Mathematical Theories of Economic Growth

Edwin Burmeister UNIVERSITY OF PENNSYLVANIA

A. Rodney Dobell UNIVERSITY OF TORONTO

WITH A FOREWORD BY **Robert M. Solow**

AND A CONTRIBUTION BY **Stephen J. Turnovsky**

MACMILLAN SERIES IN ECONOMICS

LAWRENCE R. KLEIN, CONSULTING EDITOR

Mathematical Theories of Economic Growth

Macmillan Publishing Co., Inc.
NEW YORK

Collier Macmillan Publishers
LONDON

© Copyright, Macmillan Publishing Co., Inc., 1970

Printed in the United States of America

MACMILLAN PUBLISHING CO., INC.
866 Third Avenue, New York, New York 10022
COLLIER-MACMILLAN CANADA, LTD., TORONTO, ONTARIO

Library of Congress catalog card number: 75-92080

PRINTING   5 6 7 8 9 0   YEAR   6 7 8 9 0

To Our Parents

Foreword

It is a standard gambit—I have used it myself—to describe a topic as "fit for textbook treatment," meaning that it is played out, cut and dried. But this gambit fails obviously in the case of the theory of economic growth. Burmeister and Dobell have succeeded in leading the student from a review of basic concepts, through the well-understood parts of macroeconomic growth theory, right to the frontiers of current research. It is a bit like one of those conducted military tours for politicians, except that the student will spend less time in the fleshpots, and those are real bullets in the last few chapters.

A systematic treatment like this one helps to clarify what the burst of effort in growth theory has accomplished, and what open questions remain to be studied and perhaps settled. Above all, we have quite a lot of information about the characteristics of steady states under a variety of assumptions about saving, asset preferences, and the character of technology and technological progress. It is thus possible to work out a certain amount of "comparative dynamics," statements about how differences in saving parameters or other parameters correspond to differences in the character of the associated steady states.

There is also a considerable—but incomplete—stock of knowledge about the circumstances in which an idealized model economy will—or will not—approach a steady state if it starts in some arbitrary configuration and evolves according to specified rules of the game. The permissible rules usually require that commodity and factor markets be cleared at each instant. This is pretty restrictive. One would like to allow more disequilibrium, but the literature so far has produced little beyond chitchat.

It is easy to take a dim view of this preoccupation with steady states. It must be admitted that one reason we study steady states so much is that we can actually work out their properties. There is nothing shameful in that; analysis usually proceeds by solving easier problems before harder ones. But you can make a good case that the easier problem of steady states is more than merely a finger exercise. Real economies are not in steady states; they are not in any state that can be described in a word, not even in factor- and commodity-market equilibrium. But they do not appear to be very far from, or to be rushing systematically away from, steady-state conditions. So the steady state may be a fair first approximation. Of course, that is a temporary excuse, not a permanent license.

Finally, there has been some real progress in analyzing optimal policies of capital accumulation for planned or fairly accurately steered economies. The questions at issue are a bit distant from the matters of short-run stabilization and income distribution that provide the fuel for day-to-day controversy. But for optimists it is satisfying to have a rigorous foundation for long-run economic policy.

What problems remain for the readers—or the writers—of this book to tackle? Some of them are implicit in what I have already said.

In the first place, there are problems associated with the treatment of effective demand. The rules of the game for growth models generally assume that factor and commodity markets are cleared, but provide no mechanism for clearing them. It is true that modern economies have stayed pretty close to full employment for many years, but it is anyone's guess how much this good behavior owes to the automatic and discretionary stabilization policy of governments and how much to other causes or to good luck. It would probably be a good idea to build more flesh-and-blood government into growth models. I would not expect miracles from this, however. Full employment maintained by successful stabilization policy will have qualitative consequences much like those of full employment maintained for any other reason. There will be differences worth exploring nevertheless. Stabilization policy may operate by changing the volume of public-and-private saving at different levels of income. When it does so, it helps choose which steady state corresponds to given parameters of the private economy. Moreover, the consequences of changes in private behavior parameters will depend on the way government offsets their effective-demand implications. In any case, it would be desirable for growth models to have an explicit mechanism for effective demand.

Second, there are difficult problems in models with many capital goods, connected with their convergence—or failure to converge—to steady states. The knottiest problems arise from the occurrence of capital gains and losses; any system in which the current level of a price depends strongly enough on its (expected) rate of change is vulnerable to something like a speculative boom. The objects of such a boom, or its opposite, can be capital goods as well as tulips or exotic equities. Burmeister and Dobell touch briefly on these matters at the end of Chapter 9.

Third, there are problems connected with the "paradoxes" discussed by Burmeister and Dobell in Chapter 8. The key difficulty may be one of interpretation. The paradoxes themselves show that some simple conclusions deduced from models with one capital good need not hold for more general models, but it remains to be seen how significant this is. If the paradoxes matter at all, they are likely to matter for this ubiquitous question of convergence to steady states. The simpler question is whether such paradoxes can be observed in an optimizing economy, or whether if an optimal path comes upon such a situation, it will go around it, so to speak, so "paradoxical behavior" will never be observed along an optimal path. In general, even this question remains unanswered, although some particular cases, with especially simple criterion functions, have been studied. Nobody knows what sort of path an unplanned profit-maximizing economy would follow in similar circumstances. These sound like very hard problems, but important ones.

Fourth, there is the whole problem of induced bias in technical change. Burmeister and Dobell describe the current state of play in Chapter 3. The objections they list are enough to suggest a nice program of work. In addition, the only analysis now available seems to give too little weight to the internal logic of science itself. Whatever people set out to do, what they actually achieve will depend on the discoveries that happen to lie nearest the surface. The theory of induced technical change is set up to generate labor-augmenting technical change because that is the only kind that combines with the other standard assumptions to permit a steady state. The empirical evidence is not very convincing, but such as it is it seems to indicate the presence of a small component of capital-augmenting technical change.

And that leads to the fifth and last of the open questions I want to put on the agenda. The choice at the moment seems to be between exponential steady states and paths that depart ever further from steady states. Given this choice, the steady state seems the better approximation to the facts of economic growth. Data, however, suggest systematic deviations from the steady-state pattern: partially capital-augmenting technical change, drifts in the capital-output ratio and in distributive shares. These deviations do not appear to be rapidly cumulative. Can one find a set of assumptions that will rationalize this sort of second approximation to the facts?

It is a vaguely incestuous pleasure to find that one's former students have written a book one would be glad to teach from. The sad thing about the standard-gambit meaning of "fit for textbook treatment" is that it is often accurate, so that users of textbooks get no sense of the subject as a series of problems, some easy enough that they have just been solved, some just hard enough that they haven't quite been solved yet, and some so hard that they defy the imagination. Burmeister and Dobell have escaped that trap; their later chapters do provide a sense of what is actually going on at the front, especially to anyone who works the exercises. The mind boggles at the thought of the sort of books that *their* students may write.

Robert M. Solow

Preface

This book is intended primarily as a text for graduate students. The first chapters should prove useful in basic courses on economic growth, while the contents from Chapter 7 onwards provide material suitable for more advanced seminars.

It seems to us, after teaching courses on theories of economic growth, that the already vast literature on the subject is expanding so rapidly that the student is often unable to isolate, in the many elaborate mathematical models studied, the central economic themes. Our intent is that this book serve as an introduction and a guide to the contemporary literature on mathematical theories of economic growth in such a way that the reader grasps the main economic principles from which the models are derived. The deliberate focus of the book is on the economic underpinnings of the analysis.

Almost all the topics covered are subjects of present research in a field very much in flux. New findings appear in each journal issue, and old impressions may be changed as a result. We therefore cannot hope that these pages will contain the final word on any of the topics presented, nor even a full account of the fruitful work already completed. For one particular omission we ought, perhaps, to offer some explanation. We have done little more than mention a tradition of analysis that might be labeled the "Cambridge (England) theories." Our reasons were primarily those of space and time: in a book already long, we doubted that we could do justice to an alternative approach that requires separate exposition and analysis. We concluded that it might be better to present a consistent picture of one approach to our topic, and we therefore have referred only briefly to Keynesian issues or demand-oriented models. Continuing elaboration of growth models will undoubtedly lead to further emphasis on determination of aggregate demand, along with the issues of potential supply that we have emphasized, but we believe that the material of this book provides an essential foundation for that discussion. The supply-oriented models described here can be extended to deal with issues such as unemployment or cyclical growth that arise when independent determination of aggregate demand and varying rates of capacity utilization are admitted. These extensions are important and should be developed; their omission here reflects only our reluctance to lengthen this book at this time.

In Chapter 1 we review some relevant features of the familiar analysis of static general equilibrium models, and thus prepare for the construction of a highly condensed model, the evolution of which may be traced easily. Chapter 2 introduces this simple model of growth. We study the process of capital accumulation in an economy that contains only a single good and in which production relations are unchanging. Consideration of questions of technical progress in the context of the same one-good model raises a number of further issues, which are discussed in Chapter 3.

Disaggregation of the model begins in Chapter 4. There a distinction is made between the capital good and the consumption good, and different production functions for each sector are assumed. This disaggregation serves to illustrate more clearly the general equilibrium character of the model, although the analysis of the growth process remains almost unchanged. In Chapter 5 extensions of this model to include technological change and some other refinements are discussed, but we retain the basic two-sector structure with a single durable good.

An additional durable good of a different kind—a non-produced paper asset, the supply of which is controlled by a central government—is introduced in Chapter 6. The presence of such an additional asset forces explicit consideration of price relationships that play no central role in the previous discussion, and of portfolio management problems that simply do not arise in the model with a single durable good. Analysis of the process of growth in the context of this new model leads to questions of desirable economic policy in a system of free markets where a central government may possess limited instruments.

These first six chapters, then, form a coherent unit, dealing with the issues of growth in very highly aggregated models that nevertheless illustrate several basic principles. The primary analytical tool employed is the qualitative analysis of differential equation systems by means of phase diagrams and the study of associated linear systems near an equilibrium point. We believe that these chapters give a fairly comprehensive account of most of the issues arising in these highly aggregated, strictly descriptive models.

Just as in the two-asset model of Chapter 6, disaggregation to distinguish different capital goods raises important issues with respect to the behavior of capital markets on which these alternative durable assets may be traded. Such disaggregation also raises questions as to the significance of the rate of interest in models in which there is no single capital measure. In Chapter 7 the main features distinguishing different multisector growth models are described, and three particular cases are singled out for later detailed discussion. The last of these, the closed model of production, is treated at the end of the same chapter. The main mathematical tool for this analysis and the subsequent discussion of multisector models is the theory of nonnegative matrices (summarized briefly in the Appendix).

Chapter 8 adopts a linear technology in describing production, but opens the model to incorporate primary factors and final demand for consumption goods. Chapter 9 studies the open model with the infinite variety of alternative production techniques offered by smooth neoclassical production functions.

The first step away from a strictly descriptive model is taken in Chapter 10, which studies the nature of efficient paths of accumulation in models of the types treated in the previous three chapters. Completing these models by insisting on efficiency (that is, Pareto optimality) over the whole horizon of the model goes a surprising way toward a complete determination of the character of the resulting growth path and leads, in particular, to results such as the celebrated turnpike theorems.

Moving from the weak criterion of efficiency to the introduction of an explicit social welfare function, Chapter 11 returns to the question of desirable policy in the management of instruments designed to influence the path of economic growth. Optimal paths of capital accumulation are analyzed by techniques of optimal control theory that prove to be intimately related to more familiar economic principles. In Chapter 12 we summarize our work and indicate some connections with other issues in economic theory.

This text is intended to be used with a selection of basic readings, and we have provided a bibliography at the end of each chapter from which an instructor may make his own selections. We have no illusions that the book is easy, but our experience has been that a student who reads thoughtfully and works the exercises can master the material. The exercises are important to a complete understanding of the text. As far as mathematical prerequisites are concerned, this book is accessible to any student who has a modest background in calculus and linear algebra, and who is prepared to follow the references for additional topics such as stability theory, variational methods, and some special results on nonnegative matrices.

We have many intellectual debts to be acknowledged. Colleagues, friends, and students, over more years than we now care to admit, have added thoughts and corrections to our drafts. We are particularly grateful to L. R. Klein, Kiyoshi Kuga, E. S. Phelps, Bernt Stigum, and C. C. von Weizsäcker. Stephen J. Turnovsky generously agreed to let us use an unpublished manuscript written for Leontief's seminar at Harvard. A revised version of his work now stands as Chapter 10, and his influence extends into several other chapters.

Finally, we must express our deep thanks to two former teachers, Paul A. Samuelson and Robert M. Solow. Their influence is unmistakable throughout this book, as it is, of course, throughout the profession.

We have had the privilege of studying economics at MIT and of teaching economic theory, in association with distinguished colleagues, at major graduate schools. If we have in this book successfully communicated a little of the excitement and pleasure the subject offers the credit must go to our teachers, our colleagues, and our wives, for their help and advice, and, above all, for the examples they have set.

E. B.

A. R. D.

Contents

Brief Contents

Full Contents

Chapter 1 Introduction

1–1. Introduction

The mathematician Laplace is reputed to have said, "Give me only the equations of motion, and I will show you the future of the Universe." Likewise, economists studying the evolution of a large general equilibrium system ask only for the equations of motion in order to bring their work to completion. We hope this book makes clear what sometimes seems not to be realized by students: that growth theory and growth models—the equations of motion for an economic system—are a natural development from a standard general equilibrium framework. Just as macroeconomics itself offers a way of summarizing and condensing the features of a full general equilibrium model, growth theory describes how this condensed model changes over time. It may happen that the growth model is an even more simplified description of an economy than the usual macroeconomic model; this will be the case with the first models encountered in this book. In these, production conditions will appear to dominate entirely, but that is only because in a very long run model, it might be expected, with some justice, that supply considerations, rather than demand conditions, will dominate the evolution of the system. That is, the economy, over a long period, might be expected to operate close to potential output.

Assuming individual preferences, technological possibilities, and economic institutions all to be given, the static equilibrium of an economic system is usually taken to be determined by the amounts and distribution of productive resources. Endowments of such resources change as a consequence of current decisions, and thus current decisions (based on current expectations about the future) determine tomorrow's static equilibrium. It is this feature that distinguishes theories of economic growth from conventional general equilibrium theories, in which resources are taken as given and the adjustment processes of interest are generally adjustments of prices to equilibrium from disequilibrium configurations. It is also this feature that distinguishes theories of economic growth from Keynesian macroeconomics, in which resources again are taken as given and short run adjustments of capacity utilization, particularly adjustments in the unemployment rate, are studied.

In order to concentrate on the longer run process of the growth in endowments, the models of economic growth presented here omit consideration of shorter run processes of price adjustment or alterations in the rate of capacity utilization (including, in particular, the unemployment rate). Thus, the models to be discussed will be supply-oriented models that assume the short-run adjustments of market prices and the short-run adjustments of capacity and resource utilization rates are accomplished so quickly (relative to the time scale relevant in a long-run growth model) that static market equilibrium at full employment always may be assumed.

As in most work in growth models, our analysis follows a rather standard pattern. We begin generally by identifying and studying a long-run equilibrium, a steady growth configuration of a model. At this stage the existence and uniqueness of such a path of balanced growth are the main issues. Subsequently we turn to the possible evolution toward such a long-run equilibrium of a system already in short-run equilibrium along the entire development path. We study, in other words, neoclassical equilibrium paths, and ask whether these tend toward a state of steady growth. A natural extension of this work is to deal with disequilibrium paths that adjust toward a short-run equilibrium configuration even as that target evolves toward a long-run state of rest or steady growth. But the lack of any satisfactory theory about processes of adjustment in uncleared markets or other disequilibrium states makes any complete treatment of this problem unlikely for some time to come.

In any case, we have in mind several justifications for stopping short of the full disequilibrium model and dealing instead with what is essentially classical economics. One justification is expressed by Paul Samuelson in his familiar introductory text where he says:

In a well-running system, with monetary and fiscal policies operating to validate the high-employment assumption postulated by the classical theory, that classical theory comes back into its own.[1]

In addition the analysis has a "certain austere aesthetic grace"[2]. The classical model, extended to include many capital goods, technical change, money, and other such considerations, provides a challenging theoretical structure whose study yields intellectual satisfaction in itself.

We are interested here primarily in theories—abstract and possibly artificial

---

[1] Samuelson, [19], p. 793. Kenneth J. Arrow, in his review of Samuelson's *Collected Scientific Papers* has observed that this "neoclassical synthesis" is not completely convincing, in that theorems derived for a classical system that is always (and automatically) in equilibrium at full capacity may still not accurately describe the behavior of a nonclassical system that just happens to be at full capacity by virtue of a wise government policy. That is, there are significant differences between a system identically in equilibrium and a system in equilibrium only as a result of particular circumstances. Despite this reservation, we fall back on the hope that analysis of the full-employment model retains some relevance to problems of economic policy.

[2] Samuelson, [19], p. 793.

mathematical models of economic structures—and we shall stick narrowly to that interest. We elect to do so not because there are no important issues of empirical fact or econometric techniques bearing upon our topic, nor because there are no vital questions of development in particular economies. We do so because the study of theoretical models of economic growth is already more than can be discussed in one book, and we have had to concentrate our efforts.

On the other hand, we are aware that theoretical models of economic growth are studied for a purpose, and we try to relate our discussion to that purpose, which is to illustrate the actual process of growth in real market economies. To that end we do attempt to relate our results in a simple way to the "stylized facts" of economic life.

We are convinced that study of such abstract models as follow has something to offer toward the solution of pressing contemporary problems. Although it suppresses problems of stabilization policy and some important issues such as unemployment, the classical model we follow here may still yield insight into the longer run issues of saving and investment policy, growth and decay. By examining the sacrifices and returns involved in alternative saving policies, the implications for redistribution of consumption through time (and therefore between generations), the effects of technical progress on the returns to saving at different times, the effectiveness of market mechanisms as instruments to guide the growth process, and similar questions at the level of abstract theory, it is possible to clarify the choices real communities face, even though no prepared answers are found to determine these choices.

1–2. A Brief History of Doctrine

Some perspective on the subject of this book may be suggested by the observation at the outset that there is a discernible division in economic theory between description of the growth of underlying factor endowments in an economy on the one hand and determination of the static equilibrium configuration associated at any moment with given factor endowments on the other. A complete description of an evolving economy clearly demands full specification and full integration of both features; at various times in the history of doctrine, however, one topic or the other may dominate the discussion.

Description of the processes by which wealth accumulates and population grows dominated much of the early study of the economic development of nations.[3] Later, careful elaboration of the complex character of static general

---

[3] Some discussion of what he calls this "magnificent dynamics" is given by Baumol [3]. Or one might look directly at the works of Smith, Ricardo, Malthus, and Marx

equilibrium with given factor endowments became a central theme of nine-teenth-century economic theory, culminating in the complete general equilibrium model of Walras and the *Principles* of Marshall. Following this resolution of some of the theoretical issues related to the nature of momentary equilibrium, attention turned to aggregate models in which money and financial assets were explicitly treated, and the attainment of product or labor market clearing was difficult or impossible. The *General Theory* of Keynes is the obvious reference point in that literature. Only relatively recently, justified by a presumption of national policies adequate to rule out persistent deficiencies of aggregate demand, has an emphasis on the evolution of under-lying factor endowments emerged again. Now, because static general equili-brium theory has in the meantime been so fully elaborated,[4] we can imagine in principle carrying along a full moving equilibrium in which the equation system describing momentary equilibrium is solved to the point that all current flow variables are expressed as functions of underlying endowments of capital goods, labor force, accessible resources, and any other relevant factors of production.[5] With this interpretation, therefore, we may take all flow variables, all the entries of such summary accounts as the national accounts (and flow-of-funds accounts or input-output tables) to be known as functions of factor endowments. Thus, to know everything about the economic system at any instant, that is, to specify fully the state of the system at any instant, we need only establish the momentarily given vector of factor endowments,[6] and the vector of prices for durable assets. The emphasis of this book is, therefore, on the process by which these underlying endowments and asset prices evolve over time. Of course we expect that the equilibrium established at one moment will influence the rate at which assets are accumu-lated to carry over to the next moment, so it is not possible to isolate one topic from the other. But we shall avoid issues in the theory of general equilibrium if they are not essential to the simplified models of growth we study.

What we shall try to do in this book is to trace the logical development of mathematical theories of economic growth from very simple models in which

[4] See, for example, Debreu [4], Samuelson [18], Kuenne [12], and Meade [14].

[5] Clearly there are heroic assumptions implied in this assertion. All flow variables will depend in principle upon the endowments of each individual and each firm, that is, the values of flow variables will depend upon the distribution of resources as well as their totals. Certainly a ranking of the performance of the economy would depend heavily upon the distribution of income and wealth that it generates. In growth theory it has been customary to ignore this complication and work with one or a few aggregate values. Moreover, we shall see later that in many cases there are no true demand functions for durable assets, so that the prices of these assets have to be given from the past, rather than determined by the balance of conventional supply and demand curves. In this case, the static flow con-figuration has to be taken as determined by the vector of factor endowments and the vector of durable goods prices together, both given at each instant (but evolving over time).

[6] Again, subject to the qualifications mentioned in footnote 5.

the general equilibrium features are so unimportant as to be invisible, through to examples of quite complex models in which some unresolved questions of current interest are apparent. In particular we shall try to emphasize the economic foundations upon which growth models are constructed, so that readers may see how components of the model may be extended or reformulated within the framework imposed by the traditional theoretical approach adopted here.

1–3. Structure of General Equilibrium Systems

We begin by reviewing some features and the general framework of the simplest static models. In outline, it will be recalled, the conventional general equilibrium problem has three aspects.

(i) *Decisions of firms, taking factor and goods prices as fixed.* Given a production function, or some more general specification of technologically feasible combinations of inputs and outputs, individual firms attempt to acquire factor services and produce goods in such a way as to maximize their flow of profit. Their decisions determine demand functions for factor services and supply functions for goods in terms of factor and goods prices as parameters. The theory of the firm, or the theory of production, deals with these decisions.

(ii) *Decisions of the household, taking factor and goods prices as fixed.* Given a utility function or some more general representation of preferences, the individual household attempts to offer factor services and purchase goods in such a way as to attain a maximum instantaneous utility flow, or a position ranking highest (among feasible positions) in its preference ordering. These household decisions determine demand functions for goods and supply functions for factor services in terms of factor and goods prices as parameters. The conventional theory of consumer's behavior describes the process.

(iii) *Market adjustment processes, determining equilibrium factor and goods prices.* Given the demand and supply functions just determined, the market adjusts toward a set of prices for goods and factor services that clears all goods and factor markets. Various processes of adjustment may be studied, and we may ask, first, whether such a set of (nonnegative) prices exists, and second, what processes of market adjustment result in convergence to it. We will refer to this latter issue as a question in very short-run, or market, dynamics and will not deal with it at all. We will, on the contrary, assume that markets for goods and for factor services are always in equilibrium at appropriate prices.

The basic structure thus yields conclusions of different types. Households acting as price takers develop decisions attempting to arrive at preferred positions subject to expenditure constraints and given price data; firms acting as price takers develop decisions attempting to achieve maximum profit subject to technological constraints and given price data. Analysis of these decisions yields results describing the manner in which individual decisions are affected by changes in price data taken as given.

Processes of market adjustment then alter prices until all the foregoing decisions are mutually consistent and all markets clear. Analysis of these processes yields results on the existence and uniqueness of equilibrium prices and the stability of various adjustment rules.

Two further results holding for the system as a whole can be considered central to static economic theory. These results link the descriptive concept of a competitive equilibrium with the normative concept of a Pareto-optimum. Loosely, it will be recalled, a state of the economy is said to be *Pareto-optimal*, or *efficient*, if there is no other feasible state in which some consumer feels better off and no other consumers feel worse off. On the other hand, a state of the economy is a *competitive equilibrium* if there is a set of prices such that in the given state all consumers, given their budget constraints, are doing as well as they can at the prescribed prices, and all firms, given their technological constraints, are doing as well as they can at the prescribed prices, and all markets clear. Then the first result asserts that a competitive equilibrium is Pareto-optimal.

What is even more interesting is close to the converse of that proposition; namely, that if a particular state of an economic system is Pareto-optimal, then there exists some price vector that would sustain that state as a competitive equilibrium. That is, a Pareto-optimal state is a competitive equilibrium for some choice of a price vector and (possibly) some redistribution of resources.

This description is obviously not intended to be precise.[7] The purpose is simply to remind the reader of the basic results in conventional general equilibrium theory and in particular of the fact that in order for a system to be economically efficient, it may have to satisfy conditions resembling a description of an ideal price system. A search for comparable theorems in dynamic analysis is central to much recent literature on economic growth.

There is one respect in which such a static general equilibrium framework is clearly unsuited to our interest in an evolving system. Although it is conventional enough, it fails to come explicitly to grips with one issue that is crucial in a discussion of economic growth, namely, the existence of produced durable goods and the accumulation of assets. The static profit-maximization criterion assumed to characterize the firm does not take into account expenditure on capital goods or investment in plant or equipment. Likewise the static

[7] For a very precise and elegant statement of such results, see Debreu [4].

utility-maximization criterion assumed to characterize the household does not take into account saving and the accumulation of earning assets at the expense of deferring consumption. (The ploy that treats capital goods, or savings itself, as items purchased by consumers and yielding utility is occasionally convenient in empirical work, but obscures theoretical understanding of the system.) Extension of conventional microeconomic theories to take into account these inherently dynamic aspects of the household's and firm's decisions is an active topic of research at the present time. We have to imagine that the criterion for the decision-making of firms is some net worth criterion, an integral in which the integrand is some function of profit flow net of some current expenditures whose only present justification is that they yield future returns.[8] The consequence is that firms now enter the goods market to demand capital goods produced by other firms, as well as to offer a supply of consumer goods. Similarly, we must imagine that the criterion for households is some intertemporal utility measure, an integral in which the integrand is some function of the instantaneous utility flow adopted earlier.[9] The consequence is that households may now rationally defer some purchases of consumer goods, transferring purchasing power instead to firms wishing to acquire investment goods themselves. In exchange for this transfer the consumer obtains a claim on future production.

The extension of the decision criteria of both firms and households to intertemporal forms involving future as well as present states introduces a host of questions as to financial instruments or other social contrivances designed to achieve a more effective carryover from one period into the future. It is evident that the changes we introduced in an attempt to admit the essential features of a dynamic economy—deferred consumption and the accumulation of assets—have introduced great complexity as well. Drastic simplification is essential in attacking the problem.

The first step is to eliminate consideration of a number of the individual decisions discussed earlier, either by assuming that the decision is insensitive to any changes in the system, or that when aggregated all these decisions imply some very simple rule. We shall adopt both assumptions at various times, and sometimes both at the same time. In fact, on the household side of the general equilibrium model we shall assume that factor services are always inelastically supplied and that saving decisions are described by some simple rule. Moreover, at first we shall assume that some version of Say's Law holds, so that either household saving is a direct demand for particular kinds of goods, or it is translated directly into an investment demand that

---

[8] Study of such a net worth measure is central in the work of Jorgenson [11] and his associates.

[9] The well-known life-cycle theories of saving introduced by Modigliani and Brumberg [16], Harrod [9], and Friedman [8] are examples. See Yaari [23] for detailed analysis of one interesting case.

represents a demand for goods. The point is that total aggregate demand always equals aggregate supply, since there are no alternative assets to accumulate, and the goods market clears by hypothesis. Less than full utilization of capacity therefore need not arise.

The general equilibrium problem thus reduces to a rather special case. On the goods market firms supply an output flow equal to that obtainable from full utilization of inelastically supplied factors, and demand is brought into balance with supply by adjustment of prices and the composition of output. On the markets for factor services, supply is inelastic, and firms determine their demands so as to achieve maximum profit. Again the adjustment of factor prices ensures that the markets for factor services clear.

Thus the key components of the static equilibrium are the production functions and the factor markets, along with the demand conditions describing household saving behavior. About these items we will say a word more.

1–4. The Production Function

The first component of many models, dynamic or static, is a function that attempts to describe the physical facts of a given technology, showing the terms on which services of productive input factors like capital and labor are transformed into output. A number of assumptions are usually imposed on the function that provides this description.

First, as a mathematical abstraction we assume that it is legitimate to represent the production process by some sufficiently smooth function

$$Q = F(K, L) \tag{1}$$

showing the output flow Q attainable with given inputs K and L. (Normally it is enough that the function possess continuous second partial derivatives.)

Before moving on, it is necessary to clarify the question of the dimensions attached to these variables. In our growth models, the variables K and L refer to stocks of assets—stocks of physical and human capital respectively. For our simple one-sector model, which will be discussed in Chapter 2, K is measured in units of the output good itself, as a number of machines or a number of bushels of corn, and L as a number of laborers. On the other hand, it is clear that the arguments K and L entering the production function refer to flow rates of input of services of these assets. Hence, we must keep in mind that the foregoing notation is really a shorthand in which a utilization factor showing the rate at which service is rendered by each asset stock has been omitted. Thus, for example, the stock of laborers is measured as L (men); the flow rate of labor service measured in man-years/year would be given by

$$L(\text{man-yrs/yr}) = L(\text{men}) \times 1(\text{man-yrs/yr/man}).$$

That is, the utilization factor of unity informs us that each man in the labor force renders labor service at a rate of one man-year per year. Similarly, the rate of input of capital service (measured, for example, in machine-yrs/yr) is obtained by applying the appropriate utilization factor to the existing stocks. Thus,

$$K(\text{machine-yrs/yr}) = K(\text{machines}) \times 1(\text{machine-yrs/yr/machine}).$$

This degree of detail is usually not necessary, but it is worth remembering that our growth equations deal with the variables K and L as stock variables, whereas the arguments of the production function must be flow rates of asset services. This distinction becomes important in dealing with possible un- employment of assets and with variable utilization rates less than unity. (In the meantime, of course, we may think loosely of cancelling the time dimen- sions in a flow measured as man-years per year and translate directly from the stock of labor (in men) to the flow of labor services.)

Obviously the economist is led to a relationship such as (1) on the basis of an analogy with the microeconomic static theory of production. In this theory individual production processes specified in detail involve the input of particular commodities and the transformation of these into other par- ticular commodities, all inputs and outputs being physically identifiable and quantitatively measurable in unambiguous units, with the process of trans- formation being described in conventional engineering terms. However, although such a picture may have inspired the function (1), it is clear that no such interpretation remains tenable when we interpret the inputs K and L and the output Q as statistical aggregates like "plant and equipment, building and structures," "labor force," or "gross national product." The literature contains some discussion of the question when individual engineering relations might legitimately be aggregated into a statistical abstraction like (1); we shall not go into this question here.[10] Thus, we will continue to deal with the aggregate production function (1) as a construct that may indeed be taken to be unambiguous and exact in our one commodity model in which inputs and outputs are not statistical abstractions but precisely defined, unambiguously measurable physical entities.

The properties we should like a general production function $F(Y)$ to satisfy are

(i) It should be defined and nonnegative for any vector Y of appropriate dimension, having all components nonnegative; that is, $F(Y) \geq 0$ for all $Y \geq 0$;

(ii) Sufficient smoothness: second partial derivatives with respect to all

---

[10] The interested reader is referred to Leontief [13], Robinson [17], Solow [22], Fisher [7], and a Symposium on Aggregation appearing in the *Review of Economic Studies*, October 1968.

arguments (that is, with respect to all components of Y) should be continuous;

(iii) "No free lunch": $F(0) = 0$;

(iv) Nonnegative marginal products: for any component Y_i of the vector Y, the partial derivative

$$F_i(Y) \equiv \frac{\partial F(Y)}{\partial Y_i}$$

satisfies

$$F_i(Y) \geq 0;$$

(v) Homogeneity of degree one: $F(\lambda Y) = \lambda F(Y)$ for all

$$\lambda > 0 \quad \text{and all} \quad Y \geq 0.$$

(vi) Strict quasiconcavity: for any $Y \geq 0$, $Y' \geq 0$, $0 < \lambda < 1$, and for any $c > 0$, if $F(Y) \geq c$ and $F(Y') = c$, then $F[\lambda Y + (1 - \lambda)Y'] \geq c$, with equality if and only if $Y' \equiv Y$.[11]

We will call such a production function a *neoclassical production function.* The following example illustrates properties in the case in which Y is a vector with only two components.

The well-known *constant elasticity of substitution* (CES) function may be written[12]

$$F(K, L) = \gamma[\alpha K^{-\rho} + (1 - \alpha)L^{-\rho}]^{-1/\rho}$$

where α, γ, and ρ are given parameters.

[11] Condition (vi) requires that the *contour sets* (or *level sets*)

$$S = \{Y \mid F(Y) \geq c\}$$

where c is a positive constant be strictly convex sets unless some part of the boundary of S coincides with a portion of a boundary of the nonnegative orthant. (The nonnegative orthant in E^n is the set of all vectors in E^n having all components nonnegative.) This requirement is weaker than the requirement that the function F be strictly concave except along rays from the origin. The latter requirement is expressed by the condition

$$F[\lambda Y + (1 - \lambda) Y'] \geq \lambda F(Y) + (1 - \lambda)F(Y') \quad \text{for} \quad 0 < \lambda < 1,$$
$$Y \geq 0, \ Y' \geq 0, \text{with strict inequality unless } Y = \mu Y'$$
$$\text{for some scalar } \mu > 0.$$

This implies that F is strictly quasiconcave, but it is not implied by the requirement that F be strictly quasiconcave. Thus in view of (ii) and (v), a sufficient condition is (vi)′: The Hessian matrix of F, $H = [F_{ij}]$, is negative semidefinite and of rank $n - 1$.

[12] Exercise 10 in Chapter 2 suggests that the reader investigate properties of this function by computing average and marginal products and finding the iso-product contours. It is particularly important to distinguish the various cases in which isoquants may hit the axes, become asymptotic to the axes, or are bounded away from the axes. Exercise 11 in Chapter 2 suggests that various special limiting cases of the CES function are of interest.

Observe that the elasticity of substitution, σ, is defined for the two-variable case we are presently considering as

$$\sigma \equiv \frac{F_K F_L}{F F_{KL}}.$$

Thus, by direct calculation[13]

$$\sigma = \frac{1}{1 + \rho}.$$

If we set

$$\omega = \frac{W}{R} = \frac{F_L(K, L)}{F_K(K, L)},$$

as would be appropriate under conditions of purely competitive pricing according to marginal products, then[14] (1) ω may be treated as a function of the capital/labor ratio $K/L \equiv k$ alone, (2) this function may be inverted provided the production function is neoclassical, and (3) the elasticity

$$\frac{dk}{d\omega} \frac{\omega}{k}$$

of the resulting inverse function is precisely the elasticity of substitution σ. Thus, σ has a useful interpretation in terms of the behavior of firms facing a perfect market for factors: if the relative factor price ω falls by one percent, the capital/labor ratio k in production falls by σ percent. The greater σ, the more sensitive the cost-minimizing capital/labor ratio in production. Or, turning the relationship around, the greater σ, the less relative factor prices have to adjust in order to bring about accommodation of production conditions to any change in relative factor endowments. This interpretation will be relevant later.

Of course the CES family does not include all neoclassical production functions. Exercises 9 and 15 in Chapter 2 deal with other examples, and wider families of functions with elasticity of substitution varying have been discussed.[15]

Finally, for later reference we mention in passing that the properties imposed before on $F(Y_1, Y_2, \ldots, Y_n)$ imply that the Hessian of the function

[13] See Exercise 10 in Chapter 2.
[14] See Exercise 2 in Chapter 2.
[15] See, for example a recent symposium [6] on extensions of the CES function.

F (that is, the matrix of second partial derivatives of F) must be negative semidefinite of rank $n - 1$, and that the vector $(Y_1, \ldots, Y_n)$ is a characteristic vector of this matrix associated with a characteristic value equal to zero.[16]

In summary, all of these calculations refer to a few features of specific examples of a mathematical relationship attempting to describe the terms under which an economy may transform inputs of factor services into a flow of final output. Such calculations are really part of the theory of the firm, or theory of production, if we take the function to refer to the technological possibilities open to a firm rather than to an economy.

A function, of course, is a rather restricted description of possible transformations from input to output. Some contemporary work employs more general correspondences and expresses production restrictions more generally, by defining a technology set T to describe production possibilities. In this approach an output vector Y may be produced from an input vector X (that is, the pair (X, Y) is a feasible input-output pair) if and only if $(X, Y) \in T$. Properties of the set T analogous to the restriction on production functions express assumptions as to homogeneity, divisibility, and so on. Such an approach can include a description of either activity analysis or dynamic input-output models as well as the neoclassical production function just defined.

Although it is not among the central economic issues in most growth models, the specification of production possibilities does matter: special features of particular production functions are sometimes responsible for special features in growth models employing them.

1–5. Markets for Factor Services

One of the major steps taken to reduce the general equilibrium structure outlined before to manageable proportions relates to the inputs in the production function, that is, to the supply of factor services. We shall assume that available supplies of factors are at every moment inelastically supplied and fully utilized. This means that the quantities of factor service do not vary with changes in factor prices or other shorter run economic considerations; at any moment, all existing labor and capital offers itself for use regardless of what wage or rental rates prevail.

With this assumption, that at each instant the supply curve of each factor is a vertical line, we expect factor rewards to be determined from demand or productivity considerations. Recall briefly the elementary analysis of the determination of factor intensities in production. We imagine a competitive producer facing competitive markets for labor and capital services where a

---

[16] See footnote 11 on p. 10.

wage rate W for labor service and rental rate R for capital service prevail. Facing a price P for his product, and a neoclassical production function such as (1) describing available production possibilities, the producer is assumed to select the factor inputs that maximize profits

$$\pi = PQ - WL - RK.$$

We would expect him to accomplish this maximization by selecting inputs K and L satisfying

$$\frac{\partial F}{\partial K}(K, L) = \frac{R}{P}, \qquad \frac{\partial F}{\partial L}(K, L) = \frac{W}{P}. \tag{2}$$

At first glance we appear to have two equations in two unknowns. However, because of the assumption of constant returns to scale, F_K and F_L are not independent functions of K and L. We have only one independent unknown, the capital/labor ratio $k \equiv K/L$. (The reason is that the first partial derivatives of a function homogeneous of degree one are themselves homogeneous of degree zero. Thus, the functions in equations (2) depend only on the capital/labor ratio.) This single unknown may be determined so as to satisfy

$$F_L(K/L)/F_K(K/L) = W/R = \omega, \tag{3}$$

and thus equation (3) determines the appropriate factor intensity in production for any given wage/rentals ratio ω. Having determined k from (3), we can refer to equations (2) to determine the scale of output. Exercise 1 asks you to verify that when (3) is satisfied, either both of equations (2) are satisfied or neither is. Thus, equations (2) will give the same signals: to expand output indefinitely if the marginal product of either factor exceeds its real remuneration, to contract output to zero if the marginal product of either factor falls short of its real reward, and to let output settle indifferently at any scale if the imposed values R, W, and P happen to be such that (2) can be satisfied. Thus we have completed the description of the individual producer's response to given factor and product prices.

Alternatively, we could turn the question around to ask what prices could clear the markets for factor services if endowments K^0 of capital and L^0 of labor are prescribed and the services of these offered inelastically at the fixed utilization rate. Evidently the markets for factors will absorb a positive finite flow of capital and labor services only if firms' desired output scales are neither all zero nor all infinite. That is, the markets for factors can clear only if factor prices are such that équations (2) are satisfied (and we have seen that the selection by firms of input proportions satisfying (3) guarantees that either both equations of (2) are satisfied or neither is). Hence factor prices in real terms have to settle at

$$W/P = F_L(K^0, L^0), \qquad R/P = F_K(K^0, L^0)$$

if the markets for factor services are to clear.

We shall ignore for the moment any Keynesian suggestions that no individual has the power to make bargains in terms of the real wage W/P (or for that matter, real rentals R/P), and shall assume that the output good serves as a medium of exchange and is taken as *numeraire*. We thus set $P \equiv 1$ and measure both wages and rental flows in units of the output good. We further suppose that factor markets work quickly enough so that our system always displays competitive equilibrium in factor markets. All available labor and capital is employed, and wages and rentals are given by equations (2) with $P \equiv 1$. Exercise 2 in Chapter 2 suggests that under these circumstances relation (3) may be written in terms of the per capita production function $f(k) \equiv F(k, 1)$ as

$$\omega = \frac{f(k)}{f'(k)} - k. \tag{4}$$

This relation, which we have just seen to be a consequence of competitive markets for factors and individual producer's maximizing decisions, will be useful later.

1–6. The Factor-Price Frontier

It is obvious that with the assumptions given on the production function F we may eliminate k from the expressions for wage and rental rates and obtain a function relating wage rates to rental rates in a full employment equilibrium. This important function is an example of the *factor-price frontier* introduced by Samuelson [20].

For the case at hand we see that it is possible to invert the relation $r = R/P = f'(k)$ and write this as $k = h(r)$ where $h'(r) < 0$. Substituting this expression into the expression for the real wage rate we obtain

$$w = f[h(r)] - h(r)r. \tag{5}$$

Differentiating, we find

$$\frac{dw}{dr} = f'[h(r)]h' - h(r) - rh'(r) = -h(r) < 0$$

and

$$\frac{d^2 w}{dr^2} = -h'(r) = -\frac{1}{f''(k)} > 0.$$

1–7. Saving Behavior of Households

Because saving and asset accumulation are generally undertaken not for their own sake but for the sake of future consumption, it is rather difficult to fit the saving decision into the conventional static theory of the allocation of household income among expenditures on different goods. For an explicit theory of the extent of consumer saving we must consider, as we pointed out before, more elaborate life-cycle hypotheses.

In this book we will attempt to describe the demand for goods by three simplifications of the full dynamic analysis. First, we will aggregate all expenditure on consumer goods and speak only of consumption expenditure, taking this to represent demand for a single consumer good. Second, we will aggregate all individual decisions on saving as opposed to consumption. Third, we will suppose that this aggregate saving flow so determined may be described by some very simple rule relating saving to aggregate income (perhaps classified by income categories).[17]

It is important to realize that such a saving rule is sufficient to yield full specification of demand for all output flows in single capital good models. In the case of models with many capital goods the saving rule serves to determine the composition of demand as between consumption and saving, but not the form that saving may take. We fill this latter gap by assuming that household saving flows to firms which act simply as portfolio managers for households. In the interests of their shareholders, these firms distribute the saving flow among demand for investment goods so as to maximize the present value of the portfolio. Thus, the composition of saving and investment, and hence the demand for output of each sector, are determined.

In summary, we are assuming the existence of a well-behaved neoclassical production function and the rapid (in fact, instantaneous) adjustment of factor markets to an equilibrium position in which inelastically supplied factors earn returns equal to their marginal products. (This latter distributional assumption plays no crucial role in this chapter, but the flexibility of wages and rentals justifies, in theory, our initial assumption that labor and capital are at all times fully employed.) Simple saving rules serve to complete the system and determine the momentary equilibrium of the economy.

[17] It would be conceivable to imagine reversing the order of these last two operations, asking whether individual optimizing decisions could be summarized in a *policy* or rule that told the household (at each age, asset level, and income level) how much to save, and then aggregating these saving decisions into a simple aggregate rule. Either approach is strained.

1–8. Descriptive Decomposition of the Growth Process

Even though we shall, in this book, concentrate on theoretical features of rather abstract mathematical systems, our objective is ultimately to add to the understanding of real economic activity. One challenge to such understanding is the desire to predict how present economies are growing or will grow in the future. Why might we be led, in answering this practical question, to follow a route through the domain of mathematical theory?

A time-honored procedure in forecasting the future development of an economy is to look first to two major determinants: the labor force and labor productivity. Arithmetic being what it is, we can argue that the total annual output flow can be written as the product of two terms: the size of the flow of labor services (measured, say, in man-years per year) and the average output flow per man-year. Most of the labor force to be in service twenty years from now is already present and can be counted. Hence, if we had confident predictions about the growth in productivity (and could expect stable labor force participation rates), the problem of forecasting future output would be solved simply. What, in fact, determines productivity? To go beyond naive extrapolation of past trends, trends that may not give information as to the selection of national policies that influence growth, we need a much fuller theoretical base.

Some part of the theoretical foundation may be found in the foregoing hypotheses about technology and production. From these there follows, by straightforward calculation, a simple result that suggests a useful way of regarding the process of growth when technology is unchanged, i.e., when a single function F remains valid over time as a description of production possibilities. For then all variables in (1) may be treated implicitly as functions of time. At any time t, the output $Q(t)$ is determined by the inputs $K(t)$ and $L(t)$. Thus, differentiating with respect to t (and denoting time derivatives by dots) we obtain

$$\dot{Q} = F_K \dot{K} + F_L \dot{L} \tag{6}$$

which may be rewritten

$$\frac{\dot{Q}}{Q} = \left(\frac{KF_K}{Q}\right) \frac{\dot{K}}{K} + \left(\frac{LF_L}{Q}\right) \frac{\dot{L}}{L}. \tag{7}$$

The expressions in parentheses are identified as the shares of output that would accrue to each of the factors if they were to be rewarded by rates of payment equal to their marginal products. Thus the relative rate of growth of output is a weighted sum of the relative rates of growth of factor inputs, the weights being the relative shares, under conditions of perfectly competitive factor pricing, of the factors in national income. (These same shares measure the elasticity of output with respect to the respective factors.) Euler's theorem on homogeneous functions guarantees that for this constant-returns production function, the factor shares exhaust the total product so that

$$\frac{KF_K}{Q} + \frac{LF_L}{Q} = 1 \qquad \text{for all} \qquad t.$$

Hence, letting $q = Q/L$, $k = K/L$,

$$\frac{\dot{q}}{q} = \frac{\dot{Q}}{Q} - \frac{\dot{L}}{L} = \left(\frac{KF_K}{Q}\right)\left(\frac{\dot{K}}{K} - \frac{\dot{L}}{L}\right) = \left(\frac{KF_K}{Q}\right)\frac{\dot{k}}{k}. \tag{8}$$

Thus we do have some explanation for changes in labor productivity, at least in the sense that the hypotheses about technology given before enable a transfer of the discussion about growth rates of output or labor productivity to considerations of their underlying determinants. Clearly, however, we need further economic hypotheses in order to close the system. We must complete the model by specifying how these underlying determinants themselves grow.

Eschewing further theory (except with regard to the determination of factor shares) however, we might also employ (7) to estimate how much of the observed output growth is accounted for by growth of inputs, and how much remains to be explained by other considerations, notably by advancing technology and rising quality of inputs. Works of Denison [5] and Solow [22] and other recent studies pursue this approach. Earlier work of the same type is surveyed by Abramovitz [1].

We leave the discussion at this point, and turn in the next chapter to a more formal analysis of a particularly simple model.

Exercises

1. (a) Let $F(K, L)$ be homogeneous of degree 1. Show that the Hessian

$$\begin{bmatrix} F_{KK}(K, L) & F_{KL}(K, L) \\ F_{LK}(K, L) & F_{LL}(K, L) \end{bmatrix}$$

is singular and that the functions $F_K(K, L)$ and $F_L(K, L)$ are functionally dependent.

(b) Show that if equation (3) is satisfied then both of equations (2) are satisfied or neither is, and that the sign of $F_K - R/P$ is the same as the sign of $F_L - W/P$.

(c) Let Y be a vector in Euclidean n-space E^n. Show that if a production function F is neoclassical then the Hessian of F is negative semidefinite of rank $n - 1$. Show further that Y is a characteristic vector of the Hessian H and is associated with a characteristic value of zero.

2. Show that if a function F is concave, then it is quasiconcave.

3. Compute the factor-price frontier for the production function

$$Q = AK^\alpha L^{1-\alpha}.$$

4. Verify equation (7) and show that one may therefore write $\dot{Q}/Q = \pi \dot{K}/K + (1 - \pi) \dot{L}/L$, where π is the competitively imputed share of capital. Derive the analogous result when $Q = F(K, L; t)$.

Answers and Hints

PROBLEM 1. (a) Two functions $u(x, y)$, $v(x, y)$ are *functionally dependent* if there exists a function φ such that $\varphi(u, v) \equiv 0$. A necessary and sufficient condition for the existence of such a relation is that the Jacobian determinant of u and v be identically zero. Employ Euler's theorem to obtain the required result.

PROBLEM 2. A function is *concave* if $f[\theta x + (1 - \theta)x_0] \geq \theta f(x) + (1 - \theta)f(x_0)$ for $0 \leq \theta \leq 1$. A function is *quasiconcave* if $f(x) \geq f(x_0)$ implies

$$f[\theta x + (1 - \theta)x_0] \geq f(x_0) \text{ for } 0 \leq \theta \leq 1.$$

Hence suppose f is concave, and consider x, x_0 such that $f(x) \geq f(x_0)$. The conclusion follows directly. (See, for example, K. J. Arrow and A. C. Enthoven, "Quasi-Concave Programming" *Econometrica* Vol. 29 No. 4 (October, 1961) pp. 779–800.)

PROBLEM 3. Compute competitively imputed wage rates and rentals, and eliminate the capital/labor ratio k from the resulting expressions to obtain the real wage as a function of the real rental rate.

References

[1] ABRAMOVITZ, M., "Economics of Growth," *Survey of Contemporary Economics,* Vol. II, (B. F. Haley, Ed.). Homewood, Illinois: Irwin for American Economic Association, 1952.

[2] ALLEN, R. G. D., *Macro-Economic Theory.* New York: St. Martins, 1967.

[3] BAUMOL, W., *Economic Dynamics,* 2nd ed. New York: Macmillan, 1960.

[4] DEBREU, G., *Theory of Value.* New York: John Wiley, 1959.

[5] DENISON, E. F., *The Sources of Economic Growth in the United States and the Alternatives Before Us.* New York: Committee for Economic Development, 1962.

[6] DOBELL, A. R. (Ed.), "A Symposium on CES Production Functions," *Review of Economics and Statistics*, L, *4* (November, 1968), pp. 443–479.

[7] FISHER, F. M., "Embodied Technical Change and the Existence of an Aggregate Capital Stock," *Review of Economic Studies*, XXXII, *92* (October, 1965) pp. 263–288.

[8] FRIEDMAN, M., *A Theory of the Consumption Function.* Princeton University Press, 1957.

[9] HARROD, R. F., *Towards a Dynamic Economics.* London: Macmillan, 1948.

[10] HICKS, J. R., *Capital and Growth.* Oxford: Oxford University Press, 1965.

[11] JORGENSON, D. W., "Anticipations and Investment Behavior," in the *Brookings Quarterly Econometric Model of the United States* (Duesenberry, Fromm, Klein, and Kuh, Eds.). Chicago: Rand-McNally, 1965.

[12] KUENNE, R. E., *Microeconomic Theory of the Market Mechanism.* New York: Macmillan, 1968.

[13] LEONTIEF, W. W., "Introduction to a Theory of the Internal Structure of Functional Relationships," *Econometrica*, XV (1947), pp. 361–373.

[14] MEADE, J. E., *The Stationary Economy.* Chicago: Aldine, 1965.

[15] — *The Growing Economy.* Chicago: Aldine 1968.

[16] MODIGLIANI, F. and R. BRUMBERG, "Utility Analysis and the Consumption Function: An Interpretation of Cross-section Data," *Post-Keynesian Economics.* (K. K. Kurihara, Ed.). New Brunswick, N.J.: Rutgers University Press, 1954.

[17] ROBINSON, J., "The Production Function and the Theory of Capital," *Review of Economic Studies*, XXI (1953–1954), pp. 81–106.

[18] SAMUELSON, P. A., *Foundations of Economic Analysis.* Cambridge, Mass: Harvard University Press, 1947.

[19] — *Economics, An Introductory Analysis*, 7th Ed. New York: McGraw-Hill, 1967.

[20] —"Parable and Realism in Capital Theory: the Surrogate Production Function," *Review of Economic Studies*, XXIX, *80* (June, 1962), pp. 193–206.

[21] SOLOW, R. M., "The Production Function and the Theory of Capital," *Review of Economic Studies*, XXIII, *15* (1955–1956), pp. 101–108.

[22] — "Technical Change and the Aggregate Production Function," *Review of Economics and Statistics*, XXXIX, *3* (August, 1957), pp. 312–320.

[23] YAARI, M. E., "On the Consumer's Lifetime Allocation Process," *International Economic Review*, V, *3* (September, 1964), pp. 304–317.

Chapter 2 One-Sector Growth

Models

2-1. Introduction

In this chapter we use the simplest *neoclassical one-sector model* to introduce a number of ideas basic to the later discussion. Even this simple description of an economy carries some significant insights into processes of capital accumulation and economic growth.

Mathematically, the problem is simply to study the behavior of the solution to the single differential equation

$$\dot{k} = s(k)f(k) - g(k)k,$$

in which the functions s, f, and g are assumed to have prescribed properties and the initial capital/labor ratio is given. As a mathematical question this exercise is not particularly challenging. But to justify the economic simplifications that go into the derivation of such an equation we have to consider, for example:

  (i) Markets for factor services,
 (ii) The reconciliation of independently determined saving and investment desires,
(iii) Production conditions,
and
 (iv) The determination of population growth and labor force participation rates.

Thus, though it is easy to formulate in a mechanical way a so-called one-sector growth model, we should not forget that real economic questions surround each function.

We exclude, for the moment, any questions of technical change, monetary mechanisms, or unemployment.

2–2. The One-Good Setting

The economic theme for this chapter is: A growing economy that regularly sets aside some fairly predictable portion of its output for the purpose of capital accumulation has a tendency to adjust to a state in which the requirements to meet capital depreciation and to equip the growing labor force absorb all resources provided for accumulation. Such a state, once attained, tends to perpetuate itself. Although simple in concept, this notion is fundamental, and this chapter is devoted to exploration of the basic idea in several variations.

We deal with a highly idealized model in which difficult aggregation or valuation issues do not arise. They do not arise because we assume that there is only one produced good in the economy. Labor is present and employed as a factor of production, but laborers are neither produced nor sold and need never be valued explicitly. Capital is simply a stockpile of the single produced good; that portion of the output flow that is not consumed is accumulated and increases the stock of capital. Since there is only one good, no question of changes in relative prices can arise, nor can any questions of capital composition. Various metaphorical devices have been employed to convey what some writers feel to be the appropriate flavor of fantasy to the notion: one sees mention of " meccano sets," " ectoplasm," " leets," " putty," "schmoos," and other imaginative labels, all designed to suggest an easy transmutation of the homogeneous capital substance from one use to another. More prosaically, one concrete example is the production of corn in an economy with essentially unlimited land. The corn may be eaten, or it may be added to the stock of seed used as capital to produce yet more corn. Measuring output after provision for replacement of the seed (so that accumulated capital can be treated as an infinitely durable asset), we have a picture of an economy in which some production function describes the net output flow (measured in bushels per year) of corn available for use when the services of a specified capital stock (measured in bushels of seed) and of a given labor force (measured in men) are employed.

Capital stocks such as accumulated seed have one simple feature, which is essential throughout this chapter: it is not necessary to distinguish different kinds of capital appropriate to different capital/labor ratios or to different production processes.

> *Definition:* Capital is *malleable* (in our terminology) if we need distinguish neither its previous use nor the factor proportions of its previous use. Malleable capital can be transferred instantaneously from a production process appropriate at one level of factor intensity to a different process appropriate to a different capital intensity.

There being only one durable good—one asset—problems of deficient aggregate demand do not arise. Hoarding of output in the form of non-productive inventories held by households would, of course, be possible, though not rational; in any case such hoarding of real output can create no problems in this one-asset economy. Assuming, as discussed before, that factor markets work well and that factors are inelastically supplied, there is no cause for our system ever to display less than full utilization of available factors at every moment.

Thus we assume that all saving volunteered by households is absorbed by firms for accumulation of capital.[1] The general equilibrium structure of the model is therefore very straightforward. Taking the output good as *numeraire*, there is no change possible in the price of output, and factor prices adjust to ensure full employment. The situation may be represented in unusually full detail as follows, where the superscripts d denote flows demanded, superscripts s denote flows supplied, and product exhaustion ensures that national income equals Y^s.

Product Market:

firm supply $\qquad Q^s = F(K^d, L^d)$

final demand $\qquad Q^d = C^d + I^d = C^d + S^d = C^d + (Q^s - C^d)$

market clearing $\quad Q^d = Q^s$

Market for Capital Services:

firm demand $\qquad R = \dfrac{\partial F}{\partial K}(K^d, L^d)$

household supply $\;\; K^s = K$

market clearing $\quad\; K^s = K^d$

Market for Labor Services:

firm demand $\qquad W = \dfrac{\partial F}{\partial L}(K^d, L^d)$

household supply $\;\; L^s = L$

market clearing $\quad\; L^s = L^d$

The situation can be described also in the usual national account form.

---

[1] It may, of course, require some fiscal or monetary policy in the background to bring saving desires into line with investment intentions. Generally we shall assume that it is investment intentions that are brought into line; saving plans are always realized. That is, except in a very few cases, our models will have no explicit investment demand functions; investment is passive, following saving plans. One situation in which such a hypothesis is valid, of course, is that in which public investment is designed exactly to fill any gap between saving and investment desires.

NATIONAL INCOME
AND PRODUCT

$W \cdot L$ $R \cdot K$	C $I(=S)$
$Q^s = F(K, L)$	Q^d

This exercise describes the effect, in this elementary model, of the assumptions on static allocation. If K and L are given, these market adjustments suffice to determine the momentary flow equilibrium. To complete the model, we must turn to the less trivial question of how K and L grow over time.

2–3. The Simplest Closed Model: The Solow Model

Having established the nature of the static conditions of production, it remains only to specify the allocation of expenditure and the consequent development of factor endowments in order to obtain a complete growth model. In his influential 1956 contribution to the theory of economic growth, Solow [32] suggested simple hypotheses that close the system and enable a study of the growth path generated by the model economy. At the same time Meade [19] and Swan [34] independently developed similar models leading to essentially identical conclusions. For our present objectives it is convenient to strengthen the specification of the neoclassical production function $F(K, L)$ by the additional hypothesis that both factors are essential to production and that both have strictly positive marginal products. Two further assumptions complete the model.

(i) The labor force grows at a constant relative rate g independent of any economic variables in the system. Thus we may write an equation for the growth of labor

$$\dot{L} = gL, \qquad L(0) = L_0 > 0. \tag{1}$$

(ii) A constant fraction s of total output flow is saved and set aside to be added to the capital stock. Assuming moreover that capital does not depreciate, the growth of the capital stock is given by the equation

$$\dot{K} = sQ, \qquad K(0) = K_0 > 0. \tag{2}$$

Substituting the production function $Q = F(K, L)$ into (2), the system is complete and simple. The saving function determines the composition of demand as between output to be consumed and output to be set aside for accumulation. This given, the growth of capital is known. The growth of the labor force goes on exogenously. Thus, from any starting point with specified endowments of K and L, the growth of both factors is determined, and hence all future output and future factor growth is determined. For any given function F it would be possible to follow the time path of the system from any starting point. But it is simpler and more enlightening to make use of the assumption of constant returns to scale in order to reduce the problem to consideration of the capital/labor ratio alone, rather than the two factors separately. To this end we define

$$k \equiv K/L$$

and

$$f(k) \equiv F(k, 1) \equiv F(K/L, 1) = F(K, L)/L.$$

We then observe that the per capita or "intensive" function $f(k)$ is continuous for $k \geq 0$, and satisfies (see Exercise 1)

$$f(0) = 0 \tag{3}$$

$$f'(k) > 0, \quad k \geq 0, \tag{4}$$

and

$$f''(k) < 0, \quad k \geq 0. \tag{5}$$

Differentiating and substituting from (1), we find

$$\dot{k} = (\dot{K}/K - \dot{L}/L)(K/L) = \dot{K}/L - gk = sf(k) - gk \tag{6}$$

with initial condition $k(0) = K(0)/L(0) = K_0/L_0 = k_0 > 0$. This single differential equation determines the path to be followed by the capital/labor ratio k. All variables in the system can then be calculated immediately from the known values of K and L at any instant, so that wages, rentals, saving, and consumption are all known. (Note, however, that income distribution is irrelevant in this model since it does not influence the evolution of the system.)

The simple economic content of equation (6) should be noted. Since sQ is the portion of the output flow allocated to investment and gK is the investment flow necessary to have capital grow at the same rate as labor (and hence to have the capital/labor ratio remain unchanged), the difference between these two flows is the surplus still available for investment after all provision for equipping new labor at the existing capital/labor ratio standard. The right hand side of (6) is therefore simply the surplus per worker available after equipping all new labor at the existing standard; hence, the equation tells us simply that since all saving generated in the system has to be absorbed somewhere, the capital/labor ratio must rise at a rate proportional to the surplus per worker available after provision for equipping new labor.

What does this imply, then, about the development over time of the capital/labor ratio? The answer to that question depends only on the nature of the function

$$\phi(k) = sf(k) - gk \tag{7}$$

(and perhaps on the initial value k_0). We may easily derive a result noted by Koopmans [15].

Lemma 1: *For positive values of the parameters g and s satisfying*

$$0 < g/s < f'(0), \tag{8}$$

there exists a unique positive value k* such that $\phi(k^*) = 0$.

Proof: Since $\phi(0) = 0$, and $\phi(k)$ is strictly concave for $k \geqq 0$, if there is a positive value k^* satisfying $\phi(k^*) = 0$ then it is unique.

Now for any constant $K > 0$, by continuity

$$0 = F(K, 0) = \lim_{L \to 0} F(K, L) = K \lim_{L \to 0} \frac{L}{K} F(K/L, 1).$$

Hence,

$$0 = \lim_{k \to \infty} f(k)/k. \tag{9}$$

Therefore, for any $g/s > 0$, there exists $\bar{k}$ such that $f(k)/k < g/s$ for all $k > \bar{k}$, which means $\phi(k) < 0$ for all $k > \bar{k}$. On the other hand,

$$\lim_{k \to 0} \left[\frac{f(k) - f(0)}{k} \right] = \lim_{k \to 0} [f(k)/k]$$

is precisely $f'(0)$, and

$$f'(0) > g/s \tag{10}$$

by hypothesis.[2]

---

[2]It might seem at first glance that the hypothesis that capital is essential would guarantee $f'(k) \to \infty$ as $k \to 0$, which would in turn make the hypothesis $f'(0) > g/s$ redundant. But this is not so, as the counterexample $F(K, L) = L(1 - e^{-\gamma K/L})$ demonstrates. Capital being essential tells us only that $f(0) = 0$.

Hence there exists $\underline{k} > 0$ such that $f(k)/k > g/s$ for $0 < k < \underline{k}$, which means $\phi(k) > 0$ for $0 < k < \underline{k}$.

Since $\phi(k)$ is continuous, the intermediate value theorem guarantees that there exist at least one point k^* such that

$$\phi(k^*) = 0$$

as required. This completes the proof.

For any selection of positive parameters g and s satisfying $g/s < f'(0)$, therefore, we are justified in portraying the situation as in Figure 1.

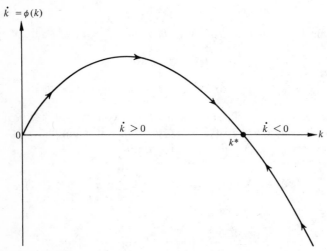

Figure 1: *Phase diagram for Solow's fundamental differential equation. The function $\phi(k)$ represents the per worker surplus available for capital deepening. Short-run equilibrium requires that the point $(k, \dot{k})$ representing the position and velocity of the economy always be on the curve $\phi(k)$.*

Figure 1 shows that no matter what the initial capital/labor ratio, provided it is positive, this system will converge toward a unique capital/labor ratio k^*. The diagram demonstrates quite convincingly that the equilibrium is stable in the interval $k > 0$; for the sake of illustrating a standard technique, we may also argue the point more formally here.

As usage differs among mathematicians, economists, and engineers, we must first digress briefly to consider what precisely we mean by stability. The following definitions will be adopted, and interested readers are referred to more elaborate mathematical treatment where appropriate. The survey by Kalman and Bertram [14] reviews the topic in detail.

Definition: A point $k*$ is an *equilibrium point* for the system described by equation (6) if

$$\phi(k*) = 0.$$

Definition: The system described by equation (6) is *globally stable* if, for any initial value $k_0 > 0$, the solution $\psi(t; k_0)$ to (6) has the property that there exists *some* equilibrium point $k*$, $0 < k* < \infty$, such that

$$\lim_{t \to \infty} \psi(t; k_0) = k*.$$

(It should be emphasized that this definition refers to a property of the system described by (6), not to a property of any one equilibrium point. The value $k*$ may depend upon k_0, but for any $k_0 > 0$, the system does approach some steady growth path.)

Lemma 2: *The system* (6) *is globally stable.*

Proof: We have already shown that there exists $\underline{k}$ such that

$$\phi(k) > 0 \quad \text{for} \quad 0 < k < \underline{k}$$

and that

$$\lim_{k \to \infty} \phi(k) < 0.$$

Moreover, the function $\phi(k)$ is continuous. Let an initial point $k_0 \in (0, \infty)$ be selected. If $\phi(k_0) > 0$, then there exists (by the intermediate value theorem) an equilibrium point $k^0 > k_0$. Defining $k* = \inf\{k \mid \phi(k) = 0, k > k_0\}$ we see that $\phi(k*) = 0$ (because ϕ is continuous) and $\lim_{t \to \infty} \psi(t; k_0) = k*$ (because $\dot{k} > 0$ for $k_0 \leq k < k*$). If $\phi(k_0) < 0$, an analogous procedure applies. If $\phi(k_0) = 0$, we have directly that $\lim_{t \to \infty} \psi(t; k_0) = k_0$. Hence from any initial value k_0, $0 < k_0 < \infty$, the solution $\psi(t; k_0)$ approaches some equilibrium point; therefore the system is globally stable. This completes the proof.[3]

Definition: An equilibrium point $k = k*$ of the system (6) is *asymptotically stable* (in the large) if for any admissible initial point k_0 the solution $\psi(t; k_0)$ to (6) satisfies $\lim_{t \to \infty} \psi(t; k_0) = k*$.

---

[3] This proof follows that of Arrow and Hurwicz [1], p. 540. A similar result is sometimes referred to as the Arrow–Block–Hurwicz theorem. See [2], p. 108.

Definition: An equilibrium point $k = k^*$ is *locally asymptotically stable* if there exists some region Ω containing k^* such that if $k_0 \in \Omega$ then $\lim_{t \to \infty} \psi(t; k_0) = k^*$.

Lemma 3: *The equilibrium point $k = k^*$ is asymptotically stable in the region $k > 0$.*

Proof: Define $\xi \equiv k - k^*$ and $V(\xi) \equiv \xi^2$.
  Then $V(\xi) \geq 0$ and $V(\xi) = 0$ if and only if $\xi = 0$.
Moreover,

$$\dot{V}(\xi) = 2\xi\dot{\xi} = 2\xi\dot{k} = 2\xi[sf(k) - gk] = 2\xi[sf(\xi + k^*) - g\xi - gk^*]$$

(by concavity)

$$\leq 2\,\xi[sf(k^*) + \xi sf'(k^*) - g\xi - gk^*] = 2\xi^2[sf'(k^*) - g]$$

$$= 2\xi^2\left[\frac{gk^*f'}{f} - g\right], \qquad \text{since} \quad s = gk^*/f(k^*),$$

$$= \frac{2g\xi^2}{f}(k^*f' - f) = \frac{-2g\xi^2}{f}(f - k^*f') < 0 \quad \text{unless} \quad \xi = 0.$$

Hence, by Lyapunov's theorem (see La Salle and Lefschetz [16]), the equilibrium $k = k^*$ is stable, as was required.[4]

Thus, we may conclude that the story of development as told by this model is summed up in a phrase: smooth convergence of the capital/labor ratio from any positive starting point to a unique equilibrium level. And, therefore, smooth convergence of the economy to an equilibrium "balanced growth path" along which capital, labor, and output grow at the same constant relative rate, while output per worker remains constant. Moreover, the rate at which the economy expands along the balanced growth path is the growth rate of labor and is completely independent of habits of thrift or the form of the production function. The economic rationale is straightforward: production possibilities admit any desired ratio of factor inputs, and since all saving must be absorbed, any surplus saving remaining after provision for

---

[4] Lyapunov's theorem is widely employed in the analysis of differential equation systems. In essence, it says simply that if one can find a function V measuring the distance (in some sense) from an equilibrium point k^*, if the distance is never negative and is zero only at the equilibrium point k^*, and if the motion of the system is such that this distance is always decreasing, then the equilibrium point must be stable. The result is obviously plausible, and it has found extensive application in economic theory.

maintaining the capital/labor ratio in the face of the growing labor force can be used only to increase the capital/labor ratio throughout the economy. The process is both simple and troublefree. What could go wrong?

Since within the model the logic is impeccable, any difficulties must arise through the failure of one of the assumptions, and there are few enough of these that we can check off all the possibilities.

Description of technology. One outstanding inadequacy in the specification of production conditions in this long-run model is, of course, that the production function certainly cannot be unchanging over time. We will deal with this question in detail in Chapter 3. Second, within the context of the no-technical-progress assumption, interest in the class of so-called constant elasticity of substitution functions makes it useful to consider cases in which the assumption that both factors are essential is dropped. (Within the class of CES functions, those having an elasticity of substitution σ exceeding unity fail to satisfy the assumption that both factors are essential.) We can at the same time illustrate the significance of the hypothesis

$$g/s < f'(0). \quad .$$

Finally, the assumption of constant returns to scale may be inappropriate.

Description of labor force growth. For a variety of reasons it can be argued that the labor supply might respond to economic conditions within the model. Rising wage rates may induce longer hours or higher labor force participation rates. Rising incomes may cause population growth rates to rise—or to fall. Such possibilities can be taken into account in the basic one-sector model; the effect, as we shall see, may be to alter some of the basic conclusions developed before.

Description of capital stock growth. Perhaps the most controversial feature of the neoclassical model of.growth we have discussed is the rule for determining the growth of capital. The rule just adopted must be interpreted primarily as a reflection of saving behavior, not a reflection of investors' decisions. More explicit consideration of the investment decision itself is required, as well as some consideration of alternative rules generating saving. In the next sections we take up in order each of these possible modifications to the basic model.

We have now discussed at some length the adjustment of the capital/labor ratio from some given initial value to some equilibrium value. This is a convenient place to introduce some terminology for later use.

In these models it is possible to think of distinguishing between investment which serves to increase capital/labor ratios, and investment which serves simply to maintain the capital/labor ratio in the face of a growing labor force; that is, which serves simply to equip new laborers as existing laborers are equipped. The former process involving increasing capital/labor ratios is often referred to as *capital deepening*, and the latter involving simple expansion of the capital stock to maintain existing capital/labor ratios is called *capital widening*.

We also note that if the economy were to begin at its equilibrium capital/labor ratio, then capital, labor, output, consumption, and investment would all grow at a constant relative rate, and the ratios between these variables would remain constant. Such a state of affairs is sometimes referred to as a *golden age*,[5] or *golden age growth*, as well as a *steady growth path*, or sometimes a *balanced growth path*.

2–4. Modification of the Production Specification: Factor Shares

It is easy to work out an explicit solution to Solow's differential equation in the special case where the production function has the well-known Cobb–Douglas form (see Exercise 4)

$$F(K, L) = AK^a L^{1-a}, \quad 0 < a < 1. \tag{11}$$

For this case, of course, we have

$$f'(k) \to \infty \quad \text{as} \quad k \to 0 \tag{12}$$

and hence have no difficulty satisfying the requirement $f'(0) > g/s \geq g > 0$ for any positive constants g and s, $s \leq 1$. Moreover we have already noted that when labor is essential to production, as it surely is for the production function (11), we are guaranteed that

$$f'(k) \to 0 \quad \text{as} \quad k \to \infty. \tag{13}$$

Hence the existence of a balanced growth equilibrium is assured for this Cobb–Douglas production function example.

But other perfectly respectable production functions do not have the feature that labor is essential, or they may not necessarily satisfy condition (12). One such example is the so-called CES function [3]. (Exercises 10 and 11 deal with properties of CES functions; these properties will be assumed without proof in the following text.) It may therefore be informative to study such an example to see the difficulties that a lack of these limiting properties creates.

[5] To emphasize its strictly mythological character; see Robinson [26].

The short answer to this question in terms of our earlier diagram may be given easily; indeed, it was given already by Solow [32]. Letting

$$F(K, L) = \gamma[\alpha K^{-\rho} + (1 - \alpha)L^{-\rho}]^{-1/\rho}, \tag{14}$$

we find that if $\rho > 0$,

$$f'(k) \to \gamma\alpha^{-1/\rho} \quad \text{as} \quad k \to 0$$

and

$$f'(k) \to 0 \qquad \text{as} \quad k \to \infty,$$

whereas if $-1 < \rho < 0$,

$$f'(k) \to \infty \qquad \text{as} \quad k \to 0$$

and

$$f'(k) \to \gamma\alpha^{-1/\rho} \quad \text{as} \quad k \to \infty.$$

Hence we might have, in place of Figure 1, either of the situations illustrated in Figures 2a or 2b. In the first case, $\phi(k)$ is never positive, and the capital/labor ratio k falls toward zero from any initial value. In the second case,

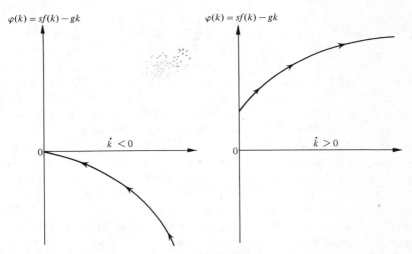

Figure 2(a). $(\rho > 0; \sigma < 1)$ **Figure 2(b).** $(-1 < \rho < 0; \sigma > 1)$
Phase diagrams possible for Solow's differential equation when F is a CES function with $\sigma \neq 1$

$\phi(k)$ is never negative, and the capital/labor ratio k rises without bound from any initial value.

In a sense, this is all that we need say about these cases in which no balanced growth path with a positive, finite equilibrium capital/labor ratio exists. But some economic explanation for why the difficulty should arise is more satisfying. A somewhat different approach to the analysis reveals an explanation in terms of factor shares and also relates the foregoing discussion to well-known work of Swan [34] and Meade [19].

Recalling that for a constant-returns-to-scale function such as (14) we may write

$$\frac{\dot{Q}}{Q} = \pi \frac{\dot{K}}{K} + (1 - \pi)\frac{\dot{L}}{L}, \tag{15}$$

where π is the competitive income share of capital (Exercise 4 in Chapter 1), we find that in the neoclassical model with constant saving rate s (where $\dot{K} = sQ$ and $\dot{L} = gL$),

$$\frac{\dot{Q}}{Q} = \pi \frac{sQ}{K} + (1 - \pi)g. \tag{16}$$

Defining $x \equiv Q/K$, we have also

$$\frac{\dot{x}}{x} = -(1 - \pi)\left[\frac{sQ}{K} - g\right] = (1 - \pi)[g - sx]. \tag{17}$$

Thus we could easily plot a phase diagram showing the way in which the output/capital ratio x behaves, starting from any initial value. Instead of the phase diagram itself, however, we may translate the horizontal axis by an amount g and plot growth rates sx and g rather than the difference between these. Clearly, from (17), when $g > sx$, $\dot{x} > 0$, and when $g < sx$, $\dot{x} < 0$ (provided always that $0 < (1 - \pi)$). Hence we conclude that x must approach x^*, provided $\pi < 1$. Moreover, we can plot the growth rate of output easily enough as the weighted average given by (16). If π were constant, that is, if the production function were Cobb–Douglas, this weighted average would appear as in Figure 3. This shows a unique equilibrium where output, labor, and capital are all growing at the same relative rate. But when π is not constant another possibility is introduced, namely, that at some point π becomes 1 and the output/capital ratio attains an equilibrium not compatible with balanced growth because output and capital grow at a common rate different from the growth rate of labor.

In economic terms we may view the issue as follows. A balanced growth equilibrium requires that output, capital, and labor all grow at the same

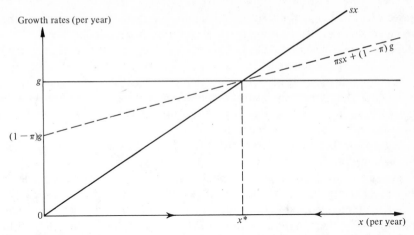

Figure 3. *Development of the output/capital ratio x and output growth rates when F is a Cobb–Douglas function.*

relative rate. If we draw a phase diagram, as we did for the Solow model, portraying the evolution of the capital/labor ratio when the system (6) has an equilibrium, then at the equilibrium the capital/labor ratio and the output/labor ratio both remain constant. It follows immediately that the output/capital ratio remains constant also. Hence an equilibrium at a positive finite capital/labor ratio in Figure 1 is automatically a balanced growth path. However, there need not be any such equilibrium, as Figure 2 illustrates. What is happening in such cases?

From Equation (17) we recognize that an equilibrium in which the output/capital ratio remains constant need not be a balanced growth path. Unless the capital/labor ratio also remains constant, that is, unless the growth rate of capital is equal to g at the equilibrium, the equilibrium cannot be a balanced growth path. Figure 3 portrays the case in which no trouble can ever arise; there is only one equilibrium output/capital ratio, and it occurs where all three of capital, output, and labor have the same growth rate. This is the case illustrated by the Cobb–Douglas function, where the output/capital ratio tends to zero or to infinity as the capital/labor ratio tends to zero or infinity, respectively.

But with CES or more general functions the output/capital ratio may be bounded above or below no matter what happens to the capital/labor ratio (see Exercise 10). As the output/capital ratio approaches these bounds, the competitively imputed share of capital in national income approaches unity, and we see from (17) that the boundary values themselves are equilibrium output/capital ratios, but they are not associated with balanced growth paths.

Thus we see that the cases in which the capital/labor ratio in Figure 2 approaches zero or infinity without achieving equilibrium correspond to cases where the capital/output ratio is approaching a boundary at which the imputed share of capital is unity. If substitution in production is neither so difficult nor so easy that this situation is plausible, then the cases illustrated in Figure 2 can be ignored.

More specifically, we see from equation (17) that there is always a value $x = g/s$ of the output/capital ratio that would represent a balanced growth path. However, when the elasticity of substitution σ is less than unity, the output/capital ratio is bounded above even as the capital/labor ratio tends to zero; if the bound is so strict that it is exceeded by the value $x = g/s$, then no balanced growth path is possible. Then the growth of capital falls short of the growth of labor, and the capital/labor ratio must decay to zero as in Figure 2a. Thus Figure 2a portrays the case where substitution of capital for labor is more restricted than in the Cobb–Douglas function, and the share of capital becomes unity at a value of the output/capital ratio too low to bring the growth rate of capital up to the growth rate of labor.

If $\sigma > 1$, on the other hand, the output/capital ratio is bounded below, even as the capital/labor ratio rises without bound. If this lower bound exceeds the value $x = g/s$, then again no balanced growth path is possible. The growth rate of capital exceeds the growth rate of labor, and the capital/labor ratio rises without bound, as in Figure 2b.

Let us summarize the point of this digression. We began with a system involving three variables of interest—labor, capital, and output—and we wished to study the balanced growth states in which all three grow at the same rate. In doing so it was convenient to look at a diagram portraying the evolution of the capital/labor ratio. But this diagram did not carry all the information relevant to our system. Particularly when there is no equilibrium capital/labor ratio at a positive finite value, it is important to know what is happening to other variables in the system. We have seen that these trouble-some cases occur when substitution of factors is either so difficult that an output/capital ratio equal to g/s is too high to be attainable even as the capital/labor ratio goes to zero (the share of wages having become zero before the output/capital ratio could be increased sufficiently), or so easy that an output/capital ratio of g/s is too low to be attainable even as the capital/labor ratio rises to infinity (the share of wages having become zero before the output/capital ratio and the growth rate of capital could be reduced sufficiently).

Exercises 12 and 14 ask for an explicit diagrammatic analysis for each of these pathological cases and for proof that their empirical relevance is un-likely to be great. Still, it should be noted that the more flexible production conditions we have introduced, relaxing the hypothesis that both factors are essential, do introduce the logical possibility that this simple economy may be unable to attain a balanced growth equilibrium, and hence also the logical possibility that shifts in saving behavior may affect the long-run growth rate.

As a separate question about production conditions, we consider briefly the assumption of constant returns to scale while retaining both the assumed saving behavior and the exogenous growth of the labor force. Here we need note only that under diminishing returns to scale, factor shares always sum to less than 1. Thus, suppose π_r and π_w are the relative shares of capital and labor, respectively, with $\pi_r + \pi_w < 1$. Then, instead of (17) we have

$$\frac{\dot{x}}{x} = \frac{\dot{Q}}{Q} - \frac{\dot{K}}{K} = \pi_r sx + \pi_w g - sx = (1 - \pi_r)s\left[\frac{\pi_w}{1 - \pi_r}\frac{g}{s} - x\right] \qquad (18)$$

so that

$$\dot{x} = 0 \quad \text{when} \quad x = \frac{\pi_w}{1 - \pi_r}\frac{g}{s} < \frac{g}{s}. \qquad (19)$$

The growth rate of labor exceeds the growth rate of capital at the point where x is stationary; thus, k and the wage rate tend perpetually toward zero. Alternatively, with increasing returns to scale, the equilibrium value of x exceeds g/s, and then the capital/labor ratio k and the wage rate tend to infinity.

Thus we see that the technical specification may be crucial to the existence of the balanced growth path. In the absence of constant returns it is, as would naturally be expected, fruitless to seek an equilibrium golden age scale expansion. Even with constant returns to scale such a golden age equilibrium need not exist if the required output/capital ratio falls outside a (possibly restricted) attainable range determined by the ease of factor substitution in production. The only CES function for which the attainable range includes all positive values is that in which the elasticity of substitution is unity. The so-called Inada conditions $f'(0) = \infty$ and $f'(\infty) = 0$ imply similar restrictions on technological specification, restrictions that are sufficient to ensure the existence of a meaningful balanced growth path.

A further issue of technical specification deserves consideration, but we shall pay no attention to it in this book. The question of depreciation in the sense of deterioration of value will arise later in the discussion of price conditions that are reminiscent of a "perfect" depreciation formula. But the process of actual physical decay and the requirements for physical replacement are not discussed. Instead, we suppose that physical deterioration may be accounted for by assuming a constant "force of mortality" so that the survival curve for all capital goods is a negative exponential. This assumption is described by saying that capital decays exponentially or radioactively. This assumption implies that replacement requirements at any time are proportional to the stock of capital at that time. Other approaches are possible but are not adopted here. Possibilities include the "one-hoss shay" hypothesis which assumes a fixed lifetime for all capital goods of any particular type, or the use of quite general survival curves permitting depreciation to depend upon age. The hypothesis of exponential decay has been defended on empirical grounds, although in principle there seems little relevance in it; its primary appeal is simply its immense convenience in computation. Extension of the model to permit the rate of physical depreciation to depend upon use (utilization rate) as well as age would obviously be desirable, but perhaps of less importance in our full employment models than in models that deal explicitly with varying utilization rates.

2–5. Modification of Labor Growth Specification

We shall indicate briefly the possible effects of introducing endogenous labor growth into the simple model with constant returns.

Dependence of the labor force on economic considerations can arise from a variety of causes. For example, the population might be growing at a constant rate g, but the labor force participation rate might depend at any moment on the prevailing wage. In such a case, the population is described by

$$P(t) = P_0 e^{gt} \tag{20}$$

and labor force by

$$L(t) = p(w)P(t) = p[w(k)]P_0 e^{gt} \tag{21}$$

where $p(w)$ denotes the labor force participation rate. Thus,

$$\dot{L} = p'w'kP_0 e^{gt} + gpP_0 e^{gt} \tag{22}$$

or

$$\frac{\dot{L}}{L} = \frac{p'w'k}{p} + g. \tag{23}$$

Hence,

$$\dot{k} = \frac{\dot{K}}{L} - \frac{\dot{L}}{L}k = sf(k) - \left(\frac{p'w}{p}\frac{w'k}{w}\frac{k}{k} + g\right)k = sf(k) - \eta_p\eta_w k - gk$$

or

$$k = \frac{sf(k) - gk}{1 + \eta_p\eta_w}, \tag{24}$$

where η_p represents the elasticity of the participation rate with respect to wages and η_w represents the elasticity of wages with respect to k. Since p' may be expected to be positive and w' is certainly positive, we have $\eta_p > 0$ and $\eta_w > 0$. Thus the balanced growth equilibrium, and hence any comparison of various steady growth equilibria, is the same in this model as in the Solow model discussed in Section 2-3. The speed of approach to equilibrium is reduced, of course, reflecting the fact that rising wage rates induce the entry of a larger proportion of the population as the capital/labor ratio rises. (Notice also that these equations imply the existence of a unique wage rate and capital/labor ratio k at any moment; see Exercise 18.)

An endogenously determined labor force may also occur because the population itself or the growth rate g is endogenous. According to this line of thought, when k, and hence the wage rate $w(k)$, is low, the population may be unable even to maintain itself, and the growth rate of labor would be negative. At higher wage rates a positive growth of population and the labor force results until the wage rate reaches such levels that the (now high-income) community's population growth rates fall off once again. Such a case might be represented by a growth rate $g(k)$ and by a phase plane as in Figure 4,

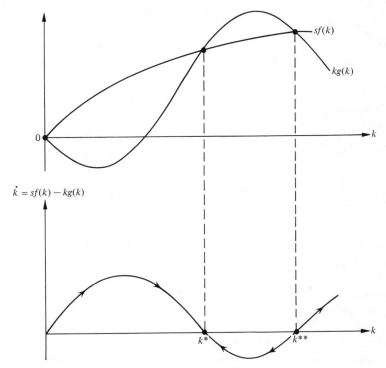

Figure 4. *Phase diagram for the differential equation $\dot{k} = sf(k) - g(k)k$.*

and might be of interest in analysis of capital accumulation in developing countries or "dual" economies.

The effect of this reasoning is to introduce the possibility of multiple equilibria and hence also of unstable equilibria. We notice that Figure 4, as already observed by Solow in 1956, illustrates the nature of a possible "low level trap" at which, for small perturbations of k, population effects oppose any increase in capital/labor ratios and force a return to the stable equilibrium. A major drive, however, which accomplished an increase in the capital/labor ratio beyond the high level unstable equilibrium point would set the economy on a path of perpetually rising capital and income per head, thus justifying the proponents of a "big push."

Other such stories could be told. We tell no more here, but the reader interested in pursuing similar issues should see the work of Phelps [23] and the references cited there.

Again, of course, if the assumption of constant returns to scale is not imposed, then the reduction to per capita terms is not possible, and the system of two differential equations must be studied directly. The effect of admitting endogenous labor force determination is then to drop the simple differential equation

$$\dot{L} = gL, \qquad L(0) = L_0,$$

with its immediate solution and to substitute a more complicated expression in which the growth of L depends on K and L through wage rates or otherwise. The work of Niehans [21] deals with the problem and also illustrates well how delicately poised between stagnation and explosion is the balanced growth path associated with constant returns to scale.

2–6. Modification of the Capital Growth Specification

Harrod's Reservation

As noted before, the path of accumulation to the equilibrium capital/labor ratio entails that rates of profit (real rentals in this one-good model) fall to their equilibrium level $f'(k^*)$. This suggests a possible difficulty: since saving decisions and investment decisions are generally made by different people, it may happen that equation (2) describes the saving desires of the community even when investors no longer find profit rates adequate to warrant any increase in capital/labor or capital/output ratios. Is there any reason, in fact, why this could not happen before the equilibrium capital/labor ratio k^* is attained? If so, what would be the behavior of the economy? Interpreting the work of Harrod [10] as an attempt to deal with these issues, we will illustrate our argument by several quotations from his discussion.

The argument stems from a concern with Keynesian difficulties due to over-saving. "The idea which underlies these lectures is that sooner or later we shall be faced once more with the problems of stagnation ..." ([10], page v). With this problem in mind, Harrod turns to "examine the necessary relations between the rates of growth of the different elements in a growing economy" and to "examine critically the mutual dependence of the steadily changing volumes of supply of each factor and the steadily changing rates of remuneration" ([10], page 19). In particular, the dependence of capital growth on profit rates is emphasized: it may happen that there is a minimum profit rate equal to the rate of interest that could be earned on financial assets (not explicitly considered thus far) beyond which accumulation will not proceed. Let us therefore ask, "What behavior of capital is required to be consistent with growth in the other elements, *on the hypothesis that the rate of interest does not change*?" ([10], page 22, italics in original). "I am not considering for the moment what will happen if the requisite fraction of income is not saved, but what saving is requisite to be consistent with a certain type of progress, if the rate of interest does not change" ([10], page 22).

In the light of what we have just said about the neoclassical model in the absence of technical progress, this is an easy question to answer.

Lemma 4: *For the rate of interest to be constant (in the absence of technical progress), the capital/output ratio must be constant, and the requisite saving rate is*

$$s = gv, \tag{25}$$

where v denotes the (constant) capital/output ratio.

Proof: Since $F(K, L)$ is homogeneous of degree one in K and L, its derivative $r = \partial F(K, L)/\partial K$ is homogeneous of degree zero in K and L. Hence, r is constant if and only if K/L is constant, which entails $\dot{K}/K = g$.

Hence, from equation (15) $\dot{Q}/Q = g$, and K/Q is a constant, denoted v. Then we have $\dot{K} = gK = gvQ$ or $\dot{K}/Q = s = gv$, as was required.

Thus the requisite fraction of income saved is the product of the rate of growth of labor and the capital/output ratio. This gives a "first approach to the question of the demand for saving in a growing economy." That is, it tells us the demand for saving—how much saving would willingly be absorbed by entrepreneurs who are not prepared to see the capital rental rate fall. What about the supply? After an extended discussion of a life-cycle hypothesis, bequest motives, and corporate saving, Harrod concludes, "There seems to be no broad presumption that the rate of saving will be precisely what is required to sustain a steady rate of advance of production with the rate of interest constant. We may have to contemplate a continuously rising or falling rate of interest" ([10], page 56). The question then is whether in fact this is plausible. Harrod's answer in summarizing the difficulty is that such development seems unlikely. "In our earlier lecture we reached the conclusion that fundamental conditions (namely, required capital growth in relation to volunteered saving) might require a steadily falling rate of interest. We found great difficulties in envisaging how the capital market could ever succeed in providing such a steady decline" ([10], page 75).

Faced with these difficulties in adjusting to an arbitrarily specified saving rate by deepening capital and reducing profit rates, we may still ask whether there are conditions under which saving behavior may be consistent with an unchanging interest rate. Clearly this will be the case if the rate of growth of income enables all saving to be absorbed without changing the capital/output ratio. This requires

$$\dot{K} = v\dot{Q} = sQ$$

or

$$\frac{\dot{Q}}{Q} = \frac{s}{v}, \qquad Q = Q_0\, e^{(s/v)t}. \tag{26}$$

In other words, whatever the parameters s and v (v being treated as a parameter because we are assuming that entrepreneurs refuse to deepen capital) all saving will be absorbed if income grows at the rate s/v. But how can this be? We know already that the capital/output ratio depends on the capital/labor ratio, and thus it will not be constant unless the capital/labor ratio is constant. Hence, unless $g = s/v$ so that capital and labor will grow at the same rate, this growth path is not consistent with full employment at the given labor growth rates. If

$$g < s/v, \tag{27}$$

it is simply not possible to sustain the path described in (26). If

$$g > s/v, \tag{28}$$

then only by admitting unemployment can the growth path (26) be followed.

Moreover, Harrod has a well-known argument to suggest that the growth path (26) is in fact an "unstable" equilibrium path, in that deviations from it cause investors to react to increase these deviations. The difficulty with the argument is that there is no explicit description of investors' behavior, and not all possible descriptions lead to this instability. Still, if such instability is present, then we can see that when s is high enough that (27) holds, the economy cannot attain the growth path (26) and is plunged into depression. This reasoning leads to a rather pessimistic conclusion: if s is too high relative to gv the warranted path (26) is unattainable, and the economy falls ever further below it. If s is too low relative to gv, then the warranted growth path (26) could actually be followed, although it would show growing unemployment as labor grew faster than the capital stock. If once the system moved above the warranted growth path it would run up to the ceiling set by labor force growth, and then demand would forever outrun capacity.

We need not ponder too long over these paradoxical issues; the point at the moment is fairly simple. We have gone through the neoclassical growth model, noting the smooth convergence to equilibrium. Following Harrod we then questioned whether in fact it was plausible to suppose all saving absorbed, as the neoclassical model demanded. In particular we argued that if monetary forces, outside the present model but implicitly in the background, determined a money rate of interest, then the money yield on machines could not fall below that level. If this monetary rate of interest were sufficiently high there would in general be no reason to expect that the saving rate would balance capital requirements; in general it might be larger, and if interest rates could not be driven down all saving could not be absorbed. In this circumstance smooth convergence to steady balanced growth is prohibited, and unemployment is one possible result.

This analysis suggests, therefore, that studying the Harrod position as if it were based essentially on a technological hypothesis about the production function, namely that it shows fixed proportions, misses the essential feature of Harrod's analysis. We have, following Eisner [8], studied Harrod's position in the context of the same smooth neoclassical production function that generated Solow's results and have isolated the hypothesis about freely falling interest rates as the crucial consideration.

It would be improper to leave this discussion without the observation that the work of Domar has also been crucial in the evolution of these ideas. His emphasis on the dual nature of capital accumulation, which at the same time represents a demand for output and creates the capacity to produce, was fundamental in later efforts to construct a consistent Keynesian system that does recognize the role of investment and thus turns the short-run macro model into a growth model. Like Harrod's work, Domar's models introduce explicitly the question of the demand for investment and hence the possible imbalance between saving desires and investment plans. It is important to emphasize that these models are equilibrium models of a different type than those studied previously in this chapter; models in the tradition of Harrod and Domar are in a very real sense demand-constrained models, setting independently determined saving and investment desires into balance and describing the growth path such an equilibrium economy would follow. These models reveal what properties the saving or investment function must possess if such a growth path is to be compatible with sustained full employment, but this question is clearly separable from the description of the growth path. All the rest of our discussion, on the other hand, has been based on supply-constrained models in which output is determined at full employment, and the resulting growth path can be analyzed. These models also reveal what behavior of investment demand is necessary to be compatible with sustained balance between saving and investment, but in this case the behavior of investment demand is the separable issue. In the remainder of this book we shall focus on the supply-constrained models that assume full employment and expect that investment decisions can always be reconciled with desired saving.

Let us consider again whether there is any justification for the hypothesis that capital can still be accumulated even though the real rental on machines falls as the capital/labor ratio rises to its equilibrium level. One defense, of course, is simply the observation that although the rate of interest falls continually, it falls only toward some asymptotic level. Along the balanced growth path it would remain constant. Nonetheless, this is no help if the interest rate available on some hypothetical alternative asset lies above the capital rental rate appropriate to the balanced growth path.

Another escape may lie in the behavior of prices. If we are prepared to introduce consideration of a financial asset like money, we may ask how the money price of goods behaves. In momentary equilibrium, with both capital goods and consumption goods being produced, the price of output is the price of the capital good as well. Because people may trade capital goods, the price of the capital good should, in principle, always settle at the present value of the stream of future rentals from the use of the capital good, discounted at the money rate of interest r_0. We have, therefore, for this price $p(t)$, the relationship[6]

$$p(t) = \int_t^\infty p(\tau)f'[k(\tau)]\exp\left[-\int_t^\tau r_0(z)\,dz\right]d\tau \tag{29}$$

or, differentiating with respect to t on the assumption that this price is always finite and the improper integral in (29) therefore always converges,

$$\frac{\dot{p}(t)}{p(t)} + f'[k(t)] = r_0(t). \tag{30}$$

Hence, even if a money rate of interest r_0 were fixed at a rate too high to permit physical capital accumulation to the steady state in the absence of

[6] This valuation relationship is discussed in more detail later.

price changes, it is possible that price inflation may raise the money rate of return to the owner of capital to the level of the money rate of interest (in other words, reduce the real rate of return on money to that on capital goods), even as the real rental on capital falls to its equilibrium level on the balanced growth track. In other words, a sufficiently high rate of capital gain as a result of inflation in the nominal price of goods may persuade investors to accumulate goods rather than alternative paper assets.

In the absence of (i) an explicit treatment of the alternative financial assets available, (ii) a fuller theory of asset desires, and (iii) investment decisions themselves, however, this discussion is not really very satisfactory. We shall undertake the necessary explicit analysis in Chapter 6; in the meantime, we turn now to some other possible mechanisms by which saving may be generated in the one-good model.

Other Saving Functions

Even apart from the Harrod-type difficulties associated with a possible floor under profit rates, the simple proportional saving hypothesis we have used can be criticized. Here we consider the modifications involved if allowance is made for a propensity to save out of wage income that differs from the propensity to save out of rental income, the former being, presumably,[7] lower than the latter. Letting s_w and s_r denote these two saving propensities and assuming $s_r \geqq s_w$, we have

$$S = s_r RK + s_w WL$$

where R and W denote the rental rate for capital and the wage rate, respectively. Under competitive pricing, we then have

$$S = s_r KF_K + s_w[F - KF_K] \tag{31}$$

and the saving flow

$$sF = S = s_r KF_K + s_w[F - KF_K],$$

or

$$sf(k) = (s_r - s_w)kf' + s_w f(k).$$

---

[7] Since the propensity to retain corporate income for reinvestment purposes is presumably higher than the propensity to save out of personal income. Also see Burmeister and Taubman [4] for some empirical evidence.

The saving rate may thus be written as a function of k:

$$s(k) = (s_r - s_w) \frac{kf'(k)}{f(k)} + s_w. \tag{32}$$

We have then

$$\dot{k} = (s_r - s_w)kf' + s_w f - gk, \tag{33}$$

and if we consider

$$\frac{d\dot{k}}{dk} = (s_r - s_w)kf'' + (s_r - s_w)f' + s_w f' - g \tag{34}$$

$$= (s_r - s_w)kf'' + s_r f' - g, \tag{35}$$

it is easy to show that at any nonzero equilibrium point where $\dot{k} = 0$ we have also (see Exercise 21)

$$\frac{d\dot{k}}{dk} < 0. \tag{36}$$

This result suffices to show uniqueness and stability (but not existence) of any nonzero equilibrium point.

As was observed by Johnson [12], we may also deal with a saving function determined by desired wealth/income ratios. For example, if it be assumed that saving is always determined by the rule

$$sf = gk + \theta[k^* - k] \tag{37}$$

where θ is an adjustment coefficient and k^* is the physical wealth per capita desired at the observed level of output per capita, determined by some desired wealth/income ratio R^*, then the saving rate is given as a function of k by

$$sf = gk + \theta[f(k)R^* - k].$$

Consequently in this case the growth equation is

$$\dot{k} = \theta[f(k)R^* - k] = \theta f(k)[R^* - k/f]. \tag{38}$$

It is then clear that the equilibrium is unique under the assumption of a neoclassical production function, with the additional condition (see Exercise 22)

$$f'(0) < \frac{1}{R*}.$$ (39)

The Two-class Model

Exercise 23 asks you to show that in our standard one-good model with population growing at a constant relative rate, if all profits are saved and reinvested and all wages are consumed, then the system approaches, from any initial point, a balanced growth equilibrium path having the property

$$f'(k) = g$$ (40)

provided that $f'(0) < g < f'(\infty)$. A little reflection on the same relationship multiplied by (positive) k

$$f'(k)k = gk$$ (41)

reveals the simple rationale for this guaranteed stable convergence to a particular balanced growth equilibrium. For if the equality were violated—say, if the left-hand side which represents per capita profits in a neoclassical distribution scheme were to exceed the right-hand side—then clearly the system could absorb all intended saving only by increasing the allotment of capital per worker. Capital widening by itself would be insufficient to absorb the flow of profits required to be reinvested. The consequent capital deepening in turn forces down the level of per capita profits and the system thus loses momentum as it approaches the designated balanced growth track. Similarly, if profits in fact fall short of the requirement for simple capital widening, reinvestment of all profits fails to equip all new workers with the pre-existing allotments of capital, and the average level of capital per worker falls.

Once this obvious mechanism is recognized, it is easy to see that if only the fraction s_r of profits is continually reinvested, the relationship becomes

$$s_r f'(k)k = gk$$

or

$$f'(k) = g/s_r.$$ (42)

The same rationale continues to apply.

What is not so obvious, and is really quite intriguing, however, is that the system can in fact continue to display the same asymptotic behavior even if there is some additional saving, determined according to quite different rules, in the system. Upon further consideration this should not appear startling; even if reinvestment of profits is only a small part of total saving we would expect that the foregoing mechanism might lead to changing capital/labor ratios whenever the equality (42) fails to hold. But working out the details is not necessarily simple if the determination of the rest of the saving flow is complex. And clearly, if the flow of profits directly reinvested becomes a completely negligible part of a saving flow dominated by the alternative sources, the theorem can no longer be expected to hold.

The observation that condition (42) (which is obvious when a fraction of profits reinvested is the only source of saving) remains valid when some additional saving flow is admitted, is the work of Pasinetti [22]. He developed this result in the context of a model in which there are distinct classes[8] in the community, and distinct components of the capital stock associated with these classes. One class receives only profits as income; its saving becomes the flow of reinvested profits just discussed. Another class receives a flow of profits from the portion of the capital stock associated with members of that class in addition to wage income. Its saving becomes the flow of alternatively generated saving introduced as an addition to saving from reinvested profits.

Labelling these two classes capitalists and laborers, respectively, gives the model color. The result we have described and Pasinetti has proved is then phrased by saying that introducing the additional saving flow generated by the laborer class (saving a constant fraction s_w of their total income) does nothing to alter either the asymptotically attained balanced growth equilibrium rate of interest, which is still given by equation (42), or the balanced growth capital/labor ratio, which in our model may be written as a function of the rate of interest.

But it would seem that introducing additional saving (thus changing the parameters of our differential equation system) must change something; in this case, of course, what is changed is the composition of the total capital stock as between capitalists' capital and laborers' capital and the composition of saving as between capitalists' saving and laborers' saving. To observe this is to confront the question alluded to before: at what point does the change in composition become sufficient that the alternative saving flow dominates the original flow of capitalists' reinvested profits, driving the proportion of capital owned by capitalists to zero? This important question, overlooked in the original Pasinetti discussion, is the subject of a thorough study by Samuelson and Modigliani [28], who demonstrate that such dominance may

---

[8] Perhaps it would be better to refer to the model as a two-caste model, thus emphasizing that the classes in this model community are distinguished not by the form of their income or their holdings of assets, but by their habits and the emphasis attributed to their actions.

occur for very small values of the saving propensity s_w. In such a case the system begins to behave just as if it were a simple Solow-type model with a constant average propensity to save and the saving of the capitalist class can be ignored. In this case, of course, we revert to our old result which says nothing directly about the equilibrium rate of profit, but tells us that

$$s_w f(k) = gk.$$

Further discussion of this result would be out of place here, but can be found in the several articles of the *Review of Economic Studies*, October, 1966, which comment upon the Samuelson–Modigliani paper [28]. The introduction of the two classes or castes of savers independently deciding on their own saving flows does, however, suggest still another interesting question; namely, what can be said about the behavior of a system in which population grows and aggregate saving is determined by adding up the individual saving decisions of a number of possibly different people in possibly different circumstances? To this question, for which we know answers only in highly simplified cases, we now turn.

A Competitively Determined Saving Policy

So far we have considered a situation in which accumulated capital remains in place forever for use in further production. However, to revert to our example in which corn was the product and stockpiled seed the accumulated capital, let us consider what might happen if, instead of the stock of seed being maintained forever, it were to be paid out each year, with interest, to those who had "invested" it at the beginning of the growing season, while from the remainder of the product the new stock of seed for next year is to be "saved." How would this system develop if the saving were coordinated through a market mechanism in which currently productive labor attempts to save and invest for its old age? The question thus takes note of two features of great interest: first, in a growing economy there is danger in adopting the crude assumption that the labor force is a constant fraction of the population (independent of the growth rate), because if people traditionally retire at the end of working lives, the ratio of the number of retired people to the number of working people depends explicitly on the growth rate. Second, market-oriented life-cycle saving behavior must also depend on growth rates and could conceivably result in a pattern of development different from that just outlined.

The determination of equilibrium interest rates and aggregate saving in a capital market that reconciles individual saving desires has been studied in a very simplified context by Samuelson [27]. The resulting saving behavior has been incorporated in a model with capital accumulation by Diamond [7] and by Cass and Yaari [5]. To illustrate the results, we will consider Diamond's analysis here.

First we identify the individuals who save, and we admit the transitory character of their lives, which has a bearing on their attitudes toward saving. We simplify drastically by supposing that these lives may be broken into two periods of equal length: a time to work and a time to rest. During the working life the individual saves in order to invest in assets that he can consume (principal and interest) during retirement. Bequest motives are absent.

Thus, in light of a given interest rate r_{t+1} ruling on investments made at time t to mature at time $t + 1$, each man working in period t must decide how much to consume and how much to save. In period $t + 1$ he is able to consume his savings and accumulated interest. In the interim, his savings form part of the capital stock used in period $t + 1$. He is repaid, with interest, from the resulting output flow.

We determine the equilibrium interest rate, as usual, by letting the demand for and the supply of saving be brought into balance. The analysis is as follows.

A man working in period t receives a wage w_t from which he may save s_t, leaving $c_t^1 = w_t - s_t$ for consumption in period t. His saving during his working years determines his retirement consumption (enjoyed in period $t + 1$) as $c_t^2 = (1 + r_{t+1})s_t$. Each man working at time t is assumed to determine his one individual choice variable s so as to yield a maximum to a utility function $U(c_t^1, c_t^2)$. For given w_t and r_{t+1}, the calculation is clearly feasible. Assuming all individuals identical, total saving in period t is given by

$$S_t = L_t s_t$$

when L_t is the number of people working at time t. If we now take this total saving as the capital stock available for period $t + 1$, we may argue that the equilibrium interest rate must satisfy

$$r_{t+1} = \frac{\partial F}{\partial K_{t+1}} (K_{t+1}, L_{t+1}) = F_1(S_t, L_{t+1}) = f'\left(\frac{S_t}{L_{t+1}}\right) = f'\left(\frac{s_t}{(1 + g)}\right). \quad (43)$$

But s_t is a function of w_t and r_{t+1}, and because of the factor-price frontier discussed in Chapter 1,

$$w_t = \phi(r_t). \quad (44)$$

Hence we have the single difference equation determining r_t, namely,

$$r_{t+1} = f'[s_t(\phi(r_t), r_{t+1})/(1 + g)]. \quad (45)$$

From this the rest of the evolution of the system follows, and it can be analyzed explicitly for particular choices of the production functions and utility functions. Exercise 17 suggests an example that illustrates the process.

Discussion of this model leads into several further fascinating questions.

(i) How would capital markets operate in more general models with individual saving decisions?

(ii) Is there anything inherently optimal or efficient about decentralized decision processes such as those admitted here?

(iii) How would this system, dependent on individual saving decisions by people of different generations, be affected by the introduction of alternative assets?

(iv) How should the problem of allocating national product between generations at the same time, and between periods, be approached in such a model?

Again we have to say that such questions can be approached only after extension of the model and after consideration of efficiency or optimality criteria. In the next section we take a first step in this direction.

2–7. The Golden Rule

In the previous section we analyzed the behavior of the simplest model when the saving flow is obtained by aggregating individually determined saving desires. We know also that with different saving propensities s imposed upon the system, the Solow model approaches different steady growth paths. It is natural to ask whether some saving rates are more appropriate than others; whether, for example, the community ought to interfere systematically with individual saving desires.

One first approach to answering this question is to ask whether some balanced growth paths are more desirable than others. Since in the Solow model particular saving rates lead to particular steady growth paths, we can translate a preference for one particular growth path into a preference for one specific saving propensity s.

Suppose, therefore, that we sought a steady growth path along which per capita consumption is a maximum (over all sustainable steady growth paths). We can identify this path by setting $\dot{k}$ equal to zero in equation (6), thus obtaining the equilibrium k^* as a function of the parameter s. Along that steady growth path, per capita consumption is

$$c = (1 - s)f[k^*(s)] = \left[1 - \frac{gk^*}{f(k^*)}\right]f(k^*) = f(k^*) - gk^*.$$

Differentiating with respect to s to obtain the maximum steady growth per capita consumption, we find

$$\frac{dc}{ds} = [f'(k^*) - g]\frac{dk^*}{ds} = 0.$$

Since $dk^*/ds > 0$, the condition for a maximum is that s satisfy

$$f'(\tilde{k}^*) = g$$

where $\tilde{k}^*$ is the capital/labor ratio yielding highest per capita consumption; then

$$s = \frac{g\tilde{k}^*}{f(\tilde{k}^*)} = \frac{\tilde{k}^*f'(\tilde{k}^*)}{f(\tilde{k}^*)}. \quad ^9$$

We learn, in other words, that if we ignore initial conditions altogether, and simply choose the constant saving rate s associated with the steady growth path on which per capita consumption is highest, then we arrive at an explicit rule: we should choose that saving rate associated with the steady growth path on which $f'(\tilde{k}^*) = g$ (the rate of profit equals the rate of labor force growth), or, alternatively which leads to that growth path on which the saving rate equals the share of profit in national income.

This calculation can be illustrated by Figure 5. If we prescribe $s = s_0$ in the Solow model, then the system has one sustainable equilibrium capital/labor ratio k_0^*. At this capital/labor ratio the system follows a path of steady growth with per capita consumption c_0. If we were to prescribe a different saving policy, say $s = s_1$, then the system would have a different equilibrium capital/labor ratio k_1^*, and, along the steady growth track associated with k_1^*, per capita consumption would be c_1. Thus, by considering different possible saving rates we arrive at that steady growth path along which per capita consumption achieves its maximum c^*, and from the diagram it is clear that this maximum should be characterized by $f'(\tilde{k}^*) = g$.

The rationale for this result is very straightforward, as Solow [33] has pointed out. We are comparing only alternative steady growth paths independent of initial conditions but subject to the requirement that once a capital/labor ratio has been selected it must be maintained forever in the face of continuing labor force growth. This commitment creates a demand for goods for capital widening, and this demand is greater at higher capital/labor ratios, as is output. At what point, i.e., at what capital/labor ratio, would an

---

⁹ Exercise 19 asks you to show that under the conditions assumed for the Solow model an interior solution to these equations exists; moreover, $f'(\tilde{k}^*) = g$ is a necessary and sufficient condition provided $f'(0) < g < f'(\infty)$.

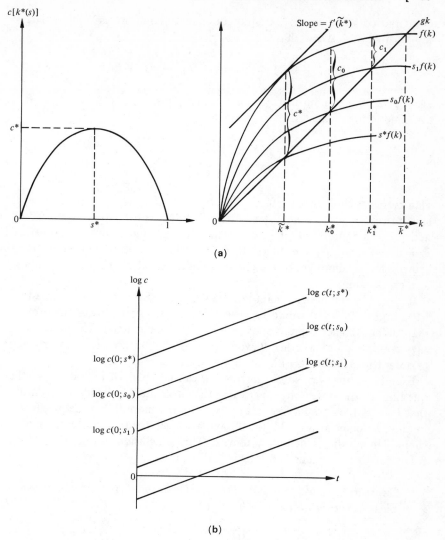

Figure 5. *Parallel consumption tracks on alternative steady growth paths. (The Golden Rule saving ratio yields the highest such path.)*

increase in the capital/labor ratio increase the commitment to capital widening more than it would increase output, and thus leave less for consumption?

We can answer this question by comparing consumption levels at some particular time, say time zero, on paths with different capital endowments. With capital stock K we find

$$C(0; K) = F(K, L_0) - gK$$

given the commitment to maintain the capital/labor ratio. With a larger capital stock $K + \Delta K$ we have

$$C(0; K + \Delta K) = F(K + \Delta K, L_0) - g(K + \Delta K),$$

again given the commitment to maintain the now larger capital stock. Will consumption be increased?

$$C(0; K + \Delta K) - C(0; K) = F(K + \Delta K, L_0) - F(K, L_0) - g(K + \Delta K) + gK$$
$$\cong [F_K(K, L_0) - g] \, \Delta K.$$

Hence, we conclude that a gift of additional capital, although it would always shift the economy to a new steady growth track with higher output, would add to consumption only if $F_K > g$. Thus, the maximum consumption track is achieved where $F_K = g$. Since the consumption tracks for different steady growth paths cannot cross, the choice is independent of the time we choose as a check point.

It should be emphasized that this calculation is relevant only to the question when a gift of capital would be welcome even though it carries the proviso that the new higher capital/labor ratio must be maintained. The calculation says nothing about whether it would be worthwhile saving and sacrificing in order to reach the new higher capital/labor ratio.

Even here, however, some information can be obtained by looking at the question a little differently. We know that if capital is already so plentiful that $F_K < g$, then even a free gift of capital hurts more than it helps. Hence, in these circumstances additional saving to get to a permanently higher capital/labor ratio is definitely unwise. This conclusion is one aspect of a result due to Koopmans and Phelps [24].

Theorem: *Consider any path $k(t)$ yielding a solution to the Solow model (6) such that for all $t \geq t_0 \geq 0$,*

$$k(t) \geq k^* + \varepsilon$$

where $\varepsilon > 0$ and k^* represents the Golden Rule capital/labor ratio. Then the path $k(t)$ is dynamically inefficient in the sense that there always exists another path which, starting from the same initial capital stock, provides more consumption at some time, and never less consumption.

Proof: Exercise 20.

An alternative interpretation of this result will appear more interesting in the light of later discussion. We note that the produced asset K yields an own-rate of return equal to F_K, whereas the nonproduced primary good L can be interpreted as having an own-rate of return g. Later we will see that a condition for efficient growth is that the own-rates of return on all produced assets should be equal. The Golden Rule result just enunciated is reminiscent of this same general requirement.

In any event, we see that this Golden Rule analysis leads us one step toward a normative judgment regarding saving policy. The result tells us that it is possible to oversave, to have too much capital. Comparing only alternative steady states, we can rank paths unambiguously in terms of the consumption flow they offer, and this ranking remains unchanged over time. The comparison of alternative growth paths thus reduces to a simple numerical ranking, and the existence of a unique maximum in this ranking is assured under our present assumptions.

Even though inefficiency can be established only for paths on which the capital/labor ratio remains *permanently* bounded above the Golden Rule value (and hence such inefficiency can never be demonstrated at any finite time), the Golden Rule analysis does provide a boundary point, a target, that will reappear in more general optimizing calculations.

We turn now to one final topic of importance in the study of the one-good model, namely, how quickly the transition to equilibrium can be completed. The answer to this question obviously affects the extent to which we can base analysis of policy merely on comparison of the alternative equilibrium growth tracks involved.

2–8. Transient Phase: The Period of Adjustment

Growth models lead to the study of differential equations, and in the study of differential equations there is no perfect substitute for an explicit solution. However, explicit solutions are rare and we must often be content with a review of qualitative features and asymptotic behavior. And the fact that asymptotic properties are often described by phrases like "equilibrium path" or "long-run rates of growth" may encourage an undue emphasis on these features.

To this point we have discussed only the equilibrium path and the general stability of the system. But clearly we cannot stop there. For it might be quite misleading, even if the simplest neoclassical growth model were an adequate representation of the accumulation process, to rest conclusions about economic policy on properties of the equilibrium steady growth track. Although we may know with certainty that the equilibrium rate of growth is always the same, and independent of the saving rate, it would not be legitimate to conclude that social policy designed to raise the rate of saving and investment cannot enhance the growth rate over a very long transitional period. Even apart from the possible effects on the rate of technical progress, and even ignoring the fact that the levels of capital per man and output per man (as opposed to rates of growth) are increased, such a conclusion would be illegitimate simply because the path of transition to steady growth may well be so long as to dominate all other considerations.

Without an explicit solution to the differential equation describing the growth process (the accumulation equation), we cannot determine the rate at which the transient path approaches equilibrium. But we can give an idea of the magnitudes possibly involved by looking at a simple example in which the explicit solution is easily obtained. From Exercise 5 we have that for the Solow model with a Cobb–Douglas production function, the output/capital ratio is given by

$$x(t) = \frac{g}{s + Be^{-\beta gt}}, \tag{46}$$

where β is the elasticity of output with respect to labor and

$$B = \frac{g}{x_0} - s.$$

If we think of a situation in which initially the economy is in equilibrium on the steady growth path appropriate to parameters g and s_0, then we know

$$s_0 x_0 = g$$

or

$$B = s_0 - s.$$

Then suppose at time $t = 0$ the saving rate is altered to s. The result is that the present position of the economy is no longer an equilibrium configuration, and the output/capital ratio must adjust until equilibrium is attained again. The adjustment is described by the rule

$$x(t) = \frac{g}{s + (s_0 - s)e^{-\beta gt}}. \tag{47}$$

As $t \to \infty$, $x \to g/s = x_\infty$, which is, of course, the equilibrium output/capital ratio appropriate to the new saving rate. But equally easily one sees that the adjustment is never quite accomplished. It does not make sense, therefore, to ask how long the adjustment process takes; it takes forever. We can only ask how long we must wait until "almost all" of the adjustment is complete.

Or, more precisely, we ask how long is required before some specified fraction α of the change from x_0 to x_∞ is complete. To compute this result we set

$$x_\alpha = x_0 + \alpha(x_\infty - x_0)$$

and define t_α by

$$x(t_\alpha) = x_\alpha$$

or

$$\frac{g}{s + (s_0 - s)e^{-\beta g t}} = x_0(1 - \alpha) + \alpha x_\infty. \tag{48}$$

Solving for t we find

$$t_\alpha = \frac{1}{\beta g} \log\left[1 + \frac{\alpha s_0}{(1 - \alpha)s}\right]. \tag{49}$$

Substituting for various values of α between zero and one, we determine the length of time t_α elapsed before the fraction α of the total adjustment has been completed.[10]

Since $g\beta < g$, and g (being a growth rate of labor) has a value in the neighborhood of 0.02, or two percent per year, we see that t_α may in general be a large number. Plotting the function t_α against α for several selections of the parameters g, s, β; and s_0, we conclude that in many cases the time required to complete two-thirds or three-fourths of the required change is very large indeed.

Such considerations led Sato [31] to conclude that startlingly long adjustment times rendered characteristics of the equilibrium growth path largely irrelevant in any applied analysis. And this warning was probably a necessary antidote to an unfortunate overemphasis that sometimes concentrated on considerations of asymptotic rates of growth. Unquestionably it is misleading to emphasize relative rates of growth to the point of ignoring the more fundamental issues of wealth per capita or consumption per capita attainable along growth paths that might show equal asymptotic growth rates. The foregoing results on the possibly long period of adjustment in response to policy initiatives should serve to discourage such simplistic tendencies.

But at the same time we must be careful not to exaggerate the scope of the

[10] Note that this calculation is even simpler for the capital/output ratio $x^{-1} = k^{1-\pi}$ in which $(s_0 - s)$ terms cancel, and the period of adjustment is independent of initial or terminal saving ratios but depends on g and β.

previous estimates of adjustment time. Being strictly correct only for the particular case of the Solow model that we actually solved, the estimate may not be at all indicative of the situation in more extensive models. Indeed, many considerations omitted from the Solow model might be expected to accelerate convergence to a new equilibrium. Sato [29] obtained substantially lower, though still quite large, estimates of the adjustment period for a model that differed only in admitting embodied technical progress[11] and capital depreciation. By following the previous calculation, he found that the adjustment time t_α is given by an expression that depends only on α and on an adjustment speed coefficient whose value he estimated to be three or four times as great as that just implied.

Different hypotheses about consumption behavior, admitting consumption lags that serve to raise saving rates temporarily in response to an increase in growth rates along the transient path, may also serve to accelerate the convergence to equilibrium. Finally, an extended model admitting unemployment and other more detailed short-run adjustment mechanisms may have the effect of speeding the adjustment process, as Conlisk [6] has observed.

2–9. Summary

We began this discussion with a simple model of a smoothly adapting economy with growing population and smoothly working markets leading investors to accommodate their capital accumulation to the community's habits of thrift. In such models we found that thriftier communities achieve greater stocks of capital and higher per capita output, but all approach the same equilibrium rate of growth, established by the rate of growth of the primary (nonproduced) factor, labor. Some qualifications arising from the technical specification of production conditions were necessary, and some reservations concerning possible feedbacks through wages onto the growth rates of labor were considered, but the basic conclusion remained generally unchanged. More crucial reservations concerning investors' behavior were voiced, raising the question as to whether deviations from full employment might not alter the whole growth process. But even leaving the unemployment issue aside, we found that the question of investment decisions forced consideration of price behavior and money into a model formerly expressed solely in "real" terms.

The attempt to incorporate more adequate representations of saving behavior also led to study of a model in which individual saving decisions are aggregated through a market process. This in turn led us to ask whether there is any criterion by which we could say whether or not certain saving patterns

---

[11] This concept will be discussed in the next chapter.

were more desirable than others. With the introduction of the criterion of dynamic inefficiency proposed by Phelps and Koopmans, we made our only departure from the strictly descriptive analysis in the rest of the chapter, and we concluded that in the simple Diamond model competitively determined saving policies could in fact be dynamically inefficient in the Phelps–Koopmans sense.

Finally, we tempered our account of asymptotic paths and equilibrium growth rates with explicit consideration of examples in which the speed of adjustment could be calculated. The possibly limited significance of the neoclassical model for purposes of social policy making became clear, even as its importance in spotlighting the crucial determinants of the smoothly working growth process provided the insights necessary to construction of a fuller model.

Formally, we have been studying the differential equation

$$\dot{k} = \phi(k) = s(k)f(k) - g(k)k. \tag{50}$$

Various economic hypotheses determine or affect the shapes of the functions $s(k)$, $f(k)$, and $g(k)$, and we have mentioned some of these. Others may be incorporated easily into the analysis, providing that one basic principle is always observed; that is, all functions should eventually be reduced to single valued functions of the capital/labor ratio k. Then if there exists a value k^* such that

$$\phi(k^*) = 0, \tag{51}$$

a balanced growth equilibrium exists for this system. If, further, we can show that for some $\varepsilon > 0$

$$\phi(k) > 0 \quad \text{for} \quad 0 < k < \varepsilon \tag{52}$$

and

$$\lim_{k \to \infty} \phi(k) < 0, \tag{53}$$

then we are assured that the system must approach some balanced growth equilibrium path, and we say that the system is globally stable. The balanced growth equilibrium may be unique; if, in addition, the system is globally stable, then the equilibrium point itself is stable. There may, however, be several solutions to equation (50), and then the question of stability of the equilibria arises. If $\phi'(k)$ exists for all k, and $\phi'(k^*) < 0$, then the equilibrium k^* is locally stable. Thus when we reduce the economic theory to its mathematical core, depending heavily on an assumption of constant returns to scale to do so, we are left finally with one "accumulation equation" whose properties are crucial.

In Chapter 4 we focus on an extension of the specification of technology to admit distinct processes of production for two distinct goods. As a step on the path to a general equilibrium structure with diverse goods and diverse methods of production, the two-sector model will highlight some of the underlying allocation and equilibration mechanisms hidden in the process of aggregating to a single-sector model.

In the next chapter we discuss the possibility that production conditions change with time. We maintain the assumption that only one homogeneous good is produced, but introduce the possibility that the output good may differ in its effectiveness as an input into production depending on the date of its manufacture, or on the date of the production activity. The role of technological progress in determining the equilibrium characteristics of the growth process is the focus of the chapter.

Exercises

1. From the hypotheses that the production function $Q = F(K, L)$ is neoclassical (as defined in Chapter 1), with strictly positive marginal products and both factors essential, show that output per unit of labor is a function of the capital/labor ratio alone and deduce the shape of this function. (This function $q \equiv Q/L \equiv f(k) \equiv F(K/L, 1)$ is sometimes referred to as the *per capita production function* or the *production function in intensive form*.) Express the marginal products of capital and labor in terms of the capital/labor ratio k and the function f, and determine the shapes of the resulting functions. On a diagram graphing average labor product q against the capital/labor ratio k, identify the marginal products of labor and the per capita earnings of capital under marginal productivity pricing.

2. Under the same production hypotheses as in Exercise 1, show that if factors are paid according to their marginal product, then the *wage/rentals ratio* ω (the ratio of the labor wage rate to the capital rental rate) may be written as a function of the capital/labor ratio k alone. Determine the function, and identify the wage rentals/ratio ω on a diagram graphing q against k.

Show that the function $\omega(k)$ may be inverted, and that the elasticity

$$\frac{dk}{d\omega}\frac{\omega}{k}$$

of the inverse function is the elasticity of substitution σ as defined in Chapter 1.

3. Investigate the Cobb–Douglas production function $Q = F(K, L) = AK^{\alpha}L^{1-\alpha}$ by calculating explicit expressions for the output/capital ratio and the output/labor

ratio as functions of the capital/labor ratio, k; determine the equation of the unit isoquant $Q = 1$. Verify that the function is neoclassical (and strictly quasi-concave). Verify that the marginal product of capital assumes all positive values as k increases from zero without limit. Compute relative income shares of factors under the assumption of competitively determined factor earnings. Verify that the elasticity of substitution for this function is unity.

4. Given that the production function has the Cobb–Douglas form, solve Solow's basic differential equation for the simplest neoclassical model with given initial capital/labor ratio $k_0 > 0$ and given saving rate s, $0 < s < 1$.
   Determine the resulting paths of real wage rates and real rentals.

5. For the simplest neoclassical model with a Cobb–Douglas production function, determine the differential equation satisfied by the output/capital ratio x, and solve this differential equation.

6. Investigate the fixed proportions production function

$$Q = F(K, L) = \min\left[\frac{K}{a}, \frac{L}{b}\right]$$

with $a > 0$ and $b > 0$ by calculating marginal and average products and determining the graph of the unit isoquant. Verify constant returns to scale and quasiconcavity. Verify that both factors are essential.

7. For the fixed proportions production function in the simplest neoclassical model, solve Solow's basic differential equation. Determine the resulting path of real wage rates, real rentals, and the output/capital ratio.

8. Discuss the solution to the simplest neoclassical model when the production function is

$$Q = F(K, L, \bar{T}) = K^\alpha L^\beta (\bar{T})^{1-\alpha-\beta}$$

and the quantity of land $\bar{T}$ is fixed.

9. (a) Let the production function be $Q(\$/\text{yr}) = 1000\ (\$/\text{man yr}) \cdot L\ (\text{men}) \cdot \log(K/L)$, for $K/L > 1$. Suppose that the labor force grows at a constant relative rate $g = 0.05/\text{yr}$, that all rental income is saved, and that all wage income is consumed. Assume there is no depreciation of capital. Determine explicitly the path of equilibrium balanced growth and the path of approach to balanced growth from an initial value $k_0 = \$10,000/\text{man}$.

   (b) Let the economy have attained the balanced growth path determined in part (a). Suppose that population policy succeeds in reducing the rate of labor force growth to $0.02/\text{yr}$. Determine the time required for the system to complete 90 percent of the adjustment to the new balanced growth track appropriate to the lower labor force growth rate.

10. Investigate the CES function

$$Q = F(K, L) = \gamma[\alpha K^{-\rho} + (1 - \alpha)L^{-\rho}]^{-1/\rho}$$

by finding average and marginal products as functions of the capital labor ratio k; determine the equation of the unit isoquant $Q = 1$.

Show that the elasticity of substitution σ is given by

$$\sigma = 1/(1 + \rho).$$

Plot the foregoing functions for cases $\sigma < 1$, $\sigma = 1$, and $\sigma > 1$. Observe particularly that if $\sigma < 1$, then Q/K is bounded above as $k \to 0$, whereas if $\sigma > 1$, then Q/K is bounded below as $k \to \infty$.

11. Show that
    (i) The limiting form of the CES as $\rho \to 0$ is the Cobb–Douglas function;
    (ii) The limiting form as $\rho \to \infty$ is the fixed proportions function;
    (iii) The limiting form as $\rho \to -1$ is a production function with straight line isoquants.
12. Expressing output per head as a function of the capital/labor ratio k for the CES production function just given, determine the differential equation describing the development of k in the simplest neoclassical model. Study the possible behavior of the solution path in a phase diagram, determining in particular the bounds on the saving rate s within which golden age equilibrium is not attainable.
13. For the CES function specified in Exercise 10, compute the function $k(\omega)$ defined along an isoproduct contour (isoquant), and show that the elasticity of this function is the elasticity of substitution σ.
14. Show that for the foregoing CES production function the share of profits in national income is given by

$$\pi = \frac{1}{1 + (1 - \alpha)k^\rho/\alpha} = \alpha \left(\frac{Q}{K}\right)^\rho.$$

Hence show that the "critical" level of the saving ratio found in Exercise 12 may be written

$$\bar{s} = \frac{gK}{Q(\pi)^{-1/\rho}} = \frac{g\pi^{1/\rho}}{x}$$

Using g, π, and x as constants and recalling that $\sigma = 1/(1 + \rho)$, plot s as a function of σ to determine what pairs $(\bar{s}, \sigma)$ would prohibit the attainment of balanced growth equilibrium.
15. (a) Determine whether the production function

$$F(K, L) = \alpha L + gK - \alpha L \exp(-\alpha K/L), \quad \alpha > 0,$$

is a neoclassical production function according to the definition given in this text.
    (b) Show that there is no point k such that $f(k) = gk$, but that for any $s < 1$ there is always a unique point k^* such that $sf(k^*) = gk^*$.
    (c) Let labor force grow at a constant relative rate g and let a constant fraction s of income be saved. Assume there is no depreciation. Discuss the character of a solution to Solow's differential equation in this case.

(d) Compare the result obtained in (c) with that obtained when saving equals profit (and other conditions remain unchanged).

16. (This problem may be omitted.) Suppose that the fraction of the labor force participating in production depends on the real wage, and hence on the capital/labor ratio. Suppose the production function is of CES form. Then we have

$$Q = F(K, L) = \gamma[\alpha K^{-\rho} + (1 - \alpha)\{p(k)L\}^{-\rho}]^{-1/\rho}.$$

What conditions on the function $p(k)$ are necessary in order that this production function display all neoclassical properties with nonnegative marginal products? What is the elasticity of substitution? (Observe, therefore, that this is a well-behaved production function with a variable elasticity of substitution.)

17. Analyze the Diamond model discussed in Section 2-6 when the production function is Cobb–Douglas.

18. Show that if a capital stock K and a population P are given at any time t, then equation (21), together with the assumptions about the model specified in Section 2-5, is adequate to determine a unique capital/labor ratio k and wage/rentals ratio ω.

19. Verify the Golden Rule result asserted in Section 2-7, show that a unique interior solution exists to the necessary condition cited, and verify that under the conditions of the problem this necessary condition is also sufficient.

20. Prove the Phelps–Koopmans result cited in Section 2-7.

21. Verify inequality (36).

22. Verify that if the condition (39) is satisfied, then equation (38) has a unique stable equilibrium.

23. Show that for a one-sector economy with any neoclassical production function, if all rental income is saved and all wage income consumed (assuming competitive pricing) then the economy converges to a balanced growth path on which

$$f'(k) = g$$

provided that $f'(0) < g < f'(\infty)$.

Answers and Hints

PROBLEM 1. To determine marginal products, observe that

$$Q = F(K, L) \equiv Lf(K/L),$$

and differentiate the last expression with respect to K and L.

PROBLEM 2. The expression $\omega(k) = f(k)/f'(k) - k$ may be inverted if $d\omega/dk$ is always positive for positive k. To complete the problem, express the elasticity of substitution σ in terms of the per capita production function f.

PROBLEM 4. Observe that the differential equation for k is a Bernoulli equation which can be solved by the substitution $Z = k^{1-\alpha}$ where α denotes the capital elasticity of output—that is, the exponent on the capital input—in the Cobb–Douglas function.

PROBLEM 5. The differential equation is $\dot{x}/x = (1 - \alpha)[g - sx]$, with solution $x = g/(s + ce^{-(1-\alpha)gt})$ where $c = g/x_0 - s$.

PROBLEM 7. Break the problem up into cases depending on $s/a \gtreqqless g$. (See Solow [32]).

PROBLEM 8. See the discussion of Swan [34].

PROBLEM 11.   (i) Take logs, then apply l'Hôpital's rule.

(ii) Deal with cases of capital redundancy or labor redundancy separately. (The computations for this exercise are set out in the Appendix to Pitchford [25].)

PROBLEM 13. The required function is $k = c\omega^\sigma$ where c is a constant depending on the parameters of the production function.

PROBLEM 14. See Sato [30].

PROBLEM 18. Consider the problem as a conventional problem in labor market equilibrium. Determine the demand for labor, the supply, and the conditions for stability of the labor market in this case.

PROBLEM 20. Consider a path $k(t)$ violating the Phelps–Koopmans dynamic efficiency condition, and construct a comparison path $k^0(t)$ satisfying, for some t_0,

$$k^0(t) \equiv k(t), \qquad t \leq t_0,$$

$$k^0(t) \equiv k(t) - \varepsilon, \quad t > t_0.$$

References

[1] ARROW, K. J. and L. HURWICZ, "On the Stability of Competitive Equilibrium, I," *Econometrica*, **XXVI**, *4* (October, 1958), pp. 522–552.

[2] — H. BLOCK, and L. HURWICZ, "On the Stability of Competitive Equilibrium, II," *Econometrica*, **XXVII**, *1* (January, 1959), pp. 82–109.

[3] —H. B. CHENERY, B. MINHAS, and R. M. SOLOW, "Capital-Labor Substitution and Economic Efficiency," *Review of Economics and Statistics*, **XLIII**, *3* (August, 1961), pp. 225–250.

[4] BURMEISTER, E., and P. TAUBMAN, "Labour and Non-labour Income Saving Propensities," *Canadian Journal of Economics*, **II**, *1* (February, 1969), pp. 78–89.

[5] CASS, D., and M. E. YAARI, "A Re-Examination of the Pure Consumption Loans Model," *Journal of Political Economy*, **LXXIV**, *4* (August, 1966) pp. 353–367.

[6] CONLISK, J., "Unemployment in a Neoclassical Growth Model: The Effect on Speed of Adjustment," *Economic Journal*, **LXXVI**, *303* (September, 1966), pp. 550–566.

[7] DIAMOND, P. A., "National Debt in a Neoclassical Growth Model," *American Economic Review*, **LV**, *5* (December, 1965), pp. 1126–1150.

[8] EISNER, R., "On Growth Models and the Neoclassical Resurgence," *Economic Journal*, **LXVIII**, *272* (December, 1958), pp. 707–721.

[9] HAHN, F. H., and R. C. O. MATTHEWS, "The Theory of Economic Growth: A Survey," *Economic Journal*, **LXXIV**, *296* (December, 1964), pp. 779–902.

[10] HARROD, R. F., *Towards a Dynamic Economics*. London: Macmillan, 1963.

[11] HICKS, J. R., *The Theory of Wages*. 2nd ed. London: Macmillan, 1963.

[12] JOHNSON, H. G., "The Neoclassical One-Sector Growth Model: A Geometrical Exposition and Extension to a Monetary Economy," *Economica*, **XXXIII**, *131* (August, 1966), pp. 265–287.

[13] KALDOR, N., and J. A. MIRRLEES, "A New Model of Economic Growth," *Review of Economic Studies*, **XXIX**, *80* (June, 1962), pp. 174–192.

[14] KALMAN, R. E., and J. E. BERTRAM, "Control System Analysis and Design via the 'Second Method' of Lyapnuov," *ASMA Journal of Basic Engineering* (June, 1960), pp. 371–393.

[15] KOOPMANS, T., "On the Concept of Optimal Growth," in *The Econometric Approach to Development Planning*. Chicago: Rand McNally, 1965, pp. 225–287.

[16] LASALLE, J., and S. LEFSCHETZ, *Stability by Liapunov's Direct Method, with Applications*. New York: Academic Press, 1961.

[17] LERNER, A. P., "Consumption-Loan Interest and Money," *Journal of Political Economy*, **LXVII**, *5* (October, 1959), pp. 512–518.

[18] McFADDEN, D. M., "Further Results on C.E.S. Production Functions," *Review of Economic Studies*, **XXX**, *83* (June, 1963), pp. 73–83.

[19] Meade, J. E., *A Neoclassical Theory of Economic Growth*. London: Allen and Unwin, 1961, pp. 1–76.

[20] — "The Rate of Profit in a Growing Economy," *Economic Journal*, **LXXIII**, *292* (December, 1963), pp. 665–674.

[21] NIEHANS, J., "Economic Growth with Two Endogenous Factors," *Quarterly Journal of Economics*, **LXXVII**, *3* (August, 1963), pp. 349–371.

[22] PASINETTI, L., "Rate of Profit and Income Distribution in Relation to the Rate of Economic Growth," *Review of Economic Studies*, **XXIX**, *81* (October, 1962), pp. 267–279.

[23] PHELPS, E. S., "Population Increase," *Canadian Journal of Economics*, **I**, *3* (August, 1968), pp. 497–518.

[24] — "Second Essay on the Golden Rule of Accumulation," *American Economic Review*, **LV**, *4* (September, 1965), pp. 793–814.

[25] PITCHFORD, J. D., "Growth and the Elasticity of Factor Substitution," *Economic Record*, **XXXVI**, *76* (December, 1960), pp. 491–504.

[26] ROBINSON, JOAN, *The Accumulation of Capital*. New York: St. Martin's Press, 1966.

[27] SAMUELSON, P. A., "An Exact Consumption-Loan Model of Interest with or without the Social Contrivance of Money," *Journal of Political Economy*, **LXVI**, *6* (December, 1958), pp. 467—482.

[28] — and F. MODIGLIANI, "The Pasinetti Paradox in Neo-Classical and More General Models," *Review of Economic Studies*, **XXXIII**, *4* (October 1966), pp. 269–298.

[29] SATO, K., "On the Adjustment Time in Neoclassical Growth Models," *Review of Economic Studies*, **XXXIII**, *85* (July, 1966), pp. 263–268.

[30] — "Growth and the Elasticity of Factor Substitution: A Comment. How Plausible is Imbalanced Growth?" *Economic Record*, **XXXIX**, *87* (September, 1963), pp. 355–361.

[31] SATO, R., "Fiscal Policy in a Neoclassical Growth Model: An Analysis of

Time Required for Equilibrating Adjustment," *Review of Economic Studies*, **XXX**, *82* (February, 1963), pp. 16–23.

[32] SOLOW, R. M., "A Contribution to the Theory of Economic Growth," *Quarterly Journal of Economics*, **LXX**, *1* (February, 1956), pp. 65–94.

[33] — "Comment," *Review of Economic Studies*, **XXIX**, *80* (June, 1962), pp. 255–257.

[34] SWAN, T. W., "Economic Growth and Capital Accumulation," *Economic Record*, **XXXII** (November, 1956), pp. 334–361.

Chapter 3 Technological Change

in the One-Sector Model

3–1. Introduction

In the previous chapter we studied how a simple neoclassical system grows under the thrust of population growth and capital accumulation. The general conclusion, subject to qualification on several points, was that the system grows toward a state of balanced growth on which capital/labor ratios and per capita output remain constant. Along the transition to balanced growth (from an initial position with a lower capital/labor ratio), the rate of profit falls and the capital/labor ratio rises.

Before we accept such a supply-constrained neoclassical system, based on a simple aggregate production function, as being descriptive of modern economies, we ought at least establish that these implications (or the system's other features) are not markedly inconsistent with recent economic history. In particular, rough agreement with the following stylized facts is surely prerequisite to acceptance of the model.

 (i) The investment/output ratio remains constant.
 (ii) The capital/output ratio remains constant.
(iii) The capital/labor ratio and output/labor ratio are rising.
(iv) The rate of interest remains constant.
 (v) The real wage is rising.
(vi) The relative shares of capital and labor, or the ratio of property income to total income, remains constant.

Of course no one argues for the strict day-to-day accuracy of these propositions; many of them may be disputed on various conceptual or empirical grounds. But as a rough characterization of secular or trend behavior they command some agreement. At least it seems to be agreed that a model that prohibited growth paths consistent with these properties could hardly be an adequate description of evolution in developed economies.

It is clear that the models discussed in Chapter 2 could admit rising capital/labor ratios (capital deepening) or rising income per head only with a simultaneous fall in the competitive interest rate and a rise in the capital/output ratio. Accordingly, we cannot accept a supply-constrained model based on an unchanging aggregate production function; in such a model the propositions (i)–(vi) could be consistent only if we postulate that the production function shifts over time, i.e., that some form of technological change occurs.[1]

A distinction is made conventionally between technological change that is *embodied* (in new equipment), and that which is not. Technological change is called *disembodied* (in some defiance of strict English usage) if, independent of any changes in the factor inputs, the isoquant contours of the production function shift inward toward the origin as time passes. Thus, even if the inputs of capital and labor are completely fixed the maximum output that can be produced from the unchanged factor supplies increases over time as a result of disembodied technological change. The increase is to be attributed, presumably, to improvements in technique or organization that enhance the productivity of old equipment along with new.

It may be objected that the hypothesis that technological change occurs in this disembodied fashion, falling like manna from heaven upon the old and the new alike, is implausible. Casual observation suggests that many inventions or improvements in technique can be introduced only by building new capital equipment of improved design, or by calling upon new labor of enhanced skill. Technological change of this sort, in which investment in new equipment or new skills is the essential carrier of improvements in technique, and old equipment is left unaltered, is called *embodied* technological change; it is built into or embodied in new capital equipment or newly trained (or retrained)[2] labor.

This chapter begins with the study of disembodied technological change and turns later to a consideration of models with embodied progress. Analysis of the former is significantly easier, and many analyses of the process of economic growth, or the sources of economic growth, do not go beyond the notion of disembodied technological progress. Moreover, in some respects the long-run behavior (that is, the behavior in states of steady growth) of models in which technological progress is embodied is, in fact, identical to that in models with disembodied change. And this should not surprise us:

---

[1] Samuelson [51], pp. 717–719 offers an excellent introductory discussion along these lines. An alternative reconciliation has been given by Ando and Modigliani [40, and the references there cited]; their model incorporates technological change, but also includes the supply side of capital markets.

[2] One of the interesting features of the study of investment in productive skills or human capital (apart from the fact that the welfare of individuals matters whereas the welfare of machines does not) is that it may be feasible generally to enhance the effectiveness of labor throughout the working life. For machines it may be much less easy. The investment decision may therefore be considerably more complex when we come to study life-cycle theories of investment in human capital.

the important effects of embodiment are to be found in transitions to steady growth paths. Nevertheless, the issue is not simple, nor is it yet fully resolved in the growth literature. We will have to deal with such comparisons before we conclude this chapter.

For now, however, we begin with a consideration of the nature and effect of disembodied technological progress.

3–2. Representation of Disembodied Technological Change

A neoclassical production function having two productive inputs and exhibiting disembodied technological change may be written in the most general form

$$Q = F(K, L; t) \tag{1}$$

where t denotes time; we assume that F has continuous second partial derivatives with respect to all three variables. Since we postulate technological improvement over time,

$$F_t \equiv \frac{\partial F}{\partial t} > 0.$$

For any given $t = \bar{t}$, we also assume that $F(K, L; \bar{t})$ has the usual neoclassical properties described in Chapter 1.

It will be convenient to rewrite $F(K, L; t)$ in per capita or intensive form

$$q = f(k; t) \tag{2}$$

where, as before, q denotes Q/L and k denotes K/L. We note that our assumptions imply $Lf_t = F_t > 0$.

One example of disembodied technological change is the *factor-augmenting* case in which (1) may be written

$$Q = F(K, L; t) = G[b(t)K, a(t)L] \tag{3}$$

where a and b are functions of time alone and G is homogeneous of degree one. We may identify $b(t)K$ and $a(t)L$ as "effective capital" and "effective labor," respectively, and, defining the ratio of effective capital to effective labor (the capital/labor ratio in *efficiency units*) as

$$z \equiv \frac{b(t)K}{a(t)L}, \tag{4}$$

we may rewrite (2) in the form

$$\frac{Q}{a(t)L} = G\left[\frac{b(t)K}{a(t)L}, 1\right] \equiv G(z, 1) \equiv g(z) \tag{5}$$

(see Exercise 2). Technological change is said to be *purely labor augmenting* if $b(t) \equiv 0$ and $\dot{a}(t) > 0$, whereas it is *purely capital augmenting* if $\dot{a}(t) \equiv 0$ and $\dot{b}(t) > 0$. It is *equally capital and labor augmenting* if $\dot{a}(t) \equiv \dot{b}(t) > 0$.[3]

We assume that the usual static efficiency conditions in production are always satisfied; thus, using the price of homogeneous output as *numeraire* ($P_Q \equiv 1$), the competitively imputed real wage rate is

$$W = F_L(K, L; t)$$

and the competitively imputed real rental rate for one unit of capital is

$$R = F_K(K, L; t).$$

As before, the relative share of capital is denoted by

$$\pi \equiv \frac{RK}{Q};$$

since F is homogeneous of degree one, labor's relative share is

$$1 - \pi = \frac{WL}{Q}.$$

The change in these relative shares provides a useful index on which to base various definitions of neutral, capital-saving, or labor-saving technological change.[4] More precisely, consider the index I defined by

$$I \equiv \left(\frac{RK}{WL}\right) \frac{\partial(WL/RK)}{\partial t}\bigg|_P \tag{6}$$

---

[3] We must warn the reader against any expectation that technological change will be capital augmenting because it is embodied in new machines or labor augmenting because it is embodied in new entries to the labor force. We are talking solely about disembodied change for the moment. In any case the factor-augmenting form has nothing to do with the question of embodiment.

[4] Historically, discussions of technological change have been particularly concerned with the effects on the welfare of labor. Hence a natural measure of the impact of technological advance is its effect on the relative share of labor. (See especially Hicks [21].)

where this notation indicates that the partial differentiation with respect to time is taken along paths in some specified class P. Once a specific class P is designated, we see that (6) measures the percentage change in the ratio of relative shares and thus gives us the following definitions (relative to the specified class):

(i) Technological change is *neutral* if and only if relative shares remain constant and $I = 0$ for movements along paths of the specified type.

(ii) Technological change is *labor saving* (*labor using*) if the relative share of labor falls (rises) along the specified paths. Since there are only two productive factors, K and L, a *labor-saving* technological change is equivalent to a *capital-using* technological change. Thus technological change is labor saving (and capital using) if and only if $I < 0$.[5]

(iii) Analogously, technological change is capital saving (and labor using) if and only if $I > 0$.

Unfortunately, these definitions depend crucially upon what path is designated; consequently, a particular technological change may be labor saving for one class of paths but capital saving for another. Later we will show how a classification of bias can be derived for the paths most frequently studied, namely paths along which there is (1) a constant capital/output ratio, (2) a constant capital/labor ratio, or (3) a constant labor/output ratio. Technological change is *Harrod neutral* if and only if $I \equiv 0$ for paths of the first type; it is *Hicks neutral* if and only if $I \equiv 0$ for paths of the second type; and we will call it *Solow neutral* if and only if $I \equiv 0$ for paths of the last type. These three cases correspond to (1) pure labor augmentation, (2) equal labor and capital augmentation, and (3) pure capital augmentation, respectively. Thus any technological change that is always neutral by one of the foregoing definitions is a special case of factor-augmenting technological change. We establish these assertions by deriving necessary and sufficient conditions for disembodied technological change to be factor augmenting.[6]

Before proceeding, however, we will illustrate Harrod- and Hicks-neutral technological changes in terms of shifts in production functions and factor-price frontiers. (These concepts can also be illustrated as shifts in the unit isoquant; indeed the resulting diagrams would appear similar to Figures 8 and 9.) Likewise it is possible to illustrate Solow neutrality diagrammatically.

Harrod-neutral technological change requires that $I = 0$ along any path

---

[5] The rationale behind the terminology labor saving, labor using, etc., can be explained by assuming that the wage/rentals ratio remains unchanged; then, e.g., a labor-*saving* technological change implies that the demand for labor *decreases* at the specified wage/rentals ratio. Hence, turning the problem around, a fixed amount of labor will find employment after a labor-saving change has occurred only if there is a fall in real wage and hence a reduced wage share in national income.

[6] An alternative proof of the theorem is given by Phelps [43].

that maintains the capital/output ratio constant; equivalently, the condition

$$\frac{d(K/Q)}{dt} = \frac{d(k/q)}{dt} = 0$$

must imply $\dot{\pi} = 0$. Since

$$\pi = \frac{f_k k}{q},$$

the constancy (over time) of k/q, π, and f_k are not all independent: if any two of the latter three variables are constant, so is the third. Thus a shift in the production function (2) is Harrod neutral if and only if f_k is constant along any ray from the origin with slope q/k. A Harrod-neutral shift is illustrated in Figure 6 for the particular output/capital ratio $q/k = \beta$.

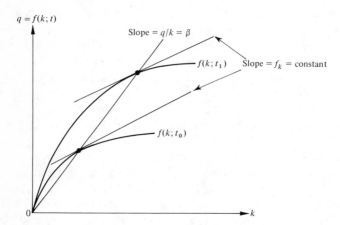

Figure 6. *Harrod-neutral technological change for the ray $q/k = \beta$ between times t_0 and t_1.*

On the other hand, Hicks-neutral technological change requires that $I = 0$ along any path that maintains the capital/labor ratio constant; equivalently, $\dot{k} = 0$ must imply

$$\frac{d(WL/RK)}{dt} = 0.$$

Defining the wage/rentals ratio $\omega = W/R$,

$$\frac{WL}{RK} = \frac{\omega}{k},$$

and therefore the constancy (over time) of k, ω, and ω/k are not all independent; if any two of the latter three variables are constant, so is the third. Thus a shift in the production function (2) is Hicks-neutral if and only if the same value of the capital/labor ratio k implies the same value of ω. A Hicks-neutral shift is illustrated in Figure 7 for one particular capital/labor ratio $k = \alpha$.

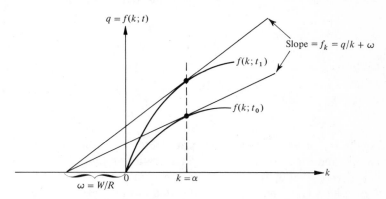

Figure 7. *Hicks-neutral technological change for the capital/labor ratio $k = \alpha$ between times t_0 and t_1.*

Samuelson [52] has proved that corresponding to any neoclassical production function there exists a dual function with the same homogeneity and convexity properties.[7] This dual function of the form

$$C(W, R) = 1 \tag{7}$$

defines the *real factor-price frontier* introduced briefly in Chapter 1. Moreover,

$$\frac{dW}{dR} = -\frac{K}{L}$$

(Exercise 3), and hence the elasticity η of the factor-price frontier is given by

$$\eta = -\frac{R}{W}\frac{dW}{dR} = \frac{RK}{WL} = \frac{\pi}{1 - \pi} \tag{8}$$

and is thus equal to the ratio of relative shares.

[7] This same duality between production and cost functions is well known in the theory of the firm. See, for example, Shephard [60] and Diewert [14]. When there are several outputs, the dual functions are the optimal transformation frontier and the factor-price frontier. These will be of interest later in this book.

In the case of disembodied technological change, the factor-price frontier shifts outward over time, reflecting an improvement in technology; thus (7) may be rewritten

$$C(W, R; t) = 1. \tag{9}$$

If there is Hicks-neutral technological change, (9) becomes

$$C\left[\frac{W}{a(t)}, \frac{R}{a(t)}\right] = 1$$

or

$$C(W, R) = a(t). \tag{10}$$

Again, the elasticity of the factor-price frontier measures the ratio of relative shares, and for a constant capital/labor ratio, or equivalently for a constant wage/rentals ratio, relative shares are constant because[8] $\hat{W} = \hat{R} = \hat{a}$ (see Exercise 4). Hicks neutrality is illustrated in Figure 8.

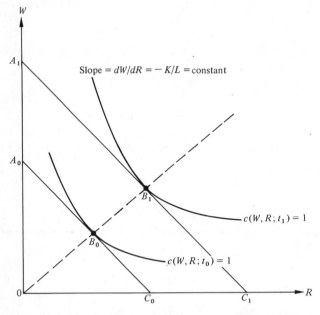

Figure 8.   *Hicks-neutral technological change between times t_0 and t_1. The elasticity η of the curve $c = 1$ measures the ratio of relative shares at time t. Since $\eta_0 = A_0 B_0/ B_0 C_0 = A_1 B_1/B_1 C_1 = \eta_1$, the ratio of relative shares has not changed.*

[8] We use the notation $\hat{x}$ to denote the relative rate of change $\dot{x}/x$.

If technological change is Harrod neutral, (9) may be rewritten

$$C\left[\frac{W}{a(t)}, R\right] = 1. \tag{11}$$

The elasticity of the factor-price frontier equals the ratio of relative shares, k/ω, and the latter is constant because $\hat{\omega} = \hat{k} = \hat{a}$ and $\hat{\omega} - \hat{k} = 0$ (see Exercise 5). Harrod neutrality is illustrated in Figure 9.

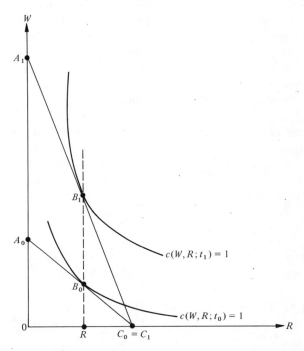

Figure 9. *Harrod-neutral technological change between times t_0 and t_1. The ratio of relative shares has remained unchanged since $\eta_0 = A_0 B_0 / B_0 C_0 = A_1 B_1 / B_1 C_1 = \eta_1$.*

Thus, to summarize, we found that our growth models of Chapter 2 appear to be unable to account, as they stand, for the character of the general trends observed in the process of evolution in a developing economy. One obvious consideration omitted from our earlier growth models is the growth of technical knowledge which enlarges production possibilities. Such expansion of possibilities may occur in many ways and have many consequences; from some points of view a crucial question is the impact that technological progress might have on the welfare of labor, as measured by competitively imputed relative shares of factors in national income. A natural dividing line is then based on types of technological progress which do not affect relative income shares. But we cannot ignore the other features of the growth path in constructing such a reference line. We have to say along what kind of growth path a particular form of technological progress leaves relative shares unaltered. Thus we say, for example, that if the growth path is such as to leave capital/labor ratios unaltered, then on that growth path Hicks-neutral technological progress would (by definition) leave relative shares unaltered. Or, if the growth path is such as to leave capital/output ratios unaltered, then along that path Harrod-neutral technological progress would (by definition) leave relative shares unaltered. (Notice therefore that it is quite possible to know that technological progress is Hicks neutral, but to observe changing relative shares.) In the previous pages we have shown how to illustrate these various types of "neutral" technological change in terms of the shape of the production function. Now we observe that technological change can be written in what we have called factor-augmenting form if and only if there is some choice of efficiency units for factors such that a neutral technological change of the above sort can be defined. Each of the categories of neutral technological change just introduced is a special case of this general form.

The following lemma provides necessary and sufficient conditions for the production function $Q = F(K, L; t)$ to admit representation in the special factor augmenting form

$$Q = G[b(t)K, a(t)L].$$

Theorems 1, 2, and 3 follow immediately and give necessary and sufficient conditions for Harrod, Hicks, and Solow neutrality, respectively.

Lemma 1: *Let the neoclassical production function $F(K, L; t)$ be given. There exist (1) positive functions $a(t)$ and $b(t)$ of time alone [with $a(0) = b(0) = 1$], having continuous first derivatives, and (2) a function G homogeneous of degree one in all its arguments such that F may be represented*

$$Q = F(K, L; t) \equiv G[b(t)K, a(t)L]$$

if and only if there exists a positive function $h(t)$ of time alone [with $h(0) = 1$] such that when the expression $h(t)k$ is constant (identically in t), then the relative share π is constant (identically in t).

The proof of this lemma and an economic interpretation are discussed by Burmeister and Dobell [8]. Moreover, we show there that the same theorem can be generalized to the case of several factor inputs with a production function of the form

$$Q = F(K_1, \ldots, K_n, L; t).$$

However, the proof itself is laborious and we omit it here, referring the interested reader to [8].

As an immediate consequence of this lemma, we obtain the following theorems.

> **Theorem 1:** *Technological change is Harrod neutral if and only if there exist functions $a(t)$ and $b(t)$ such that F may be represented in the factor-augmenting form with $b(t) \equiv 1$.*

> **Theorem 2:** *Technological change is Hicks neutral if and only if F may be represented in the factor-augmenting form with $b(t) \equiv a(t)$.*

> **Theorem 3:** *Technological change is Solow neutral if and only if F may be represented in the factor-augmenting form with $a(t) \equiv 1$.*

Theorem 2 is easy to prove (Exercise 6), but Theorems 1 and 3 require more argument to permit expression of the path restrictions in the form we require; the interested reader is referred to Burmeister and Dobell [8] for proofs of Theorems 1, 2, and 3.

The significance of the lemma just given is not obvious, but the following comments may provide some interpretation of the result. In the first place, let us emphasize that the parameter t is only an index and does not represent time, technology, temperature, or anything else in particular. But because we are thinking primarily of applications in the study of growth models, we have in fact chosen to interpret the parameter t as time. Nothing depends on this interpretation; the essence of the problem is simply that for each fixed t, the function F describes a production surface (giving Q as a function of K and L) in two independent variables of the usual sort; as t changes, the function F generates a whole family of such surfaces in the three-dimensional space of points K, L, and Q. Curves in this space pass through successive production surfaces indexed by t. We suppose the entire family to be completely known, and we attempt to describe some features of the family itself. To assert, for example, that "technical progress is everywhere Hicks neutral" is to assert that along any particular path in the class of paths having the capital/labor ratio constant, factor shares are likewise constant. In other words, the family has the property that factor shares, which are, in general, functions of the capital/labor ratio and the index t, are in fact functions of the capital/labor ratio alone, independent of the index t. Thus it is obvious that the factor-augmenting representation of disembodied change is restrictive in the sense that not all production functions $F(K, L; t)$ can be written as $G[b(t)K, a(t)L]$.

(This conclusion follows immediately from the fact that in general Q depends on the three variables K, L, and t, whereas in the factor-augmenting case Q depends only on the two variables $b(t)K$ and $a(t)L$.)

Because we are interested in applications to growth models, we have taken the range of values assumed by the parameter t to be all positive real numbers and the partial derivative F_t to be defined for all positive arguments. Our method of proof does depend on this feature. (Of course, this does not restrict our interpretation of t to time alone: we could think of the family of surfaces as describing the characteristics of a chemical process conducted at different temperatures.)[9]

In this problem we are not thinking of the inputs K and L directly as functions of time, as we would in a truly dynamic growth model; in formulating the problem, these are to be considered as independent variables. In our method of proof, however, we do assume that all relevant paths in the three-dimensional space of points $(K, L; t)$ may actually be represented in the parametric form

$$K = K(t),$$

$$L = L(t),$$

and thus

$$k = k(t).$$

Then the essence of our lemma is that technological change may be represented as factor augmenting if and only if there exists some class of such paths that may be expressed by

$$k(t) = \frac{k(0)}{h(t)},$$

where $h(t)$ is independent of the initial value $k(0)$, along which relative competitive income shares are constant. That is, the family of surfaces represented by F must be such that the paths having factor shares constant are scale replicas of one another in the sense that at any time t all ratios $k(t)/k(0)$ are completely independent of the actual values of $k(t)$ and $k(0)$.[10]

Thus we see why it is possible for Solow to assert that the factor-augmenting representation is restrictive and for Phelps to assert that no econometric evidence would enable us to reject the hypothesis that technological change has been factor augmenting. The following experiment, for example, could

---

[9] Rose [50] develops a somewhat different formulation of the condition justifying the factor-augmenting representation when the parameter t assumes values only in some arbitrary index set, and he obtains some further economic interpretation.

[10] Provided, of course, that such paths, defined by the requirement that factor shares be constant, are unique. See footnote 11.

identify a case in which technological progress was not factor augmenting. Suppose we select an initial capital/labor ratio k_0. Then an initial ratio of imputed income shares is determined. It will be possible, in general, to find some path $k(t)$ that maintains income shares constant as time passes and the production function shifts. Take the resulting path $k(t)$ as a standard for later comparison. Now return to the initial time and select a different initial value k_0'. Again some initial ratio of imputed income shares is determined. Now find a new path $k'(t)$ that maintains this ratio constant at its new value. Unless there is some function $\lambda(t)$ independent of the initial values k_0 and k_0' such that $k'(t) = \lambda(t)k(t)$ for all t, we must conclude, using our lemma, that the family of production functions could not be represented in the factor-augmenting form. The description of this experiment—the necessity of going back to the starting point and comparing two histories of the world—makes it obvious why econometric time series evidence can never reject the factor-augmentation hypothesis.[11]

We conclude with an important warning about a common misconception. Although an increase in $a(t)$ is labor augmenting and increases the *efficiency unit measure* of the labor input, it does not follow that technological change has occurred because the "quality" of workers has improved. Conversely, an improvement in the quality of workers, e.g., through improved education, does not necessarily imply an increase in $a(t)$, but rather $a(t)$, $b(t)$, or both may change. In fact, $a(t)$ may actually decrease providing $b(t)$ increases sufficiently and the net effect is a technological improvement with $F_t > 0$. An analogous comment applies to the capital input.

3–3. The Role of Disembodied Technological Change in Growth Models

We would like an economic model whose theoretical implications are consistent with the observed "empirical realities" (stylized facts) (i)–(vi) enumerated in Section 3-1. Regardless of the nature of technological change, it is trivial to fulfill (i) by assuming that a constant fraction s of output is saved. However, in a one-sector, constant returns to scale model (with constant exponential decay) in which the growth rate of labor and the saving rate I/Q are both constant, the only form of disembodied technological progress consistent with an equilibrium balanced growth path on which all

---

[11] This discussion assumes that when a starting point k_0 is specified and initial factor, shares are therefore determined, then the requirement that factor shares remain constant defines a unique path $k(t)$ in the input space. For the two-factor case we are considering here, this requirement of uniqueness is met provided only that the production function F does not have elasticity of substitution equal to unity, except perhaps for isolated values of t. (The Cobb-Douglas function must obviously be excluded as a degenerate case from all the foregoing discussion.) The proof of this result is Exercise 9 of Chapter 5.

variables grow at a constant relative rate is Harrod-neutral progress. This fact may be proved simply by observing that if investment is to be positive and the saving rate constant, then capital grows at a constant relative rate only if the capital/output ratio is constant. Thus,

$$\frac{Q}{K} = \frac{f(k, t)}{k} = A, \qquad \text{a constant.}$$

Differentiating with respect to time,

$$f_k k + f_t = A\dot{k}$$

or

$$\frac{f_t}{f} = (\lambda - g)(1 - \pi)$$

where λ is the common (and constant) growth rate of capital and output. Diamond [11, 12] has shown that if $(f_t/f)/(1 - \pi)$ is a function of time alone, then technical progress is Harrod neutral.[12] By our previous result, we may represent the function f in factor-augmenting form.

Thus we see that when the growth rate of labor and the saving rate are constant, and the production function is homogeneous of degree one, satisfaction of the stylized facts (ii)–(vi) demands that technological progress be representable in the Harrod-neutral form. We can also show that all the properties (i)–(vi) can be realized in a model with the above factor growth assumptions and a constant returns to scale production function in the Harrod-neutral form

$$Q = F(K, L; t) = G[K, a(t)L]. \tag{12}$$

Since G is homogeneous of degree one in its two arguments K and $a(t)L$, we may define a new production function

$$\tilde{q} \equiv \frac{Q}{\ell} = G\left(\frac{K}{\ell}, 1\right) \equiv g(\tilde{k}) \tag{13}$$

---

[12] Note that it is not enough for us simply to observe (ii) and (vi) and conclude that if we assume that relative income shares are constant, then the constancy of the capital/labor ratio implies the constancy of the rate of interest. Although this sounds like a definition of Harrod neutrality, it is not; it is simply an observation about one particular growth path, not a characterization of the complete family of production functions.

where *labor measured in efficiency units* is $\ell \equiv a(t)L$ and $\tilde{k} \equiv K/\ell$. For simplicity, assume that $\hat{a} = \gamma$, an exogenous constant. It is then easy to show that the growth equation is

$$\dot{\tilde{k}} = sg(\tilde{k}) - (g + \delta + \gamma)\tilde{k} \tag{14}$$

(where δ is the exponential depreciation rate of capital) with $d(\dot{\tilde{k}}/\tilde{k})/d\tilde{k} < 0$ (Exercise 8). Thus, a positive root $\tilde{k}^*$ to the equation

$$\dot{\tilde{k}} = sg(\tilde{k}) - (g + \delta + \gamma)\tilde{k} = 0,$$

if it exists, is unique and stable and

$$\lim_{t \to \infty} \tilde{k} = \tilde{k}^*.$$

Consequently we may establish that (iii)–(vi) hold *asymptotically* (i.e., as $t \to \infty$):

(iii) $k = a(t)\tilde{k}^*$ or $\hat{k} - \hat{a} = \gamma > 0.$

(iv) $r = F_K - \delta = G_1 - \delta = g'(\tilde{k}^*) - \delta = \text{constant}.$

(v) $W = F_L = a(t)G_2 = a(t)[g(\tilde{k}^*) - \tilde{k}^*g'(\tilde{k}^*)]$ or
    $\hat{W} = \hat{a} = \gamma > 0.$

(vi) $\omega/k = F_L L/F_K K = F_L/F_K k$ and
    $\hat{\omega} - \hat{k} = \hat{F}_L - \hat{F}_K - \hat{k} = \gamma - 0 - \gamma = 0.$

We conclude that there are models consistent with (i)–(vi) if we assume the existence of Harrod-neutral technological change.

Unless technological change is *ultimately* Harrod neutral, one-sector models generally cannot approach an equilibrium balanced growth path that is economically meaningful. To illustrate the type of issue involved, we will outline a model with Hicks-neutral technological change and demonstrate that a constant capital/output ratio implies that one factor share approaches zero.[13]

Thus, suppose that the production function is

$$Q = F(K, L; t) = G[a(t)K, a(t)L] = a(t)G(K, L)$$

or

$$q = a(t)g(k).$$

---

[13] On the other hand, if (1) technological change is Hicks neutral, (2) $\sigma \neq 1$, and (3) $\hat{\pi} = 0$, then it is clear that $\hat{k} = 0$, a contradiction to the stylized facts (Exercise 9).

Differentiation of the latter gives

$$\hat{q} = \hat{a} + \pi \hat{k},$$

and, consequently,

$$\hat{x} \equiv \hat{q} - \hat{k} = \hat{a} - (1 - \pi)\hat{k}$$

where $x \equiv q/k$ is the output/capital ratio. Since we insist on a growth path along which $\hat{x} = 0$, the condition

$$\hat{k} \equiv \frac{\hat{a}}{1 - \pi}$$

must be satisfied identically in t. By assumption technological change is Hicks neutral and we may derive (see equation 9 in Chapter 5)

$$\hat{\pi} = \left(1 - \frac{1}{\sigma}\right)\hat{a}. \tag{15}$$

Now if $\hat{a}$ is bounded from below by some positive number ε, i.e., if $\hat{a} - \varepsilon > 0$ and if σ is bounded away from unity, it is clear that (15) implies

$$\lim_{t \to \infty} \pi(t) = \infty \text{ if } \sigma > 1, \quad \text{or} \quad \lim_{t \to \infty} \pi(t) = 0 \text{ if } \sigma < 1.$$

Thus, for this example a growth path along which the output/capital ratio is constant is possible only if one relative share falls to zero (either in finite time or asymptotically), and earlier we rejected such results. Similar difficulties arise for other paths and for forms of technological change other than Harrod neutral.

3–4. Induced Technological Change

We have argued that the observed empirical facts can be explained if we assume that technological change is always Harrod neutral, but this explanation is open to the valid criticism that we have no *a priori* reason for accepting the Harrod-neutrality postulate. Some authors, e.g., Drandakis and Phelps [15], Kennedy [31], and von Weizsäcker [75] have attempted to circumvent this objection by introducing an *invention possibility frontier* that gives a functional relationship between the attainable rates of factor augmentation $\hat{a}$ and $\hat{b}$. This function is shaped like an ordinary production possibility frontier with

$$\hat{a} = \psi(\hat{b}),$$

$$\psi'(\hat{b}) < 0,$$

$$\psi''(\hat{b}) < 0, \qquad (16)$$

and

$$\psi(0) > 0.$$

At any given point in time it is supposed that firms maximize the current rate of technological progress $\tau \equiv F_t/F$, which is equivalent to maximizing the current rate of cost reduction at given factor prices. However, τ is maximized subject to the given constraint $\hat{a} = \psi(\hat{b})$, and thus $\hat{a}$ and $\hat{b}$ cannot be increased simultaneously: by assumption, an increase in the rate of labor augmentation necessitates a decrease in the rate of capital augmentation, and vice versa.

We will discuss several objections to this model later, but first we shall outline an analysis similar to that of Drandakis and Phelps [15]. We assume that $\hat{a}$ and $\hat{b}$ are bounded from above by $\hat{a} < \hat{a}_0$, and $\hat{b} < \hat{b}_0$. Since we also assume that $\psi(0) > 0$, both $\hat{a}_0$ and $\hat{b}_0$ are positive and the curve $\hat{a} = \psi(\hat{b})$ has a segment in the first quadrant of the $\hat{b}$-$\hat{a}$ plane. Therefore we can always find a positive value of

$$\tau = \pi\hat{b} + (1 - \pi)\hat{a}$$

by selecting any point $(\hat{b}, \hat{a})$ in the first quadrant. Consequently, the *maximum* value of τ is positive for any given value of π.

Maximization of τ subject to the constraint $\hat{a} = \psi(\hat{b})$ requires that

$$\frac{\partial \tau}{\partial \hat{b}} = \pi + (1 - \pi)\frac{\partial \hat{a}}{\partial \hat{b}} = \pi + (1 - \pi)\psi'(\hat{b}) = 0; \qquad (17)$$

since

$$\frac{\partial^2 \tau}{\partial \hat{b}^2} = (1 - \pi)\psi''(\hat{b}) < 0,$$

a maximum exists and is unique. The solution of (17) gives the condition

$$\psi'(\hat{b}) = -\frac{\pi}{1 - \pi}, \qquad (18)$$

as illustrated in Figure 10. Thus our assumption that τ is maximized at every point of time implies that $\hat{a}$ and $\hat{b}$ are both functions of π, and differentiating (18) gives (see Exercise 10)

$$\frac{d\hat{b}}{d\pi} = -\frac{1}{(1-\pi)^2 \psi''(\hat{b})} > 0, \tag{19}$$

$$\frac{d\hat{a}}{d\pi} = \psi'(b)\frac{d\hat{b}}{d\pi} = -\frac{\pi}{1-\pi}\frac{d\hat{b}}{d\pi} < 0, \tag{20}$$

and if $\hat{h} \equiv \hat{b} - \hat{a}$,

$$\frac{d\hat{h}}{d\pi} = -\frac{1}{(1-\pi)^3 \psi''(\hat{b})} > 0 \tag{21}$$

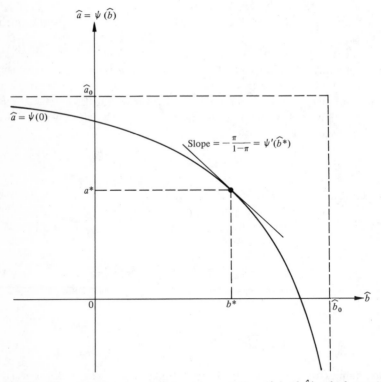

Figure 10. *The optimal rates of factor augmentation $\hat{a}^*$ and $\hat{b}^*$ which maximize τ are determined by the tangency of a line with slope $-\pi/(1-\pi)$ and the invention possibility frontier. It is assumed that $\hat{a}$ and $\hat{b}$ are bounded above by $\hat{a}_0$ and $\hat{b}_0$, respectively, and that $\psi(0) > 0$.*

If the savings ratio s is constant,[14] the rate of growth of capital is

$$\hat{K} = s\frac{Q}{K} - \delta$$

and the rate of growth of the capital/labor ratio is

$$\hat{k} = \hat{k}(x) = sx - (g + \delta) \tag{22}$$

where (as previously) $x \equiv q/k$, $g = \dot{L}/L$, and δ is the exponential depreciation rate of capital. Since $\hat{q} = \pi\hat{k} + \tau$,

$$\hat{x} \equiv \hat{q} - \hat{k} = \tau - (1 - \pi)\hat{k}, \tag{23}$$

and substituting $\tau = \pi\hat{b} + (1 - \pi)\hat{a}$ and (22) into (23) we obtain

$$\hat{x} = \hat{x}(\hat{x}, \pi) = \tau(\pi) - (1 - \pi)\hat{k}(x) = \pi\hat{b}(\pi) + (1 - \pi)\hat{a}(\pi) - \\ (1 - \pi)[sx - (g + \delta)]. \tag{24}$$

Similarly, $\hat{\pi}$ is a function of x and π because (Exercise 11)

$$\hat{\pi} = (1 - \pi)\left(1 - \frac{1}{\sigma}\right)(\hat{k} + \hat{b} - \hat{a}) = (1 - \pi)\left(1 - \frac{1}{\sigma}\right)[\hat{k}(x) + \hat{b}(\pi) - \hat{a}(\pi)]$$

$$= (1 - \pi)\left(1 - \frac{1}{\sigma}\right)[\hat{k}(x) + \hat{h}(\pi)] = \hat{\pi}(x, \pi). \tag{25}$$

The two differential equations (24) and (25) determine the behavior of the model over time for any given initial values of x and π. The point (x^*, π^*) is an equilibrium if and only if $\hat{x}(x^*, \pi^*) = \hat{\pi}(x^*, \pi^*) = 0$, and the existence, uniqueness, and stability of equilibrium can all be studied by examining the equations $\hat{x} = 0$ and $\hat{\pi} = 0$. However, we need the additional assumption that $\sigma \neq 1$ to avoid the case in which $\hat{\pi} \equiv 0$.

Consider first the equation $\hat{\pi} = 0$. Since $0 < \pi < 1$, (25) implies that $\hat{\pi} = 0$ if and only if

$$\hat{k} = \hat{a} - \hat{b} \equiv -\hat{h}$$

or

$$x = \frac{1}{s}[(g + \delta) - \hat{h}(\pi)] \equiv N(\pi), \tag{26}$$

[14] Drandakis and Phelps [15] also consider an exponentially declining savings ratio.

and thus for any value of π,

$$\hat{\pi}[N(\pi), \pi] = 0;$$

because $d\hat{h}/d\pi > 0$ by (21),

$$N'(\pi) < 0. \tag{27}$$

Similarly, (24) implies that $\hat{x} = 0$ if and only if

$$\hat{k} = \frac{\tau}{1 - \pi}$$

or

$$x = \frac{1}{s}\left[\frac{\tau(\pi)}{1 - \pi} + (g + \delta)\right] = \frac{1}{s}\left[\frac{\pi}{1 - \pi}\,\hat{b}(\pi) + \hat{a}(\pi) + (g + \delta)\right] \equiv M(\pi), \tag{28}$$

and for any value of π,

$$\hat{x}[M(\pi), \pi] = 0.$$

Both $\hat{x}$ and $\hat{\pi}$ equal zero at the equilibrium point (x^*, π^*), and therefore the equation

$$M(\pi) - N(\pi) = \frac{\hat{b}(\pi)}{s(1 - \pi)} = 0$$

is satisfied when $\pi = \pi^*$. Consequently, π^* must be a root of the equation $\hat{b}(\pi) = 0$, and since $d\hat{b}/d\pi > 0$ by (19), π^* is unique and

$$\hat{b}(\pi) \gtreqless 0 \quad \text{as} \quad \pi \gtreqless \pi^*. \tag{29}$$

Thus, x^* is also unique and is given by

$$x^* = M(\pi^*) = N(\pi^*).$$

Moreover, we may differentiate (28), obtaining

$$M'(\pi) = \frac{1}{s}\left[\frac{\hat{b}(\pi)}{(1 - \pi)^2} + \frac{\pi}{1 - \pi}\frac{d\hat{b}}{d\pi} + \frac{d\hat{a}}{d\pi}\right],$$

and substituting (20) into the latter gives

$$M'(\pi) = \frac{\hat{b}(\pi)}{s(1 - \pi)^2}.$$

Thus (29) implies that

$$M'(\pi) \gtreqqless 0 \quad \text{as} \quad \pi \gtreqqless \pi^*. \tag{30}$$

Equations (26)–(30) enable us to graph the functions $M(\pi)$ and $N(\pi)$ (the curves along which $\hat{x} = 0$ and $\hat{\pi} = 0$, respectively) in the x-π plane. The limiting behavior of $N(\pi)$ as π approaches zero or one is determined by observing that (1) $\hat{a} \to \hat{a}_0$ and $\hat{b} \to -\infty$ as $\pi \to 0$, and (2) $\hat{a} \to -\infty$ and $\hat{b} \to \hat{b}_0$ as $\pi \to 1$, as may be verified from Figure 10. Therefore,

$$\lim_{\pi \to 0} N(\pi) = \frac{g + \delta}{s} + \frac{1}{s} \lim_{\pi \to 0} [\hat{a}(\pi) - \hat{b}(\pi)] = +\infty \tag{31}$$

and

$$\lim_{\pi \to 1} N(\pi) = \frac{g + \delta}{s} + \frac{1}{s} \lim_{\pi \to 1} [\hat{a}(\pi) - \hat{b}(\pi)] = -\infty. \tag{32}$$

However, the exact limiting behavior of

$$M(\pi) = \frac{1}{s} \left[\frac{\pi}{1 - \pi} \hat{b}(\pi) + \hat{a}(\pi) + (g + \delta) \right]$$

is indeterminate unless additional assumptions are made, although it can be shown that (Exercise 12)

$$M(\pi^*) < \lim_{\pi \to 0} M(\pi) < \frac{1}{s} [\hat{a}_0 + (g + \delta)] \tag{33}$$

and

$$\lim_{\pi \to 1} M(\pi) > M(\pi^*). \tag{34}$$

Finally, (29) implies that $\hat{b}(\pi^*) = 0$, and thus (18) and (28) may be solved for

$$\pi^* = \frac{\psi'(0)}{\psi'(0) - 1} = \text{constant } (0 < \pi^* < 1) \tag{35}$$

and

$$x^* = \frac{1}{s}[\psi(0) + (g + \delta)] = \text{constant} > 0, \tag{36}$$

respectively. Substitution of (36) in (22) gives

$$\hat{k}^* = \hat{k}(\pi^*) = \psi(0) > 0, \tag{37}$$

and in equilibrium the capital/labor ratio grows at the constant rate $\psi(0)$.
The two curves $N(\pi)$ and $M(\pi)$ in Figures 11 and 12 have the shapes asserted

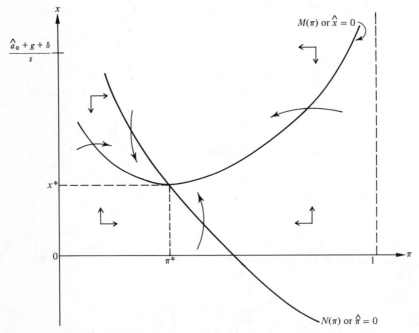

Figure 11. *Phase diagram of the differential equations $\hat{x} = \hat{x}(x, \pi)$ and $\hat{\pi} = \hat{\pi}(x, \pi)$ when $\sigma < 1$. The equilibrium point (x^*, π^*) is stable, and therefore starting from any initial point (x_0, π_0) for which $x_0 > 0$ and $0 < \pi_0 < 1$, $\lim_{t \to \infty}(x_t, \pi_t) = (x^*, \pi^*)$. Observe that a limit cycle cannot exist because all the phase arrows that cross the boundary of the region enclosed by $N(\pi)$, $M(\pi)$, and the x-axis point inward.*

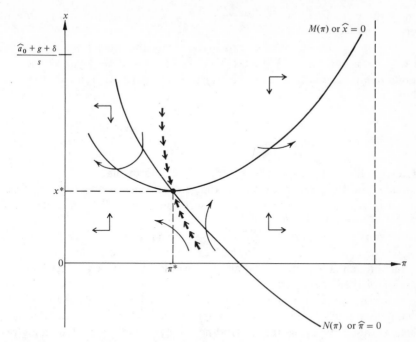

Figure 12. *Phase diagram of the differential equations* $\hat{x} = \hat{x}(x, \pi)$ *and* $\hat{\pi} = \hat{\pi}(x, \pi)$ *when* $\sigma > 1$. *The equilibrium point* (x^*, π^*) *is a* saddlepoint, *and unless initially* (x_0, π_0) *lies exactly on the dashed curve,* $\lim_{t \to \infty} \pi(t) = 0$ *or* 1.

by the foregoing discussion. Consider any point (x_0, π_0) in the plane. If $x_0 > M(\pi_0)$, from (28) we deduce that $\hat{k} > \tau/(1 - \pi)$, and hence (24) implies that $\hat{x} < 0$; likewise if $x_0 < M(\pi_0)$, $\hat{x} > 0$. Accordingly, in both phase diagrams the arrows in the x-direction point down (up) for all points above (below) the curve $M(\pi)$. The analysis of the motion in the π-direction is similar: if $x_0 > N(\pi_0)$, (26) implies that $\hat{k} + \hat{h} > 0$, and thus from (25) we see that $\hat{\pi} \lessgtr 0$ as $\sigma \lessgtr 1$, whereas if $x_0 < N(\pi_0)$, $\hat{\pi} \gtrless 0$ as $\sigma \gtrless 1$. Therefore, in Figure 11 where $\sigma < 1$, the arrows in the π-direction point to the left (right) for all points above (below) the curve $N(\pi)$, whereas if $\sigma > 1$ as in Figure 12, the arrows in the π-direction are reversed.

Examination of Figure 11 ($\sigma < 1$) reveals that all the phase arrows that cross the boundary of the region enclosed by $N(\pi)$, $M(\pi)$, and the x-axis *point inward*. Therefore a limit cycle around the equilibrium point (x^*, π^*) cannot exist, and we conclude that the equilibrium is *stable*. In other words, starting from any economically meaningful initial point (x_0, π_0) with $x_0 > 0$ and $0 < \pi_0 < 1$, (x_t, π_t) asymptotically approaches (x^*, π^*) as t approaches infinity. However, when $\sigma > 1$ as in Figure 12, the equilibrium point (x^*, π^*) is a *saddlepoint*, and unless the initial point (x_0, π_0) lies exactly on the dashed curve, the system will not converge to (x^*, π^*), but instead π will approach zero or one.

Solow has given an intuitive explanation why this model is stable when $\sigma < 1$; his argument ([62], pp. 32–35) is as follows: If we again define the capital/labor ratio *measured in efficiency units* as $z \equiv bK/aL$, it is easy to show that

$$\frac{d\pi}{dz}\{\gtreqless\}0 \qquad \text{if and only if} \quad \sigma\{\gtreqless\}1$$

(Exercise 13). Suppose $\sigma < 1$ and initially z is growing; then π decreases initially, and from Figure 10 we see that τ is maximized only if $\hat{b}$ decreases and $\hat{a}$ increases. Clearly this process must continue until (1) z is constant, (2) $\hat{b} = 0$, and (3) $\hat{a} = \psi(0) = \hat{k}^*$.

Of course, in general σ is a function of x and π and need not be always bigger than or less than one. In the latter case a more complicated analysis of the differential equations (24) and (25) would be necessary to describe the motion of the system.

However, if σ is always less than one, the model of induced technological change presented here does offer an explanation of the observed empirical facts without requiring the Harrod-neutrality assumption. Technological change is asymptotically Harrod neutral since $\hat{b}(\pi^*) = 0$, but this fact is an implication rather than an assumption. Moreover, examination of (35)–(37) shows that there are other significantly different implications of this model. In particular, (35) and (37) imply that in equilibrium both the relative share of capital π^* and the rate of growth of the capital/labor ratio $\hat{k}^*$ depend only on $\psi'(0)$ and $\psi(0)$, respectively, and therefore both are independent of the savings ratio s. On the other hand, (36) implies that the equilibrium output/capital ratio x^* does depend on s with $dx^*/ds < 0$. Thus, for values of s between zero and one, there exist corresponding balanced growth paths (Golden Ages) that are stable providing that $\sigma < 1$, and only x^* (not π^* or $\hat{k}^*$) changes from path to path as s changes. It is also possible to show that per capita consumption is maximized along the unique balanced growth path for which

$$r \equiv F_K - \delta = g + \hat{a} = g + \psi(0) \tag{38}$$

and

$$s = \pi^* = \frac{\psi'(0)}{\psi'(0) - 1} \tag{39}$$

(Exercise 14).

It can be shown that the qualitative behavior of the model remains essentially unchanged if the assumption that gross investment equals $s(RK + WL)$ is replaced by the more general assumption that gross investment equals $s_r RK + s_w WL$, where s_r and s_w are the fixed savings propensities from profit and wage income respectively, as in Chapter 2. Using the latter savings assumption with $s_r \geqq s_w$, it can be proved that there exists a unique equilibrium point (x^{**}, π^{**}) that is stable if $\sigma < 1$ and a saddlepoint if $\sigma > 1$. Moreover,

$$\pi^{**} = \frac{\psi'(0)}{\psi'(0) - 1} \tag{40}$$

and

$$\hat{k}^{**} = \hat{a}(\pi^{**}) = \psi(0), \tag{41}$$

exactly the same results we obtained with the previous savings assumption. However, now the equilibrium output/capital ratio is

$$x^{**} = \frac{\psi(0) + (g + \delta)}{s_r \pi^{**} + s_w(1 - \pi^{**})}, \tag{42}$$

which, of course, equals x^* if $s_r = s_w = s$. The proof of these facts is Exercise 15.

Several objections to this model have been raised by Drandakis and Phelps [15], Samuelson [53, 54], and Solow [62]. The most serious criticisms are:

(i) No resources (i.e., capital and labor) are required to achieve technological progress, and factor augmentation is restricted only by the invention possibility frontier $\hat{a} = \psi(\hat{b})$.

(ii) The invention possibility frontier is stationary and cannot be shifted outward over time by allocating resources to a "research sector."

(iii) The model assumes maximization of the rate of technological progress τ or (equivalently) the current rate of cost reduction at given factor prices. But this assumption implies a myopic behavior since factor prices do change over time, except in steady-state equilibrium. In a model with competitive pricing and no uncertainty it is more appropriate to postulate the *minimization of the present discounted value of all future costs*.

(iv) Although the assumptions of a stationary frontier and the instantaneous maximization of τ may be an appropriate approximation to reality in the very short run (especially if factor prices are changing slowly), it is then that the assumption of factor-augmenting technological change is dangerous because it is precisely in the very short run that technological progress is probably embodied in new capital equipment.

Several authors have attempted to meet some of these objections by considering the effect of education upon technological progress and by explicitly introducing a research sector that produces inventions; in particular, the interested reader is referred to papers by Drandakis and Hu [16], Nelson and Phelps [41], Nordhaus [42], Shell [55], Uzawa [72, 74] and von Weizsäcker [75].

3–5. Embodied Technological Change

In the previous discussion technological change, whether induced or exogenous, has been of the disembodied type—the productivity of input factors has depended only upon the date at which production takes place. We now wish to consider a different possiblity, namely that the productivity of produced factors may depend not upon the date of current activity, but upon the date of manufacture of the factors. Technological change, in other words, does not affect new and old machines alike, but rather technological progress must be embodied in design changes built into new machines alone. Old machines reflect the technology and economic conditions prevailing at their date of birth, not the best practice at the present moment.

We shall see that analysis of models with embodied technical change can be extremely complex, challenging the manipulative skills of successive generations of graduate students. On some questions, results for these models are still rather sketchy, and many questions remain unanswered. In this present discussion we shall attempt to do little more than specify the model and to outline some of the issues.

We begin with the well-known article of Solow [63] which describes the technology taken as the point of departure for most of the later contributions to this literature. It is assumed that a machine is identified by a number v denoting its date of manufacture or vintage. It is further assumed that machines of different vintages are operated independently, as separate processes, so that we may write total output $Q(t)$, measured as a flow of physical units, in the additive form

$$Q(t) = \int_{-\infty}^{t} Q(v, t) \, dv.$$

Here $Q(v, t)$ is like a density function in that the expression $Q(v, t) \, dv/Q(t)$ denotes the fraction of the output flow $Q(t)$ at time t that is produced by employing labor to work those machines manufactured between times v and $v + dv$. Thus we are assuming that only a single kind of capital good, together with labor, is required to produce an output flow, and we aggregate the resulting output flows of identical goods. This approach contrasts with the procedure we have used until now: that of supposing the existence of an aggregate capital stock representing some measure of all machines of different types presently in existence and entering this measure into a single production function. (Thus far we have in fact assumed only one kind of capital good in existence, so no problem has arisen in construction of any aggregates.)

The output flow from machines of a particular type is given by a *vintage production function* having a standard form

$$Q(v, t) = F[K_v(t), L_v(t), v]$$

where $L_v(t)$ is the allocation of labor to work on machines of vintage v. The form of this function pinpoints the assumption that it is the date of manufacture v of the capital good, rather than the current time t, that determines productivity.[15]

Assuming that existing labor is allocated to machines of different vintages in such a way as to obtain maximum output subject to the constraint $L(t) = \int_{-\infty}^{t} L(v, t)dv$, we may determine the function $L(v, t)$, and hence determine output $Q(t)$ completely.

If we add assumptions concerning

(i) Labor force growth,
(ii) Saving and investment in new machines, and
(iii) Deterioration of existing machines,

then we have a complete growth model with a determinate future.

We should note an interesting sidelight to the foregoing calculations. If we assume a Cobb–Douglas form for the vintage production functions as Solow did in his original analysis, it is easy to solve the labor allocation problem explicitly. Output can then be expressed as a function of the total labor force and a constructed measure that depends only upon the number of machines and their distribution over vintages. It is possible, in other words, to construct explicitly a measure of an aggregate capital stock that is suitable as an argument in an aggregate production function. This feature sparked a resurgence of interest in problems of aggregation that had been a matter of debate somewhat earlier (see Robinson [49] and Solow [66]), and it led to a number of investigations into the conditions that permit the construction of such factor aggregates. Among these are the works of Fisher [18], Stigum [70, 71], and a number of others appearing in a recent *Symposium on Aggregation* in the *Review of Economic Studies* (October, 1968).

[15] In Solow's original work on this model the vintage production functions were

$$Q(v, t) = Be^{\lambda v}K_v(t)^\alpha L_v(t)^{1-\alpha},$$

in which the productivity shift factor $e^{\lambda v}$ depends only upon the vintage of the capital good and not on time.

Although obviously relevant to the construction of growth models, this aggregation question is beyond our present interest, and we will not pursue the matter here. Instead we will return to the properties of growth paths arising in a one-sector model with embodied technological change. But first it is worthwhile to consider the kind of parable that would validate this Solow model. One such scheme is the following. The process of production yields an output flow of ubiquitous animals called schmoos. A proportion of the output flow (measured in schmoos per year) is separated and flows to consumption, these animals being instantly adaptable to serve as a universal consumption good pleasing all tastes. The remainder of the flow is added to the capital stock to aid in further production. Because of continual design changes, the schmoos of later years are more efficient in production, but not at all different as a consumption good. The latter assumption permits the output flow to be measured in an unchanging consumption good unit. At the same time a schmoo of later date may be thought of as equivalent in production to more than one schmoo produced in year zero.

The difficulties that arise in this model when technological progress causes rising quality of consumption goods as well as increasing efficiency in production have been discussed by Green [20]. The significance of the discussion for our present analysis is that this model demands some natural unit of measurement with unchanging consumption value. The design changes that make the output good more productive when it is stockpiled as capital must not make it more desirable when consumed, or else we would face a difficult problem of measuring and comparing national income over time. The one-sector model that permits us to think of a unique flow of national income independently of its composition as between consumption and investment becomes strained under these circumstances.

A great many strands develop from this base. One strand deals with the effect of the embodiment hypothesis upon predictions as to the power of saving policy to influence the growth of an economy with a neoclassical technology. Phelps [44] discussed this question in detail under the assumption that the vintage production functions are all of the Cobb–Douglas form. For this case he showed that in balanced growth equilibrium the average age of the capital stock (and in fact the whole age distribution of the capital stock) is independent of the extent to which technical progress may be embodied rather than disembodied. Further, he showed for this Cobb–Douglas case that the sensitivity of the steady growth output track to changes in the saving rate does not depend on the extent of embodiment of technological change. Instead we can calculate that the elasticity of output with respect to the saving rate is given by the ratio of the imputed share of capital to that of labor. With the Cobb–Douglas function, this ratio is evidently constant. On the other hand, Phelps observed that the transition from one equilibrium path to an equilibrium path with higher saving is faster in case technological change is embodied, because of the "modernizing" effect of the temporary reduction in the average age of the capital stock.

Matthews [39] suggested that this result hinges crucially on the fact that with Cobb–Douglas production functions only physical depreciation reduces the stock of capital; no vintage of capital goods will ever be discarded for economic reasons. Operation with a sufficiently small crew will always yield returns in excess of wage costs. With more general production functions this result does not hold; machines can be scrapped because of economic obsolescence as well as for physical deterioration. Matthews therefore suggested that the sensitivity of output to saving will be different for models in which technological change is embodied than for those in which it is disembodied, the direction of difference depending upon the elasticity of substitution.[16]

Subsequently Levhari and Sheshinski [38] studied a vintage model with a general production function and derived the same relation showing the elasticity of equilibrium output with respect to changes in the saving rate to be equal to the ratio of capital's imputed share to labor's. From this they concluded that Phelps' early result extended to models with general vintage production functions and that the sensitivity to saving policy does not depend upon the extent to which technological progress is embodied. However, A. B. Atkinson of Cambridge University has pointed out in an unpublished note that although their analysis is correct the conclusion is not general, since usually imputed factor shares will be predicted differently by models that differ in their degree of embodiment. The same observation has been made in a note by Fisher, Levhari, and Sheshinski [38], but they argue further that the Sheskinski–Levhari conclusion just stated is a valid approximation for small changes in the saving rate.

Thus we conclude from this group of studies that when technological change is embodied we may expect transitions between steady growth paths and the sensitivity of output to changes in policy parameters to be different from that when technological change is disembodied. However, long-run equilibrium rates of growth are the same in both models, and higher growth rates can be sustained only by a continual increase in the saving ratio.

All the foregoing discussion of embodied change stems from an initial concern with identification of the sources of economic growth and with the character of the technological progress that could account for that growth. The emphasis is on the comparison of results with earlier statistical estimates obtained for models with disembodied change. In particular, study focused on the sensitivity of output to changes in saving rates, in order to determine whether earlier pessimistic conclusions as to the ineffectiveness of saving policy might simply reflect failure to recognize the role of investment as a carrier of

---

[16] In response to this comment Phelps and Yaari [46] extended the analysis to a more general accumulation equation valid when technical progress is embodied, but did not resolve the question.

technical change and the benefits from reducing the average age of the capital stock. Now we wish to turn from this particular issue to examine more general properties of the growth paths possible when technological change is embodied.

We do not wish to discuss this complex topic in great detail. Many of the major results may be surveyed by reviewing briefly the contents of an elegant paper by Bliss [6]. The paper deals with an extended version of a vintage model in which the characteristics of a capital good may be varied at the time it is manufactured, but may not be altered (at least not so easily) once the capital good is in place.[17] As a result, we must specify an *ex ante* production function describing the production possibilities of newly designed equipment, and an *ex post* production function describing the output obtainable from operation of the specific equipment in place. Therefore the production specification would include

$$Q(t) = \int_{-\infty}^{t} Q(v, t) \, dv$$

where the *ex ante* production function is given by

$$Q(v, v) = F[I(v), L(v, v), v].$$

(The presence of embodied technological change is, of course, suggested by the fact that the date of manufacture v appears in the *ex ante* production function. We could also incorporate the same distinction between *ex ante* and *ex post* production conditions in the absence of technological change.)

We shall assume, as Bliss does, that once the machine is built it must be operated with fixed complements of labor so that the *ex post* production function is

$$Q(v, t) = Q(v, v)L(v, t)/L(v, v),$$

with the additional constraint $L(v, t) \leq L(v, v)$ to rule out operation with redundant labor.

As before, the allocation of labor must satisfy

$$\int_{-\infty}^{t} L(v, t) \, dv = L(t)$$

where $L(t)$ is a given time path for the available labor force. The function $L(t)$ thus gives our specification of labor force growth.

---

[17] The idea for this representation was Johansen's [25]; his work provided the stimulus for many studies along these lines, including those of Phelps [45], Solow [64], and several others [58, 33].

The specification of capital stock growth may be obtained by assuming a one-sector structure, so that output $Q(t)$ may be taken equal to aggregate demand. Assuming also a specified saving function $s(t)$, we may write

$$Q(t) = C(t) + I(t) = \int_{-\infty}^{t} Q(v, t)\, dv$$

where

$$I(t) = s(t)Q(t).$$

With specified initial conditions (including the whole initial age distribution of the capital stock), these equations form a complete model. It is of interest to investigate the properties of this model.

The results may be summarized as follows. We define a *feasible* growth path $\{C(t), I(t), Q(t)\}$ satisfying all the previous equations for some specified function of time $L(t)$. We define an *efficient* growth path as a feasible path $\{C(t), I(t), Q(t)\}$ such that there exists no other feasible path $\{C'(t), I'(t), Q'(t)\}$ having the property that $C'(t) \geq C(t)$ for all t and $C'(t) > C(t)$ for some choice of t.[18]

We define a *competitive equilibrium* path as a feasible path (with an associated wage rate defined) on which there exists a discount rate at which the net present values V of all investment options are maximized (over choices of k) and zero. A *first order competitive equilibrium* is a feasible path on which all necessary conditions for V to be maximized are satisfied, and also V is zero. (The difference is that sufficient conditions for a maximum to V may not be satisfied.) We say that there is *equilibrium on the investment market* if for a positive lifetime T, positive rates of return r, and positive capital/labor ratio k, the present value of new equipment is maximized and the maximum value is zero.

Bliss demonstrates the following propositions.

(i) A balanced growth path is possible in this technology if and only if technological progress is Harrod neutral and proceeds at a constant (exponential) rate.

(ii) On any efficient balanced growth track the economic life T of machines is constant.

(iii) On any balanced growth path which is a competitive equilibrium path, the rate of return r is a constant.

(iv) There exists a value w_0 (which may be infinite) such that for any prescribed wage $w \leq w_0$ there exists a unique positive rate of return r and

---

[18] Actually, the property must hold for some set of values $\{t\}$ having nonzero measure. For our present expository purposes, we disregard details of this kind.

positive values k and T such that equilibrium on the investment market is assured. (This result, which sounds like a more general statement of a factor-price frontier, is also reminiscent of results developed in our later discussion of dynamic linear models in Chapters 7 and 8.)

(v) A growth path is efficient only if it is a first-order competitive equilibrium. (This result is obviously part of a dynamic analog to the theorems mentioned in Chapter 1, linking Pareto-optimality and competitive equilibrium allocations.)

(vi) A balanced growth path with rate of return r less than the natural rate of growth n is inefficient. (This result evidently corresponds to our earlier Golden Rule.)

These results are representative of those obtained in various studies of similar models in which possibilities for factor substitution in production after an investment is in place may be more limited than the possibilities for designing new equipment with varying factor input requirements. They have the effect of demonstrating that limited substitutability in production need not invalidate many of the familiar neoclassical relationships derived from less complete representation of technological possibilities. Since the detailed computations become extremely burdensome, we shall leave the subject of these so-called putty-clay models and the various special cases with this brief sketch.

For the same reason we shall also omit discussion of the important "learning-by-doing" models in which technological progress is embodied but endogenous. In these models improvements in productivity occur as a result of economic activity—experience—and this is indexed by cumulative gross investment. The result is that investment may yield social returns that cannot be captured privately. The existence and stability of balanced growth equilibrium paths in this model, introduced by Arrow [1], have been investigated in a series of papers by Levhari [35, 36, 37] and by Bardhan [3, 4].

Finally, we conclude this discussion by drawing attention to skeptical observations concerning the need for the embodiment hypothesis (Dennison [10], Jorgenson and Griliches [27]) and indeed questioning whether the hypothesis is empirically meaningful (Jorgenson [26]).

3–6. Summary

This chapter has reviewed some of the ways in which technological change may be represented, and it has outlined some of the consequences of introducing technological change into the simple growth model we studied in Chapter 2. We discussed two main ways in which the expansion of production possibilities over time as a result of improvements in techniques could be represented. The first of these assumes simply that changing conditions or changing organization result in an inward movement of isoquants, thus implying increased output with unchanged factor inputs. As a special case of this type of disembodied technological change we introduced the factor-augmenting representation, and we found that special cases of factor augmentation correspond to well-known classes of neutral technological change. We learned that the modified technology that includes specification of a shift over time due to technological improvements represented as factor augmenting can sustain balanced growth only if, in fact, technological change takes the particular Harrod-neutral or labor-augmenting form.

We wished to probe further, however, to discover some mechanism which explains why technological change occurs in a particular way or at a particular rate. One step toward an answer to this question was outlined in our discussion of induced technological change (of the disembodied type). In this analysis the rate and direction of technological change become endogenous, being the consequences of some cost-minimization decision. The explanation falls far short of being complete, however, since we still lack any representation of the way in which the economic system generates opportunities for technological change and how expenditure on research might enlarge these opportunities.

The second main way in which the continuing improvements in technology could be represented recognizes that factor inputs stem from stocks of items produced within the system at various dates, and it is assumed that the productivity of newly produced items increases continually over time. This representation of embodied technological change leads to questions about the effects of investment decisions or saving policy, and it also leads naturally to models in which the possibilities for technical substitution are more limited after an investment is made than they are at the time the investment decision is made. Models of this latter sort require a distinction between the *ex ante* production function on which investment decisions are based and an *ex post* production function describing the operating characteristics of a machine once it is in place.

Again it would be desirable to go beyond the simple description of exogenous technological change to some indication of how the rate of technical improvement may be affected by other variables within the model. The class of learning-by-doing models takes us in this direction by assuming technological change to be labor augmenting at a rate that depends upon cumulated gross investment.

There are many particular models that could be investigated in discussing technological change, and many have, in fact, been subject to intense study. But our brief survey indicates that basically the same questions recur. What characteristics of technical change are necessary if a balanced growth path is to be permanently sustainable (given a constant saving rate)? How is the economic life of machines determined in a particular model, and will that economic life be constant along a balanced growth path? What must be the characteristics of technological change if the construction of some factor aggregates is to be possible, and when can a pseudo-production function be defined that expresses output as a function of such factor aggregates?

We now will concentrate on other features of the process of economic growth, and in the next chapter we move toward disaggregating the one-sector model, distinguishing the processes producing investment goods from those producing consumption goods.

Exercises

1. Prove that $Lf_t = F_t$.

2. Consider equation (3) and define

$$\frac{\partial G}{\partial (bK)} \equiv G_1 \quad \text{and} \quad \frac{\partial G}{\partial (aL)} \equiv G_2.$$

(a) Derive $F_K = bG_1$, $F_L = aG_2$ and $F_t = bKG_1 + \dot{a}LG_2$.

(b) Show that G is homogeneous of degree one in its two arguments bK and aL.

(c) Derive equation (5).

3. Derive equation (8)

4. (a) With a method similar to that used in Exercise 3, prove that

$$\left. \frac{\partial W}{\partial R} \right|_t = - \frac{K}{L}$$

if technological change is Hicks neutral and $q = a(t)g(k)$.

(b) Prove that $\hat{W} = \hat{R} = \hat{a}$ if $\hat{k} = 0$ and thereby deduce that the ratio of relative shares is constant if $\hat{k} = 0$.

(c) Justify equation (10).

5. (a) With a method similar to that used in Exercise 3, prove that

$$\left. \frac{\partial W}{\partial R} \right|_t = - \frac{K}{L}$$

if technological change is Harrod neutral and $Q = G[K, a(t)L]$.

(b) Prove that $\hat{\omega} = \hat{k} = \hat{a}$ if $\hat{R} = 0$ and thereby deduce that the ratio of relative shares is constant if $\hat{R} = 0$.

(c) Justify equation (11).

6. Prove Theorem 2.
7. Consider the production function $Q = F(K, L; t) = K^{\alpha(t)}L^{1-\alpha(t)}$ defined only for $K > L$, $0 < \alpha(t) < 1$, and $\dot{\alpha} > 0$.
   (a) Verify that $\sigma = 1$.
   (b) Verify that $\tau > 0$.
   (c) Prove that $Q = K^{\alpha(t)}L^{1-\alpha(t)}$ *cannot* be written as $Q = G[b(t)K, a(t)L]$.
8. Derive equation (14) and prove that $d(\dot{\tilde{k}}/\tilde{k})/d\tilde{k} < 0$.
9. Prove that if (1) technological change is Hicks neutral, (2) $\sigma \neq 1$, and (3) $\dot{\pi} = 0$, then $\hat{k} = 0$. (*Hint:* Refer to Section 3 of Chapter 5.)
10. Derive equations (19)–(21).
11. Derive equation (25).
12. Derive the inequalities (33) and (34).
13. Prove that $d\pi/dz\{\gtreqless\}0$ if and only if $\sigma\{\gtreqless\}1$, where $z = bK/aL$.
14. (a) Consider the model of induced technological change presented in Section 3-5. Prove that (38) and (39) are necessary conditions for the maximization of per capita consumption in *steady-state eqilibrium*.
    (b) Show the *existence* of a balanced growth path satisfying (38) and (39).
15. Consider a model of induced technological change with all the assumptions stated in Section 3-5, *except* suppose that gross investment equals $s_r RK + s_w WL$ with $s_r \geq s_w$. Derive the equilibrium conditions (40)–(42), and prove that the unique equilibrium point (x^{**}, π^{**}) is stable if $\sigma < 1$ and is a saddle-point if $\sigma > 1$.

Answers and Hints

PROBLEM 3. Consider the production function

$$\frac{Q}{L} \equiv q = f(k)$$

and set the price of output $P_Q \equiv 1$. Then

$$R = f'(k)$$

and

$$W = f(k) - kf'(k)$$

are the parametric equations for the factor-price frontier with parameter k. Calculate

$$\frac{dW}{dR} = \frac{dW/dk}{dR/dk} = -k.$$

PROBLEM 4.

(a) Derive

$$W = a(t)[g(k) - kg'(k)],$$

$$R = a(t)g'(k),$$

and calculate

$$\left. \frac{\partial W}{\partial R} \right|_t = \frac{a(t)[g'(k) - kg''(k) - g'(k)]}{a(t)g''(k)} = -k.$$

(b) Set $\hat{k} = 0$ in the equations for $\dot{W}$ and $\dot{R}$ to obtain $\hat{W} = \hat{R} = \hat{a}$ when $\hat{k} = 0$.

(c) Define *efficiency units* $\tilde{L} \equiv a(t)L$, $\tilde{K} \equiv a(t)K$. The production function $Q = G[a(t)K, b(t)L]$ then becomes $Q = G(\tilde{K}, \tilde{L})$ or $\tilde{q} = g(\tilde{k})$ where $\tilde{q} \equiv Q/\tilde{L}$ and $\tilde{k} \equiv \tilde{K}/\tilde{L} = k$.

If we denote the wage rate and the rental rate for capital *in efficiency units* by $\tilde{W}$ and $\tilde{R}$, respectively,

$$\tilde{R} = g'(k) = \frac{R}{a(t)}$$

and

$$\tilde{W} = g(k) - kg'(k) = \frac{W}{a(t)}$$

are the parametric equations for $C(\tilde{W}, \tilde{R}) = 1$ (see Hint 3). Calculate

$$\frac{d\tilde{W}}{d\tilde{R}} = -k,$$

and therefore conclude that

$$C(\tilde{W}, \tilde{R}) = C\left[\frac{W}{a(t)}, \frac{R}{a(t)} \right] = 1.$$

PROBLEM 5.

(a) Define the capital/labor ratio *in efficiency units* as

$$\tilde{k} \equiv \frac{K}{a(t)L}$$

and write

$$\frac{Q}{L} = a(t)G\left[\frac{K}{a(t)L}, 1 \right] = a(t)G(\tilde{k}, 1) \equiv a(t)g(\tilde{k}).$$

Calculate

$$R = \frac{\partial Q}{\partial K} = g'(\tilde{k}), \qquad W = \frac{\partial Q}{\partial L} = a(t)[g(\tilde{k}) - \tilde{k}g'(\tilde{k})],$$

and

$$\frac{\partial W}{\partial R}\bigg|_t = -a(t)\tilde{k} = -k.$$

(b) Set $\dot{R} = 0$ in the equations for $\dot{W}$ and $\dot{R}$ to obtain $\hat{W} = \hat{a}$ and $\hat{k} = \hat{a}$, respectively.

(c) Again using the notation for measurements *in efficiency units*, derive

$$\tilde{W} = g(\tilde{k}) - \tilde{k}g'(\tilde{k}) = \frac{W}{a(t)}$$

and

$$R(=\tilde{R}) = g'(\tilde{k});$$

then proceed as in Hint 4c.

PROBLEM 6. Necessity is immediate; establish sufficiency by using $h(t \equiv 1.)$

PROBLEM 7.

(a) Calculate

$$\sigma = \frac{F_K F_L}{F F_{KL}}.$$

(b) $\tau \equiv \dfrac{1}{Q} \dfrac{\partial Q}{\partial t} = \dot{\alpha}(\log K - \log L).$

(c) $D \equiv \dfrac{\partial(F_L/F_K)/\partial t}{F_L/F_K} = \alpha(1 - \alpha) \neq 0.$

(d) It can be shown that $\hat{\omega} - \hat{k} = D$ when $\sigma = 1$ (see equation (9) in Chapter 5). Hence there is no path for which relative shares are constant.

PROBLEM 8. Calculate $\dot{\tilde{k}}/\tilde{k} = \dot{K}/K - \dot{L}/L - \dot{a}/a$ and prove

$$\frac{d[g(\tilde{k})/\tilde{k}]}{d\tilde{k}} < 0.$$

PROBLEM 9. Since technological change is Hicks neutral, $D = 0$; $\sigma \neq 1$, and therefor equation (9) of Chapter 5 and $\hat{\tau} = 0$ imply $\hat{k} = 0$.

PROBLEM 10. Differentiate (18).

PROBLEM 11. See equations (8)–(10) in Chapter 5.

PROBLEM 12. Use (30).

PROBLEM 13. (i) Derive $\pi = zg'(z)/g(z)$ and $\sigma = -(1 - \pi)g'(z)/zg''(z)$.

(ii) Differentiate π with respect to z and substitute to obtain

$$\frac{d\pi}{dz} = \frac{\pi(1 - \pi)}{z}\left[1 - \frac{1}{\sigma}\right].$$

PROBLEM 14.

(a) Since we consider only steady-state equilibrium growth, equations (35)–(37) must be satisfied and technological change must be Harrod neutral. Therefore

$$\frac{C}{L} = (1 - s)\frac{F[K, a(t)L]}{L} \equiv (1 - s)a(t)f(\tilde{k})$$

where $\tilde{k} \equiv K/a(t)L$ and $\hat{a} = \psi(0)$. Equation (37) is equivalent to

$$\dot{\tilde{k}} = sf(\tilde{k}) - (g + \delta + \hat{a}) = 0, \qquad \hat{a} = \psi(0).$$

Maximizing C/L subject to the latter constraint gives the necessary condition

$$f'(\tilde{k}) = F_K = g + \delta + \hat{a}.$$

Using this condition, equation (36) and $\pi = F_K/x$, we obtain

$$\pi^* = s = \frac{\psi'(0)}{\psi'(0) - 1}.$$

(b) $F_K^* = \pi^* x^* = [\psi'(0)/(\psi'(0) - 1)][g + \delta + \hat{a}]/s$, and therefore $dF_K^*/ds < 0$. Thus the minimum value of F_K^* occurs when $s = 1$ and $F_K^* = [\psi'(0)/(\psi'(0) - 1)][g + \delta + \hat{a}]$. Since $\psi'(0) < 0$, $0 < \psi'(0)/(\psi'(0) - 1) < 1$ and there must exist a root to

$$f'(\tilde{k}) = g + \delta + \hat{a}, \qquad \hat{a} = \psi(0).$$

PROBLEM 15. The fundamental equations now are

$$\hat{k} = [s_r\pi + s_w(1 - \pi)]x - (g + \delta) \equiv \hat{k}(x, \pi),$$
$$\hat{x} = \tau(\pi) - (1 - \pi)\hat{k}(x, \pi) \equiv \hat{x}(x, \pi),$$

and

$$\dot{\pi} = (1 - \pi)\left(1 - \frac{1}{\sigma}\right)[\hat{k}(x,\pi) + \hat{h}(\pi)] \equiv \dot{\pi}(x,\pi).$$

After deriving these equations, analyze them by the same methods used in Section 3-4.

References

[1] ARROW, K. J., "The Economic Implications of Learning by Doing," *Review of Economic Studies*, **XXIX**, *80* (June, 1962), pp. 155–173.

[2] ATTIYEH, R., "Estimation of a Fixed Coefficients Vintage Model of Production," Cowles Foundation Discussion Paper No. 210, Yale University (mimeo.), 1966.

[3] BARDHAN, P. K., "International Trade Theory in a Vintage-Capital Model," *Econometrica*, **XXXIV**, *4* (October, 1966), pp. 756–767.

[4] — "Equilibrium Growth in a Model with Economic Obsolescence of Machines, *The Quarterly Journal of Economics*, **LXXXIII**, *2* (May, 1969), pp. 312–323.

[5] BERGLAS, E., "Investment and Technological Change," *Journal of Political Economy*, **LXXIII**, *2* (April, 1965), pp. 173–180.

[6] BLISS, C. J., "Problems of Fitting a Vintage Capital Model to U.K. Manufacturing Time Series," paper presented to the First World Congress of the Econometric Society, September, 1965. Abstracted in *Econometrica*, **XXXIV**, *5* (Supplementary Issue 1966) pp. 63–64.

[7] — "On Putty-Clay," *Review of Economic Studies*, **XXXV**, *102* (April, 1968), pp. 105–132.

[8] BURMEISTER, E., and R. DOBELL, "Disembodied Technological Change with Several Factors," *Journal of Economic Theory*, **1**, 1 (June, 1969), pp. 1–8.

[9] CHAMPERNOWNE, D. G., "The Production Function and the Theory of Capital: A Comment," *Review of Economic Studies*, **XXI** (1954), pp. 112–135.

[10] DENISON, E. F., "The Unimportance of the Embodiment Question," *American Economic Review*, **LIV**, *2* (March, 1964), pp. 90–94.

[11] DIAMOND, PETER A., "Disembodied Technical Change in a One-Sector Model," unpublished.

[12] — "Disembodied Technical Change in a Two-Sector Model," *Review of Economic Studies*, **XXXII**, *90* (April, 1965), pp. 161–168.

[13] — "Technical Change and the Measurement of Capital and Output," *Review of Economic Studies*, **XXXII**, *92* (October, 1965), pp. 289–298.

[14] DIEWERT, W. E., "Functional Forms for Profit and Transformation Functions," mimeo. (1969).

[15] DRANDAKIS, E. M., and E. S. PHELPS, "A Model of Induced Invention, Growth and Distribution," *Economic Journal*, **LXXVI**, *304* (December, 1966), pp. 823–839.

[16] — and S. C. HU, "On Optimal Induced Technical Progress," University of Rochester, paper presented at the Econometric Society Meeting, Evanston, Illinois (1968).

[17] FEI, J. C. H., and G. RANIS, "Innovational Intensity and Factor Bias in the Theory of Growth," *International Economic Review*, VI, 2 (May, 1965), pp. 182–198.

[18] FISHER, F. M., "Embodied Technical Change and the Existence of an Aggregate Capital Stock," *Review of Economic Studies*, XXXII, 92 (October, 1965), pp. 263–288.

[19] GORMAN, W. M., "Measuring the Quantities of Fixed Factors," pp. 141–192 in *Value, Capital, and Growth* (J. N. Wolfe, Editor). Chicago: Aldine, 1968.

[20] GREEN, H. A. J., "Embodied Progress, Investment, and Growth," *American Economic Review*, LVI, 1 (March, 1966), pp. 138–151.

[21] HICKS, J. R., *Theory of Wages*. 2nd ed., London: Macmillan, 1963.

[22] INADA, K., "Fixed Factor Coefficients and Harrod-Neutral Technical Progress," *Review of Economic Studies*, XXXIV, 105 (January, 1969), pp. 89–98.

[23] — "Economic Growth and Factor Substitution," *International Economic Review*, V, 3, (September, 1964), pp. 318–327.

[24] — "Endogenous Technical Progress and Steady Growth," *Review of Economic Studies*, XXXVI, 105 (January, 1969), pp. 99–107.

[25] JOHANSEN, L., "Substitution Versus Fixed Production Coefficients in the Theory of Economic Growth: A Synthesis," *Econometrica*, XXVII, 2 (April, 1959), pp. 157–176.

[26] JORGENSON, D., "The Embodiment Hypothesis," *Journal of Political Economy*, LXXIV, 1 (February, 1966), pp. 1–17.

[27] — and Z. GRILICHES, "The Explanation of Productivity Change," *Review of Economic Studies*, XXXIV, 99 (July, 1967), pp. 249–283.

[28] KEMP, M. C., and P. C. THANH, "On a Class of Growth Models," *Econometrica*, XXXIV, 2 (April, 1966), pp. 257–282.

[29] —, E. SHESHINSKI, and P. C. THANH, "Economic Growth and Factor Substitution," *International Economic Review*, VIII, (June, 1967), pp. 243–251.

[30] KENNEDY, C., "Harrod on Neutrality," *Economic Journal*, LXXII, 285 (March, 1962), pp. 249–250.

[31] — "The Character of Improvements and of Technical Progress," *Economic Journal*, LXXII, 288 (December, 1962), pp. 899–911.

[32] — "Samuelson on Induced Innovation," *Review of Economics and Statistics*, XLVIII, 4 (November, 1966), pp. 442–444.

[33] KURZ, M., "Substitution Versus Fixed Production Coefficients: A Comment," *Econometrica*, XXXI, 1–2 (January-April, 1963), pp. 209–217.

[34] LEONTIEF, W. W., "Introduction to a Theory of the Internal Structure of Functional Relationships," *Econometrica*, 15, 4, (October, 1947), pp. 361–373.

[35] LEVHARI, D., "Extensions of Arrow's Learning by Doing," *Review of Economic Studies*, XXXIII, 94 (April, 1966), pp. 117–131.

[36] — "Further Implications of Learning by Doing," *Review of Economic Studies*, XXXIII, 93 (January, 1966), pp. 31–38.

[37] — "Learning by Doing Once Again," Technical Report #10, February 1, 1968, Institute for Mathematical Studies in the Social Sciences, Serra House, Stanford University.

[38] — and E. SHESHINSKI, "On the Sensitivity of the Level of Output to Savings: Embodiment and Disembodiment," *Quarterly Journal of Economics*, LXXXI, 3 (August, 1967), pp. 524–528. See also FISHER, F. M., LEVHARI, D., SHESHINSKI, E., "On the Sensitivity of the Level of Output to Savings: Embodiment and Disembodiment: A Clarificatory Note," *The Quarterly Journal of Economics*, LXXXIII, 2 (May, 1969), pp. 347–348.

[39] MATTHEWS, R. C. O., "The New View of Investment: Comment," *Quarterly Journal of Economics*, LXXVIII, *1* (February, 1964), pp. 164–172.

[40] MODIGLIANI, F., "Comment," pp. 39–50 in *The Behavior of Income Shares*. (C. L. Schultze and L. Weiner, Eds.). NBER, Princeton: Princeton University Press, 1964.

[41] NELSON, R. R., and E. S. PHELPS, "Investment in Humans, Technological Diffusion, and Economic Growth," *American Economic Review*, LVI, *2* (May, 1966), pp. 69–75.

[42] NORDHÄUS, W. D., "The Optimal Rate and Direction of Technical Change," in *Essays on the Theory of Optimal Economic Growth* (K. Shell, Ed.). Cambridge: M.I.T. Press, 1967, pp. 53–66.

[43] PHELPS, E. S., *Golden Rules of Economic Growth*. New York: W. W. Norton, 1966.

[44] — "The New View of Investment: A Neoclassical Analysis," *Quarterly Journal of Economics*, LXXVI, *4* (November, 1962), pp. 548–567.

[45] — "Substitution, Fixed Proportions, Growth and Distribution," *International Economic Review*, IV, *3* (September, 1963), pp. 265–288.

[46] — and M. E. YAARI, "The New View of Investment: A Reply," *Quarterly Journal of Economics*, LXXVII, *1* (February 1964), pp. 172–176.

[47] ROBINSON, JOAN, "The Classification of Inventions," *Review of Economic Studies*, V, (February, 1938), pp. 139–142.

[48] — *Essays in the Theory of Economic Growth*. New York: St. Martin's Press, 1962.

[49] — "The Production Function and the Theory of Capital," *Review of Economic Studies*, XXI, *12* (1953–54), pp. 81–106.

[50] ROSE, H., "The Condition for Factor-Augmenting Technical Change," *Economic Journal*, LXXVIII, *312* (December, 1968), pp. 966–971.

[51] SAMUELSON, P. A., *Economics*. 7th ed. New York: McGraw Hill, 1967.

[52] — "Parable and Realism in Capital Theory: The Surrogate Production Function," *Review of Economic Studies*, XXIX, *80* (June, 1962), pp. 193–206.

[53] — "A Theory of Induced Innovation Along the Kennedy-Weizsäcker Lines," *Review of Economics and Statistics*, XLVII, *4* (November, 1965), pp. 343–356.

[54] — "Rejoinder: Agreements, Disagreements, Doubts, and the Case of Induced Harrod-Neutral Technical Change," *Review of Economics and Statistics*, XLVIII, *4* (November, 1966), pp. 444–448.

[55] SHELL, K., "A Model of Inventive Activity and Capital Accumulation," in *Essays on the Theory of Optimal Economic Growth* (K. Shell, Ed.). Cambridge, Mass.: M.I.T. Press, 1967, pp. 67–86.

[56] SHESHINSKI, E., "Optimal Accumulation with Learning by Doing," in *Essays on the Theory of Optimal Economic Growth* (K. Shell, Ed.). Cambridge: M.I.T. Press, 1967, pp. 31–52.

[57] — "Factor-Augmenting, Disembodied, Technical Change," unpublished, 1965.

[58] — "Balanced Growth and Stability in the Johansen Vintage Capital Model," *Review of Economic Studies*, XXXIV, *2* (April, 1967), pp. 239–248.

[59] — "Tests of the 'Learning by Doing' Hypothesis," *The Review of Economics and Statistics*, XLIX, *4* (November, 1967), pp. 568–578.

[60] SHEPHARD, R. W., *Cost and Production Functions*. Princeton: Princteon University Press, 1953.

[61] SIMS, C. A., *The Dynamics of Productivity Change: A Theoretical and Empirical Study*, Ph.D. dissertation, Department of Economics, Harvard University, Cambridge, Massachusetts (August, 1967).

[62] SOLOW, R. M., "Some Recent Developments in the Theory of Production," in *The Theory and Empirical Analysis of Production*, (Murray Brown, Ed.). N.B.E.R., New York: Columbia University Press, 1967, pp. 225–250.

[63] — "Investment and Technical Progress," pp. 89–104 in *Mathematical Methods in the Social Sciences* (K. J. Arrow, S. Karlin, and P. Suppes, Eds.). Stanford, Calif.: Stanford University Press, 1960.

[64] — "Substitution and Fixed Proportions in the Theory of Capital," *Review of Economic Studies*, **XXIX**, *80* (June, 1962), pp. 207–218.

[65] — "Heterogeneous Capital and Smooth Production Functions: An Experimental Study," *Econometrica*, **XXXI**, *4* (October, 1963) pp. 623–645.

[66] — "The Production Function and the Theory of Capital," *Review of Economic Studies*, **XXIII**, *15* (1955–56), pp. 101–108.

[67] — "Technical Progress, Capital Formation and Economic Growth," *American Economic Review Papers and Proceedings*, **LII**, *2* (May, 1962), pp. 76–86.

[68] — *Capital Theory and the Rate of Return*. Amsterdam: North-Holland, 1963.

[69] — J. TOBIN, C. VON WEIZSÄCKER, and M. YAARI, "Neoclassical Growth with Fixed Factor Proportions," *Review of Economic Studies*, **XXXIII**, *94* (1966), pp. 79–115.

[70] STIGUM, B. P., "On Certain Problems of Aggregation," *International Economic Review*, **VIII**, *3* (October, 1967), pp. 349–367.

[71] — "On a Property of Concave Functions," *Review of Economic Studies*, **XXXV**, *104* (October, 1968), pp. 413–416.

[72] UZAWA, H., "A Note on Professor Solow's Model of Technical Progress," *The Economics Studies Quarterly*, **XIV**, *3* (1964).

[73] — "Neutral Inventions and the Stability of Growth Equilibrium," *Review of Economic Studies*, **XXVIII**, *76* (February, 1961), pp. 117–124.

[74] — "Optimum Technical Change in an Aggregative Model of Economic Growth," *International Economic Review*, **VI**, *1* (January, 1965), pp. 18–31.

[75] VON WEIZSÄCKER, C. C., "Tentative Notes on a Two-Sector Model with Induced Technical Progress," *Review of Economic Studies*, **XXXIII**, *95* (July, 1966), pp. 245–251.

Chapter 4 Two-Sector

Growth Models

4–1. Introduction

The one-sector models discussed in Chapter 2 necessitate the unrealistic assumption that one unit of homogeneous output can be transformed instantaneously without cost into either one unit of a consumption good or one unit of a capital good. Two-sector models of economic growth recognize, however, that consumption and capital goods are inherently different commodities produced in two distinct sectors of the economy. In this chapter, then, each sector has its own production function obtained by aggregating the production functions of each sector's individual firms. Frequently it is assumed that the firms in each sector, but not in different sectors, all have production functions identical to the aggregate production function for that sector. A two-sector model is equivalent to a one-sector model only in the very special case where, for any given wage/rental ratio, the two sectors select the same capital/labor ratio.

The following assumptions characterize most two-sector models; as illustrated in the next chapter, they may be weakened in various ways.[1]

Assumption (A.1): *There is a single malleable[2] capital good used as an input in both sectors.*

Assumption (A.2): *Labor is homogeneous, grows at an exogenously given exponential rate g, and has a supply curve of zero elasticity.*

---

[1] Many of the principal results in this chapter stem from Uzawa's original contributions [15, 16].
[2] See Chapter 2, p. 21.

Assumption (A.3): *Both capital and labor can be shifted instantaneously and without cost from either sector to the other.*

Assumption (A.4): *The usual static efficiency conditions of pure competition or Lerner–Lange socialism are assumed to hold at every instant of time. Consequently the economy is always in competitive equilibrium, even though this equilibrium position may change over time if the capital/labor ratio changes.*

Assumption (A.5): *The gross savings propensities, both average and marginal, from wage income and profit (or rental) income are nonnegative constants denoted by s_w and s_r, respectively. Thus, when $s_w = s_r = s$, the value of consumption is equal to a constant fraction $(1 - s)$ of Gross National Product.*

Assumption (A.6): *Capital depreciates at a constant exponential decay rate δ which is independent of use:*

Certain results can be obtained in a two-sector model that are impossible in a one-sector model. In particular,

(i) For some values of the capital/labor ratio k, a unique competitive equilibrium position may not exist, and

(ii) The capital/labor ratio at time t, denoted by k^t, may not asymptotically approach a constant value as t approaches infinity, but rather k^t may oscillate around an unstable equilibrium value k^*.[3] The occurrence of (i) and (ii), which is possible despite the strong assumptions (A.1)–(A.6), may be attributed to the distinction between the consumption good and the capital good, and to the fact that the production possibility frontier is now a smooth curve rather than a straight line as in one-sector models. Consequently the two-sector case is a simple example of a full general equilibrium problem, and in retrospect it is no surprise that the usual problems of the existence and stability of equilibrium arise. It is reasonable to conjecture that more general models with many different consumption and capital goods can give further new results; the following analysis can thus be regarded as an exploratory study preliminary to the examination of an n-sector general equilibrium model.[4]

---

[3] This result will be discussed in the next chapter.

[4] As noted in the next chapter, under certain assumptions a model with many consumption goods and *one* capital good is equivalent to a two-sector model; thus it appears that the introduction of many distinct types of *capital* goods is most likely to yield new results. Chapters 8 and 9 also support this view.

4–2. Notation and Description of the Model

Notation

The following economic variables should all include a superscript t designating time;[5] however, by convention the superscript t is omitted except when it is needed for clarification.[6] The subscripts 1 and 2 denote the capital-good sector and the consumption-good sector, respectively.

Y_1: output of new capital goods

Y_2: output of consumption goods

P_1: price of one unit of new capital

P_2: price of the consumption good

K: total quantity of available capital

L: total labor supply

k: the capital/labor ratio in the economy (K/L)

W: wage rate of homogeneous labor (which is equal in both sectors)

R: rental rate for one unit of capital. Because the depreciation rate δ is independent of use, by assumption (A.6), this rental rate applies to both sectors.

ω: the wage/rentals ratio (W/R)

K_i: quantity of capital employed in the ith sector, $i = 1, 2$

L_i: quantity of labor employed in the ith sector, $i = 1, 2$

k_i: capital/labor ratio in the ith sector (K_i/L_i), $i = 1, 2$

y_i: output/labor ratio in the ith sector (Y_i/L_i), $i = 1, 2$

ρ: ratio of labor employed in the capital-good sector to total labor (L_1/L)

δ: depreciation rate of capital. See assumption (A.6).

s_w and s_r: gross saving propensities. See assumption (A.5).

Production Functions

The production functions are $Y_i = F^i(K_i, L_i)$ and are both *neoclassical*.[7]

---

[5] The notation later introduced in our multisector chapters could be employed since two-sector models are obviously very special cases of the latter. However, two-sector models have received exceptional attention from economists, and therefore merit discussion using a notation consistent with the existing literature.

[6] In addition it should be noted that "the value of a variable x at time t" is denoted by $x(t)$ in some chapters and by x^t in others, depending upon which convention is most convenient at the time.

[7] See Chapter 1, pp. 9–10.

Thus they may be written in the intensive form

$$y_i = f_i(k_i), \qquad i = 1, 2, \tag{1}$$

where $f_i'(k_i) > 0$ and $f_i''(k_i) < 0$ for $0 < k_i < \infty$.

Competitive Equilibrium or Efficiency Conditions

Using $F_L^i \equiv f_i(k_i) - k_i f_i'(k_i)$ and $F_K^i \equiv f_i'(k_i)$, we may express the familiar equilibrium conditions

$$\omega = \frac{W/P_i}{R/P_i} = \frac{F_L^i}{F_K^i}, \qquad i = 1, 2,$$

as

$$\omega = \frac{f_i(k_i)}{f_i'(k_i)} - k_i, \qquad i = 1, 2. \tag{2}$$

Static efficiency also requires full employment of both capital and labor, i.e., $K_1 + K_2 = K$ and $L_1 + L_2 = L$. This requirement may be written

$$\rho k_1 + (1 - \rho)k_2 = k. \tag{3}$$

(See Exercise 1.)

Savings Assumption

From assumption (A.5), total gross saving in the economy is

$$s_r RK + s_w WL.$$

The only possible investment in the economy is the production of new capital, and since the value of gross investment must equal the value of gross saving in equilibrium,

$$P_1 Y_1 = s_r RK + s_w WL.$$

Assuming the efficiency condition $F_K^1 = R/P_1$ is satisfied, we may write the latter equation as

$$\rho f_1(k_1) = f_1'(k_1)(s_r k + s_w \omega). \tag{4}$$

(See Exercise 2.)

Growth Process

Net capital formation is identically equal to the output of new capital minus depreciation, i.e.,

$$\dot{K} \equiv Y_1 - \delta K.$$

Thus the instantaneous change in the capital/labor ratio is

$$\dot{k} = f_1'(k_1)(s_r k + s_w \omega) - nk \qquad (5)$$

where $n \equiv g + \delta$ (see Exercise 3).

Note that although the static (momentary) efficiency conditions for this model are exactly analogous to those derived in Chapter 2 for the one-sector model, the growth equation is not immediately written as a simple function $\dot{k} = k(k)$; for the two-sector case, (5) is of the more complicated form $\dot{k} = k(k, \omega, k_1)$. This important distinction is relevant to our discussion in Section 4-3.

4–3. Equilibrium Conditions and the Concept of Causality

Equilibrium Conditions

The equilibrium conditions that are *assumed satisfied at every instant of time* are given by the preceding equations (1)–(4). They may be rewritten

$\Psi^1 = f_1(k_1) - y_1 = 0$ (intensive production function for sector 1)

$\Psi^2 = f_2(k_2) - y_2 = 0$ (intensive production function for sector 2)

$\Psi^3 = \dfrac{f_1(k_1)}{f_1'(k_1)} - k_1 - \omega = 0$ (static efficiency condition for sector 1)

$\Psi^4 = \dfrac{f_2(k_2)}{f_2'(k_2)} - k_2 - \omega = 0$ (static efficiency condition for sector 2)

$\Psi^5 = \rho k_1 + (1 - \rho)k_2 - k = 0$ (full employment of capital and labor)

$\Psi^6 = \rho f_1(k_1) - f_1'(k_1)(s_r k + s_w \omega) = 0$ (savings-investment equation), or

$\Psi(x; k) = 0$

where the vector $x = (x_1, \ldots, x_6)$ is the vector $(y_1, y_2, k_1, k_2, \omega, \rho)$.

At any instant of time, the capital/labor ratio is assumed given, and in principle the six equations $\Psi^1 = 0, \ldots, \Psi^6 = 0$ can be solved for a unique vector x. However, unless additional restrictive assumptions are made, values of k may exist for which a unique x is not determined, and other values of k may exist for which there is no solution to $\Psi(x; k) = 0$. These difficulties will be examined in the next section.

The Concept of Causality

The concept of *causality* in a general model is described as follows. Consider any system of differential equations

$$\frac{dk_i^t}{dt} \equiv \dot{k}_i^t = f^i(x_1^t, \ldots, x_n^t; k_1^t, \ldots, k_m^t), \qquad i = 1, \ldots, m,$$

and suppose that for all t the vectors $x^t = (x_1^t, \ldots, x_n^t)$ and $k^t = (k_1^t, \ldots, k_m^t)$ are subject to n constraints of the form

$$\Psi^j(x^t; k^t) = 0, \qquad j = 1, \ldots, n.$$

The latter constraints may be considered the laws of nature governing behavior; in economics they are the equilibrium conditions that are assumed satisfied.

We ask the following question: Given (1) regularity conditions on f^i and Ψ^j, and (2) an initial starting point $k^0 = (k_1^0, \ldots, k_m^0)$, when can we solve explicitly for a unique solution $\dot{k}_m^0$? If we can solve for unique $\dot{k}_i^0$, the system might be termed *causal at time zero*. In other words, *if the system is causal at time zero, then given a starting point we can predict the motion at that instant.* More generally, a system describing the evolution over time of a point k^t is *causal* if, from any specified initial vector k^0 all subsequent motion is determined (so that only the laws of the system and the initial point k^0, and no other information, need be known in order to determine the whole future path of the system point). It is clear that if we can find functions $x^t = \Phi(k^t)$, the system is causal, since by substitution we could obtain $\dot{k}^t = f[\Phi(k^t); k^t] \equiv h(k^t)$.

In two-sector models the growth equation (5) for the capital/labor ratio may be written as $\dot{k} = f(x; k)$. (Remember that a superscript t designating time has been omitted from each variable.) If a unique vector x is determined for any given value of k, then $x_1 \equiv y_1 = \Phi^1(k), \ldots, x_6 \equiv \rho = \Phi^6(k)$ or

$$x = \Phi(k).$$

In this case the model is termed causal because given any initial value of the capital/labor ratio k^0, a unique vector $x^0 = \Phi(k^0)$ is determined, and consequently the initial motion of the capital/labor ratio at time $t = 0$ is uniquely given by

$$\dot{k}^0 = f(x^0; k^0) = f[\Phi(k^0); k^0] \equiv H(k^0).$$

Moreover, under the stated conditions it is clear that the entire path k^t is determined for all $t > 0$ (given k^0) by the differential equation

$$k^t = f(x^t; k^t) = f[\Phi(k^t); k^t] \equiv H(k^t).$$

Consequently, it is easily shown that *uniqueness of static (momentary) equilibrium at all times* and *causality* are equivalent concepts in two-sector models (see Exercise 6).

4–4. Causality of the Two-Sector Model

A Necessary and Sufficient Condition

We wish to derive a necessary and sufficient condition for the existence of a unique solution $x = \Phi(k)$, $a < k < b$, to the system of simultaneous equations $\Psi(x; k) = 0$.[8] The special structure of the two-sector model and the assumptions that have been made greatly simplify the problem because $\Psi(x; k) = 0$ can be reduced to a single function $k = k(\omega)$. Thus, as we shall see, causality of a two-sector model depends on the properties of the derivative $k'(\omega)$.

Assume for the moment that ω is taken as the independent variable. Solving $\Psi^3 = 0$ and $\Psi^4 = 0$ for ω, we obtain

$$\omega = \frac{f_i(k_i)}{f'_i(k_i)} - k_i \tag{6}$$

and calculate

$$\frac{d\omega}{dk_i} = -\frac{f_i(k_i)f''_i(k_i)}{[f'_i(k_i)]^2}, \qquad i = 1, 2.$$

Since $f_i(k_i) > 0$ and $f''_i(k_i) < 0$ by assumption, $d\omega/dk_i > 0$. Thus, (6) can be inverted, and therefore for any given positive value of ω, say $\omega = \bar{\omega}$, unique values $k_i = \bar{k}_i$ are determined, i.e., the equilibrium conditions $\Psi^3 = 0$ and $\Psi^4 = 0$ imply the existence of functions

$$k_i = k_i(\omega), \qquad i = 1, 2. \tag{7}$$

Thus, for a given factor-price ratio ω, (7) gives the equilibrium capital/labor ratio that minimizes the cost of production for firms operating under constant

---

[8] The nonnegative numbers a and b will be defined precisely in subsequent discussion.

returns to scale. One geometric illustration is given in Figure 13.[9] Positive values of the wage/rentals ratio ω are measured leftward from the origin along the horizontal axis and downward from the origin along the vertical axis, and the production function $y_i = f_i(k_i)$ is plotted in the first quadrant.

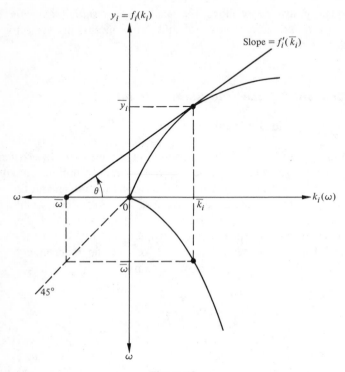

Figure 13

Starting from a given value $\bar{\omega}$ on the horizontal axis, a line is drawn tangent to the production function $f_i(k_i)$ and which, therefore, has slope $f_i'(k_i)$. This tangency point determines a unique value $\bar{k}_i$ corresponding to $\bar{\omega}$. It represents an equilibrium value consistent with $\Psi^3 = 0$ or $\Psi^4 = 0$ because, by construction,

$$\tan \theta = f_i'(k_i) = \frac{f_i(k_i)}{k_i + \omega}.$$

The resulting function $k_i = k_i(\omega)$ is plotted in the fourth quadrant.

[9] It should be noted that Figure 13 is only illustrative and does not reflect all admissible production functions.

Although k_i can assume any value between zero and infinity, the range of ω given by (6) may not include all positive numbers. For example, if $f_i(k_i) = \log(k_i + 2)$, in equilibrium

$$\omega = \frac{f_i(k_i)}{f_i'(k_i)} - k_i = (k_i + 2)\log(k_i + 2) - k_i$$

and

$$\lim_{k_i \to 0} \omega = 2 \log 2 > 0.$$

This difficulty is avoided by considering only values of ω contained in the open interval $(\omega_{\min}, \omega_{\max})$ where

$$\omega_{\min} = \max_{i=1,\,2} \left\{ \lim_{k_i \to 0} \left[\frac{f_i(k_i)}{f_i'(k_i)} - k_i \right] \right\}$$

and

$$\omega_{\max} = \min_{i=1,\,2} \left\{ \lim_{k_i \to \infty} \left[\frac{f_i(k_i)}{f_i'(k_i)} - k_i \right] \right\}.$$

Thus, for any $\omega \in (\omega_{\min}, \omega_{\max})$, the equilibrium values of k_i are uniquely determined by the functions $k_i = k_i(\omega)$, $i = 1, 2$, and the equalities $\Psi^3 = 0$ and $\Psi^4 = 0$ are both satisfied.

If (1) the Inada derivative conditions [8, 9] $f_i'(0) = \infty$ and $f_i'(\infty) = 0$, $i = 1, 2$, are satisfied, or (2) $f_i(k_i)$ are both constant-elasticity-of-substitution (CES) production functions, then $\omega_{\min} = 0$ and $\omega_{\max} = \infty$; see Exercise 4.

Now consider any given $\bar{\omega} \in (\omega_{\min}, \omega_{\max})$; since $\bar{k}_1$ and $\bar{k}_2$ are uniquely determined, $\Psi^5 = 0$ and $\Psi^6 = 0$ may be written as two linear equations in the variables ρ and k:

$$(\bar{k}_1 - \bar{k}_2)\rho - k = -\bar{k}_2 \tag{8}$$

$$f_1(\bar{k}_1)\rho - [s_r f_1'(\bar{k}_1)]k = s_w \bar{\omega} f_1'(\bar{k}_1) \tag{9}$$

The relevant determinant $\Delta = -s_r f_1'(\bar{k}_1)(\bar{k}_1 - \bar{k}_2) + f_1(\bar{k}_1)$ is always positive (Exercise 5), and therefore (8) and (9) can be solved for

$$\rho = \frac{s_w \bar{\omega} f_1'(\bar{k}_1) + s_r f_1'(\bar{k}_1)\bar{k}_2}{\Delta} \tag{10}$$

and

$$k = \frac{s_w \bar{\omega} f_1'(\bar{k}_1)(\bar{k}_1 - \bar{k}_2) + \bar{k}_2 f_1(\bar{k}_1)}{\Delta}. \tag{11}$$

We may rewrite (11) as

$$k = k(\omega), \quad \omega_{min} < \omega < \omega_{max}, \tag{12}$$

and if $k'(\omega)$ is strictly of one sign[10] there exists an inverse function

$$\omega = k^{-1}(k) \tag{13}$$

where

$$a \equiv \lim_{\omega \to \omega_{min}} k(\omega) < k < \lim_{\omega \to \omega_{max}} k(\omega) \equiv b.$$

If the inverse function $\omega = k^{-1}(k)$ exists ($a < k < b$), then from (7),

$$k_1 = k_1(\omega) = k_1[k^{-1}(k)] \equiv \Phi^3(k) \tag{14}$$

and

$$k_2 = k_2(\omega) = k_2[k^{-1}(k)] \equiv \Phi^4(k). \tag{15}$$

Likewise, from $\Psi^1 = 0$ and $\Psi^2 = 0$,

$$y_1 = f_1(k_1) = f_1[\Phi^3(k)] \equiv \Phi^1(k) \tag{16}$$

and

$$y_2 = f_2(k_2) = f_2[\Phi^4(k)] \equiv \Phi^2(k). \tag{17}$$

Finally, define

$$\omega = k^{-1}(k) \equiv \Phi^5(k), \tag{18}$$

and from (10), we may obtain

$$\rho = \Phi^6(k). \tag{19}$$

[10] Although $k'(\omega) > 0$ (or <0) for all $\omega \in (\omega_{min}, \omega_{max})$ is *sufficient* for the existence of the inverse (13), it is not necessary. Since $k(\omega)$ is a continuous function it is *necessary* that (1) $k'(\omega)$ does not *change* sign, and (2) the roots of $k'(\omega) = 0$ are isolated, i.e., if ω^* is any root of $k'(\omega) = 0$, $k'(\omega)$ must not be identically zero on any deleted neighborhood of ω^*.

Equations (14)–(19) are written in vector notation as

$$(x_1, \ldots, x_6) = [\Phi^1(k), \ldots, \Phi^6(k)]$$

or

$$x = \Phi(k), \qquad a < k < b.$$

Our results may be summarized in the following theorem:

Theorem 1: *The vector x is uniquely determined by $x = \Phi(k)$, $a < k < b$, if and only if the function $k = k(\omega)$, $\omega_{min} < \omega < \omega_{max}$, has an inverse. Thus a two-sector model is causal and has a unique static (momentary) equilibrium for all $k \in (a, b)$ if and only if $\omega = k^{-1}(k)$, $a < k < b$, exists.*[11]

An Equivalent Condition

Let

$$J = J(x; k) = \det\left[\frac{\partial(\Psi^1, \ldots, \Psi^6)}{\partial(y_1, \ldots, \rho)}\right] = \det[\Psi^i_j]$$

be the Jacobian determinant[12] of the system $\Psi(x; k) = 0$, and let $(x^*; k^*)$ be a point for which (1) $\Psi(x^*; k^*) = 0$ and (2) $J(x^*; k^*) \neq 0$. Then the implicit function theorem[13] guarantees that there exist a neighborhood of k^* and a unique function $x = \Phi(k)$ defined on that neighborhood such that $x^* = \Phi(k^*)$ and $\Psi[\Phi(k); k] = 0$. It is well known that some systems of simultaneous equations do not have a global inverse even if the Jacobian determinant never vanishes. (See Exercise 7.) However, the special economic structure of the two-sector model and the assumptions that have been made allow us to obtain the following result.

Theorem 2: *Define the set $S \equiv \{(x, k) \mid \Psi(x; k) = 0, a < k < b\}$ where $\Psi(x; k) = 0$ is the system of equilibrium conditions given above, and assume that the roots of $J(x; k) = 0$, $(x, k) \in S$, are isolated. There exists a solution $x = \Phi(k)$ which is globally unique ($a < k < b$) if and only if $J(x; k)$ does not change sign for all $(x, k) \in S$. That is, for any given capital/labor ratio $k \in (a, b)$, the two-sector model has a unique static (momentary) equilibrium and the system is causal if and only if J does not change sign.*

---

[11] The "only if" conclusion follows immediately from Exercise 6.
[12] This Jacobian can be calculated explicitly as in Exercise 8.
[13] For a clear statement of the implicit function theorem, see [2], pp. 141–148.

Proof: We have shown that y_1, y_2, k_1, k_2, ρ and k are all uniquely determined for given $\omega \in (\omega_{min}, \omega_{max})$. In particular, k may be written as a function of ω and the existence of an inverse depends on the monotonicity of that function $k(\omega)$. Moreover, $J(x; k)$ is a continuous function of ω and we may write $J = J(\omega)$, $\omega_{min} < \omega < \omega_{max}$ (see Exercise 8). Consider any point $(\tilde{x}; \tilde{k}) \in S$ for which $J(\tilde{\omega}) \neq 0$; by the implicit function theorem, $d\omega/dk = N^5/J$ where N^5 is the determinant formed by replacing the fifth column of J with $[-\Psi_k^i] = [0, 0, 0, 0, 1, s_r f_1^i(k_1)]$. Since it is easily shown that N^5 is strictly positive for all $(x, k) \in S$ (Exercise 9),

$$\text{sgn}(d\omega/dk) = \text{sgn}(N^5/J) = \text{sgn}(J), \qquad J \neq 0.$$

Because the roots of $J(\omega) = 0$ are isolated by assumption,[14] $d\omega/dk$ does not change sign if and only if J does not change sign. Thus the function $k = k(\omega)$ can be inverted (and $x = \Phi(k)$ exists) if and only if J does not change sign. QED

We may note that k must be restricted to the domain (a, b) to ensure that there is any solution to $\Psi(x; k) = 0$. If $k < a$ or $k > b$, it may be necessary to examine corner solutions obtained by replacing the equalities in the system $\Psi = 0$ with appropriate inequalities; to avoid such difficulties we will assume that $k \in (a, b)$. However, if $\omega_{min} = 0$ and $\omega_{max} = \infty$, then $a = 0$ and $b = \infty$ (Exercise 4c).

Theorem 2 provides a necessary and sufficient condition for causality.[15] Figures 14a, 14b, and 14c illustrate the nature of the issue. In Figure 14a the Jacobian determinant is always positive and ω is uniquely determined for any given $\bar{k}$; in 14b J changes sign twice and at most three equilibrium configurations are possible for a given $k = \bar{k}$; and in 14c the numerous changes in the sign of J allow the possibility of more than three equilibrium positions for a given $k = \bar{k}$. A numerical example shows that the behavior illustrated in Figure 14b can definitely be encountered (see Exercise 10). The behavior illustrated in Figure 14c can be ruled out for some special cases.[16]

A revealing interpretation of causality is obtained by considering the

---

[14] This assumption is satisfied if the function $J(\omega)$ is analytic; see [2], Theorem 16-9, p. 518. Although the assumption that $J(\omega)$ is an analytic function is quite restrictive, it does not seem unreasonable since the production functions $f_i(k_i)$ are analytic for most standard examples.

[15] Yet another necessary and sufficient causality condition in terms of the weak axiom of revealed preference has been given by Hahn; the interested reader is referred to [6], p. 341.

[16] If both $f_1(k_1)$ and $f_2(k_2)$ are constant elasticity of substitution production functions, then the Jacobian determinant either never changes sign or it changes sign exactly twice. See Burmeister [4].

production possibility frontier for a two-sector model. This frontier may be written as

$$Y_2 = T(Y_1; K, L),$$

or, in per capita form,

$$Y_2/L = T(Y_1/L; k, 1), \tag{20}$$

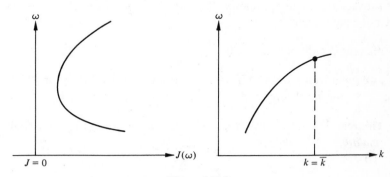

Figure 14(a)

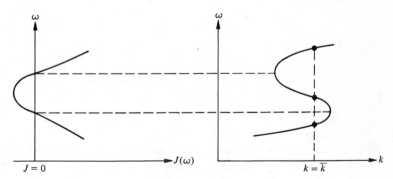

Figure 14(b)

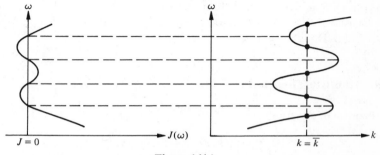

Figure 14(c)

and it implicitly contains all the information about production functions and the efficiency conditions that are explicitly formulated in $\Psi^1 = 0, \ldots,$ $\Psi^5 = 0$. The only remaining indeterminateness is the selection of some point Q on the frontier. If Q is to be an equilibrium position, it must not only lie on the production possibility frontier (thereby satisfying $\Psi^i = 0, i = 1, \ldots, 5$), but it must also satisfy $\Psi^6 = 0$. We can now reformulate our notion of causality: If there is only one point on the production possibility frontier that satisfies the savings equation $\Psi^6 = 0$, then the system is causal and J does not change sign.

Sufficient Conditions for $J > 0$

As we have seen $k'(\omega) > 0$ if and only if $J(\omega) > 0$, and therefore we may state the following theorem.

> **Theorem 3:** $J(\omega)$ *is strictly positive for all* $\omega \in (\omega_{\min}, \omega_{\max})$ *if any of conditions* (i)–(v) *hold for all* $\omega \in (\omega_{\min}, \omega_{\max})$.
>   (i) $s_r = s_w = s$
>   (ii) $s_r > s_w$ *and* $k_1 < k_2$
>   (iii) $s_r < s_w$ *and* $k_1 > k_2$
>   (iv) $k_1 = k_2$,
> or
>   (v) $\sigma_1 + \sigma_2 \geqq 1$
> *where* σ_i *is the elasticity of substitution*[17] *in the ith sector. Thus if any of* (i)–(v) *hold for all* $\omega \in (\omega_{\min}, \omega_{\max})$, *the vector function* $x = \Phi(k)$ *exists,* $a < k < b$, *and the two-sector model is causal.*

Proof: Exercise 11.[18]

Condition (i) means that the saving propensities out of profit and wage incomes are equal, and condition (ii) means that the capital intensity hypothesis holds (the capital-good sector must be less capital intensive than the consumption-good sector) and $s_r > s_w$; (iii) has a similar interpretation. The two-sector model is equivalent to a one-sector model if condition (iv) holds (see Exercise 12). Finally, note that condition (v) is satisfied if either sector has a Cobb–Douglas production function.

4–5. Stability Theorems

The growth equation

$$\dot{k} = f'_1(k_1)(s_r k + s_w \omega) - nk$$

----

[17] The elasticity of substitution is defined in Chapter 1, p. 11.
[18] The above conditions (i)–(v) were derived by Drandakis [5].

may be written

$$\dot{k}/k = f_1'(k_1)\,\frac{s_r k + s_w \omega}{k} - n$$

for all $k \in (a, b)$ since a ≥ 0. We will assume in this section that the system is causal; the behavior of $\dot{k}$ when the system is not causal will be discussed in Section 4-7. Thus there exists a function $x = \Phi(k)$ and the latter growth equations may be written

$$\dot{k} = H(k) \qquad \text{or} \qquad \dot{k}/k = H(k)/k \equiv h(k).$$

There need not exist any root $k^* \in (a, b)$ satisfying $h(k^*) = 0$ unless some restrictions are placed on $n \equiv g + \delta$ and/or the production functions. However, for any positive n the Inada derivative conditions $f_i'(\infty) = 0$ and $f_i'(0) = \infty$, $i = 1, 2$, are sufficient for the existence of at least one root k^*, providing $s_r > 0$ (see Exercise 16). Moreover, if $h'(k) < 0$ for all $k \in (a, b)$, then clearly any root k^* (if it exists) is unique, and thus starting from any initial value $k^0 \in (a, b)$, k^t asymptotically approaches a unique constant k^*. In other words, the model has a unique balanced growth path that is asymptotically approached from all initial points $k^0 \in (a, b)$.

In general, the equation

$$\dot{k}/k = h(k) = 0$$

may have more than one root. Any such root is called *locally* (asymptotically) *stable* if there exists a neighborhood of k^*, $N(k^*)$, such that

$$\lim_{t \to \infty} k^t = k^* \qquad \text{for all initial} \qquad k^0 \in N(k^*).$$

Since $h(k)$ is a continuous function, clearly k^* is locally stable if $h'(k^*) < 0$,[19] and we may prove the following theorem.

Theorem 4: *Let k^* be any root of $h(k) = 0$ and let $x^* = (y_1^*, y_2^*, k_1^*, k_2^*, \omega^*, \rho^*) = \Phi(k^*)$. If either*

(i) $\dfrac{s_w}{n} \leq \dfrac{k^*}{f_1(k_1^*)}$

or

(ii) $\dfrac{s_r}{n} \geq \dfrac{k_1^*}{f_1(k_1^*)}$ *(= capital/output ratio in the capital-good sector),*

then $h'(k^*) < 0$ and k^* is locally stable.

---

[19] k^* is a locally stable root if and only if there exists a *deleted* neighborhood of k^* on which $h'(k) < 0$. For example, k^* may be an inflection point with $h'(k^*) = 0$, but it is nevertheless a locally stable root if there exists $\varepsilon > 0$ such that $h'(k) < 0$ for all $k \in (k^* - \varepsilon, k^* + \varepsilon), k \neq k^*$.

Proof: It may be established that $h'(k) \gtreqless 0$ if and only if $(s_w - \rho) \times d\omega/dk - s_w \omega/k \gtreqless 0$ (Exercise 13). Writing $h(k) = [\rho f_1(k_1)/k] - n$, we see that $h(k) = 0$ when $\rho = nk/f_1(k_1)$. Thus $h'(k^*) < 0$ if $s_w \leq nk^*/f_1(k_1^*)$, which completes the proof of (i). Using $\Psi^3 = 0$ and $\Psi^6 = 0$, we find that $s_w = \rho(k_1 + \omega)/\omega - s_r k/\omega$; thus $s_w - \rho = [\rho k_1 - s_r k]/\omega \leq 0$ if $\rho k_1 - s_r k \leq 0$. Substituting $\rho = nk/f_1(k_1)$ gives the condition $nkk_1/f_1(k_1) - s_r k \leq 0$. Thus, $h'(k^*) < 0$ if $nk_1^*/f_1(k_1^*) - s_r \leq 0$, and (ii) is proved.   QED

Theorem 4 provides sufficient conditions for local stability. Any of the stronger sufficient conditions given in Theorem 5 guarantee that if a balanced growth path exists, it is unique and stable. These sufficient conditions are based on the obvious mathematical fact that if $h(k) = 0$ implies $h'(k) < 0$, then (1) there exists at most one root k^* satisfying $h(k^*) = 0$ (because $h(k)$ is a continuous function), (2) if such a k^* exists, it is locally stable by Theorem 4 and the hypothesis $h'(k^*) < 0$, and finally, (3) $\lim_{t \to \infty} k^t = k^*$ starting from any (admissible) initial capital/labor ratio k^0. Chapter 2 contains a more detailed discussion of this issue, and therefore we omit further repetition here.

Theorem 5: *If any of the following conditions are satisfied for all $\omega \in (\omega_{min}, \omega_{max})$, then (1) $h'(k) < 0$ for all $k \in (a, b)$, and (2) any root k^* of $h(k) = 0$ is* unique and stable, *i.e., for all initial $k^0 \in (a, b)$, $\lim_{t \to \infty} k^t = k^*$.*
  (i) $s_r \geq s_w$ and $k_1 \leq k_2$.
  (ii) $\sigma \equiv (\omega/k)(dk/d\omega) \geq 1$.
  (iii) $\sigma_2 \geq 1$.
  (iv) $s_r = 1$ and $J(\omega) > 0$.
  (v) $s_w = 0$ and $J(\omega) > 0$.

Proof: Observe that any one of (i)–(v) implies $k'(\omega) > 0$, $\omega_{min} < \omega < \omega_{max}$, because (i) and (iii) satisfy the sufficient conditions (ii) and (v) given in Theorem 3, respectively, and (ii), (iv), and (v) assume that $k'(\omega) > 0$, or equivalently, that $J(\omega) > 0$. Thus the system is causal and the function $\dot{k}/k = h(k)$ exists. As already noted (Exercise 13), $h'(k) \gtreqless 0$ if and only if $(s_w - \rho)d\omega/dk - s_w(\omega/k) = s_w(d\omega/dk - \omega/k) - \rho(d\omega/dk) \gtreqless 0$, and therefore conditions (ii) and (v) follow immediately. Condition (iv) is obtained by proving that $(s_w - \rho) < 0$ if $s_r = 1$ (Exercise 14), and condition (i) may be derived from Theorem 4 (Exercise 15). The proof of condition (iii) is laborious, and the interested reader is referred to [5].   QED

We cannot, of course, hope to give any complete verbal interpretation of Theorem 5. But it may be useful to present in a general way an economic explanation of the stability conditions. Suppose, therefore, that a two-sector economy is initially in balanced growth equilibrium, and that it then receives an exogenous injection of new capital, say a gift from a foreign country. In order to accommodate the increased capital stock, the wage/ rentals ratio must rise if the system is causal. In response to this change in the factor-price ratio, the equilibrium capital/labor ratios adopted by the firms in each sector will change through a reallocation of capital and/or labor. If the model is stable, all these adjustments must imply that the output of the capital goods sector is not increased sufficiently further. For if an exogenous rise in the capital/labor ratio were to cause the output of the capital goods sector to rise sufficiently above its initial steady-state equilibrium value, the capital/labor ratio would increase still further with instability resulting.

Thus, it is easy to see why a high elasticity of substitution in the consumption goods sector might offer a stability condition, for then an exogenous increase in capital can be absorbed primarily in the consumption good sector; (iii) in Theorem 5 is precisely such a sufficient condition. Likewise (i) is a slightly more general form of the capital intensity hypothesis employed by Uzawa [15] in his original discussion, and the economic interpretation of this hypothesis has been expounded by Solow [12]; the interested reader should study this reference. Condition (ii) requires that the system as a whole be able to absorb changes in the capital/labor ratio without extreme repercussions on the equilibrium wage/rentals ratio, and (iv) and (v) show that with extreme savings behavior, stability can be ensured in a causal system without any further restrictions.

We emphasize that the foregoing informal observations cannot substitute for a precise statement and proof of Theorem 5. However, with the benefit of hindsight we can see an underlying economic logic in the results.

The following examples serve to illustrate two important features of two-sector models, namely: (1) there may exist a unique and stable balanced growth path even when all of Theorem 5's sufficient conditions are violated (as illustrated by Example 1), and (2) in general, unstable balanced growth paths may exist (as illustrated by Example 2). In both examples $s_r = s_w = s$, and therefore $J(\omega) > 0$ from Theorem 3. Thus, $\dot{k} = H(k)$ may be written

$$\dot{k} = H[k(\omega)] \equiv G(\omega) \tag{21}$$

where $\dot{k} = 0$ if and only if $G(\omega) = 0$. We may also derive

$$\rho(\omega) = \frac{s(k_2 + \omega)}{(1 - s)k_1 + sk_2 + \omega} \tag{22}$$

and

$$k(\omega) = \frac{k_1 k_2 + (1 - s)\omega k_2 + s\omega k_1}{(1 - s)k_1 + sk_2 + \omega} \tag{23}$$

by substituting $s_r = s_w = s$ into equations (10) and (11).

Example 1. Let $y_1 = k_1^{1/2}$ and $y_2 = (k_2^{-1} + 2^{-2})^{-1}$ $(\sigma_1 = 1$ and $\sigma_2 = 1/2)$, and assume that $s = 2/5$ and $n = 1/3$. From $\Psi^3 = 0$ and $\Psi^4 = 0$ it is easily verified that $k_1 = \omega$ and $k_2 = 2\omega^{1/2}$, and substituting the latter in (22) and (23) gives

$$\rho(\omega) = \frac{2 + \omega^{1/2}}{2 + 4\omega^{1/2}} \quad \text{and} \quad k(\omega) = \frac{8\omega + \omega^{3/2}}{2 + 4\omega^{1/2}}.$$

Thus, $\dot{k} = \rho y_1 - nk = G(\omega) = 0$ if and only if $\omega + 5\omega^{1/2} - 6 = (\omega^{1/2} - 1) \times (\omega^{1/2} + 6) = 0$. Since the only admissible root of the latter equation is $\omega^* = 1$, we find $k^* = 3/2$. Likewise,

$$x^* = \Phi(k^*) = \Phi(3/2) = (1, 4/3, 1, 2, 1, 1/2).$$

Both conditions (i) and (ii) of Theorem 4 are satisfied since

$$k_1^*/y_1^* = 1 < s/n = 6/5 < 3/2 = k^*/y_1^*.$$

Hence, the system is stable, and starting from any initial capital/labor ratio k^0, k^t will asymptotically converge to the unique value $k^* = 3/2$. However, all of the sufficient stability conditions given in Theorem 5 are violated; in particular, note that $k_1 = \omega > 2\omega^{1/2} = k_2$ if $\omega > 4$ (i.e., for ω or k sufficiently large).

Example 2. Consider the production functions $y_i = \beta_i[k_i^{-\rho_i} + \alpha_i^{-\rho_i-1}]^{-1/\rho_i}$ where $\sigma_i \equiv 1/(1 + \rho_i)$, $i = 1, 2$. Setting $\beta_1 = \alpha_1 = \sigma_1 = \alpha_2 = 1$, $\sigma_2 = 1/4$, and $s = n = 1/28$, we may derive $k_1 = \omega$, $k_2 = \omega^{1/4}$, and $\dot{k} = G(\omega) = 0$ when

$$\omega^{5/4} - 28\omega^{3/4} + 55\omega^{2/4} - 28 = 0.$$

Two roots of the latter equations are $(\omega^*, \omega^{**}) = (1, 16)$, and $\omega^* = 1$ is locally stable since it satisfies the sufficient conditions given in Theorem 4. We wish to show that there exists an unstable root. If ω^{**} is unstable (and ω^{**} does violate Theorem 4's sufficient conditions), there is nothing left to prove. Assume ω^{**} is stable with $H'[k(\omega^{**})] < 0$; then there must exist another unstable root ω^{***} with $H'[k(\omega^{***})] > 0$, $\omega^* < \omega^{***} < \omega^{**}$, since $H[k(\omega)]$ is a continuous function.

4–6. Global Stability

A two-sector model is called *globally stable* if, starting from any initial $k^0 \in (a, b)$, k^t asymptotically approaches some constant value.[20] If the model

---

[20] See Chapter 2, p. 27.

is causal, the function $\dot{k}/k = h(k)$ exists for all $k \in (a, b)$. If, in addition

$$\lim_{k \to a} h(k) > 0$$

and

$$\lim_{k \to b} h(k) < 0,$$

then, since $h(k)$ is continuous and differentiable on (a, b), there must exist at least one root k^* of $h(k) = 0$ for which $h'(k^*) < 0$ and $a < k^* < b$. It may be shown that the latter inequalities hold if $s_r > 0$ and the Inada derivative conditions $f_i'(0) = \infty$ and $f_i'(\infty) = 0$, $i = 1, 2$, are satisfied (Exercise 16). Thus a causal system with $s_r > 0$ which satisfies the Inada derivative conditions is globally stable. It is important to note that the Inada derivative conditions are not necessary for global stability as Example 2 in Section 4-5 clearly illustrates.

4–7. Concluding Remarks

In Chapter 2 the central issue was the behavior of a simple accumulation equation of the form

$$\dot{k} = sf(k) - nk.$$

In this chapter, however, the analogous equation is

$$\dot{k} = \rho f_1(k_1) - nk,$$

and the latter cannot be written as a function of k alone unless the model is causal. However, since ρ, k_i, and k are all functions of the wage/rentals ratio ω, if ω is uniquely determined for any given value of $k \in (a, b)$, or equivalently, if there exists a function $\omega = \Phi^5(k)$, then we can write the accumulation equation in the causal form

$$\dot{k} = \rho[\Phi^5(k)]f_1\{k_1[\Phi^5(k)]\} - nk \equiv H(k), \qquad a < k < b.$$

This complexity, of course, results from the general equilibrium character of two-sector models. One-sector models have a trivial mechanism for allocating outputs and no mechanism at all for allocating factors, whereas in the two-sector case both the demands for outputs and factors depend on the factor-price ratio ω. Hence the crucial questions are (1) whether or not the system can generate a unique factor-price ratio for all admissible capital/

labor ratios $k \in (a, b)$, and (2) given an affirmative answer to (1), whether or not the system is capable of convergence to a balanced growth path with $\dot{k} = 0$.

The overall system of equations is highly interrelated. We have seen, however, that one small part can be considered separately: cost-minimizing firms operating under constant returns to scale and facing a given factor-price ratio ω will select unique capital/labor ratios k_i in each sector, and thus we are able to derive the equilibrium conditions $k_i = k_i(\omega)$, $i = 1, 2$. But an equilibrium factor-price ratio ω that clears all markets can be determined only by solving a simultaneous system of equations in which factor endowments and demand conditions are explicitly taken into account. What, therefore, do we learn from the study of two-sector models? The following conclusions seem important.

 (i) There is a nontrivial general equilibrium problem of finding a factor-price ratio ω that simultaneously determines the equilibrium values of (1) the capital/labor ratios k_i in each sector, (2) the demand for new capital goods (the demand for consumption goods is then determined from Walras' law), and (3) the quantities of labor allocated to each sector, which must be such that both factors of production are fully employed for the given overall capital/labor ratio k. Thus it is no wonder that the two-sector model has been called a "miniature Walrasian equilibrium" problem.[21]

 (ii) We can write the accumulation equation in the causal form

$$\dot{k} = H(k), \qquad a < k < b,$$

if and only if a unique equilibrium value of ω is determined for all $k \in (a, b)$.

(iii) Causality itself requires restrictive sufficient conditions. Except in the case of extreme savings behavior where $s_r = 1$ or $s_w = 0$, sufficient conditions for stability require further restrictive conditions.

(iv) As Hahn has observed, "The two-sector story has been unwinding slowly and is not always easy to read."[22] The reader who glances at the list of references for this chapter can only agree. In fact, it is the extreme complexity of the two-sector model that serves as a warning: a detailed and rigorous analysis of more general models with heterogeneous capital and consumption goods will not be easy. However, now that we have studied the two-sector case in detail, we are better prepared for the more difficult multisector models examined in several subsequent chapters.

---

[21] Solow [12], p. 49.
[22] Hahn [7], p. 339.

Exercises

1. (a) Prove that $K_1 + K_2 = K$ and $L_1 + L_2 = L$ if and only if $\rho k_1 + (1 - \rho)k_2 = k$, and $(1 - \rho) = L_2/L$ where $\rho \equiv L_1/L$.
   (b) Generalize this result to the case

$$\sum_{i=1}^n K_i = K \quad \text{and} \quad \sum_{i=1}^n L_i = L.$$

2. Show that in equilibrium $P_1 Y_1 = s_r RK + s_w WL$ is equivalent to $\rho f_1(k_1) = f_1'(k_1)(s_r k + s_w \omega)$ when $F_K^1 = R/P_1$.

3. Derive the growth equation

$$k = f_1'(k_1)(s_r k + s_w \omega) - nk.$$

4. Prove that $\omega_{\min} = 0$ and $\omega_{\max} = \infty$ if either
   (a) $f_i'(0) = \infty$ and $f_i'(\infty) = 0$, $i = 1, 2$, or
   (b) $f_i(k_i)$ are both CES production functions.
   (c) Show that $\omega_{\min} = 0$ and $\omega_{\max} = \infty$ is a sufficient condition for $a = 0$ and $b = \infty$. (Can you show that it is not necessary?)

5. Show that $\Delta \equiv -s_r f_1'(k_1)(k_1 - k_2) + f_1(k_1)$ is strictly positive in equilibrium.

6. Prove that a two-sector model is causal if and only if $x = \Phi(k)$, $a < k < b$.

7. Consider the simultaneous equations

$$y_1 = x_1 \cos x_2$$

and

$$y_2 = x_1 \sin x_2.$$

Prove that $x_1 = f(y_1, y_2)$ and $x_2 = g(y_1, y_2)$ do not exist even though

$$J = \begin{vmatrix} \partial y_1/\partial x_1 & \partial y_1/\partial x_2 \\ \partial y_2/\partial x_1 & \partial y_2/\partial x_2 \end{vmatrix}$$

is positive for all $x_1 > 0$.

8. Calculate the Jacobian determinant J of the system $\Psi(x; k) = 0$ and show that J is a continuous function of ω.

9. Prove that $N^5 > 0$ for all $(x; k) \in S$.

10. Let the production functions be[23]

$$y_1 = f_1(k_1) = 0.001(k_1^{-3} + 7^{-4})^{-1/3}$$

[23] See Uzawa [15].

and

$$y_2 = f_2(k_2) = (k_2^{-3} + 1)^{-1/3}$$

with

$$s_r = 1, \ s_w = 0, \quad \text{and} \quad \sigma_1 = \sigma_2 = 1/4.$$

Show that (a) J changes sign, and (b) three equilibrium positions are possible for some values of k between 3 and 4.5.

11. Prove Theorem 3.
12. Prove that a two-sector model is equivalent to a one-sector model if $k_1 = k_2$ for all $\omega \in (\omega_{min}, \omega_{max})$.
13. Prove that $h'(k) \gtreqless 0$ if and only if

$$(s_w - \rho) \frac{d\omega}{dk} - s_w \frac{\omega}{k} \gtreqless 0.$$

14. Prove that $(s_w - \rho) < 0$ if $s_r = 1$.
15. Prove that $s_r > s_w$ and $k_1 < k_2$ imply both
    (a) $s_w/n < k^*/f_1(k_1^*)$ and
    (b) $s_r/n > k_1^*/f_1(k_1^*)$,
    where k^* is any root of $h(k) = 0$ and $x^* = \Phi(k^*)$.
16. Prove that $\lim_{k \to 0} h(k) > 0$ and $\lim_{k \to \infty} h(k) < 0$ if $f_i'(0) = \infty, f_i'(\infty) = 0, i = 1, 2,$ and $s_r > 0$.

Answers and Hints

PROBLEM 1.

(b) Define $\rho_i \equiv L_i/L, k_i \equiv K_i/L_i$, and $k \equiv K/L$; then $\sum_{i=1}^{n} \rho_i k_i = k$ where

$$\rho_n = 1 - \sum_{i=1}^{n-1} \rho_i.$$

PROBLEM 3. $\dot{k}/k = \dot{K}/K - \dot{L}/L$ or $k = \dot{K}/L - gk$ since $\dot{L}/L = g$. Substituting $\dot{K}/L = Y_1/L - \delta k$ into the latter and calculating Y_1/L from the savings equation gives the result.

PROBLEM 4.

(a) Calculate the appropriate limits from

$$\omega = \frac{f_i(k_i)}{f_i'(k_i)} - k_i.$$

(b) A CES production function may be written

$$y = f(k) = (\beta^* k^{-\rho} + \alpha^*)^{-1/\rho}$$

where the elasticity of substitution is $\sigma \equiv (1 + \rho)^{-1}$. By introducing the transformations $\beta^* = \beta^{-\rho}$ and $\alpha^* = \beta^{-\rho}\alpha^{-\rho-1}$, derive $y = \beta(k^{-\rho} + \alpha^{-\rho-1})^{-1/\rho}$, and then use the equilibrium condition $f(k)/f'(k) - k - \omega = 0$ to obtain $k = \alpha\omega^\sigma$ and $\omega = (k/\alpha)^{1/\sigma}$.

(c) Use $\Psi'^5 = 0$.

PROBLEM 5. It is sufficient that $f_1(k_1) - s_r f_1'(k_1)k_1 > 0$; use $\Psi'^3 = 0$ and $0 \leqq s_r \leqq 1$ to obtain the result.

PROBLEM 6. Sufficiency is obvious. Necessity is established by assuming that ω is not a (single-valued) function of k and finding a contradiction.

PROBLEM 7. $J = x_1$; however, for any $x_1 > 0$ and for all x_2, $x_2 \pm 2\pi$ give the same y_i.

PROBLEM 8. $J = f_1(k_1)[(1 - \rho)\xi_1 + \rho\xi_2] + s_w \xi_1\xi_2(k_1 - k_2)f_1'(k_1) - (k_1 - k_2)\gamma\xi_2$ where $\xi_i \equiv d\omega/dk_i$ and $\gamma \equiv \rho f_1'(k_1) - f_1''(k_1)(s_r k + s_w \omega)$. Continuity is assured by the assumption that $f_i''(k_i)$, $i = 1, 2$, are continuous.

PROBLEM 9. $N^5 = \xi_1\xi_2[f_1(k_1) - s_r f_1'(k_1)(k_1 - k_2)]$, and use the result obtained in Exercise 5.

PROBLEM 11. Use the expression for J obtained in Exercise 8; then manipulate!

PROBLEM 12. Show that $f_1(k_1) = \alpha f_2(k_2)$ for some positive constant α if $k_1(\omega) = k_2(\omega)$ for all $\omega \in (\omega_{\min}, \omega_{\max})$; then redefine the units of measurement for the output of consumption goods to make the two production functions identical.

PROBLEM 13. Calculate $h'(k)$ and use $\Psi(x; k) = 0$.

PROBLEM 14. Derive $s_w \omega = \rho k_1 + \rho\omega - k$ from $\Psi'^3 = 0$ and $\Psi'^6 = 0$, and substitute $\rho k_1 - k = -(1 - \rho)k_2$.

PROBLEM 15. The hypothesis implies that $s_w k_1^* < s_r k^*(< s_r k_2^*)$ or $s_w[1 - \omega^*/(\omega^* + k_1^*)] < s_r[k^*/(\omega^* + k_1^*)]$, and then use $\Psi'^3 = 0$ to obtain

$$s_w < \frac{f_1'(k_1^*)}{f_1(k_1^*)} (s_r k^* + s_w \omega^*).$$

Substitute $nk^* = f_1'(k_1^*)(s_r k^* + s_w \omega^*)$, which may be derived from $h(k) = 0$ and $\Psi'^6 = 0$, into the latter to obtain (a) and (b).

References

[1] AMANO, A., "A Further Note on Professor Uzawa's Two-Sector Model of Economic Growth," *Review of Economic Studies*, **XXXI**, *86* (April, 1964), pp. 97–102.

[2] APOSTOL, T. M., *Mathematical Analysis*. Reading, Mass.: Addison-Wesley, 1957.

[3] ARROW, K., H. B. CHENERY, B. MINHAS, and R. M. SOLOW, "Capital-Labor Substitution and Economic Efficiency," *The Review of Economics and Statistics*, **XLIII**, *3* (August, 1961), pp. 225–250.

[4] BURMEISTER, E., "The Role of the Jacobian Determinant in the Two-Sector Model," *International Economic Review*, **IX**, *2* (June, 1968), pp. 195–203.

[5] DRANDAKIS, E. M., "Factor Substitution in the Two-Sector Growth Model" *Review of Economic Studies*, **XXX**, *84* (October, 1963) pp.217–228.

[6] HAHN, F. H., "On Two-Sector Growth Models," *Review of Economic Studies*, **XXXII**, *92* (October, 1965), pp. 339–346.

[7] — and R. C. O. MATTHEWS, "The Theory of Economic Growth: A Survey," *Economic Journal*, **LXXIV**, *296* (December, 1964), pp. 779–902.

[8] INADA, K., "On a Two-Sector Model of Economic Growth: Comments and a Generalization," *Review of Economic Studies*, **XXX**, *86* (April, 1964), pp. 119–127.

[9] — "On the Stability of Growth Equilibria in Two-Sector Models," *Review of Economic Studies*, **XXXI**, *86* (April, 1964), pp. 127–142.

[10] KURZ, M., "A Two-Sector Extension of Swan's Model of Economic Growth: The Case of No Technical Change," *International Economic Review*, **IV**, *1* (January, 1963), pp. 68–79.

[11] SAMUELSON, P. A., "The Canonical Model of Capital," unpublished.

[12] SOLOW, R. M., "Note on Uzawa's Two-Sector Model of Economic Growth," *Review of Economic Studies*, **XXIX**, *78* (October, 1961), pp. 48–50.

[13] TAKAYAMA, A., "On a Two-Sector Model of Economic Growth: A Comparative Statics Analysis," *Review of Economics Studies*, **XXX**, *83* (June, 1963), pp. 95–104.

[14] — "On a Two-Sector-Model of Economic Growth with Technological Progress," *Review of Economic Studies*, **XXXII**, *91* (July, 1965), pp. 251–262.

[15] UZAWA, H., "On a Two-Sector Model of Economic Growth," *Review of Economic Studies*, **XXIX**, *78* (October, 1961), pp. 40–47.

[16] — "On a Two-Sector Model of Economic Growth: II," *Review of Economic Studies*, **XXX**, *83* (June, 1963), pp. 105–118.

Chapter 5 Extensions of the

Two-Sector Model

5–1. Introduction and Summary

As noted in the previous chapter, in two-sector models the capital/labor ratio may oscillate around an unstable value, a feature that is impossible in the one-sector models we have studied. This new possibility is examined more closely in the next section, and a simple example is provided to illustrate the result.

Section 5-3, a brief digression, classifies different kinds of technological change bias. The formulas derived here facilitate the subsequent study of Harrod- and Kennedy-neutral technical progress in Sections 5-4 and 5-5, respectively. An economic discussion of Harrod versus Kennedy neutrality follows in Section 5-7, and it is seen that the fundamental issue is an interpretation of the stylized facts stated in Chapter 3. Finally, we conclude this chapter with a brief survey of some modifications of the standard two-sector model.

5–2. Cyclic Behavior

Inada [13] has shown that two-sector models may have cyclic solutions for the capital/labor ratio, and we will follow his demonstration closely. Note that a model with a cyclic solution cannot be globally stable.

In order to facilitate a diagrammatic description, we will assume that both production functions are CES, $s_r = 1$ and $s_w = 0$. The following discussion will show that a cyclic solution can exist only if the system is not causal and $J(\omega)$ changes sign for $\omega \in (\omega_{\min}, \omega_{\max})$. Therefore, $J(\omega)$ must change sign, and none of the sufficient conditions given in Theorem 3, p. 120 is satisfied.

In particular, we must assume that the elasticity of substitution of the production function for the capital-good sector is less than one, and thus

$$\lim_{k_1 \to 0} f_1'(k_1) = \beta_1$$

where β_1 is a positive constant. Substituting $s_r = 1$ and $s_w = 0$ into the growth equation derived in Chapter 4,

$$\dot{k}/k = f_1'(k_1)\left[\frac{s_r k + s_w \omega}{k}\right] - n,$$

we find

$$\dot{k}/k = f_1'(k_1) - n. \tag{1}$$

We will also assume that $n \equiv g + \delta < \beta_1$ so that the equation $f_1'(k_1) - n = 0$ has a root k_1^*, easily seen to be unique, for which $\dot{k}/k = 0$.

It is important to realize that (1) cannot be written as a function $\dot{k}/k = h(k)$ because, as we have stated, the system is not causal and therefore no function $k_1 = \Phi^3(k)$ exists. However, the functions $k_i = k_i(\omega)$, $i = 1, 2$, and $k = k(\omega)$ always exist, and we may rewrite (1) as

$$\dot{k}/k = f_1'[k_1(\omega)] - n \equiv G(\omega), \qquad \omega_{\min} < \omega < \omega_{\max}. \tag{2}$$

A cyclic solution is illustrated in Figure 15; because both production functions are CES, the equation $J(\omega) = 0$ has exactly two roots, ω_1 and ω_2 (see footnote 16 on p. 118). The equation

$$\dot{k}/k = G(\omega)/k(\omega) = 0$$

has only one root ω^*, and assume $J(\omega^*) < 0$, or, equivalently, that $k'(\omega^*) < 0$.

Suppose also that the initial capital/labor ratio is k^0 and the system starts at the points labeled **1**. Since initially $\dot{k}$ is negative, k falls and eventually reaches the points labeled **2** where $k = k^U$. At this point $\dot{k}$ is still negative, and thus k must continue to fall. However, for all values of k satisfying the inequality

$$k^L \leqq k \leqq k^U,$$

exactly three values of ω and three corresponding values of $\dot{k}$ are consistent with the equilibrium condition $\Psi(x; k) = 0$ derived in Chapter 4 and the growth equation (1). It is reasonable to suppose that the economic variables, y_1^t, y_2^t, k_1^t, k_2^t, ω^t, ρ^t, and k^t will move, if possible, along continuous time

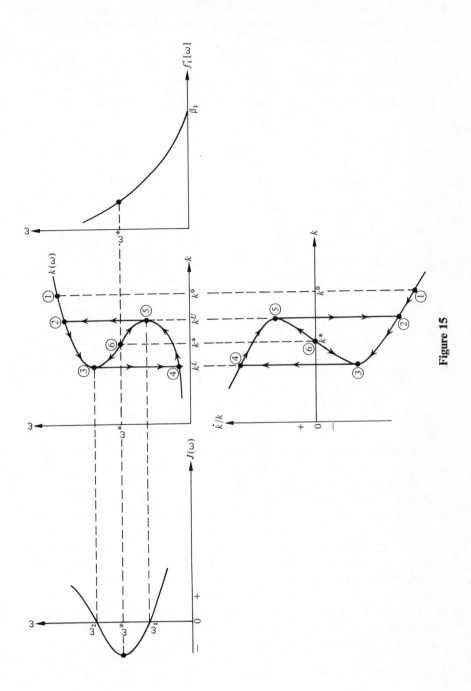

Figure 15

paths. If the system does, in fact, behave in this way, it will move along the curves illustrated in Figure 15 from the points labeled **2** and in finite time will reach the points labeled **3** where $k = k^L$.

Once the system reaches the points labeled **3**, it cannot continue to move along the branch **3-6-5** because (ω^*, k^*) is an unstable singular point for which $G'(\omega^*) > 0$. Since it is physically impossible for k to change abruptly under the full-employment assumption, there must be an instantaneous change in y_1, y_2, k_1, k_2, ω, and ρ for which k is constant at $k = k^L$. We see from Figure 15 that the only other points satisfying $k = k^L$ and the equilibrium condition $\Psi(x; k) = 0$ are labeled **4**; thus there is an instantaneous "jump" from **3** to **4**.

At **4** $\dot{k}/k > 0$ and k begins to rise, moving eventually to **5**. From **5** there is another instantaneous jump to **2**, and the cycle **2-3-4-5-2** repeats itself with $k^t \in [k^L, k^U]$.

A graph of k and k_1 versus time is given in Figure 16. At times $t_1, t_2, t_3, \ldots$, there is an instantaneous jump in k_1. Even though we may be willing to assume that capital is perfectly malleable and can be used for the production of either output good, it is an other matter to assume that the capital/labor ratios k_1 and k_2 can be adjusted instantaneously by shifting capital and labor between the capital- and consumption-good sectors; a more reasonable hypothesis is that it takes some finite time merely to move capital and labor from one sector to another. The source of the difficulty lies in the fact that when we write the condition $\Psi(x; k) = 0$, we have implicitly assumed that the variables can *instantaneously* adjust to achieve static equilibrium. In other words, the model we have specified is void of short-run disequilibrium dynamics, and therefore we are led to an unreasonable conclusion.

Similar results are found in physics: in certain types of electronic circuits that undergo relaxation oscillations, current (but not voltage) may jump if inductance is ignored. The cyclic solution for such circuits is exactly the same as that pictured in Figure 15 with current playing the role of k_1 and voltage the role of k (see [1], pp. 163–181). Inductance, which is a resistance to a change in current, can be thought of as a kind of friction that prevents current from jumping. When inductance is taken into account, current can no longer change abruptly, although it may change with high velocity.

What kind of friction has been ignored in this model? From the foregoing it follows that the time paths not only for k_1 and k_2, but also for the wage/rentals ratio ω, must possess a discontinuous jump. A reasonable conjecture is that the wage/rentals ratio ω may not be able to adjust *instantaneously* to its short-run equilibrium value; a smooth time path for ω, in turn, would prevent abrupt changes in k_1 and k_2 if the equations $k_i = k_i(\omega)$, $i = 1, 2$, are always satisfied.

Uzawa [30] has briefly considered the same problem and assumes that both ω and k are independent variables. In this case, the full employment

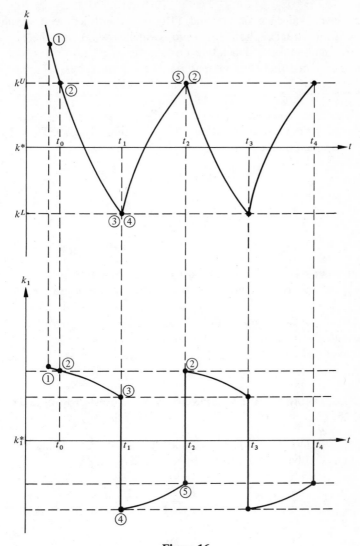

Figure 16

equation ($\Psi^5 = 0$) is not necessarily satisfied and must be replaced by the inequalities

$$K_1^t + K_2^t \leqq K^t \tag{3}$$

and

$$L_1^t + L_2^t \leqq L^t. \tag{4}$$

For any given value of ω, (3) and (4) can be satisfied with *equality* if and only if the actual capital/labor ratio is equal to $k(\omega)$, and there are two different equations for $\dot{k}$ depending on whether $k \geqq k(\omega)$ or $k < k(\omega)$ (see [30]). It is assumed that the time path ω^t is determined by

$$\dot{\omega} = \Omega[k - k(\omega)] \tag{5}$$

where Ω is some continuous sign-preserving function of (ω, k). Thus, Uzawa obtains two differential equations

$$\dot{k} = \Lambda^1(\omega, k)$$

and

$$\dot{\omega} = \Lambda^2(\omega, k)$$

which, given any starting point (ω^0, k^0), determine the time paths ω^t and k^t. A limit cycle may result, but, in contrast to our previous results, the time paths y_1^t, y_2^t, k_1^t, k_2^t, ω^t, ρ^t, and k^t are all continuous and the possibility of instantaneous jumps is eliminated. However, it is clear that the variables may adjust to full-employment equilibrium with very high velocity for some forms of the function Ω in (5).

5–3. A Digression: A Classification of Technological Change Bias

Diamond [7] has shown that disembodied technological change with two factor inputs can be completely described by the two indices

$$\tau \equiv \frac{F_t}{F} = \frac{f_t}{f} \tag{6}$$

and

$$D \equiv \frac{\dfrac{\partial (F_L/F_K)}{\partial t}}{F_L/F_K} = \frac{F_{Lt}}{F_L} - \frac{F_{Kt}}{F_K}. \tag{7}$$

The index τ measures the rate of increase of output attributable to time alone (with factor inputs held constant) and is called the *rate of technological progress*, while the index D measures the percentage change in the marginal rate of substitution between capital and labor with inputs held constant.

Clearly, technological change is Hicks labor saving, Hicks neutral, or Hicks capital saving if and only if $D < 0$, $D = 0$, or $D > 0$, respectively,[1] and thus D is called a measure of the *Hicks bias*.

Alternative indices of bias have been proposed that equal zero if technological change is Harrod neutral or Solow neutral.[2] For example, the index

$$\frac{\dfrac{\partial(Q/K)}{\partial t}}{Q/K}\bigg|_{F_K}$$

is one possible measure of Harrod bias. However, we can achieve a symmetric classification of bias by defining indices that measure the percentage change in relative shares $(\hat{\omega} - \hat{k})$ for designated paths. These indices are derived by calculating

$$\hat{\omega} - \hat{k} = -\frac{\hat{\pi}}{1-\pi} = \frac{1}{1-\pi}(\hat{f} - \hat{k} - \hat{f_k}) \tag{8}$$

$$= (1/\sigma - 1)\hat{k} + D \tag{9}$$

(Exercise 1) and using the alternative path restrictions; σ is the elasticity of substitution between capital and labor for any fixed t.

If we *assume* that technological change is factor augmenting, we may calculate (Exercise 2)

$$D = (1/\sigma - 1)(\hat{b} - \hat{a}). \tag{10}$$

Using Theorems 1, 2, and 3 from Chapter 3 and equation (10), we can obtain the following indices for bias:[3]

$$I_{\text{Harrod}} = (1/\sigma - 1)\hat{b}, \tag{11}$$

$$I_{\text{Hicks}} = D = (1/\sigma - 1)(\hat{b} - \hat{a}), \tag{12}$$

and

$$I_{\text{Solow}} = -(1/\sigma - 1)\hat{a}. \tag{13}$$

---

[1] Since D is defined with constant K and L (constant k), the ratio of relative shares WL/RK is constant if and only if $F_L/F_K = W/R$ is constant. See the discussion in Chapter 3.
[2] See, e.g., Fei and Ranis [10] and Sheshinski [24].
[3] Similar indices can be derived without the factor-augmenting hypothesis.

Thus, if $I_{\text{Harrod}} < 0$, the technological change is called *Harrod labor saving*; if $I_{\text{Hicks}} < 0$, the technological change is called *Hicks labor saving*; etc.[4] Of course, not all the indices are independent since

$$I_{\text{Harrod}} + I_{\text{Solow}} \equiv I_{\text{Hicks}} \equiv D. \tag{14}$$

Moreover, if $\sigma = 1$, then technological change is neutral by any of the above three definitions.[5] Likewise observe that the indices of bias can have different signs if $\sigma \neq 1$. Suppose, for example, that technological change is Hicks neutral with $\hat{a} = \hat{b} > 0$; then it is also Harrod labor saving if $\sigma > 1$ and Harrod capital saving if $\sigma < 1$. However, once it is realized that the various definitions of bias depend crucially on the particular path of the capital/labor ratio and therefore can conflict, there is no reason to proceed with a complete classification.

5–4. Harrod Neutrality in the Two-Sector Model

If there exists *Harrod neutral* or *purely labor-augmenting* technical progress in each sector, the production functions become

$$Y_i = F^i(K_i, \ell_i), \qquad i = 1, 2,$$

where ℓ_i are measures of *effective labor*. We shall assume

$$\ell_i = L_i e^{\gamma_i t}, \qquad i = 1, 2,$$

with γ_i equal to the exponential rates of Harrod-neutral technical progress in each sector. For simplicity we will assume further that these rates are the same and write $\gamma_1 = \gamma_2 = \gamma$.[6] We then define new variables in terms of *labor-efficiency units*:

$$\tilde{y}_i \equiv Y_i/\ell_i,$$

$$\tilde{k}_i \equiv K_i/\ell_i,$$

$$\ell \equiv \ell_1 + \ell_2,$$

$$\tilde{\rho} \equiv \ell_1/\ell$$

$$\tilde{k} \equiv \frac{K_1 + K_2}{\ell_1 + \ell_2} = \frac{K}{\ell},$$

---

[4] See the discussion of nonneutral disembodied technological change in Chapter 3.

[5] This observation is also proved by noting that $Q = a(t)K^\alpha L^{1-\alpha}$ may be written in the equivalent forms $Q = \{[a(t)]^{1/\alpha}K\}^\alpha L^{1-\alpha}$ or $Q = K^\alpha\{[a(t)]^{1/(1-\alpha)}L\}^{1-\alpha}$.

[6] This is a very restrictive simplification; the interested reader is referred to Diamond [7, 8] for a discussion of more complicated cases. Also see Takayama [28].

and

$$\tilde{\omega} \equiv \omega^{-\gamma t}. \tag{15}$$

It may be shown (Exercise 3) that the new system of equilibrium conditions is functionally identical with the old conditions, and therefore we may write

$$\Psi(\tilde{x}; \tilde{k}) = 0;$$

likewise the growth equation is

$$\dot{\tilde{k}} = \tilde{\rho}_1 f_1(\tilde{k}_1) - \tilde{n}\tilde{k}, \qquad \tilde{n} \equiv g + \delta + \gamma,$$

which is of the same functional form as the previous equation for $\dot{k}$. Thus, all the previous causality and stability theorems apply to this case when $(x; k)$ is replaced by $(\tilde{x}; \tilde{k})$ and n is replaced by $\tilde{n}$. If the system is stable,

$$\lim_{t \to \infty}(\tilde{x}; \tilde{k}) = (\tilde{x}^*; \tilde{k}^*),$$

and then the output/capital ratios are asymptotically *constants* given by

$$\frac{Y_i}{K_i} = \frac{Y_i/\ell_i}{K_i/\ell_i} = \frac{\tilde{y}_i^*}{\tilde{k}_i^*}, \qquad i = 1, 2. \tag{16}$$

Similarly, per capita output grows at the rate

$$\frac{d(Y_i/L)/dt}{Y_i/L} = \frac{\dot{Y}_i}{Y_i} - \frac{\dot{L}}{L} = (\gamma + g) - g = \gamma, \qquad i = 1, 2, \tag{17}$$

and the capital/labor ratio grows according to the equation

$$k^t = \frac{K^t}{L^t} = \tilde{k}^* e^{\gamma t}. \tag{18}$$

We shall return to this example and give a more complete economic discussion in Section 5-6.

5–5. A Different Definition of Neutrality: The Kennedy Theorem

There is still another distinctly different definition of neutral technological change due to Kennedy [17, 18].[7] We denote the capital/output ratio for the

---

[7] Also see Joan Robinson [21], pp. 88–91.

consumption-good sector *in value terms* by

$$P_1 K_2 / P_2 Y_2$$

or

$$\beta \equiv p K_2 / Y_2$$

where $p \equiv P_1/P_2$ is the relative price of one unit of capital to the price of the consumption good. Kennedy has proved that the expression β is constant when the interest rate r is constant if (1) there is no technological change in the investment-good sector (*Warning:* this assumption is crucial.), and (2) technological change in the consumption-good sector is Hicks neutral with $Y_2 = F^2(K_2, L_2, t) = a(t)G(K_2, L_2)$. This result may be established as follows.

Since ω is the same in each sector, equilibrium in the factor markets and equation (9) imply

$$\frac{\hat{k}_1}{\sigma_1} + D_1 = \frac{\hat{k}_2}{\sigma_2} + D_2 \tag{19}$$

where 1 and 2 denote the investment-good sector and the consumption-good sector, respectively. Because the rate of interest, which is positive by assumption, is equal to the own-rate of return to capital in the investment-good sector in steady states where $\dot{p} = 0$, i.e., because $r = F_1^1 - \delta$ when $\dot{p} = 0$, the assumption $\dot{r} = 0$ implies $\hat{F}_1^1 = 0$. For any production function $F(K, L; t)$ we may calculate

$$\hat{F}_K = \hat{f}_k = \tau - (1 - \pi) D - [(1 - \pi)/\sigma]\hat{k}$$

(Exercise 4), and thus $\hat{F}_1^1 = 0$ implies

$$\hat{k}_1/\sigma_1 = [\tau_1/(1 - \pi)] - D_1.$$

Since by assumption there is no technological change in the investment-good sector and $\tau_1 = 0$, the latter becomes

$$\hat{k}_1/\sigma_1 = - D_1. \tag{20}$$

Substituting (20) into (19) we find the condition

$$\hat{k}_2 = -\sigma_2 D_2. \tag{21}$$

But from (9) we find

$$\hat{\pi}_2 = (1 - \pi_2)[(1 - 1/\sigma_2)\hat{k}_2 - D_2]; \tag{22}$$

consequently, (21) implies

$$\mathring{\pi}_2 = -\sigma_2(1 - \pi_2)D_2.$$ (23)

However, as previously noted technological change in the consumption-good sector is Hicks neutral if and only if $D_2 = 0$, and thus we have proved that $\mathring{\pi}_2 = 0$ when $\mathring{r} = 0$.

Accordingly,

$$\pi_2 = \frac{F_K^2 K_2}{Y_2} = \frac{(R/P_2)K_2}{Y_2} = \text{constant},$$ (24)

and multiplying (24) by the constant $P_1/R = 1/F_K^1 = 1/(r + \delta)$ gives another constant, i.e.,

$$\frac{(P_1/R)(R/P_2)K_2}{Y_2} = \frac{pK_2}{Y_2} = \beta = \text{constant},$$

as was to be proved.

The equilibrium conditions for the foregoing model are very similar to those derived in Chapter 4. In particular, we may define

$$y_2 \equiv Y_2/L_2 = a(t)G(K_2/L_2, 1) = a(t)G(k_2, 1) \equiv a(t)g(k_2)$$ (25)

where

$$\frac{\partial Y_2}{\partial K_2} = a(t)g'(k_2)$$

and

$$\frac{\partial Y_2}{\partial L_2} = a(t)[g(k_2) - k_2 g'(k_2)].$$

Since $\partial Y_2/\partial K_2 = R/P_2$ and $\partial Y_2/\partial L_2 = W/P_2$ in equilibrium,

$$\omega = \frac{W/P_2}{R/P_2} = \frac{g(k_2)}{g'(k_2)} - k_2$$

or

$$\frac{g(k_2)}{g'(k_2)} - k_2 - \omega = 0,$$ (26)

which is formally identical to $\Psi^4 = 0$ in Chapter 4. The rest of the model is unchanged except that now $y_2 = a(t)g(k_2)$. However, for any given t, the causality conditions derived in Chapter 4 are identical to the causality conditions for this model if we replace $f_2(k_2)$ by $g(k_2)$; this fact follows immediately from the observation that for a fixed t we need only work with $\Psi^3 = 0$, $\Psi^4 = 0$, $\Psi^5 = 0$, and $\Psi^6 = 0$ to determine the function $\omega = \Phi^5(k)$ in a causal model. Since $k_i = k_i(\omega)$, the output y_2 is given by (25) for any value of t. The reason the causality conditions remain virtually unaltered, except that we replace $f_2(k_2)$ by $g(k_2)$, is that the function $a(t)$ does not appear in the crucial equation (26).

For exactly the same reasons, the reader may easily verify that the growth process and its stability properties remain unchanged. Consequently, if the system is causal and stable and

$$\lim_{t \to \infty} k^t = k^*,$$

then

$$\lim_{t \to \infty} r^t = f'_1[k_1(k^*)] - \delta = r^* = \text{constant}, \tag{27}$$

$$\lim_{t \to \infty} \dot{r} = 0 \tag{28}$$

and therefore we conclude that

$$\lim_{t \to \infty}(pK_2/Y_2) = \text{constant}. \tag{29}$$

Moreover, for any stable model in which r is asymptotically constant and Kennedy's theorem applies, the ratio of total capital to total output in value terms is constant, i.e., as $t \to \infty$,

$$v \equiv \frac{pK}{Y_2 + pY_1} = \text{constant}. \tag{30}$$

For as $t \to \infty$, in the limit $\hat{Y}_2 - \hat{L} = \hat{a}$, $\hat{p} = \hat{F}_1^2 - \hat{F}_1^1 = \hat{a} - 0 = \hat{a}$, $\hat{K} = \hat{L}$, and $\hat{Y}_1 = \hat{L}$ (Exercise 5). Thus,

$$\lim_{t \to \infty} \hat{v} = \lim_{t \to \infty}\left[\hat{p} + \hat{K} - \left(\frac{Y_2}{Y_2 + pY_1}\right)\hat{Y}_2 - \left(\frac{pY_1}{Y_2 + pY_1}\right)(\hat{p} + \hat{Y}_1)\right]$$

$$= \hat{a} + \hat{L} - \left(\frac{Y_2}{Y_2 + pY_1}\right)(\hat{a} + \hat{L}) - \left(\frac{pY_1}{Y_2 + pY_1}\right)(\hat{a} + \hat{L})$$

$$= \hat{a} + \hat{L} - \left(\frac{Y_2 + pY_1}{Y_2 + pY_1}\right)(\hat{a} + \hat{L}) = 0.$$

Similarly, real GNP $(Y_2 + pY_1)$ and consumption (Y_2) both grow at the rate $\hat{a} + \hat{L}$, whereas real per capita GNP and real per capita consumption both grow at the rate $\hat{a}$.

Finally, we may note that the production possibility frontier for this Kennedy–Robinson model is of the form

$$Y_2 = a(t)T(Y_1; K, L). \tag{31}$$

If, on the other hand, we consider the model discussed in the previous section where

$$\ell_i = L_i e^{\gamma t}, \qquad i = 1, 2,$$

and where in general $e^{\gamma t} = a(t)$, then the production possibility frontier is

$$Y_2 = T[Y; K, a(t)L] \tag{32}$$

Equations (31) and (32), in addition to the assumption that the models under consideration are stable, are fundamental and enable us to distinguish clearly between the economic implications of Harrod versus Kennedy neutrality; we now turn to this issue.

5–6. Discussion of Harrod versus Kennedy Neutrality

In order to compare the economic implications of Harrod versus Kennedy neutrality, we must assume that both models are stable. More precisely, consider first the Harrod-neutrality case discussed in Section 5-4. We then have

$$Y_i = F^i(K_i, L_i e^{\gamma t}), \qquad i = 1, 2,$$

and the model is stable in the sense that

$$\lim_{t \to \infty} \tilde{k} = \lim_{t \to \infty} (K/Le^{\gamma t}) = \tilde{k}^*. \tag{33}$$

On the other hand, in the Kennedy model we have

$$Y_1 = F^1(K_1, L_1)$$

(no technological change in the investment-good sector), and

$$Y_2 = e^{\gamma t}F^2(K_2, L_2)$$

(Hicks-neutral technological change in the consumption-good sector; for comparative purposes we now assume the latter technological change is at the exponential rate γ). Stability in this model implies

$$\lim_{t \to \infty} k = \lim_{t \to \infty}(K/L) = k^*. \tag{34}$$

In the following we shall assume that both (33) and (34) are satisfied, and we now wish to compare the asymptotic values of the economic variables.

Recall our discussion in Chapter 3 in which we stated that technological change is one way to explain certain empirical facts that seem characteristic of most advanced economies. The first seven variables listed in Table 1 include many of these facts, and as indicated we have no basis for preferring a model with Harrod neutrality over one with Kennedy neutrality: both provide exactly the same explanation for the behavior of the first seven economic variables.

However, the two models yield different conclusions for the economic variables listed on lines 8–13 of Table 1. In particular, consider p, line 8, and k, line 9. The Kennedy model predicts $\hat{p} = \gamma$ and $\hat{k} = 0$, i.e., the price of the capital good in terms of the consumption good rises at the percentage rate γ, whereas the capital/labor ratio in physical units remains constant. On the other hand, if there is Harrod-neutral technological change (at the same exponential rate γ in each sector), then $\hat{p} = 0$ and $\hat{k} = \gamma$. Of course, as an immediate consequence of the latter two statements, we see that the capital/labor ratio *in value terms*, line 1, grows at the percentage rate γ in both models.

It is not our objective to accept or reject either model on the basis of the results stated in Table 1. However, it does seem very strange to conclude that $\hat{p} = \gamma$ in steady-state equilibrium,[8] although it is precisely this fact that is responsible for most of the results in the case of Kennedy neutrality.

The reason that p is rising in the Kennedy model is evident from

$$Y_2 = a(t)T(Y_1; K, L)$$

$$= e^{\gamma t}T(Y_1; K, L). \tag{35}$$

Because $\partial Y_2/\partial Y_1 = -P_1/P_2$ in competitive equilibrium, we may calculate

$$\partial Y_2/\partial Y_1 = e^{\gamma t}T_1 = -p$$

and

$$\dot{p} = \gamma\, e^{\gamma t}T_1 + e^{\gamma t}(dT_1/dt). \tag{36}$$

---

[8] Remember that here we are not observing an "inflation" caused by monetary factors, although the latter question will be of primary concern in Chapter 6.

TABLE 1

VARIABLE	HARROD	KENNEDY
1. Capital/labor ratio in value terms [pK/L]	γ	γ
2. Real wage rate [W/P_2]	γ	γ
3. Capital/output ratio in value terms [$pK/(Y_2 + pY_1)$]	0	0
4. Net own rate of return on capital or the interest rate [$r \equiv F_K^1 - \delta$]	0	0
5. Relative share of labor [$1 - \pi = WL/(P_1Y_1 + P_2Y_2)$]	0	0
6. Per capita GNP in value terms [$(Y_2 + pY_1)/L$]	γ	γ
7. Capital/output ratio in physical units for each sector [$K_i/Y_i, i = 1, 2$]	0	0
8. Price level in terms of the consumption good as *numeraire* [$p \equiv P_1/P_2$]	0	γ
9. Capital/labor ratio in physical units [$k \equiv K/L$]	γ	0
10. Capital/output ratios in value terms for each sector [$pK_i/Y_i, i = 1, 2$]	0	γ
11. Capital/labor ratio in physical units for each sector [$K_i/L_i, i = 1, 2$]	γ	
12. Per capita output for each sector [$Y_i/L, i = 1, 2$]	γ	$\begin{cases} 0, i = 1 \\ \gamma, i = 2 \end{cases}$
13. Wage/rentals ratio [$\omega \equiv W/R$]	γ	0

Table 1 compares the asymptotic behavior of various economic variables under two alternative assumptions; namely, (1) there is a *stable* two-sector model with Harrod-neutral technological change in both sectors at the same rate $a(t) = e^{\gamma t}$, versus, (2) there is a *stable* two-sector model with Kennedy-neutral technological change at the rate $a(t) = e^{\gamma t}$. The numbers in the columns labelled *Harrod* and *Kennedy* give the *percentage rate of change* of the variables on the corresponding lines for the models (1) and (2), respectively. Note that the conclusions are identical for lines 1–7, but the results differ for lines 8–13.

It should be remembered that there is a great deal of interdependence among the variables listed on lines 1–13, but we have intentionally included this redundancy for emphasis; e.g. lines 2 and 6 imply line 5. The entries in Table 1 may all be calculated in a straight-forward manner by employing results obtained in the previous two sections, and the reader is urged to test his understanding by doing a few such calculations.*

* For example, consider the variable $w \equiv W/P_2$ in the Harrod case. Then

$$\hat{w} = (dF_L^2/dt)/F_L^2 = \frac{d[y_2 - k_2 f_2'(k_2)]/dt}{y_2 - k_2 f_2'(k_2)}$$
$$= \hat{f}_2(y_2/x) - [\hat{k}_2 - \hat{f}_2'(k_2)][k_2 f_2'(k_2)/x]$$

where $x \equiv y_2 - k_2 f_2'(k_2)$. But $\hat{f}_2 = \hat{k}_2 = \gamma$, whereas $\hat{f}_2' = 0$; hence, $\hat{w} = \gamma$.

However, T_1 is *homogeneous of degree zero*, and hence

$$T_1(Y_1; K, L) \equiv T_1(Y_1/L; K/L, 1).$$

But, Y_1/L and K/L approach constants as $t \to \infty$ given our stability assumption which in turn implies that $dT_1/dt = 0$. Thus from (36) we conclude that

$$\dot{p}/p \equiv \hat{p} = \gamma.^{9}$$

On the other hand, our Harrod model implies

$$Y_2 = T[Y_1; K, e^{\gamma t}L]. \tag{37}$$

Thus, $\partial Y_2/\partial Y_1 = T_1 = -p$ and $\dot{p} = 0$ because $Y_1/e^{\gamma t}L$ and $K/e^{\gamma t}L$ both approach constants as $t \to \infty$. All the results listed in Table 1 may be derived from (35) and (37) by using analogous methods, and thus these production possibility frontiers, plus the stability assumptions, implicitly contain all the relevant economic implications.

We conclude this section with a warning. If there is any moral to be learned from our comparison of Harrod versus Kennedy neutrality, it is that the same facts may be explained by more than one theory; and, moreover, the rejection of a model on the basis of its inconsistency with empirically observed facts may depend crucially upon the precise interpretation of those facts.[10]

5–7. A Brief Survey of Some Modifications of the Standard Two-Sector Model

Labor Supply

Drandakis [9] has shown that the labor supply may be made a function of the real wage $w \equiv W/P_2$ without significantly altering the two-sector model. Since the real wage is a function ω with

$$w'(\omega) > 0,$$

(Exercise 6), labor supply may be written as a function of ω where by assumption

$$L'(\omega) > 0.$$

[9] Less formally, we see that the Kennedy model hinges on the assumption of Hicks-neutral technological change in the consumption-good sector, for given this assumption the output of the consumption sector must rise and the price of the consumption good, measured with any other good as *numeraire*, must fall.

[10] E.g., is the capital/labor ratio in fact constant in physical units or in value terms?

The assumption that labor is fully employed is now expressed by

$$L_1 + L_2 = L(\omega).$$

Variable Savings Ratios

In principle the savings ratios s_r and s_w may depend on all the other variables in the system, i.e.,

$$s_r = s_r(x; k)$$

and

$$s_w = s_w(x; k).$$

In particular, let us define

$$y_I \equiv Y_1/L = \text{per capita output of capital goods,}$$
$$y_C \equiv Y_2/L = \text{per capita output of consumption goods,}$$
$$p \equiv P_1/P_2 = \text{price of the capital good relative to the}$$
$$\text{price of the consumption good,}$$

and

$$y \equiv y_C + py_I = \text{real per capita Gross National Product.}$$

If $s_r = s_w = s$, we may assume that s is a function of y, i.e.,

$$s_r = s_w = s = s(y),$$

Inada [13] has shown that a two-sector model with such a savings function is, under certain assumptions, always *globally stable*, and, moreover, has a unique stable equilibrium if the capital intensity condition $(k_1 \leqq k_2)$ is satisfied.

We may also note that a two-sector model might always be causal if there existed a concave *social utility function* of the form

$$u = u(y_I, y_C).$$

If it is assumed that such a social utility function exists and that it is maximized for all t, then clearly there would exist a unique point on the production possibility frontier satisfying equilibrium. However, this approach has serious logical difficulties because it is not clear what economic meaning can be attached to a utility function defined over the outputs of consumption goods and new capital goods. Clearly, new capital goods yield utility only to the extent that they contribute to future consumption, and thus we are forced to consider explicitly utility defined over future consumption streams. From such a criterion function an optimal savings path s^t and a corresponding optimal path (x^t, k^t) can sometimes be derived. This problem is the subject of Chapter 11.

Malleability of Capital

We have assumed that capital is perfectly malleable and that one unit of capital (one machine) can be shifted instantaneously between sectors, without cost, to achieve equilibrium (assumption A.1 in Chapter 4). Alternatively, it might be assumed that capital cannot be shifted between sectors and that a new machine, once it is installed in a particular sector, must remain in that sector for its lifetime. Inada [16] has examined a two-sector model with this and other assumptions and has proved causality and stability theorems.

We may note, however, that in particular circumstances the assumption of malleability is not a restriction; such is true in cases for which the flows of new capital to each sector are both nonnegative. Assume, for example, that $s_r = 1$, $s_w = 0$, and the production function for the consumption goods sector is Cobb–Douglas with $\sigma_2 = 1$. In this case it is easily shown that ρ is a *constant* (Exercise 7), and, hence,

$$\dot{L}_i/L_i = g, \qquad i = 1, 2.$$

Since

$$\dot{K}_i \equiv Z_i - \delta K_i, \qquad i = 1, 2,$$

where Z_i is the flow of new capital to the ith sector, Z_i is nonnegative if

$$-\delta < \dot{K}_i/K_i, \qquad i = 1, 2.$$

However,

$$\dot{K}_i/K_i = \dot{k}_i/k_i + \dot{L}_i/L_i,$$

and for this example the requirement becomes

$$-\delta < \dot{k}_i/k_i + g.$$

Moreover, there exists a unique and stable growth path, and thus for any $k^0 \in (a, b)$ for which $k^0 \leq k^*$, we know that $\dot{k} \geq 0$. Therefore,

$$\frac{\dot{k}_i}{k_i} = \frac{1}{k_i} \left[\frac{dk_i}{d\omega} \frac{d\omega}{dk} \right] \dot{k} \geq 0, \quad i = 1,2,$$

and thus $Z_i \geq 0$, $i = 1, 2$, for all t. In other words, starting from any initial capital/labor ratio less than k^*, the growth of the system toward k^* will never require a reduction in the amount of capital K_i in either sector, and thus the malleability assumption is not in fact restrictive.

Fixed Coefficients

The smooth neoclassical production functions

$$Y_i = F_i(K_i, L_i)$$

may be replaced by fixed-coefficient production functions of the Leontief form

$$Y_i = \min \left(\frac{K_i}{a_{Ki}}, \frac{L_i}{a_{Li}} \right), \quad i = 1, 2,$$

where the a_{Ki} and the a_{Li} are technological constants assumed positive. The capital/labor ratios are now given by

$$k_i = \frac{K_i}{L_i} = \frac{K_i/Y_i}{L_i/Y_i} = \frac{a_{Ki}}{a_{Li}}, \quad i = 1, 2,$$

and are constants. If full employment of capital and labor is assumed, equilibrium is determined by the two equations

$$\rho k_1 + (1 - \rho)k_2 - k = 0$$

and

$$\omega \rho + k_1 \rho - s_r k - s_w \omega = 0.$$

This Robinsonian model has been examined by Shinkai [25], Corden [6], and Samuelson [23] under various assumptions. Here we will demonstrate only that the essential features of two-sector growth models are exhibited in the simple fixed-coefficient case; namely, there exist

(i) A lack of causality under certain circumstances, and
(ii) The possibility of cyclical movements around an unstable equilibrium point.

For given values of K and L, the capital constraint is

$$Y_2 = \frac{K - a_{K1} Y_1}{a_{K2}}$$

and the labor constraint is

$$Y_2 = \frac{L - a_{L1} Y_1}{a_{L2}};$$

the inner envelope of these constraints is the production possibility frontier of the form

$$Y_2 = T(Y_1; K, L)$$

as shown in Figure 17 for the case $k_1 > k_2$. Assume that $s_r = 1$, $s_w = 0$, and

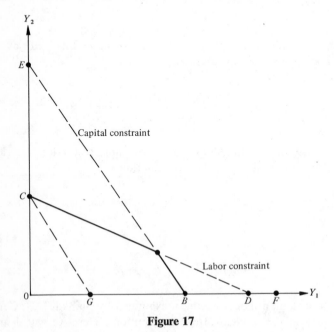

Figure 17

$k_1 > k_2$; as observed by Samuelson [23], if full employment is not assumed, the system need not start out at the only full-employment point A. To see this fact, observe that the savings equation

$$P_1 Y_1 = RK$$

is satisfied at point C where $Y_1 = 0$, capital is unemployed (redundant), and $R = 0$; likewise, point B (where $Y_2 = 0$, labor is unemployed, and $W = 0$) is consistent with equilibrium if full employment is not assumed. Thus, the model is not causal if $k_1 > k_2$, i.e., equilibrium is not unique.

Suppose that the system starts out at point B. If $g = 0$, the labor constraint (the line C–A–D) does not move, and if

$$1/a_{K1} > \delta,$$

the capital constraint (the line E–A–B) shifts outward over time (Exercise 8). Eventually there will be an instantaneous equilibrium at point D. However, from D the capital constraint continues to move outward, and thus the labor constraint will become binding with $W > 0$, and therefore no point such as F can be an equilibrium position; the equilibrium point must lie on the labor constraint C–A–D. If equilibrium is established at C where $Y_1 = 0$, the capital constraint will start to shift inward, and it is possible to remain at point C until the capital constraint becomes the line C–G.

We conclude that various cyclic time paths are possible in the Y_1-Y_2 plane.

Generalization to Several Consumption Goods

Generalization of the neoclassical two-sector model with one consumption good and a single malleable capital good to an $(n + 1)$-sector model with n distinct consumption goods requires an assumption about demand conditions. Assume that a constant proportion of income is spent on capital goods (is saved). Whether this is a result of a life-cycle savings behavior or just some rule of thumb for dividing future income from present income we may leave unspecified. The rest of the income is spent on the various commodities. Suppose that society, in its choice of consumption goods, acts to maximize a concave homothetic utility function. Accordingly, society chooses the proportion of income to be spent on each good, and these proportions will depend only on the relative prices of the n consumption goods.

With these assumptions it is possible to prove that utility is a function of the *total* quantities of capital and labor allocated to the n different consumption-good sectors if the marginal utility of expenditure on consumption goods is used as *numeraire*; moreover, this function has all the properties of a neoclassical production function (see [4]). Thus, all the causality and stability theorems apply with equal validity to the extended model. For example, if the capital/labor ratio in the investment-good sector is less than the *aggregate* capital/labor ratio of all the n consumption-good sectors, then the model is causal and there exists a unique balanced growth path that is stable.

Two-Sector Models with Classes

Stiglitz [27] has studied a modified two-sector model in which he assumes that there are two identifiable classes of people: *capitalists*, who derive their incomes solely from the ownership of capital, and *workers*, who receive both wage income and returns from capital ownership. Let k_c denote the ratio of capital owned by the capitalists to total labor, and let k_w denote the ratio of capital owned by workers to total labor. Further, let (k_c^*, k_w^*) be an equilibrium point for which $\dot{k}_c$ and $\dot{k}_w$ both are zero. Under various assumptions Stiglitz shows that there exists an equilibrium point $(k_c^*, k_w^*) > (0, 0)$ that is locally stable. However, sufficient conditions for nonlocal stability apparently are not easily derived, and consequently the existence of stable and unstable limit cycles cannot be excluded; the interested reader is referred to Stiglitz [27].

Exercises

1. (a) Derive equation (8).
   (b) Derive equation (9).
2. Derive equation (10).
3. Assume that there is purely labor augmenting technological change in each sector at the exponential rate γ. Derive
   (a) $\Psi(\tilde{x}; \tilde{k}) = 0$ and
   (b) $\dot{\tilde{k}} = \tilde{\rho} f_1(\tilde{k}_1) - \tilde{n}\tilde{k}$.
4. Derive $\hat{F}_K = \hat{f}_k = \tau - (1 - \pi)D - [(1 - \pi)/\sigma]\hat{k}$.
5. Consider a stable Kennedy–Robinson model and prove that in the limit (as $t \to \infty$) $\hat{Y}_2 - \hat{L} = \hat{a}, \hat{p} = \hat{a}, \hat{K} = \hat{L}$, and $\hat{Y}_1 = \hat{L}$.
6. Prove that $w = w(\omega)$, $\omega \in (\omega_{\min}, \omega_{\max})$ exists and that $w'(\omega) > 0$.
7. Prove that $\rho = constant$ if $s_r = 1$, $s_w = 0$, and $\sigma_2 = 1$.
8. Consider a system that starts at point B in Figure 17 (where $s_r = 1$, $s_w = 0$, and $k_1 > k_2$). Prove that $\dot{k} > 0$ if $1/a_{K1} > g + \delta$.
9. Let a family $F(K, L; t)$ be given, such that the elasticity of substitution is different from zero except possibly at isolated values of t. Assume that the function may be represented in factor augmenting form. Show that the requirement that factor shares remain constant defines a unique path $k(t)$ through any initial point k_0.

Answers and Hints

PROBLEM 1.
  (a) Differentiate $\omega/k = (1-\pi)/\pi$ to calculate $\hat{\omega} - \hat{k} = -\hat{\pi}/(1-\pi)$; then use $\pi = f_k k/f$.
  (b) (i) Derive $\tau = \pi F_{Kt}/F_K + (1-\pi)F_{Lt}/F_L$.
  (ii) Derive $\hat{q} = \hat{f} = \pi\hat{k} + \tau$.
  (iii) Derive $k f_{kk}/f_k = -[(1-\pi)/\sigma]$ using $\sigma = F_K F_L/F F_{KL}$, and then calculate

$$\hat{f_k} = -[(1-\pi)/\sigma]\hat{k} + f_{kt}/f_k.$$

  (iv) To derive (9) substitute (i), (ii), and (iii) into

$$\hat{\omega} - \hat{k} = (\hat{f} - \hat{k} - \hat{f_k})/(1-\pi).$$

PROBLEM 2.
  (i) Differentiate $Q = F(K, L; t) = G[b(t)K, a(t)L]$ to obtain

$$D \equiv \frac{F_{Lt}}{F_L} - \frac{F_{Kt}}{F_K} = (\hat{a} - \hat{b}) + \left[\frac{G_{21}bK}{G_2} - \frac{G_{11}bK}{G_1}\right]\hat{b} + \left[\frac{G_{22}aL}{G_2} - \frac{G_{12}aL}{G_1}\right]\hat{a}.$$

  (ii) Calculate $\sigma = G_1 G_2/G G_{12}$.
  (iii) Use $G \equiv G_1 bK + G_2 aL$, $bKG_{11} + aLG_{21} \equiv 0$, $bKG_{12} + aLG_{22} \equiv 0$, and (ii) to simplify the expression for D obtained in (i).

PROBLEM 3.
  (b) Derive $\hat{\ell}/\ell = g + \gamma$ and use

$$\frac{\dot{\hat{K}}}{\hat{K}} = \frac{\dot{K}}{K} - \frac{\dot{\ell}}{\ell}.$$

PROBLEM 4. See Hints for Exercise 1(b).

PROBLEM 6. $w = f_2(k_2) - k_2 f_2'(k_2)$ and $k_2 = k_2(\omega)$;
  $dw/d\omega = (dw/dk_2)(dk_2/d\omega) = k_2 f_2(k_2)[f_2'(k_2)/f_2''(k_2)]^2.$

PROBLEM 7. Use $\Psi'^6 = 0$.

PROBLEM 9. Use equations (9) and (10) of Section 5-3 and apply the standard uniqueness theorem of ordinary differential equations theory.

References

[1] ANDRONOW, A. A., and C. E. CHAIKIN, *Theory of Oscillations*. Princeton: Princeton University Press, 1949.

[2] ARROW, K. J., H. B. CHENERY, B. MINHAS, and R. M. SOLOW, "Capital-Labour Substitution and Economic Efficiency," *Review of Economics and Statistics*, **XLIII**, *3* (August, 1961), pp. 225–250.

[3] BURMEISTER, E., "The Role of the Jacobian Determinant in the Two-Sector Model," *International Economic Review*, **IX**, *2* (June, 1968) pp. 195–203.

[4] — and G. AKERLOF, "Substitution and Aggregation," Working Paper No. 222, Center for Research in Management Science, University of California at Berkeley, June ,1967.

[5]— and R. DOBELL, "Disembodied Technological Change with Several Factors," *Journal of Economic Theory* **1**, *1* (June, 1969), pp. 1–8.

[6] CORDEN, W. M., "The Two Sector Growth Model with Fixed Coefficients," *Review of Economic Studies*, **XXXIII**, *95* (July, 1966), pp. 253–262.

[7] DIAMOND, P. A., "Disembodied Technical Change in a Two-Sector Model," *Review of Economic Studies*. **XXXII**, *90* (April, 1965), pp. 161–168.

[8] — "Technical Change and the Measurement of Capital and Output," *Review of Economic Studies*, **XXXII**, *92* (October, 1965), pp. 289–298.

[9] ·DRANDAKIS, E. M., "Factor Substitution in the Two-Sector Growth Model," *Review of Economic Studies*, **XXX**, *84* (October, 1963), pp. 217–228.

[10] FEI, J. C. H., and G. RANIS, "Innovational Intensity and Factor Bias in the Theory of Growth," *International Economic Review*, **6**, *2* (May, 1965), pp. 182–198.

[11] HAHN, F. A., and R. C. O. MATTHEWS, "The Theory of Economic Growth: A Survey," *Economic Journal*, **LXXIV**, *296* (December, 1964) pp. 779–902.

[12] HICKS, J. R., *Theory of Wages*, 2nd ed. London: Macmillan, 1963.

[13] INADA, K., "On a Two-Sector Model of Economic Growth: Comments and a Generalization," *Review of Economic Studies*, **XXX**, *83* (June, 1963), pp. 119–127.

[14] — "On the Stability of Growth Equilibria in Two-Sector Models," *Review of Economic Studies*, **XXXI**, *86* (April, 1964), pp. 127–142.

[15] — "On Neoclassical Models of Economic Growth," *Review of Economic Studies*, **XXXII**, *90* (April, 1965), pp. 151–160.

[16] — "Investment in Fixed Capital and the Stability of Growth Equilibrium," *Review of Economic Studies*, **XXXIII**, *93* (January, 1966), pp. 19–30.

[17] KENNEDY, C., "Harrod on 'Neutrality'," *Economic Journal*, **LXXII**, *285* (March, 1962), pp. 249–250.

[18] — "The Character of Improvements and of Technical Progress," *Economic Journal*, **LXXII**, *288* (December, 1962), pp. 899–911.

[19] — "Samuelson on Induced Innovation," *Review of Economics and Statistics*, **48**, *4* (November, 1966), pp. 442–444.

[20] ROBINSON, JOAN, "The Classification of Inventions," *Review of Economic Studies*, **V** (February, 1938), pp. 139–142.

[21] — *Essays in The Theory of Economic Growth*. New York: St. Martin's Press, 1962.

[22] ROSE, H., "The Condition for Factor-Augmenting Technical Change," *Economic Journal*, **LXXVII**, *312* (December, 1968), pp. 966–971.

[23] SAMUELSON, P. A., "The Canonical Model of Capital," unpublished.

[24] SHESHINSKI, E., "Factor-Augmenting, Disembodied, Technical Change," unpublished.

[25] SHINKAI, Y., "On Equilibrium Growth of Capital and Labor," *International Economic Review*, **I**, *2* (May, 1960), pp. 107–111.

[26] SOLOW, R. M., "Some Recent Developments in the Theory of Production," pp. 225–250, in *The Theory and Empirical Analysis of Production*, (Murray Brown, Ed.) NBER, Studies in Income and Wealth. New York: Columbia University Press, 1967.

[27] STIGLITZ, J. E., "A Two Sector Two Class Model of Economic Growth," *Review of Economic Studies*, **XXXIV**, *98* (April, 1967), pp. 227–238.

[28] TAKAYAMA, A., "On a Two-Sector Model of Economic Growth with Technological Progress," *Review of Economic Studies*, **XXXII**, 91 (July, 1965), pp. 251–262.

[29] UZAWA, H., "On a Two-Sector Model of Economic Growth," *Review of Economic Studies*, **XXIX**, *81* (October, 1961), pp. 40–47.

[30] — "On a Two-Sector Model of Economic Growth: II," *Review of Economic Studies*, **XXX**, *83* (June, 1963), pp. 105–118.

[31] VON WEIZSÄCKER, C. C., "Tentative Notes on a Two-Sector Model with Induced Technical Progress," *Review of Economic Studies*, **XXXIII**, *95* (July, 1966), pp. 245–251.

Chapter 6 Money and Economic Growth

6-1. Introduction

Thus far our study of economic growth has been based upon models in which only actual flows of goods and actual stocks of a single capital good have appeared. Yet, much theorizing about economic issues focuses on the fact that in modern economies there exist financial assets, paper claims that offer alternative forms in which to hold wealth. Indeed, it might be argued that all of the central Keynesian problems of deficient aggregate demand and unemployment have relevance only to an economy in which there exists a money supply whose value can be augmented without giving rise to employment. In this chapter we will continue to avoid the problems of capacity utilization and unemployment by continuing to assume that there are no independently determined investment desires, but rather that all saving plans are realized. We shall, however, introduce some of the features of a monetary economy by assuming the presence of a paper currency in addition to a single capital good. Such a model was introduced by Tobin [21, 22].

One feature of the resulting model is that wealth may be held in alternative forms, so that some specification of portfolio behavior is necessary. Further, the production side of the model is taken to be identical to the one-sector models discussed in Chapter 2, in that the capital good combines with labor to produce a homogeneous output that can be used either for consumption or for gross capital formation.

On the other hand, it should be emphasized that the following model omits a number of features that probably would be of real importance in a monetary economy—disequilibrium phenomena involving unemployment, short-run adjustments of asset prices to equilibrium levels, and requirements for financing temporary shortfalls in liquid balances due to timing of transactions are all among the possible examples. Explicit treatment of portfolio demands for money requires consideration of the problems of risk and uncertainty.

Incorporating such considerations, however, necessitates paying attention to the institutional peculiarities of the economic community and the special characteristics of financial markets. In particular, a realistic treatment is impossible without the recognition of other financial assets that differ in liquidity from money, e.g., time deposits and bonds.

We cannot aspire to this degree of realism for present objectives, but rather limit ourselves to the fairly abstract issues arising from use of a nonproduced paper asset in the system. This asset, termed money, is issued costlessly by the government. It serves as *numeraire* and is desired for both transactions and investment purposes.

It should be noted that our analysis is based on a differential equation structure. We take a price level and capital stock to be given by the past. Then all that we may choose is the rate of change of the price level and of the capital stock, and we choose these so as to satisfy a money market equilibrium condition and a saving hypothesis. These choices determine the new values of the price level and the capital stock for the " next instant," and the process is repeated.

Our procedure thus appears to say nothing directly about the level of prices, as opposed to the rate of price inflation. It is therefore in marked contrast to the usual theorizing about money market equilibrium that purports to determine the equilibrium price level. But we must remember that this traditional theorizing is based on comparative statics, and it corresponds to a comparison of different stationary solutions to our differential equation system (possibly with the capital stock taken as fixed).

That is, much of the usual theorizing about money markets and price level determination is based on a Keynesian structure, with the time period short enough so that the capital stock may be treated as fixed, but long enough so that adjustments in employment and prices may be accomplished. In this context we study equilibrium configurations in which prices have adjusted fully to a stationary equilibrium value. Such theorizing leads to conclusions about the neutrality of money, the dichotomy of the real and monetary systems, and so on. But since it fails to take capital gains and losses explicitly into account in the formal equation structure, the analysis is really quite difficult. It has to deal implicitly with qualifications arising from changing prices without having an explicit mechanism for incorporating these in the model studied.

The present model does circumvent some of this difficulty. By determining the rate of price change so as to achieve equilibrium in portfolios and in the money market, we continue to deal with a full equilibrium model in which the price level and price change are just appropriate to induce portfolio managers to hold the existing supplies of money and capital goods. We are thus able to incorporate explicitly the dynamic considerations that are implicit, for example, in Keynesian liquidity preference arguments. As in all such models our argument continues to be crucially based on the requirement that at each moment all existing asset stocks must be willingly held in their given proportions, and this condition suffices to determine the required rate of capital gain. Note, finally, that the discussion of the chapter also reflects the traditional distinction between the decision to accumulate wealth, described by a saving hypothesis, and the decision on the composition of wealth, described by a portfolio management rule or liquidity preference function.

6–2. Demand for Money

In general, the demand for money must be sensitive to the distribution of income and wealth. However, neglecting these influences we postulate, for purposes of aggregate analysis, that the per capita demand for money is a function only of per capita money income, per capita money wealth, and the expected yield on capital (the only other asset). We further assume money demand per capita (m^d) always equals the actual money supply per capita (m), and, consequently, we assume that the equilibrium condition[1]

$$m^d = G(y, w, r) = m \qquad\qquad (1)$$

is always satisfied where

$m \equiv M/L$ = per capita money stock
p = price of output in terms of money as *numeraire*[2]
$y \equiv pF(K, L)/L$
$\quad \equiv pf(k)$ = per capita value of output
$k \equiv K/L$ = capital/labor ratio
$w \equiv \overline{W}/L \equiv (pK + M)/L = pk + m$ = per capita money wealth
$r \equiv f'(k) - \delta + E(\dot{p}/p)$
$\quad$ = expected money yield on the capital good.[3]

Absence of "money illusion" would require that (1) be homogeneous of degree one in its first two arguments. Consequently we may write

$$m/p = G(y/p, w/p, r)$$

---

[1] This equation could in principle be derived by aggregating the money demand functions of individuals having identical tastes, income, and wealth. More forthrightly, it may be assumed that the aggregate relationship will be of the same form as the individually determined demand functions.

[2] The price of money in terms of output is $p_m \equiv 1/p$.

[3] As in previous chapters, we assume that capital decays physically at the exponential rate δ, and $f'(k) - \delta$ is thus the net own rate of return on capital. The *expected* rate of inflation is denoted by $E(\dot{p}/p)$.

or

$$x = G[f(k), k + x, r] \tag{2}$$

where $x \equiv m/p$ denotes *per capita real money balances*.

We assume $G_1 > 0$, $1 > G_2 > 0$,[4] and $G_3 < 0$ (where G_i is the partial derivative of G with respect to its ith argument) for variables in the relevant ranges. Thus there exists a function

$$x = g(k, r), \tag{3}$$

describing the per capita real cash balances consistent with equilibrium at various levels of capital stock and yield (with $g_1 > 0$, $g_2 < 0$), and another function

$$r = \varphi(k, x), \tag{4}$$

which determines the yield necessary to maintain equilibrium with various portfolios of cash and real capital (with $\varphi_1 > 0$, $\varphi_2 < 0$)[5] (Exercise 1).

Various monetary models depend crucially on alternative forms and properties of (1) and hence of (3) and (4), including the ranges of the variables for which they are defined. In particular, we may identify the following cases.

Case 1   Assume we have the form

$$m^d = G(pk, w, r) = m \tag{1a}$$

instead of (1), with $G_1 > 0$, $1 > G_2 > 0$, and $G_3 < 0$, and assume further that (1a) is homogeneous of degree one in its first two arguments. We may again solve for (3), and it may be proved that the latter function is homogeneous of degree one in k; hence we have

$$x/k = g(1, r) \equiv \mathscr{L}(r) \tag{5}$$

with $\mathscr{L}'(r) < 0$. Thus the ratio M/pK is a declining function of the expected money yield on capital, which is exactly the liquidity preference model introduced by Tobin [21, 22] and later studied by Sidrauski [16], Nagatani [9], and others.

[4] The assumption $1 > G_2$ simply implies that an extra dollar of wealth will not all be held in the form of money balances.

[5] It should be emphasized that equations (3) and (4) are derived from equation (1), which explicitly assumes money market equilibrium.

Case 2 Suppose a second alternative to (1) is

$$m = m(y, r) \tag{1b}$$

where m is homogeneous of degree one in y, $\partial m/\partial y > 0$, and $\partial m/\partial r < 0$. Clearly then,

$$m/y = m/pf(k) = m(1, r) \equiv 1/v(r)$$

or

$$Mv(r) = pF(K, L) \tag{6}$$

where $v'(r) > 0$. Obviously (6) represents a standard transactions demand equation in which the velocity of circulation is an increasing function of r.[6] The classic Cambridge form of equation (6) assumed that $1/v(r)$ is an institutionally determined constant.

Case 3 Monetary models in which the demand for money is purely speculative have been studied by Shell, Sidrauski, and Stiglitz [15] and Hahn [5]. If money is held only for asset purposes, then the expected money yield on capital, r, must equal zero, the money yield on money. For if $r > 0$, and if the variance of expected returns does not matter, as it would not in a model with perfect certainty, then everyone would want to hold all his wealth in the form of capital, whereas if $r < 0$, desired portfolios would consist only of money.[7] Consequently, pure speculation models are equivalent to the special case in which (4) becomes

$$r = \varphi(k, x) \equiv 0. \tag{4a}$$

Case 4 If money is desired both for speculative and transaction purposes, as in the Keynesian tradition, then $g(k, r)$ is not necessarily homogeneous of degree one in k. The dynamic characteristics of a complete growth model will depend on the properties of $g(k, r)$. In the next section we will assume certain specific properties; these properties, which may have some economic justification, enable us to provide a complete description of the dynamic characteristics of our model.

---

[6] See, e.g., Modigliani [8] pp. 104–105.

[7] Since $r = f'(k) - \delta + E(\dot{p}/p)$, $r = 0$ implies $f'(k) - \delta = -E(\dot{p}/p)$. But, as $p_m \equiv 1/p$, the latter implies $f'(k) - \delta = E(\dot{p}_m/p_m)$, an equation that says that the net real rate of return on capital must equal the expected real rate of return on money. See Samuelson [14], pp. 488–496, for the observation that these conditions are characteristic of perfect capital markets under perfect certainty.

It is important to realize that Cases 1–4 represent different assumptions about economic behavior, and in principle one or more of them could be rejected or accepted for either theoretical or empirical reasons. In Case 1 the concern is with portfolio balance as first discussed by Tobin [21, 22], whereas Case 2 can be regarded as a modified version of the quantity theory of money. Case 3 is very special, and we examine it separately in Section 5-10.

Our preference, therefore, is Case 4, which is not only in the Keynesian tradition but which also provides most general representation in the sense that it includes all the behavioral motivations that underlie the other cases.

6–3. Behavioral Hypotheses

As already noted the equilibrium condition (1) may be taken to yield functions

$$x = g(k, r) \tag{3}$$

and

$$r = \varphi(k, x) \tag{4}$$

defined for relevant ranges of the variables k, x, and r. In all that follows, we shall assume that the capital/labor ratio is bounded away from zero, i.e.,

$$k \geq \varepsilon > 0. \tag{7}$$

We assume also $g(k, r)$ has the property, that, given any k, $0 < \varepsilon \leq k < \infty$, there exists a sufficiently large finite value $\bar{r} = \bar{r}(k)$ such that

$$g[k, \bar{r}(k)] = 0. \tag{8}$$

Since

$$r = f'(k) - \delta + E(\dot{p}/p), \tag{9}$$

this assumption states that corresponding to any finite, positive value of the capital/labor ratio k there exists some expected rate of price inflation, $E(\dot{p}/p)$, at which the per capita demand for real money balances is zero. In other words, given a fixed k, we assume there exists a yield $\bar{r}(k)$ on the alternative asset so large that no money balances are desired and the economy resorts to barter or manages to synchronize payments and purchases perfectly.

We further assume that the function $\bar{r}(k)$ has the shape illustrated in Figure 18 with $\infty > \bar{r}(k) > 0$, $\bar{r}'(k) > 0$, $0 < \varepsilon \leq k < \infty$ and $\lim_{k \to \infty} \bar{r}(k) \equiv \bar{R} \leq \infty$. Note that the condition $\bar{r}(k) > 0$ implies that there is a positive transactions demand for money; the case in which there is no transactions demand is treated as the case of pure speculative demand in Section 6-10.[8]

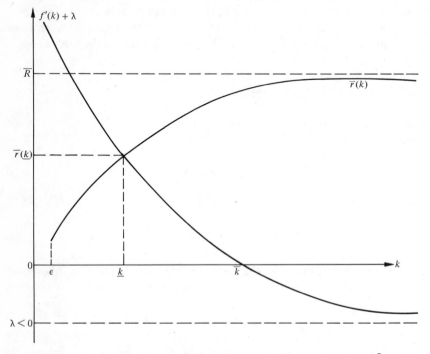

Figure 18. *A graph of the function $\bar{r}(k)$ is illustrated. The numbers $\underline{k}$ and $\bar{k}$ and the parameter λ will be defined later in the text.*

We also require

$$\bar{R} > \lambda$$

where $\lambda \equiv \theta - \delta - n$, $n \equiv \dot{L}/L$, and $\theta \equiv \dot{M}/M$ is the constant rate of increase in the nominal stock of money.[9] Observe that $\bar{R} > \lambda$ whenever $n + \delta$ exceeds θ and λ is negative, the case that seems most likely to prevail for reasonable values of the parameters.

---

[8] Setting $x = 0$ and $r = \bar{r}(k)$ in (3), we may derive $\bar{r}'(k) = -g_1/g_2 > 0$ as an implication of $g_1 > 0$ and $g_2 < 0$.

[9] It is assumed that the value of θ is set exogenously by the government and maintained constant forever.

The exact role of these assumptions will become clear in the subsequent discussion; essentially it is to ensure the existence and uniqueness of a steady state with positive money balances. Alternative assumptions, e.g., restrictions on the elasticities of x with respect to k and r, serve the same purpose.[10]

Finally, we impose the following commonly invoked regularity conditions on the per capita production function $f(k)$:

$$f(k) > 0, \quad 0 < k < \infty; \qquad f(0) = 0; \qquad f(\infty) = \infty;$$

$$f'(k) > 0, \quad 0 < k < \infty; \qquad f'(0) = \infty;$$

$$f'(\infty) = 0; \qquad f''(k) < 0, \qquad 0 < k < \infty.$$

The latter conditions are not indispensable, but they do avoid difficulties that might arise at boundaries and are therefore convenient for our present expository purposes.[11]

6–4. A Digression: The Liquidity Trap and Disequilibrium Dynamics

For any positive, finite value of the capital/labor ratio there may exist a positive expected yield on capital so low (that is, the expectation of capital losses may be so strong) that no one wishes to hold his wealth in the form of capital. In such a situation the equilibrium level of per capita real money balances becomes indefinitely large, a situation that corresponds to the traditional Keynesian liquidity trap illustrated in Figure 19.

Whether or not such liquidity traps exist for different values of k within the relevant region is of no consequence in our model. The reason for this fact is that we have assumed the money market is always in equilibrium with equality between the exogenously given m and the money demand m^d, as stated by equation (1). This equality must be achieved by instantaneous adjustments in the expected rate of inflation.

The exact mechanism is most easily seen if we take the expected rate of inflation to be always equal to the actual rate of inflation, i.e.,

$$E(\dot{p}/p) = \dot{p}/p. \tag{10}$$

This assumption is sometimes referred to as the assumption of *perfect myopic foresight*, and until stated otherwise we will assume (10) holds. Accordingly,

[10] See, e.g. Sidrauski [16], p. 800.
[11] Chapter 2 has already indicated the type of qualifications necessary to take care of the various boundary cases likely to arise if these assumptions are violated.

we find from (9) that the expected money yield on capital is

$$r = f'(k) - \delta + \dot{p}/p. \tag{11}$$

Consider now any point in time with known k and x. Stock equilibrium in the money market necessitates that (4) be satisfied, which together with (11) implies that the rate of inflation required for portfolio equilibrium is

$$\dot{p}/p = r - f'(k) + \delta = \varphi(k, x) - f'(k) + \delta. \tag{12}$$

Thus, $\dot{p}/p$ is a function only of k and x, and we may view (12) as determining the rate of inflation that establishes stock equilibrium in the money market. Therefore we have assumed implicitly that $\dot{p}/p$ adjusts instantaneously to satisfy (12), and with such perfectly flexible prices a full-employment solution is ensured even if there are liquidity traps.

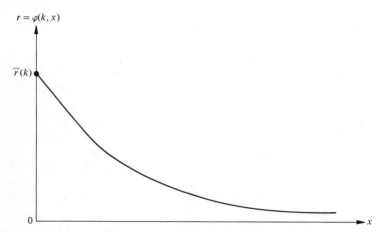

Figure 19. *Consider a fixed value of k, $0 < \varepsilon \leqq k$. The equilibrium level of per capita real money balances becomes infinite as r decreases toward zero, and everyone then would want to hold all his wealth in the form of money. The latter is possible, of course, for fixed values of k ($0 < \varepsilon \leqq k < \infty$) and m only if the price level p becomes zero.*

Alternatively, the equilibrium condition (1) may be dropped and a dis-equilibrium model can be constructed by assuming that the rate of inflation is a function of the excess flow supply of real balances.[12] Suppose, in addition, the excess flow supply is equal to the excess stock supply times an appropriate

[12] The following discussion follows Stein [18].

proportionality factor. We then may assume the rate of inflation is determined by a simple functional form such as

$$\dot{p}/p = \gamma[x - g(k, r)] \tag{13}$$

where $\gamma > 0$ is the finite speed of adjustment.[13] Equation (13) has a simple interpretation, namely when the actual flow supply exceeds the desired flow supply of real balances, then there is inflation; a rising p *lowers* the value of per capita real money balances since $x = m/p$. Accordingly, a positive rate of inflation reduces the excess flow supply of real balances. Similar reasoning applies when the excess supply is negative, and $\dot{p}/p = 0$ if and only if there is equilibrium in the money market with a zero excess flow (and, by assumption, also stock) supply of per capita real balances.

Walras' law implies that the sum of the excess flow supplies must equal zero. Suppose desired net saving and desired net investment in the form of capital are S and I, respectively, and are functions of k, x, and L (population). The excess flow demand for capital is then

$$I - S,$$

and Walras' law is expressed by

$$I - S - (\dot{p}/p)/\gamma = 0. \tag{14}$$

The crucial problem is to determine the actual rate of net capital formation in these circumstances. Stein [18, 19, 20] and Rose [10, 11, 12] impose arbitrarily the hypothesis that the actual rate of net capital formation is some linear function of net desired investment and saving in capital, i.e.,

$$\dot{K} = \alpha I + (1 - \alpha)S \tag{15}$$

where α is an exogenous *constant* between zero and one. On the other hand, Nagatani [9] assumes the investment plan is always realized, which is equivalent to setting $\alpha = 1$ in (15).

If we accept (15), the actual rate of net capital formation is, by substitution from (14),

$$\dot{K} = \alpha(\dot{p}/p)/\gamma + S. \tag{16}$$

Since S is a function of k, x, and L, an equation for the actual change in the capital/labor ratio can be derived from (13) and (16) and is of the form

$$\dot{k} = \dot{k}(k, x). \tag{17}$$

---

[13] By rescaling the parameter γ, we may always choose the proportionality factor to be unity.

This disequilibrium approach is interesting primarily because the possibility of unemployment can arise in such models; see, e.g., Rose [10, 11, 12]. The serious difficulty, however, is that there is no economic mechanism to determine α, and the assumption that α is an exogenous constant, perhaps determined by the institutional environment, seems most implausible. Indeed, we agree with Hahn when he says,

> One has, in the present state of knowledge, great latitude in the construction of disequilibrium models; that is one of the reasons they are so unattractive and so great a variety of results can be produced.[14]

We therefore analyze a simple dynamic equilibrium model; in so doing we emphasize money market clearing conditions and portfolio balance, thus following the tradition set by Tobin [21, 22].

6–5. The Saving Hypothesis

Following Tobin [21, 22], we define *real wealth* and *real net disposable income*[15] by

$$W = K + M/p \tag{18}$$

and

$$Y = F(K, L) - \delta K + d(M/p)/dt \tag{19}$$

respectively. Since real total output is identically equal to consumption (C) plus depreciation (δK) plus net capital formation ($\dot{K}$), i.e. since

$$F(K, L) \equiv C + \delta K + \dot{K}, \tag{20}$$

we find that

$$Y = \dot{W} + C. \tag{21}$$

In other words, real net disposable income is equal to the change in real wealth plus real consumption, which is the rationale behind the definition (19). We assume that real consumption is always a constant (exogenous) fraction of real net disposable income:

$$C = (1 - s)Y, \qquad 0 < s < 1. \tag{22}$$

---

[14] Hahn [5].
[15] Note that the term "real" means "deflated by the price level p."

Equation (22) is a flow equilibrium condition satisfied at all points in time; clearly it may be written in the equivalent form

$$\dot{W} = sY. \tag{23}$$

It should be noted that all variables are deflated by the price level and hence are measured in *real* terms. Alternatively, the *money* value of wealth is

$$\overline{W} = pK + M = pW, \tag{24}$$

and if we insist on the flow equilibrium condition

$$\overline{Y} = \dot{\overline{W}} + pC, \tag{25}$$

which is analogous to (21), then the *money* value of net disposable income must equal

$$\overline{Y} = pF(K, L) - p\delta K + \dot{M} + \dot{p}K \neq pY.$$

Consequently, if $pC = (1 - s)\overline{Y}$, we conclude that the capital gains on the capital stock $\dot{p}K$ influence the money value of consumption, and therefore the two foregoing formulations are not equivalent.

Whether or not the savings-consumption behavior of an actual economy is best described in real or money terms is presumably a matter that can be tested empirically. However, behavioral relations cast in money terms may imply the existence of *money illusion*[16]; therefore we will use the Tobin formulation in real terms given by equations (18)–(23).

Finally, it is crucial to realize that equations (18)–(23) may not be consistent with the requirement that total consumption never exceed gross output, i.e., that

$$(1 - s)Y = C \leq F(K, L). \tag{26}$$

Whenever (26) is violated, the model itself breaks down and must be rejected. We shall return to this observation later in Section 6-7.

6–6. Derivation and Properties of $\dot{x} = \dot{x}(k, x)$

From the definition of real per capita money balances $x \equiv M/pL$, we derive

$$\dot{x} = \left(\frac{\dot{M}}{M} - \frac{\dot{L}}{L} - \frac{\dot{p}}{p}\right)x = (\theta - n - \dot{p}/p)x. \tag{27}$$

[16] See, e.g., Shell, Sidrauski, and Stiglitz [15].

The equation

$$\dot{x} = \dot{x}(k, x) = [f'(k) + \lambda - \varphi(k, x)]x \tag{28}$$

follows by substitution from (12) where $\lambda \equiv \theta - \delta - n$. We should like to know the behavior implied by this equation.

Consider the case $x = 0$; clearly $\dot{x} = 0$ if the bracketed term in (28) is finite, and the latter must equal

$$f'(k) + \lambda - \varphi(k, 0) \equiv f'(k) + \lambda - \bar{r}(k). \tag{29}$$

Since by assumption the terms $\bar{r}(k)$ and $f'(k)$ are both finite for $0 < \varepsilon \leq k < \infty$, we conclude that

$$\dot{x}(k, 0) = 0, \qquad 0 < \varepsilon \leq k < \infty. \tag{30}$$

Now consider $x > 0$; then $\dot{x}(k, x) = 0$ if and only if

$$H(k, x) \equiv f'(k) + \lambda - \varphi(k, x) = 0. \tag{31}$$

Because

$$H_x = -\varphi_x > 0,$$

$H(k, x) = 0$ may be solved for

$$x = h(k) = g[k, f'(k) + \lambda] \tag{32}$$

where $h'(k) > 0$ (Exercise 2). A solution to (32) is meaningful only if $x > 0$, which necessitates $f'(k) + \lambda < \bar{r}(k)$. Accordingly, $\dot{x} = 0$, $x > 0$, whenever

$$x = h(k), \qquad k > \underline{k}, \tag{33}$$

where $\underline{k}$ is defined as the root to

$$f'(k) + \lambda = \bar{r}(k).$$

Clearly such a $\underline{k} > 0$ exists and is unique, as shown in Figure 18.

The complete locus of points along which $\dot{x} = 0$ is illustrated by the heavy lines in Figure 20. If there exists a liquidity trap and

$$g[\bar{k}, f'(\bar{k}) + \lambda]$$

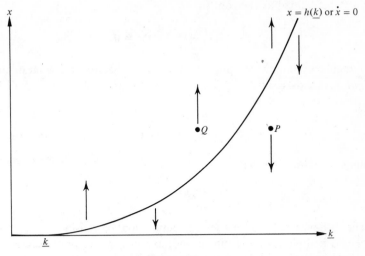

Figure 20

becomes *infinite* as k approaches some sufficiently large value $\bar{k}$, then the curve $h(k)$ has an asymptote at $k = \bar{k}$ and is defined only for $\underline{k} < k < \bar{k}$.[17] However, as already noted, this issue is of no consequence for our model.

Consider any point

$$(k, x) > [h^{-1}(x), 0]$$

which is to the right of $h(k)$ and above the k-axis, as is point P in Figure 20. Examination of (28) reveals that $\dot{x} < 0$ at any such point, as indicated by the arrows in Figure 20. Similarly, $\dot{x} > 0$ at any point such as Q, to the left of $x = h(k)$.

6–7. Derivation and Properties of $\dot{k} = \dot{k}(k, x)$

Manipulation of (18)–(23) and (27) yields

$$\dot{k} = sf(k) - (n + s\delta)k - (1 - s)(\theta - \dot{p}/p)x \qquad \textbf{(34a)}$$

$$= sf(k) - (n + s\delta)k - (1 - s)(\dot{x} + nx) \qquad \textbf{(34b)}$$

(Exercise 3), and substituting (12) in (34a) we obtain

$$\dot{k} = \dot{k}(k, x) = sf(k) - (n + s\delta)k - (1 - s)[f'(k) - \delta + \theta - \varphi(k, x)]x. \qquad \textbf{(35)}$$

---

[17] If λ is in fact negative, then there presumably will exist such a $\bar{k}$, no larger than the value of k satisfying $f'(k) + \lambda = 0$; see Figure 18.

Let k^{**} be defined as the root to

$$sf(k) - (n + s\delta)k = 0.$$

The regularity conditions imposed on $f(k)$ in Section 6-3 guarantee that a *unique* root exists satisfying $0 < \varepsilon \leq k^{**} < \infty$ for sufficiently small ε. Consequently, since

$$f'(k^{**}) - \delta + \theta - \varphi(k^{**}, 0) = f'(k^{**}) - \delta + \theta - \bar{r}(k^{**})$$

is finite, we conclude that

$$\dot{k}(k^{**}, 0) = 0.$$

The behavior of the model for any initial conditions $k^0 \geq \varepsilon > 0$ and $x^0 = 0$ is completely determined, and, except for interpretation, is identical to the one-sector model discussed in Chapter 2.[18]

A simple one-sector model without money in which *net* capital formation is a constant fraction (s) of *net* income implies the differential equation

$$\dot{k} = sf(k) - (n + s\delta)k = \dot{k}(k) \tag{36}$$

with $\dot{k}(k^{**}) = 0$ (Exercise 4). The behavior of such a model is completely illustrated in Figure 21; note that k^{**} is a stable equilibrium.

Our objective is to find a solution $(k^*, x^*) > (0, 0)$ for which

$$\dot{k}(k^*, x^*) = \dot{x}(k^*, x^*) = 0.$$

Since for $k \leq \underline{k}$, $\dot{x} = 0$ only if $x = 0$ (see Figure 20), we need deal only with the case where

$$\underline{k} < k^{**}. \tag{37}$$

(We know that if (37) is not satisfied, then $\dot{x} = 0$ can occur only for $x \equiv 0$; and when $x \equiv 0$, $\dot{k} = 0$ can occur only at $(k^{**}, 0)$. Hence we need consider only the case $\underline{k} < k^{**}$.)

---

[18] In this case stocks of nominal money are forever zero, and equation (12) yields

$$\dot{p}/p = \bar{r}(k) - f'(k) + \delta.$$

Prices do not themselves affect anything in this model with no money, however; nevertheless, the price change may be interpreted as essential to ensure that the existing capital stock is willingly held and the rate of accumulation dictated by (35) is maintained. It is in this sense that the Solow model of Chapter 2 implicitly involves capital goods prices, and it is this kind of price equation that links the stable Solow model to unstable models of optimal saving. We return to this issue briefly in Chapter 11.

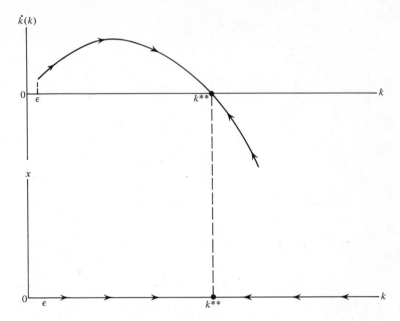

Figure 21. *Behavior of the model with no money balances and $x \equiv 0$ for all t.*

Consider now the equation

$$\dot{k}(k, x) = sf(k) - (n + s\delta)k - (1 - s)[f'(k) - \delta + \theta - \varphi(k, x)]x = 0,$$

$$x > 0,\ 0 < \varepsilon \leqq k < k^{**}.$$
(38)

Calculating

$$\frac{\partial \dot{k}}{\partial x} = (1 - s)\varphi_x x - (1 - s)[f'(k) - \delta + \theta - \varphi(k, x)],$$

we see that

$$\left.\frac{\partial \dot{k}}{\partial x}\right|_{\dot{k}=0} < 0, \qquad x > 0,\ 0 < \varepsilon \leqq k < k^{**},$$

because (1) $\varphi_x < 0$, and (2) $f'(k) - \delta + \theta - \varphi(k, x) = [sf(k) - (n + s\delta)k]/(1 - s)x > 0$ when $\dot{k} = 0$, $x > 0$, and $0 < \varepsilon \leqq k < k^{**}$. Thus there exists a function $x = x(k) > 0$, $0 < \varepsilon \leqq k < k^{**}$, $x(k^{**}) = 0$, obtained by solving the implicit equation $\dot{k} = 0$. This function is shown in Figure 22 where the

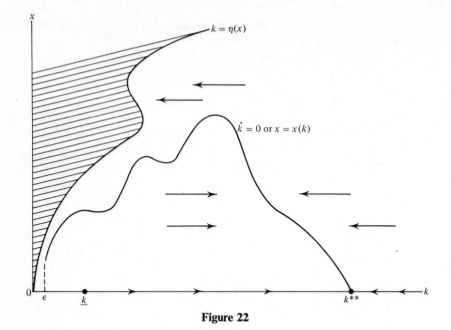

Figure 22

arrows indicate motion in the k-direction at points not on the $x = x(k)$ locus.[19]

We must now return to the important observation made at the end of Section 6-5, namely, consumption can never exceed gross output. Consider first the case in which

$$(1 - s)Y = C = F(K, L)$$

or

$$\Lambda(k, x) = x(\theta - \dot{p}/p) - sf(k)/(1 - s) + \delta k = 0.$$

Since

$$\frac{\partial \Lambda}{\partial k} = x(-\varphi_k + f'') - sf'/(1 - s) - \delta < 0,$$

there exists a function $k = \eta(x)$ along which $C = F(K, L)$, but the sign of

[19] Apparently the possibility of points $(k, x) > (k^{**}, 0)$ at which $\dot{k}(k, x) = 0$ has not been ruled out, but the matter is not sufficiently important to pursue here because there cannot exist an equilibrium point with $\dot{k} = \dot{x} = 0$ for $k > k^{**}$.

$\eta'(x)$ is indeterminate. Moreover, it can be proved that the locus of points for which

$$C \geqq F(K, L),$$

lies entirely above the $\dot{k} = 0$ curve in the k-x plane (Exercise 5).

Accordingly, our model is valid only for points that are on or below the curve $k = \eta(x)$. In other words, there is a region in the k-x plane, indicated by the shaded area in Figure 22, for which our behavioral hypotheses simply are not satisfied and the model ceases to make sense. This situation is not surprising; for "extreme" values of the economic variables, there is every reason to expect that the behavior of the economic agents in the community will change, and then our model is no longer valid. We shall simply avoid this difficulty by invoking the following assumption.

Define the set

$$\Omega \equiv \{(k, x) \mid 0 < \varepsilon \leqq k < \infty \quad \text{and} \quad k \geqq \eta(x)\}.$$

In all our subsequent discussion we shall assume $(k, x) \in \Omega$, although for expositional convenience we neither mention this fact again nor indicate the set Ω in our later illustrations.

6–8. Existence and Uniqueness of a Positive Equilibrium (k^*, x^*)

The existence of at least one equilibrium solution $(k^*, x^*) > (0, 0)$ satisfying

$$\dot{k}(k^*, x^*) = \dot{x}(k^*, x^*) = 0$$

is already implied by combining Figures 20 and 22. More formally, however, assume $\dot{x} = 0$, $x > 0$; then (31) and (32) must both be satisfied, and substituting these into (35) we find

$$\Psi(k) \equiv \dot{k}\big|_{\dot{x}=0,\, x>0} = sf(k) - (n + s\delta)k - (1 - s)ng[k, f'(k) + \lambda]. \tag{39}$$

Observe that

(i) $sf(k) - (n + s\delta)k > 0, \qquad 0 < \varepsilon \leqq k < k^{**},$
(ii) $g[\underline{k}, f'(\underline{k}) + \lambda] = 0,$
(iii) $\underline{k} < k^{**},$ by assumption (37).

Consequently,

$$\Psi(\underline{k}) > 0.$$

As $\Psi(k)$ is a continuous function in k, the existence of a root k^* satisfying $\Psi(k^*) = 0$, $\underline{k} < k < k^{**}$, is ensured if

$$\lim_{k \to k^{**}} \Psi(k) < 0.$$

But

$$\lim_{k \to k^{**}} g[k, f'(k) + \lambda] = \lim_{k \to k^{**}} h(k) = h(k^{**}),$$

and $h(k^{**}) > 0$ because $h(\underline{k}) = 0$, $h'(k) > 0$, $\underline{k} < k < \infty$. Thus,

$$\lim_{k \to k^{**}} \Psi(k) = -n(1 - s)h(k^{**}) < 0.$$

The *uniqueness* of such a root k^* is guaranteed if

$$\Psi'(k)|_{\Psi(k)=0} < 0. \tag{40}$$

At the present level of generality, however, it may be impossible to justify (40), and we choose instead to invoke the following assumption: *The elasticity of $x = h(k)$, $\underline{k} < k < \infty$, is larger than one,*[20] i.e.,

$$kh'(k)/h(k) > 1$$

or

$$h'(k) > h(k)/k, \quad \underline{k} < k < \infty. \tag{41}$$

Consider a new function defined by

$$\Gamma(k) \equiv \Psi(k)/(1 - s)n = \frac{sf(k) - (n + s\delta)k}{(1 - s)n} - h(k) \tag{42}$$

and let

$$\gamma(k) \equiv [sf(k) - (n + s\delta)k]/(1 - s)n. \tag{43}$$

---

[20] This assumption can be illustrated by Figure 20; it implies that a line drawn from the origin to any point on the curve $x = h(k)$ has a slope *less* than that of the tangent to the curve at the corresponding point. See also Sidrauski [16], p. 800. Exercise 17 asks the reader to prove that (41) is always satisfied for the portfolio balance case in which (5) holds.

Clearly any root k^* to $\Psi(k) = 0$ also satisfies $\Gamma(k^*) = 0$. Since the elasticity of $\gamma(k)$ is smaller than one for all $0 < k < k^{**}$ (Exercise 6),

$$\gamma'(k) < \gamma(k)/k. \tag{44}$$

Now the condition

$$\Gamma(k) = \gamma(k) - h(k) = 0$$

for some k satisfying $\underline{k} < k < k^{**}$, together with (41) and (44), implies

$$\gamma'(k) < \gamma(k)/k = h(k)/k < h'(k) \tag{45}$$

at this value of k. Thus,

$$\Gamma'(k)|_{\Gamma(k)=0} = \gamma'(k) - h'(k) < 0,$$

and the uniqueness of a root k^* is proved. The foregoing proof is illustrated by Figure 23; note also that a root to $\Psi(k) = 0$ or $\Gamma(k) = 0$ is impossible for $k > k^{**}$.

Now let

$$x^* = h(k^*)$$

and we have proved Theorem 1.

Theorem 1: *Assume equations* (3), (4), (8), (10), (18)–(23), (26), *and* (41) *are all satisfied, in addition to the regularity conditions stated in the text. Then, there exists a unique root* k^*, $0 < \varepsilon \leqq k^* < k^{**}$, *and a unique corresponding root* $x^* = h(k^*) > 0$ *such that*

$$\dot{k}(k^*, x^*) = \dot{x}(k^*, x^*) = 0.^{21}$$

Before turning to the stability properties of (k^*, x^*), we conclude this section with some comparative statics. Suppose the government increases θ, the exogenous rate of growth of the nominal money stock $\dot{M}/M$. If no other parameters change, we may ask the effect on (k^*, x^*). Since (39) implies that

$$sf(k^*) - (n + s\delta)k^* - (1 - s)ng[k^*, f'(k^*) + \lambda] = 0 \tag{46}$$

[21] Observe that $(k^*, x^*) \in \Omega$, the feasible set defined in the previous section for which our behavioral hypotheses are consistent and assumed valid. This conclusion follows directly from (d) in Exercise 5.

and $\lambda = \theta - n - \delta$, we find that

$$\frac{dk^*}{d\theta} = \frac{(1-s)ng_2}{sf' - (n+s\delta) - (1-s)n(g_1 + g_2 f'')}\bigg|_{(k^*,\, x^*)}. \qquad (47)$$

However, we have proved $\Gamma'(k^*) < 0$, which implies that $\Psi'(k^*) < 0$. But the denominator of (47) is simply $\Psi'(k^*)$, as seen from (39), whereas g_2 is negative. Thus,

$$\frac{dk^*}{d\theta} > 0.$$

Similarly, it may be proved that

$$\frac{dx^*}{d\theta} \gtreqqless 0 \qquad \text{as} \qquad k^* \lesseqqgtr \tilde{k},$$

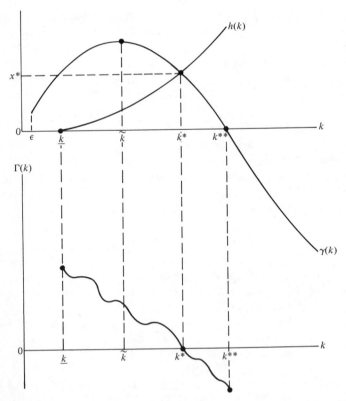

Figure 23

where $\tilde{k}$ is the unique root to both $sf'(k) - (n + s\delta) = 0$ and $\gamma'(k) = 0$ (Exercise 7). When $\dot{x} = 0$, the rate of inflation is

$$\left(\frac{\dot{p}}{p}\right)^* = \theta - n \tag{48}$$

as seen from (27). Thus,

$$d(\dot{p}/p)^*/d\theta = 1.$$

The conclusion, of course, is that "money matters," at least in a comparative statics sense. Comparing only *equilibrium* positions $(k^*, x^*) > (0, 0)$, we have deduced that an increase in the nominal rate of monetary expansion will

(i) Always increase the equilibrium capital/labor ratio k^*,
(ii) Increase or decrease the equilibrium value of per capita real balances x^* as $k^* \gtreqless \tilde{k}$, and
(iii) Increase the equilibrium rate of inflation $(\dot{p}/p)^*$.

Two further observations are important.

(iv) In equilibrium the rate of price change $(\dot{p}/p)^*$ may be either positive, negative, or zero, as $\theta \gtreqless n$. Since there is only one policy parameter in this model, once θ is chosen the equilibrium point (k^*, x^*) is completely determined.
(v) The equilibrium point *without* money, $(k^{**}, 0)$, has a higher capital/labor ratio than the equilibrium point with money, $(k^*, x^*) > (0, 0)$, i.e., $k^* < k^{**}$. In this very narrow sense, the existence of a government debt—which in this case consists of only paper currency—is a "burden" because the equilibrium capital/labor ratio k^* is smaller than k^{**}.[22] We note, however, that this burden is negative if k^{**} exceeds the Golden Rule capital/labor ratio, for then per capita consumption is increased by a reduction in the capital/labor ratio.

6–9. Stability Properties of Equilibrium Points

The qualitative behavior of the possible time paths (k^t, x^t) is illustrated in Figure 24. Observe that the (k^*, x^*) equilibrium is a *saddlepoint*, and therefore

[22] Note also that (i) and (ii) above imply that for $k > \tilde{k}$ an increase in θ will increase k^* and decrease x^*. As θ continues to increase, the equilibrium point occurs closer to $(k^{**}, 0)$, and in the limit with infinitely high rates of expansion of the nominal money supply, the rate of price change becomes infinite; apparently the economy then reverts to a situation in which real per capita money balances $x \to 0$ because $p \to \infty$. Alternatively, for sufficiently large θ, we may find a solution to $0 = g[k^{**}, f'(k^{**}) + \theta - n]$. Indeed if $0 = g[k, \bar{r}(k)]$ holds for $k = k^{**}$, which is the barter case, then we can always find a θ so large that $f'(k^{**}) + \theta - n = \bar{r}(k^{**})$ since $f'' < 0$ and $\bar{r}' > 0$.

$\lim_{t\to\infty}(k^t, x^t) = (k^*, x^*)$ only from initial positions (k^0, x^0) lying on the heavy curve labeled AA. On the other hand, the $(k^{**}, 0)$ equilibrium point is stable, and $\lim_{t\to\infty}(k^t, x^t) = (k^{**}, 0)$ starting from all initial positions (k^0, x^0) lying below the AA curve.

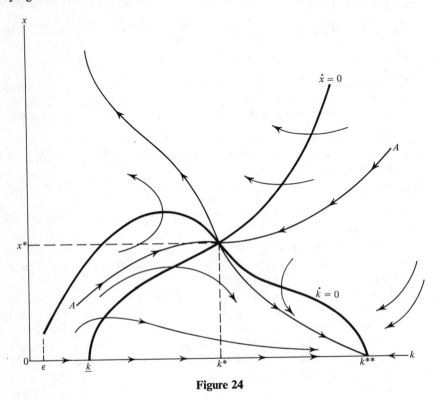

Figure 24

The exact manner in which the economy might approach the $(k^{**}, 0)$ equilibrium depends on the values of the parameters. Of course

$$x^t = (M^0/L^0)e^{(\theta - n)t}/p^t \tag{49}$$

is always valid. Now if $(M^0/L^0) > 0$, which is necessary for $x^0 > 0$, and, if further $\theta \geqq n$, then

$$\lim_{t\to\infty} x^t = 0$$

implies

$$\lim_{t\to\infty} p^t = \infty.$$

The reason is simple: if initially M^0 is positive and the government increases the nominal money stock so fast that the per capita money stock rises, then the price level must become infinite if real per capita money balances become zero.

On the other hand, a slower rate of increase in the nominal money stock, with $\theta < n$, implies that

$$\lim_{t \to \infty} x^t = 0$$

for any value of

$$\lim_{t \to \infty} p^t > 0.$$

The asymptotic behavior of the model starting from initial points (k^0, x^0) above the AA curve is not evident. However, this matter is not of sufficient economic interest to pursue here.[23]

For completeness we now show that (k^*, x^*) is locally a saddlepoint. It is sufficient to prove that

$$\det J^* < 0$$

where

$$J^* = \begin{bmatrix} J_{11}^* & J_{12}^* \\ J_{21}^* & J_{22}^* \end{bmatrix}$$

is the Jacobian of the system

$$\dot{k} = \dot{k}(k, x), \qquad \dot{x} = \dot{x}(k, x)$$

evaluated at the equilibrium point (k^*, x^*). It is easily verified (Exercise 8) that

$$(\partial \dot{k}/\partial k)^* = J_{11}^* = sf' - (n + s\delta) - (1 - s)(-\varphi_k + f'')x$$
$$(\partial \dot{k}/\partial x)^* = J_{12}^* = (1 - s)(\varphi_x x - n) < 0$$
$$(\partial \dot{x}/\partial k)^* = J_{21}^* = (f'' - \varphi_k)x < 0$$
$$(\partial \dot{x}/\partial x)^* = J_{22}^* = -\varphi_x x > 0.$$

---

[23] Apparently all such trajectories eventually pass out of the feasible set Ω, in which case our model no longer makes sense. Exactly the same difficulty arises in the paper by Shell, Sidrauski, and Stiglitz [15], although their interpretation differs slightly from ours. In any event, further discussion of the issue is beyond the scope of this chapter.

Consequently, $\det J^* < 0$ if and only if

$$J_{11}^* J_{22}^* - J_{12}^* J_{21}^* = -\varphi_x x[sf' - (n + s\delta)] + (1 - s)nx(f'' - \varphi_k) < 0 \quad (50)$$

(Exercise 9). Furthermore, we have proved that

$$\Psi'(k) = sf' - (n + s\delta) - (1 - s)n[g_1 + g_2 f''] < 0 \quad (51)$$

at (k^*, x^*), whereas by straight-forward calculation

$$g_1 + g_2 f'' = (f'' - \varphi_k)/\varphi_x. \quad (52)$$

Multiplying (51) by $-\varphi_x x > 0$ and substituting from (52), we conclude that (50) is valid and $\det J^* < 0$, as was to be proven.

6–10. Another Digression: The Pure Speculative Motive

We have already observed in Section 6-2 that in some models there is no transactions demand for money, in which case the existing money stock will be held if and only if the expected yield on the only other asset, capital, is equal to zero, the yield on money. In such instances where "money" is not used for transaction purposes, it may be thought of as the outstanding government debt, which, accordingly, no longer need be nonnegative. Thus, if "per capita real 'money' balances" are negative $(x < 0)$, the interpretation is simply that the public is in debt to the government. Under these circumstances it may be convenient to think of "bonds" rather than "money".[24]

Equations (4a), (11), and (27) imply that

$$\dot{x} = \dot{x}(k, x) = [\theta - n - \delta + f'(k)]x = [f'(k) + \lambda]x, \quad (53)$$

while (4a), (11), and (34a) imply

$$\dot{k} = \dot{k}(k, x) = sf(k) - (n + s\delta)k - (1 - s)[f'(k) - \delta + \theta]x. \quad (54)$$

We will confine our attention to $x \neq 0$, and consequently k^* is determined by (53) alone provided that λ is negative, a necessary assumption if this model is to be meaningful. In other words, the rate of nominal money expansion (θ) must be less than the sum of population growth and depreciation $(n + \delta)$.

Shell, Sidrauski, and Stiglitz [15] have studied this system, and they have proved that $(k^*, x^*) > 0$ is a saddlepoint, whereas $(k^{**}, 0)$ is locally stable, with $k^* < k^{**}$. These results seem exactly the same as those we obtained in

---

[24] See [15].

the previous section, but there is one crucial difference, namely, the possibility of an equilibrium point (k^*, x^*) with $k^* > k^{**} > 0$ and $x^* < 0$ cannot be excluded. Moreover, the stability properties of the latter equilibrium point are drastically different.

The phase diagram for the latter situation is pictured in Figure 25. The crucial observations are

(i) The "no money equilibrium" $(k^{**}, 0)$ is now a saddlepoint with the k-axis as the stable arm.

(ii) The equilibrium with *negative* "money" (bonds) is locally stable, and, moreover, $k^* > k^{**}$.[25]

We now turn to the question of when $k^* > k^{**}$ so that Figure 25 prevails. Clearly it suffices to prove that

$$f(k^*)/k^* < f(k^{**})/k^{**}, \tag{55}$$

where as before,

$$f(k^{**})/k^{**} = (n/s) + \delta.$$

Let α be the relative share of capital at the equilibrium point (k^*, x^*), i.e.,

$$\alpha = k^* f'(k^*)/f(k^*);$$

then,

$$(n + \delta - \theta)/\alpha = f'(k^*)/\alpha = f(k^*)/k^*$$

at (k^*, x^*). Clearly, (55) holds if

$$(n + \delta - \theta)/\alpha < (n/s) + \delta$$

or if

$$\theta > \frac{n}{s}(s - \alpha) + (1 - \alpha)\delta. \tag{56}$$

For "reasonable" values of the parameters, we would certainly expect the right-hand side of (56) to be negative.[26] Accordingly, unless the government

---

[25] See Exercise 10.

[26] For example, $n(s - \alpha)/s + (1 - \alpha)\delta = 0.04(0.1 - 0.2)/0.1 + (1 - 0.2)(0.03) = -0.016$.

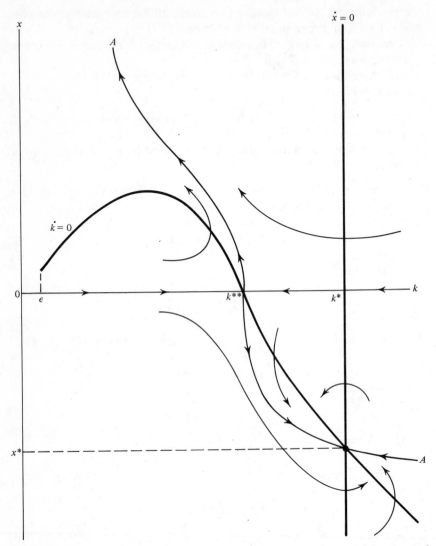

Figure 25. *The equilibrium point* $(k^{**}, 0)$ *with no money is now a saddlepoint, and the point* (k^*, x^*), $x^* < 0$, $k^* > k^{**}$, *is locally stable.*

selects a negative value of θ, we would expect that the situation depicted by Figure 25 is valid.

Given these observations, we reject the pure speculation money models as economically meaningless. Indeed, in such models money has no important role to perform, and it is not surprising that nonsensical conclusions can result.

6–11. Stability in a Simplified Model

In general there is a real balance effect—or, in other words "money matters"—if the equilibrium value of k^* is influenced by the monetary policy of the government, which in our case is represented by a single parameter θ. In our preceding discussion we have found that money does matter and that $dk^*/d\theta > 0$. This result, however, need not hold if the equation for k is independent of x (or θ).

For example, suppose that we postulate a simple rule: desired and realized net saving is a constant fraction (s) of net income and always equals realized net investment. This rule, although consistent with the one-sector models studied in Chapter 2, is unlike the more sophisticated saving behavior discussed in Section 6-5. For under this postulate,

$$\dot{k} = sf(k) - (n + s\delta)k, \tag{57}$$

and consequently $\dot{k}$ is independent of θ or x. Indeed, if (57) holds, then $\dot{k} = \dot{k}(k^*) = 0$ if and only if

$$f(k^*)/k^* = (n + s\delta)/s, \tag{58}$$

and by our previous notational convention we find that $k^* \equiv k^{**}$.[27] However, for analytical convenience it is useful at the moment to consider a model composed of (57) and (28), i.e.,

$$\dot{k} = \dot{k}(k) = sf(k) - (n + s\delta)k \tag{57}$$

and

$$\dot{x} = \dot{x}(k, x) = [f'(k) + \lambda - \varphi(k, x)]x. \tag{28}$$

We retain the assumptions previously stated in Sections 6-3, 6-4, and 6-6.[28].

We emphasize that the reason for substituting equation (57) in place of (35) is convenience alone. Real balance effects may be theoretically and/or empirically important, but their exclusion is a great analytical convenience in studying the present stability questions. Moreover, as the zealous reader

[27] The use of (57) led Johnson [6] into an error which has been corrected by Tobin [23], Nagatani [9], and others.

[28] However, it is important to realize that for this special case in which our model consists of (57) and (28), the set of (k, x) consistent with the behavioral equations is $\overline{\Omega} \equiv \{(k, x)| \ 0 < \varepsilon \leqq k < \infty$ and $0 \leqq x < \infty\} \supset \Omega$. In this sense also the version now being discussed is a simplification.

may verify, the qualitative conclusions that follow are not sensitive to our simplification, excepting the qualification made in the preceding footnote. Although we now consider (57) and (28), exactly the same results would be obtained in our more general model comprised of equations (35) and (28).

The new phase diagram is illustrated in Figure 26, but we leave its derivation as Exercise 11. The root k^* is now defined by (58), and as already noted, it is identical to k^{**} in our previous notation.

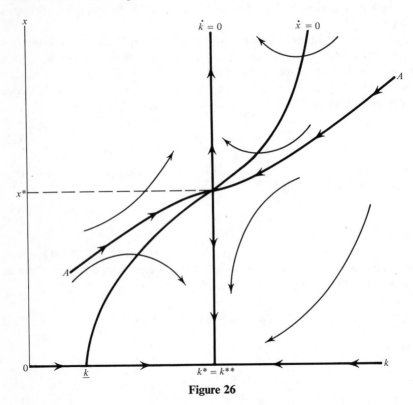

Figure 26

Observe the strong similarities between the phase diagrams depicted by Figures 24 and 26. In particular, in both instances (1) $(k^*, x^*) > (0, 0)$ is a saddlepoint, (2) the point $(k^*, 0)$ without money is stable, and (3) starting from any initial point (k^0, x^0) below the line AA,

$$\lim_{t \to \infty} k^t = k^*$$

and

$$\lim_{t \to \infty} x^t = 0.$$

We now wish to answer two crucial questions.

(i) Retain the perfect myopic foresight assumption $\dot{p}/p = E(\dot{p}/p)$. Is there any government policy $\theta = \theta^t$ that will result in a stable equilibrium $(k^*, x^*) > (0, 0)$?
(ii) Retain the assumption that the government sets $\theta = constant$. Is there any behavioral hypothesis about expectations for which $(k^*, x^*) > (0, 0)$ is stable?

The first question is easy to answer. Consider, for example, the policy

$$\theta^t = n + \delta + qr^t$$

where q is an exogenous constant; as before $\lambda \equiv \theta - \delta - n$ and

$$r^t = \varphi(k^t, x^t) = f'(k^t) - \delta + (\dot{p}/p)^t.^{29}$$

The system of equations now becomes

$$\dot{k} = \dot{k}(k) = sf(k) - (n + s\delta)k$$
$$\dot{x} = \dot{x}(k, x) = [f'(k) + (q - 1)\varphi(k, x)]x. \tag{59}$$

The derivation of (59) is Exercise 12.

Consider now the Jacobian determinant of the system (59) evaluated at the equilibrium point $(k^*, x^*) > (0, 0)$:

$$\det J^* = \det \begin{bmatrix} sf'(k^*) - (n + s\delta) & 0 \\ [f''(k^*) + (q - 1)\varphi_k(k^*, x^*)]x^* & (q - 1)\varphi_x(k^*, x^*)x^* \end{bmatrix}$$

with $\det J^* = J_{11}^* J_{22}^*$. Clearly, (k^*, x^*) is (locally) stable if both J_{11}^* and J_{22}^* are negative, for then

(i) $\det J^* > 0$,

and

(ii) Trace $J^* = J_{11}^* + J_{22}^* < 0$,

which are sufficient conditions. However, it is easy to show that $J_{11}^* < 0$ (Exercise 13), and clearly $J_{22}^* < 0$ for all $q > 1$ because $\varphi_x < 0$.

[29] As previously, the superscripts t denote time and are not exponents.

Closer examination of this stablizing policy is of interest. From (59) we see that

$$\frac{\dot{M}}{M} - \frac{\dot{p}}{p} - n \equiv \frac{\dot{x}}{x} = f'(k) + (q - 1)\varphi(k, x) \tag{60}$$

and

$$\theta^t = \frac{\dot{M}}{M} = q(\dot{p}/p) + qf'(k) + (1 - q)\delta + n \tag{61}$$

may be derived (Exercise 14).

Such a stabilizing policy may seem "perverse" because in times of "excessive" inflation, the stock of money is also increasing. Note, however, that the perversity is a consequence of the fact that p is an asset price—a perfect asset price—and p is only coincidentally a goods price because of the one-sector assumption. When should there be excessive inflation in this model? It is when the yield required on capital (required if the existing portfolios, i.e., capital and money stocks, are to be willingly held) is so high that it must consist primarily of expected capital gains. That is, people would really wish more money, but they are persuaded to hold the existing capital stock by the promise of very high capital gains. This situation can be interpreted as a case in which money is scarce relative to capital goods in the eyes of the portfolio managers. The stabilizing policy calls for the government to supply cash in these times of scarcity. What is perverse about that? Remember, there is simply no way a demand inflation can occur in this model because the goods market always clears.

Possible confusion about this issue may arise from a failure to distinguish goods prices and asset prices, and from a mistaken identification of this situation as an inflation resulting from rising goods market prices because people are trying to substitute money for goods. Here prices are rising because people have to be persuaded to hold goods as assets. Inflation in this model is a sign of scarcity of cash, high demand for money, and is not a sign of too many dollars chasing too few goods.

In the next section we turn to our second question, namely, is there a behavioral hypothesis other than perfect myopic foresight for which $(k^*, x^*) > (0, 0)$ is stable?

6–12. Adaptive Expectations

If we reject perfect myopic foresight, a behavioral replacement for

$$\dot{p}/p = E(\dot{p}/p) \tag{10}$$

must be found. We have already rejected a flow (or stock) adjustment mechanism of the form

$$\dot{p}/p = \gamma[x - g(k, x)] \tag{13}$$

(see Section 6-4). However, it is possible to retain the spirit of a dynamic equilibrium model without (10), and the *adaptive expectations* postulate is most convenient.

This postulate, used by Cagan [2], states that *the rate of adjustment in the current expected rate of inflation depends on the error made in predicting the current rate of change.* If we denote $E(\dot{p}/p)$ by π, the latter assumption is expressed in symbols by

$$\dot{\pi} = \beta(\dot{p}/p - \pi) \tag{62}$$

where $\beta \geq 0$ is the speed of adjustment in expectations. We may note that $\beta = 0$ and $\beta = \infty$ are analogous to " static expectations " and " perfect myopic foresight," respectively. In other words, larger values of β imply smaller time lags in the adjustment of expectations.

It is now convenient to work with the variables (k, π) instead of (k, x). We may calculate

$$\dot{x} = d[g(k, r)]/dt = [g_k \dot{k} + g_r \dot{r}]. \tag{63}$$

Similarly, we differentiate

$$r \equiv f'(k) - \delta + \pi,$$

and substituting into (63), obtain

$$\dot{x} = g_k \dot{k} + g_r[f''(k)\dot{k} + \dot{\pi}]. \tag{64}$$

However,

$$\dot{p}/p = \theta - n - \dot{x}/x, \tag{65}$$

and combining (62), (64), and (65), we may derive

$$\dot{\pi} = \frac{\beta x(\theta - n - \pi) - \beta[g_k + g_r f''(k)]\dot{k}}{\beta g_r + x} \tag{66}$$

(Exercise 15).

Since $k = k(k)$, given by (57), our final system is of the form

$$k = k(k, \pi), \qquad \dot{\pi} = \dot{\pi}(k, \pi) \qquad (67)$$

and again we seek the existence, uniqueness, and stability of a point $(k^*, \pi^*) > (0, 0)$.[30]

We ignore the questions of existence and uniqueness of an equilibrium point $(k^*, \pi^*) > (0, 0)$; reasoning similar to that employed in the previous sections reveals identical conclusions. The local stability of (k^*, π^*), on the other hand, can be shown to hinge solely on the sign of

$$\left.\frac{\partial \dot{\pi}}{\partial \pi}\right|_{(k^*, \pi^*)} = -\frac{\beta x^*}{\beta g_r + x^*} \qquad (68)$$

which must be negative for stability (Exercise 16).

Thus a sufficient local stability condition is

$$\beta < -x^*/g_r(x^*, r^*). \qquad (69)$$

Since g_r is negative and likely to be small in absolute value, at least as suggested by empirical evidence, condition (69) may not be too restrictive. In any event, the important conclusion is that sufficiently large values of β (very high speeds of adjustment in expectations) lead to

$$\left.\frac{\partial \dot{\pi}}{\partial \pi}\right|_{(k^*, \pi^*)} > 0$$

and a saddlepoint equilibrium.

Again, comparative statics of equilibrium positions are of some interest. Since $\dot{\pi} = 0$ in equilibrium, we conclude that

$$\beta(\dot{p}/p - \pi^*) = 0 \qquad (70)$$

or

$$(\dot{p}/p)^* = \theta - n, \qquad (71)$$

as might be expected. If the rate of increase in the nominal stock of money $(\theta \equiv \dot{M}/M)$ exceeds the rate of growth of the labor force, $(n \equiv \dot{L}/L)$, then there is inflation in equilibrium.

---

[30] Observe that $x = g(k, r) = g[k, f'(k) - \delta + \pi]$ implies the existence of $x = x(k, \pi)$.

We have already stressed that monetary policy cannot affect $k*$ because we have made a simplifying assumption in this section that serves to expedite the analysis. In general, however, the real balance effect is important even in stable models using the adaptive expectations postulate. As in our previous model (Section 6-8) $dk*/d\theta > 0$, so that a rise in the rate of increase in the money supply has a stimulating effect on the economy. However, as is clear from (70) and (71), this result is achieved only with a higher value of $(\dot{p}/p)*$.

Moreover, although $dk*/d\theta > 0$ in a *comparative statics sense*, the motion from k_1^* to k_2^* $(k_2^* > k_1^*)$ due to an increase in θ from θ_1 to θ_2 *may not be monotonically increasing in k^t*. The latter observation, which was also made by Sidrauski ([16], pp. 805–807) in the context of a similar model, could conceivably play a most crucial role in choosing between expansionary policy alternatives.

6–13. Additional Policy Parameters

Many monetary growth models are exceedingly limited in their policy implications because they assume that there is only one parameter under government control, namely $\theta = \dot{M}/M$. A common assumption is that the government creates money in only one way: it distributes it as "gifts" to the public. Clearly there are simple alternatives. The government might create money to purchase new capital goods that would then be rented to firms in the private sector at the competitive rental rate. The latter may be interpreted as an "open market operation." In this section we will briefly analyze a model built upon this possibility, and then comment on the implications.

The following model was suggested by Hahn [5], and we have introduced only minor modifications. In this model the government always owns a constant fraction α of the capital stock, $0 \leq \alpha < \bar{\alpha} \leq 1$, where $\bar{\alpha}$ will be defined precisely in footnote 32; however, the selection of some $\alpha \in [0, \bar{\alpha})$ is a matter of government choice. Constancy of α means that the government must purchase capital at the flow rate $\alpha \dot{K}$ for all points in time. As before, we assume the nominal money stock increases at the constant rate θ, but we may identify two distinct roles by writing

$$\theta = \dot{M}/M = \dot{M}_1/M + \dot{M}_2/M;$$
(72)

here we interpret $\dot{M}_1/M$ as the flow rate of money "gifts," whereas $\dot{M}_2/M$ is the rate of change in the money supply required to purchase capital at the *net* flow rate $\alpha \dot{K}$, thereby keeping α constant. Consequently, we have

$$\dot{M}_2 = \alpha p(\dot{K} + \delta K),$$

or, equivalently,

$$(\dot{M}_2/M)(M/pL) = (\dot{M}_2/M)x = \alpha(\dot{K}/L + \delta K/L) = \alpha[\dot{k} + (n + \delta)k]. \quad \text{(73)}$$

Further assumptions are needed regarding the government's use of its capital and the savings behavior of individuals when $\alpha > 0$. Suppose all the rentals received on the capital stock owned by the government, αK, are distributed to the public as transfer payments; then net disposable income includes the term

$$\alpha F_K K + (1 - \alpha)F_K K + F_L L - \delta K = F_K K + F_L L - \delta K = F(K, L) - \delta K, \quad \text{(74)}$$

as before.[31]

However, *real net disposable income* is no longer

$$Y = F(K, \dot{L}) - \delta K + d(M/p)/dt \quad \text{(19)}$$

since $\dot{M}_2/p$ does not add to disposable income—it is not a "gift" but rather a "trade"—net government purchases of capital must be subtracted to give

$$Y(\alpha) = F(K, L) - \delta K + d(M/p)/dt - \alpha\dot{K}. \quad \text{(75)}$$

Furthermore, our basic flow equilibrium condition which is analogous to (23), is

$$\dot{W}(\alpha) = s\,Y(\alpha) \quad \text{(76)}$$

where

$$W(\alpha) \equiv (1 - \alpha)K + M/p = \textit{real private wealth.} \quad \text{(77)}$$

Manipulation of (75), (76), and (77) yields the differential equation

$$\dot{k} = \frac{sf(k) - [s\delta + (1 - \alpha)n + s\alpha n]k - (1 - s)(\theta - \dot{p}/p)x}{(1 - \alpha) + s\alpha}; \quad \text{(78)}$$

observe that (78) and (34a) are equivalent when $\alpha = 0$.

---

[31] Thus we are assuming that individuals are indifferent as to whether (1) they own the entire capital stock and receive all rental payments $F_K K$ directly, or, alternatively (2) the government owns a fraction α of the capital stock, but turns back all rental income to the public as transfers with individuals still receiving exactly the same total income.

As before,

$$r = f'(k) - \delta + E(\dot{p}/p)$$
$$= f'(k) - \delta + \dot{p}/p$$

under the assumption of perfect myopic foresight. However, it is reasonable to suppose that the demand for money depends on privately owned wealth, and hence, (2) must be replaced by

$$x = G[f(k), (1 - \alpha)k + x, r] \tag{79}$$

where $(1 - \alpha)k + x \equiv w(\alpha)$ is *real per capita private wealth*. Again we may solve (79) for x and r, but now we obtain

$$x = g(k, r; \alpha) \tag{80}$$

with

$$g_\alpha \equiv \frac{\partial x}{\partial \alpha}\bigg|_{k,\,r} = -kG_2/(1 - G_2) < 0 \tag{81}$$

and

$$r = \varphi(k, x; \alpha) \tag{82}$$

with

$$\varphi_\alpha \equiv \frac{\partial r}{\partial \alpha}\bigg|_{x,\,k} = kG_2/G_3 < 0. \tag{83}$$

Although (81) and (83) may be derived by calculation, economic intuition will suffice here. Consider (81); with k and r fixed, so is $\dot{p}/p = r - f'(k) + \delta$. Hence, an increase in α decreases $(1 - \alpha)k$, which tends to decrease the demand for money x, and feedback effects can only tend to decrease x further because $0 < G_2 < 1$ by assumption. Similarly, consider (83); if the demand for money x is to remain constant with constant k as α increases, the expected yield on the alternative asset r surely must fall.

Consequently, (12) must be replaced by

$$\dot{p}/p = \varphi(k, x; \alpha) - f'(k) + \delta, \tag{84}$$

and analogously to (32), we may conclude that $\dot{x} = 0$, $x \neq 0$, whenever

$$x = h(k; \theta, \alpha) = g[k, f'(k) + \lambda; \alpha], \tag{85}$$

where $0 < \varepsilon \leqq k(\alpha) \leqq \underline{k}$, $d\underline{k}(\alpha)/d\alpha > 0$, $0 \leqq \alpha < \bar{\alpha} \leqq 1$, and with

$$\frac{\partial h}{\partial \alpha}\bigg|_{k,\,\theta} < 0 \qquad (86)$$

implied by (81).[32] Accordingly, the curve $h(k; \theta, \alpha)$ shifts downward and to the right with an increase in α.

In summary, we may again derive a differential equation system

$$\dot{k}(k, x; \theta, \alpha) = \{ sf(k) - \xi k - (1-s)[f'(k) - \delta + \theta - \varphi(k, x; \alpha)]x \}/[(1-\alpha) + s\alpha],$$

$$\xi = s\delta + (1 - \alpha)n + s\alpha n, \qquad (87)$$

$$\dot{x}(k, x; \theta, \alpha) = [f'(k) + \lambda - \varphi(k, x; \alpha)]x.$$

Now (87) is written in a form that indicates explicitly that θ and α enter as government policy parameters subject to choice, but assumed constant. The existence and uniqueness of an equilibrium point $(k^*, x^*) > (0, 0)$ for $\alpha \in (0, \bar{\alpha})$ are proved in the same manner as in Section 6-8 under exactly analogous assumptions, and we need not repeat the argument here.

A glance at the system of differential equations (87) shows that the stability properties are the same for all $\alpha \in [0, \bar{\alpha})$, and the case $\alpha = 0$ has already been treated in detail. Similarly, a stable model with adaptive expectations and sufficiently slow speeds of adjustment will have properties analogous to those stated in Section 6-12 where $\alpha = 0$. Since the comparative static properties of such a stable model are qualitatively identical to the system (87) with a

---

[32] Observe that $\underline{k}$ is determined by the intersection of the curves $\bar{r}(k)$ and $f'(k) + \lambda$ where $\bar{r}(k)$ is the solution to

$$0 = g[k, \bar{r}(k); \alpha],$$

and where, as assumed previously, $\bar{r}'(k) > 0$ (see Figure 18). Hence,

$$0 = g_1\, dk + g_2\, d\bar{r} + g_\alpha\, d\alpha$$

or

$$\frac{\partial \bar{r}}{\partial \alpha}\bigg|_k = -g_\alpha/g_2 < 0.$$

The latter means that the $\bar{r}(k)$ curve shifts downward with an increase in α, implying the stated conclusion $d\underline{k}(\alpha)/d\alpha > 0$.

Finally, recall that the assumption $\underline{k} < k^{**}$ was required for the existence of a root $(k^*, x^*) > (0, 0)$ when $\alpha = 0$; see (37) and the subsequent discussion. Therefore, for any fixed θ it is necessary to restrict our attention to $\alpha \in [0, \bar{\alpha})$ where $\bar{\alpha}$ is defined as the root to $\underline{k}(\bar{\alpha}) = k^{***}$ and k^{***} satisfies $sf(k^{***}) - \xi k^{***} = 0$, where ξ is a parameter representing $s\delta + (1 - \alpha)n + s\alpha n$. It is important to realize that $\bar{\alpha}$ may be substantially less than one, depending, of course, upon the function $f(k)$ and the exogenous parameters s, δ, and n.

For similar reasons very high values of θ may preclude the existence of an equilibrium point $(k^*, x^*) > (0, 0)$, as was true in the model with $\alpha = 0$.

saddlepoint equilibrium, we need only investigate the comparative statics of (87).

We have already stated that the curve $x = h(k; \theta, \alpha)$, along which $\dot{x} = 0$, $x \neq 0$, shifts downward and to the right for increases in either θ or α. Now, analogously to (43), define

$$\gamma(k; \alpha) \equiv [sf(k) - \xi k]/(1 - s)n; \tag{88}$$

clearly

$$\left.\frac{\partial \gamma}{\partial \alpha}\right|_k = k > 0. \tag{89}$$

Likewise, $d\tilde{k}/d\alpha = -n(1 - s)/sf''(\tilde{k}) > 0$, where $\tilde{k}$ is the root to $sf'(k) - \xi = 0$. Consequently the curve $\gamma(k; \alpha)$, pictured in Figure 23 for $\alpha = 0$, shifts upward and to the right for increases in α.

All the features just discussed are illustrated in Figure 27. The policy implications are immediately evident. For example, suppose the government insists upon zero inflation in equilibrium, which necessitates fixing $\theta = n = \dot{L}/L$. If $\alpha = 0$, as in our previous models, the equilibrium point (k^*, x^*) is completely determined and no further government control is possible. For illustrative purposes, suppose the equilibrium point A depicted in Figure 27 is possible with $\alpha = 0$ and $\theta = n$. By choosing a value of $\alpha \in [0, \bar{\alpha})$ a whole locus of equilibrium points is now possible. For example, any point on the curve labeled AB in Figure 27 is now a feasible equilibrium position.[33] (In Figure 27 it has been assumed that $\alpha < \bar{\alpha}$.)

[33] The proper slope of the AB curve in Figure 27 is not evident either graphically or intuitively. However, it is clear that any root k^* must satisfy

$$\Psi(k^*; \theta, \alpha) = sf(k^*) - \xi k^* - (1 - s)ng[k^*, f'(k^*) + \lambda; \alpha] = 0,$$

and the proof that (k^*, x^*) is unique implies

$$D^* \equiv \partial\Psi(k^*; \theta, \alpha)/\partial k^* < 0.$$

Consequently we find

$$\left.\frac{\partial k^*}{\partial \alpha}\right|_\theta = [g_\alpha - (1 - s)nk^*]/D^*,$$

which is clearly positive because g_α is negative; see (81). Since $x^* = g[k^*, f'(k^*) + \lambda; \alpha]$, we may calculate

$$\left.\frac{\partial x^*}{\partial \alpha}\right|_\theta = [g_1 + g_2 f''(k^*)](\partial k^*/\partial \alpha) + g_\alpha,$$

and although the first term of the latter expression is clearly positive, g_α is negative. Therefore an increase in α, for any fixed θ, may either increase or decrease x^*.

However, observe from (81) that $g_\alpha^* = -k^*G_2/(1 - G_2)$ where G_2 represents the partial derivative of the demand for real per capita money balances with respect to real per capita private wealth. We may anticipate that G_2 is very near zero, in which case it is likely that $\partial x^*/\partial \alpha|_\theta$ is positive, as implied by the upward-sloping AB curve in Figure 27.

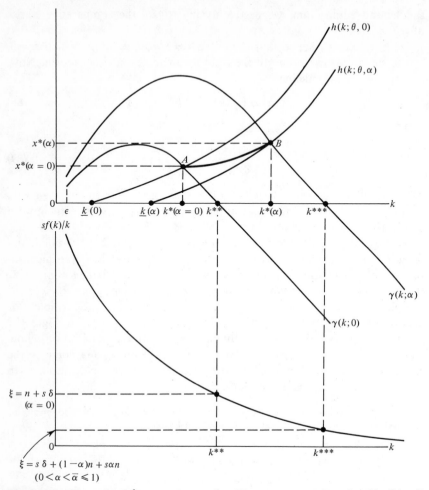

Figure 27. *For a fixed θ, any point on the AB curve represents a feasible (k*, x*) equilibrium corresponding to a value of α satisfying $0 \leqq \alpha < \tilde{\alpha} \leqq 1$. However, this example is illustrative only.*

As an immediate consequence of our analysis, we can prove the following theorem (see Burmeister and Phelps [1]).

Theorem 2: *Let the real per capita debt in equilibrium be denoted by $b^* \equiv x^* - \alpha k^*$. Further, let θ be fixed and assume $\alpha \in [0, \bar{\alpha})$. Then for any feasible equilibrium value of the capital/labor ratio k^* there corresponds one and only one value of the real per capita debt b^*. The exact relationship is*

$$b^* = \gamma(k^*; 0) = [sf(k^*) - (n + s\delta)k^*]/(1 - s)n$$

where $\gamma(k; \alpha)$ is defined by (88).

Proof: Equilibrium prevails if and only if $sf(k^*) - \xi k^* - (1 - s)nx^* = 0$, where $\xi = s\delta + (1 - \alpha)n + s\alpha n$. Substituting $x^* = b^* + \alpha k^*$ into the latter and simplifying yield the conclusion.   QED.

As an immediate consequence of Theorem 2 we have Corollary 2.1.

Corollary 2.1: *Let the conditions stated in Theorem 2 be satisfied. Further, assume that for some fixed θ there exists a value of $\alpha \in (0, \bar{\alpha})$ for which $k^* = k^{**}$ is the equilibrium capital/labor ratio, i.e., assume k^{**} is a feasible equilibrium value. Then $k^* = k^{**}$ if and only if $b^* = 0$, where k^{**} is the no-money Solow equilibrium point at which*

$$sf(k^{**}) - (n + s\delta)k^{**} = 0.$$

As suggested in Section 6-11, the government may pursue policies that stabilize the system. Thus we have a second corollary of Theorem 2.

Corollary 2.2: *Any stabilizing policy for which*

$$\lim_{t \to \infty} k^t = k^{**} \Rightarrow \lim_{t \to \infty} b^t = 0.$$

Conversely, any stabilizing policy for which

$$\lim_{t \to \infty} b^t = 0 \Rightarrow \lim_{t \to \infty} k^t = k^{**}.$$

From Corollary 2.1 we conclude that the Solow point capital/labor ratio k^{**} represents an equilibrium if and only if the net indebtedness of the government (in the sense defined earlier) is zero. More generally, this analysis suggests that the additional policy instrument arising from government owner-ship of a portion of the capital stock provides, as expected, additional freedom in influencing the location of the equilibrium points for the system, but does not alter the structure of the system itself in any drastic fashion.

6–14. Conclusions and Other Issues

Let us summarize briefly the results of this chapter. In Section 6-2 we intro-duced a function describing the level of money balances desired (for specula-tive, as well as for transactions, purposes) in the economy. From the beginning we assumed that the yield on capital is always at the level required to bring about equilibrium on the money market (and hence on both asset markets).

That is, we have in the system at any time stocks of two assets, capital goods and paper money, and we assumed that the money yield on the capital good is uniquely determined at each instant by the requirement that the existing stocks be willingly held. Since the real rental on the capital good is determined by the stock of capital (and the known depreciation rate), and the price of the capital good is fixed at each instant, the requirement of money market equilibrium suffices to determine the rate of asset price inflation (the rate of capital gain on the capital good) each instant. With both the nominal stock of money and the labor force expanding at exogenously determined constant rates, the rate of change of real balances per capita is determined directly by the rate of asset price inflation. As in our previous models, a saving hypothesis determines the rate of change in the capital/labor ratio. Hence the model may be reduced to two differential equations determining real balances per capita and capital per capita.

Section 6-3 elaborates properties of the demand for money function, while Section 6-4 indicates one approach to models in which money market clearing may not always be realized, either as a result of a conventional liquidity trap or otherwise. Though such models are important because of their relevance to situations of unemployment, we do not pursue them here. Instead we specify a saving hypothesis in Section 6-5, and develop the properties of the resulting differential equation system in Sections 6-6, 6-7, 6-8, and 6-9.

The central result is that there apparently exist two equilibrium points for the system, a saddlepoint equilibrium with positive real balances, and a stable equilibrium with zero real balances. (The fact of the saddlepoint equilibrium confirms results of Tobin [22] and Nagatani [9] in a slightly different context, but for the whole class of paths approaching the stable no-money equilibrium, it appears that money is indeed neutral in the long run). Section 6-10 analyzes a particularly special case where money is desired only as an asset, and hence will only be held if the rate of price deflation brings the money yield on capital down to zero.

The only policy instrument available in these models (apart from the saving rate which we have discussed before) is the rate of expansion of the nominal money supply. The only policy question at which the models can be directed is the effect of the paper asset on the real accumulation of the system. Interestingly, the analysis suggests that the presence of the paper asset does reduce the equilibrium capital/labor ratio for the system (in this sense conferring a burden on later generations), but that, given a positive money stock, a higher rate of nominal money expansion raises saving rates and thus leads to higher capital/labor ratios in equilibrium.

Slightly richer policy choices may also be considered. Given the saddlepoint character of the equilibrium with positive real balances, one may ask whether a policy permitting changing rates of growth of the money supply might change that equilibrium to a stable one. Section 6-11 shows (in a simplified model) that a policy relating the rate of growth of the money supply to the revealed desire for money to hold does indeed stabilize the system, a result which should hardly be startling. (One must, however, ask whether this stabilizing policy is desirable, since the stable no-money Solow point may be a preferable target at which to be aiming.) It is also true that sluggish adjustment of expectations serves to stabilize the system as Section 6-12 shows (again in the context of a simplified model). Finally, Section 6-13 analyzes a model similar to that of Sections 6-7 to 6-9, but in which the government is imagined to own a fraction of the capital stock, and this fraction is itself a policy parameter. The additional instrument does yield additional scope for policy, but the structure of the model is not much altered.

As we stated in the introductory section to this chapter, the models we have presented and analyzed relate to somewhat subordinate aspects of the role of money in economic theory. In particular, we have retained the hypothesis that runs through our entire book, namely the assumption that there are no aggregate demand deficiencies and labor is fully employed. Section 6-4 mentions some of the serious pitfalls that may be encountered when more general models are attempted.

Our models also suffer from a defect noted in another context by Sidrauski:[34]

The major limitation of this analysis is given by the fact that we have postulated a saving function and a demand function for real cash balances that are not explicitly derived from the maximizing behavior of the individual economic units of the economy. A more reasonable procedure would be to consider a representative economic unit in this simplified world and to analyze first how this economic unit would behave in a monetary economy if it attempted to maximize its well-being over its economic horizon. Once this is done, demand functions for assets and real consumption can be derived on the basis of which one could build a macroeconomic model that will describe the economy's time path under different assumptions about the behavior of the monetary authority.

The difficulty is to develop a satisfactory treatment of *uncertainty*. Other work by Sidrauski [17] and more recently by Levhari and Patinkin [7] attempts to circumvent the uncertainty problem in part by including real money balances in the utility functions of individuals and/or the production functions of firms. Samuelson [13] has also introduced money into the utility function, because, as he writes, "... one can put M into the utility function,

[34] [16], pp. 809–810.

along with other things, as a real convenience in a world of stochastic uncertainty and indivisible transaction charges."[35]

Undoubtedly, there is a great deal of merit to these heuristic arguments, but a rigorous uncertainty framework is beyond our reach at this moment. Hence we have followed simple saving-consumption hypotheses, and these at least have some empirical support, even if they do not rest upon an explicit derivation from a foundation of individual preference orderings.

The role of money in society is rather complex, but we see that to a substantial extent it serves as a mediating entity necessary because barter is not feasible and capital markets are not perfect or frictionless. In a world with institutional restrictions on modes of financing, where bankruptcy and liquidity crises may be real threats to firms with quite promising prospects of future earnings, money serves as a buffer stock smoothing transactions and providing liquidity. Thus, "money" is more than the artificial "outside" money considered in the previous pages; to deal adequately with important aspects of monetary problems we would have to examine descriptions of financial markets and financial institutions. Perhaps we also should question the assertion that some part of government liabilities can be treated as outside money. Why outside? Is it really accurate to suggest that government operations can be separated so thoroughly that agents in the economy do not see the government as conforming to the same double-entry accounting requirements as other economic institutions? Perhaps we require a descriptive theory bringing government decisions into the model on the same basis as other institutions that can borrow now only against future power to obtain earnings (through tax levies or otherwise).

To the extent these issues are important, the foregoing models fail to deal adequately with important features of a monetary economy. We can argue for our analysis only as a starting point. In the long run, we may hope that results are little changed from the real models earlier studied. Certainly this might be expected as a consequence of the emphasis on the simple mediating role played by money stocks.[36] On the other hand, we must remember that the presence of money offers an alternative form in which to hold wealth. To the extent that a saving flow is diverted in part from accumulation of physical assets to the acquisition of paper claims on an outside government, the equilibrium of the system and associated per capita income levels clearly may be affected, as demonstrated by this chapter.

---

[35] Samuelson [13], p. 8.

[36] The expectation is reinforced by the fact that in most of these monetary growth models there is a stable equilbrium (at the Solow point) which can be attained from a whole range of initial positions. Convergence to this point, where money balances effectively become irrelevant, is in these models a perfectly feasible and acceptable outcome, with none of the difficulties associated in recent growth models with divergence from the balanced growth (saddlepoint) equilibrium.

Exercises

1. Show that if $x = G[f(k), k + x, r]$ has $G_1 > 0$, $1 > G_2 > 0$, and $G_3 < 0$, then there exists a function of the form $x = g(k, r)$ with $g_1 > 0$ and $g_2 < 0$. Likewise, prove the existence of a function $r = \varphi(k, x)$ with $\varphi_1 > 0$, $\varphi_2 < 0$.

2. Prove that (31) may be solved for $x = h(k)$ with $h'(k) > 0$.

3. Derive the equations 34(a) and 34(b).

4. Show that a simple one-sector model without money in which net capital formation is a constant fraction (s) of net income implies the differential equation

$$\dot{k} = sf(k) - (n + s\delta)k = \dot{k}(k)$$

with

$$\dot{k}(k^{**}) = 0.$$

5. (a) Prove that $(1 - s)Y = C = F(K, L)$ if and only if $\Lambda(k, x) = x(\theta - \dot{p}/p) - sf(k)/(1 - s) - \delta k = 0$.

   (b) Show that there exists a function $k = \eta(x)$ such that $C \gtreqless F(K, L)$ as $k \gtreqless \eta(x)$.

   (c) Show $\eta'(x)$ is of indefinite sign in general.

   (d) Prove $k \leq \eta(x)$ implies $\dot{k}(k, x) < 0$.

6. Show that the elasticity of $\gamma(k)$ is less than one for all $0 < \varepsilon \leq k < k^{**}$.

7. Show that $dx^*/d\theta \gtreqless 0$ as $k \gtreqless \tilde{k}$ where $\tilde{k}$ is defined by $sf'(\tilde{k}) - (n + s\delta) = 0$.

8. Obtain expressions for $J_{11}^*, J_{12}^*, J_{21}^*, J_{22}^*$.

9. Derive equation (50).

10. Derive equations (53) and (54), and prove assertions (i) and (ii) on p. 181 of the text.

11. Derive the phase diagram illustrated in Figure 26.

12. Derive the equation $\dot{x} = \dot{x}(k, x)$ in (59).

13. Show that $J_{11}^* < 0$ for the simplified model discussed in Section 6-11.

14. Derive the equation (61).

15. Derive the expression for $\dot{\pi}$ given in equation (66).

16. Prove that $(k^*, \pi^*) > (0, 0)$ is locally stable if and only if $\partial\dot{\pi}/\partial\pi\big|_{(k^*, \pi^*)}$, given by equation (68), is negative.

17. Prove that equation (41) is always satisfied when (5) holds.

Answers and Hints

PROBLEM 3. Substitute into (20) $C = (1 - s)Y$, using the expression for Y given in (19).

PROBLEM 5.

(b) $\dfrac{\partial \Lambda}{\partial k} = x(-\varphi_k + f'') - sf'/(1 - s) - \delta < 0.$

(d) It suffices to prove that $(1 - s)Y = C \geq F(K, L)$ implies $\dot{k} < 0$. But, from (a) and (b) of this problem, $C \geq F(K, L)$ if and only if $\Lambda(k, x) \geq 0$, which in turn holds if and only if $(1 - s)x(\theta - \dot{p}/p) \geq sf(k) + (1 - s)\delta k$. Therefore

$$\dot{k} = sf(k) - (n + s\delta)k - (1 - s)(\theta - \dot{p}/p)x$$

$$\leq sf(k) - (n + s\delta)k - sf(k) - (1 - s)\delta k = -(n + \delta)k < 0.$$

PROBLEM 6. Derive an expression for the elasticity of $\gamma(k)$ and show that it is less than 1 as long as $f'(k)k < f(k)$ (which always holds).

PROBLEM 15. Derive an expression for $\dot{x}$ in terms of x, $\dot{\pi}$, π by combining (62) and (65); then equate the latter to the formulation for $\dot{x}$ given in (64).

References

[1] BURMEISTER, E., and E. S. PHELPS, "Money, Public Debt, Inflation and Real Interest," Discussion Paper No. 122, Department of Economics, University of Pennsylvania, Philadelphia, Pa. (June, 1969).

[2] CAGAN, P., "The Monetary Dynamics of Hyperinflation," in *Studies in the Quantity Theory of Money* (M. Friedman, Ed.). Chicago: University of Chicago Press, 1956, pp. 25–117.

[3] FOLEY, D., K. SHELL, and M. SIDRAUSKI, "Optimal Fiscal and Monetary Policy, and Economic Growth," *Journal of Political Economy*, **77**, 4, Part 2 (July–August, 1969), pp. 698–719.

[4] — and M. SIDRAUSKI, *Monetary and Fiscal Policy in a Growing Economy.* New York: Macmillan, to be published in 1970.

[5] HAHN, F. H., "On Money and Growth," *Journal of Money, Credit and Banking* **I**, 2 (May, 1969), pp. 172–187.

[6] JOHNSON, H. G., "The Neoclassical One-Sector Growth Model: A Geometrical Exposition and Extension to a Monetary Economy," *Economica*, **XXXIII**, *131* (August, 1966), pp. 265–287.

[7] LEVHARI, D., and D. PATINKIN, "The Role of Money in a Simple Growth Model," *American Economic Review*, **LVIII**, 4 (September, 1968), pp. 713–753.

[8] MODIGLIANI, F., "The Monetary Mechanism and Its Interaction with Real Phenomena," *Review of Economics and Statistics*, **XLV**, *1* (February, 1963), pp. 79–107.

[9] NAGATANI, K., "Professor Tobin on Money and Economic Growth," forthcoming in *Econometrica*.

[10] ROSE, H., "On the Non-Linear Theory of the Employment Cycle," *Review of Economic Studies*, **XXXIV**, *98* (April, 1967), pp. 153–174.

[11] — "Real and Monetary Factors in the Business Cycle," *Journal of Money, Credit and Banking*, **I**, 2 (May, 1969), pp. 138–152.

[12] — "Unemployment in a Theory of Growth," *International Economic Review*, **7**, *3* (September, 1966), pp. 260–282.

[13] SAMUELSON, P. A., "What Classical and Neoclassical Monetary Theory Really Was," *The Canadian Journal of Economics*, **I**, *1* (February, 1968), pp. 1–15.

[14] — "Some Aspects of the Pure Theory of Capital," *Quarterly Journal of Economics*, **LI** (May, 1937), pp. 469–496.

[15] SHELL, K., M. SIDRAUSKI, and J. E. STIGLITZ, "Capital Gains, Income and Saving," *Review of Economic Studies*, **XXXVI**, *105* (January, 1969), pp. 15–26.

[16] SIDRAUSKI, M., "Inflation and Economic Growth," *Journal of Political Economy*, **75**, *6* (December, 1967), pp. 796–810.

[17] — "Rational Choice and Patterns of Growth in a Monetary Economy," *American Economic Review*, **LVII**, *2* (May, 1967), pp. 534–544.

[18] STEIN, J. L., "Growth in a Monetary Economy: Comment," *American Economic Review*, **LVIII**, *4* (September, 1968), pp. 944–950.

[19] — "Money and Capacity Growth," *Journal of Political Economy*, **LXXXIV**, *5* (October, 1966), pp. 451–465.

[20] — "Neoclassical and Keynes-Wicksell Monetary Growth Models," *Journal of Money, Credit and Banking*, **I**, *2* (May, 1969), pp. 153–171.

[21] TOBIN, J., "A Dynamic Aggregative Model," *Journal of Political Economy*, **LXIII**, *2* (April, 1955), pp. 103–115.

[22] — "Money and Economic Growth," *Econometrica*, **33**, *4* (October, 1965), pp. 671–684.

[23] — "The Neutrality of Money in Growth Models: A Comment," *Economica*, **XXXIV**, *133* (February, 1967), pp. 69–72.

Chapter 7 A Preview of
Multisector Growth Models

7-1. Introduction

In the previous six chapters we studied several different models, all of which displayed essentially the same production characteristics. They postulated the existence of a single produced durable asset, the capital good, and a single nonproduced primary factor, labor. They assumed that technological possibilities were described by neoclassical production functions with no joint production. Analysis of static equilibria in these models was straightforward in the simple cases we considered, although a complete analysis of the dynamic behavior was not always easy.

In the following chapters we wish to study multisector models involving several produced durable goods. However, in specifying such a model we have choices to make regarding the features just mentioned: we must decide whether to include any nonproduced or primary factors of production; whether the models should contain linear or neoclassical production functions; if linear, whether they should allow only a single activity for producing each good or a whole spectrum of feasible activities. And in all the latter cases, we may or may not exclude joint production. A complete exposition would require that we deal with all possible combinations of these features, but that is clearly neither feasible nor efficient. Instead we will outline in this chapter the technological specifications for two models we study in detail in later chapters, and for a third model we will study later in this chapter. By this selective sketch we indicate the variety of possible alternatives and develop from the simplest cases some technical results that are useful for subsequent applications. An elegant review of some of this material and related topics may also be found in Nikaido [29].

7–2. A Multisector Neoclassical Technology without Joint Production

Probably the most natural multisector extension of our basic models (developed in Chapters 2 and 4) would be simply to add more sectors, each corresponding to an additional durable good produced by a neoclassical production function of the type employed earlier. Such an extension would have the form outlined as follows, involving several produced durable goods and a single primary factor, labor, growing at a given exogenous rate.

Specifically, assume there are n distinct capital goods, each produced in a separate sector of the economy. (Joint production of two or more goods simultaneously in a single process is excluded.) To concentrate upon the consequences arising from the presence of heterogeneous capital goods, we continue to assume that labor is homogeneous and that there is a single consumption good. (Of course, this consumption good may be a composite of several different goods provided that the proportions between these remain constant; this "fixed basket" case is well known.)

We therefore assume the economy consists of $n + 1$ production sectors, with the subscripts $1, 2, \ldots, n$ designating the sectors producing the n capital goods, and the symbols $K_1, K_2, \ldots, K_n$ denoting the stocks of these capital goods. The sector producing the consumption good is identified by the subscript 0. The services of each capital good and of labor may be used in each of the $n + 1$ sectors; K_{ij} denotes the quantity of the ith capital good employed in the jth sector, and L_j denotes the quantity of labor employed in the jth sector ($i = 1, \ldots, n; j = 0, 1, 2, \ldots, n$).

In each sector, production is governed by a neoclassical production function[1]

$$Y_j = F^j(L_j, K_{1j}, \ldots, K_{nj}), \quad (j = 0, 1, \ldots, n), \tag{1}$$

giving the flow output Y_j (measured unambiguously in physical units) of the sector as a function of the capital and labor services employed in that sector. Since in particular these functions are homogeneous of degree one, we may write

$$1 = F^j(a_{0j}, a_{1j}, \ldots, a_{nj}), \quad (j = 0, 1, \ldots, n), \tag{2}$$

where we define

$$a_{0j} \equiv L_j/Y_j, \quad (j = 0, 1, \ldots, n), \tag{3}$$

and

$$a_{ij} \equiv K_{ij}/Y_j, \quad (i = 1, \ldots, n; j = 0, 1, \ldots, n). \tag{4}$$

[1] A neoclassical production function is defined in Chapter 1, pp. 9–10.

Together with the full employment conditions

$$\sum_{j=0}^{n} a_{0j} Y_j = L \tag{5}$$

and

$$\sum_{j=0}^{n} a_{ij} Y_j = K_i, \qquad (i = 1, \ldots, n; j = 0, 1, \ldots, n), \tag{6}$$

equations (2) completely determine the technology for the multisector neoclassical model. We would like to know how, given particular endowments of capital goods and labor, an allocation of these factors to the various sectors (and hence the output of each sector) is determined, and whether this allocation is unique. Moreover, if the allocation is unique for each endowment vector, we can then study the properties of the dynamic system

$$\dot{K}_i = Y_i - \delta_i K_i, \qquad K_i(0) = K_i^0, \qquad (i = 1, \ldots, n). \tag{7}$$

Equations (7) determine the accumulation path for each capital good (under the assumption that each decays exponentially).

These questions are studied in Chapter 9. Prior examination of a model more restricted in some respects than the present one is useful, however, and we now turn to one such example.

7–3. Leontief Technologies with Alternative Techniques

Although the model just described is the most natural extension of the preceding chapters, it is convenient to deal first with a model in which the production functions are of a Leontief (or fixed proportions) form. However, the other crucial assumptions—in particular that of a single primary factor growing at a fixed rate and the absence of joint production—are retained. We study this model in Chapter 8, treating both the case in which alternative activities produce each nonprimary output and the case in which only a single activity produces each output. In the latter case the model studied in Chapter 8 may be identified as one version of the open dynamic Leontief (or input-output) model.

The production functions (2) now take the familiar Leontief, rather than the neoclassical, form. If there were only one method of production in each sector we would write

$$Y_j = \min\left[\frac{L_j}{a_{0j}}, \frac{K_{1j}}{a_{1j}}, \ldots, \frac{K_{nj}}{a_{nj}}\right], \qquad (j = 0, 1, \ldots, n), \tag{8}$$

where the input coefficients a_{ij} $(i, j = 0, 1, \ldots, n)$ are given, nonnegative, technical constants. The vector $(a_{0j}, 0, a_{1j}, \ldots, a_{nj})$ is called an *activity vector* for producing the jth good.[2] However, we wish also to consider alternative methods of producing the same output good. Hence we introduce an index μ_j that may assume any integer value from 1 to m_j where m_j denotes the number of alternative activity vectors for producing the jth good. Then we may write the production functions (8) as

$$Y_j = \min\left[\frac{L_j}{a_{0j}(\mu_j)}, \frac{K_{1j}}{a_{1j}(\mu_j)}, \ldots, \frac{K_{nj}}{a_{nj}(\mu_j)}\right], \quad (j = 0, 1, \ldots, n), \quad (9)$$

where for any choice of the index μ_j the vector[3] $[a_{0j}(\mu_j), 0, a_{1j}(\mu_j), \ldots, a_{nj}(\mu_j)]$ is one of the admissible activity vectors for producing the jth good.

We assume static efficiency in production so that no input is ever redundant,[4] and the equalities

$$a_{ij}(\mu_j) = K_{ij}/Y_j, \quad (i = 1, \ldots, n; j = 0, 1, \ldots, n), \quad (10)$$

and

$$a_{0j}(\mu_j) = L_j/Y_j, \quad (j = 0, 1, \ldots, n), \quad (11)$$

always hold. (These relationships justify our use of the same notation here as in the previous model.)

An $(n + 2) \times (n + 1)$ matrix with activity vectors in the columns is called a *technique matrix* or a *technique of production*. For example, if $\mu_j = 1$ for all $j = 0, 1, \ldots, n$, the corresponding technique matrix is

$$\begin{bmatrix} a_{00}(1) & a_{01}(1) & \cdots & a_{0n}(1) \\ \hline 0 & 0 & \cdots & 0 \\ a_{10}(1) & a_{11}(1) & \cdots & a_{1n}(1) \\ \vdots & \vdots & & \vdots \\ a_{n0}(1) & a_{n1}(1) & \cdots & a_{nn}(1) \end{bmatrix}.$$

[2] The introduction of the zero component in this vector reflects the fact that the consumption good is never used as an input in production. This notational convention causes our terminology to deviate slightly from the usual, but will prove convenient for later matrix manipulations.

[3] Throughout the remainder of the book we follow a standard vector notation described in the Appendix.

[4] It should be noted that this assertion is not intended to mean that no factor is ever unemployed or in excess supply, but rather that efficiency in each sector will ensure that no production process will demand more of any input than can be used. There may still be some factors less than fully utilized, simply because total demand of all sectors falls short of factor supplies.

(Again, the second row of zeros is introduced for later notational convenience and reflects the fact that the consumption good is never used as a factor input.) Because the activity vectors may be selected independently, there are M alternative technique matrices where

$$M = \prod_{j=0}^{n} m_j.$$ (12)

The set of these M alternative technique matrices is the *technology*; it contains all the technical knowledge of production methods and is sometimes called the economy's book of blue prints or the spectrum of techniques. The technique matrices will be referred to as Technique α, Technique β, Technique γ, and so on.[5]

As in the previous section our analysis of the model investigates the existence and uniqueness of a static equilibrium determining the allocation of factors in production (and hence the output of each sector), and the stability of the accumulation process determined by the static allocation. We undertake this analysis in Chapter 8; here we specialize the model further to eliminate the primary factor. The resulting model is described in the following section.

Thus, to summarize, we are postponing discussion of the multisector neoclassical model with a single primary factor until Chapter 9, even though this model may be thought the most natural extension of our previous discussion in Chapters 2 and 4. Instead, in the remainder of this chapter, we develop some useful background by studying closed models of production, and then in Chapter 8 we turn to open linear models.

In the transition to the models to be discussed in the next five sections of this chapter, one point may cause confusion. Throughout this book until now the technology has been specified explicitly in terms of factor stocks and the allocation of services of these stocks to production in various sectors. The activity vectors we just defined refer to such allocations of (services of) factor stocks to output flows. However, when we admit joint production it is easy to introduce stocks in the system by having capital goods enter as inputs to production, and then the depreciated capital goods emerge as outputs. Thus, when we work in a difference equation form, as we do in the following sections, we may think conveniently in terms of a point-input, point-output model, where the outputs of one period become the inputs of the next, and any factor stocks may be numbered among the inputs and outputs by the simple device just mentioned. For the next few sections it will be convenient to follow this practice and omit any explicit mention of factor stocks.

---

[5] This terminology, which was introduced by Joan Robinson [31], is now widely used; see, e.g., Morishima [25] and Samuelson [32].

7–4. The Closed Model of Production

In this section we study one example of a "closed" multisector model[6] of production, obtained by dropping the assumption of a fixed primary factor—indeed by dropping explicit consideration of factor stocks altogether. Within this framework it is easy to admit joint production and nonlinear production functions, and we do so in the following.

For this closed model of production we will demonstrate the existence and, with an additional assumption, the uniqueness of a balanced growth path displaying the maximum rate of balanced growth attainable with the specified technology. Since it is only the technology that is specified at this stage, however, and no output allocation decisions are included, the actual dynamics of a complete system are not at issue here. That is, the model only determines a class of feasible paths and demonstrates that among them there is one (possibly unique) balanced growth path that attains the maximal rate of expansion. No selection among these feasible paths is undertaken, so no actual growth path is determined, and no questions of stability or asymptotic behavior arise.

The first modern analysis of an expanding multisector economic model was carried out by von Neumann in 1937 [35]. Under rather stringent assumptions as to technological possibilities he proved the existence of a maximum attainable rate of steady growth of the economy. Moreover, he proved the existence of an equilibrium path along which all sectors grow at the same maximal rate; further, all prices and the interest rate remain constant along this path. The paper is rather complicated, achieving the main result by use of Brouwer's fixed-point theorem[7] to assert the existence of a solution to a set of inequalities. More recently the von Neumann results have been established using more elementary techniques and less severe restrictions. In particular, they have been proved using game theory [13], the duality theorem of linear programming [9], ordinary set theory [9, 12], and the Frobenius theorems of matrix algebra [24, 25]. The most general formulation is due to Karlin [12], and it is his version that we outline here.

It must be stressed that (with the exception of generalizations to be considered presently) the von Neumann model deals with a closed economy. Labor is regarded not as a primary resource but as produced by the system

[6] We call attention to the adjective in quotation marks because the word "closed" is used here to indicate that there is no primary factor, not in the more usual sense which implies that the model is self-contained and determinate.

[7] Fixed-point theorems such as Brouwer's or Kakutani's [11] play an important role in the proofs of many theorems in economics. Brouwer's theorem states that if a convex set S is nonempty, closed, and bounded, then a continuous mapping H of S into itself has a fixed-point, i.e. there exists a point $V^* \in S$ such that $V^* = H(V^*)$; the reader is referred to Lefschetz [16] and Karlin [12] for further discussion.

like any other commodity; consumption is merely an input to processes that have labor as outputs. It is further assumed that labor is paid a subsistence wage and is perfectly elastic in supply at that wage; moreover, capitalists do not consume but automatically reinvest all their income, and perfect competition prevails.

Suppose that the economy produces n distinct commodities and that the technologically given production possibilities can be described by the transformation set T where T is a set of pairs (x, y) of n-vectors such that the production of output $y = (y_1, \ldots, y_n)$ is technologically possible from input $x = (x_1, \ldots, x_n)$ if and only if (x, y) belongs to T.[8] The following assumptions will be made about the set T.

Assumption (A.1): *T is a closed convex cone in the nonnegative orthant of $2n$-dimensional Euclidean space.[9] (The fact that the transformation set is closed implies that the boundary points are feasible activities, whereas convexity implies that any weighted average[10] of two feasible activities is also feasible, and the conical property implies constant returns to scale.)*

Assumption (A.1'): *T is a closed cone in the nonnegative orthant. (This weaker assumption, which drops the convexity requirement of (A.1), is used in Chapter 10.)*

Assumption (A.2): *If $(x, y) \in T$, $x' \geq x$ and $0 \leq y' \leq y$, then $(x', y') \in T$. This condition asserts that the disposal activity is costless.*

Assumption (A.3): *If $(0, y) \in T$, then $y = 0$. This implies that it is impossible to produce something from nothing, that there really is no "free lunch" or Land of Cockaigne.*

Assumption (A.4): *For all i, $i = 1, \ldots, n$, there exists $(x^i, y^i) \in T$ such that $y_i^i > 0$. That is, every commodity can be produced. In view of (A.1), (A.4) is equivalent to (A.4').*

---

[8] Vectors normally will be understood to be column vectors. Transposes of vectors are denoted by primes and the inner product of two vectors x and y is written $x'y$. Superscripts distinguish different vectors, whereas subscripts denote components of a particular vector. The Appendix contains further details on vector notation conventions used in the remainder of this book. We sometimes may use a superscript T to denote transpose when that notation is more convenient.

[9] T is a closed convex cone if (1) T is a closed set in E^{2n}—i.e., it contains its limit points, (2) if (x_1, y_1) and $(x_2, y_2) \in T$ then $(x_1 + x_2, y_1 + y_2) \in T$, and (3) if $(x, y) \in T$ and if $\alpha \geq 0$, then $\alpha(x, y) \in T$.

[10] The term "weighted average" as used here actually means "convex combination"—that is, a weighted average in which the weights are nonnegative and sum to unity.

Assumption (A.4'): *There exists* $(x^0, y^0) \in T$ *such that* $y^0 > 0$.

Definition: For a nonzero input-output relation $(x, y) \in T$, the *rate of expansion* $\lambda(x, y)$ will be defined by

$$\lambda(x, y) = \max\{\lambda \mid y \geqq \lambda x\}. \tag{13}$$

Using assumptions (A.1) and (A.3) it follows that

$$0 \leqq \lambda(x, y) < \infty. \tag{14}$$

Under these assumptions the von Neumann theorem asserts the following.

Theorem 1 (Karlin):
   (i) *There exists a pair* $(x^*, y^*) \in T$ *such that*

$$y^* = \lambda^* x^*, \qquad \lambda^* = \lambda(x^*, y^*), \qquad (x^* \geq 0) \tag{15}$$

and

$$\lambda^* \geqq \lambda(x, y) \quad \text{for each} \quad (x, y) \in T \quad \text{with} \quad x \geq 0. \tag{16}$$

(*The vector pair* (x^*, y^*) *is referred to as a* balanced growth pair *and* λ^* *is the maximal* balanced growth factor. *The input-output pair* (x^*, y^*) *is a pair that grows at the maximum balanced growth rate of which the economy is capable, and* $(\lambda^* - 1)$ *is the corresponding maximum balanced growth rate.*) *Associated with the balanced growth path we have an equilibrium price system as follows.*
   (ii) *There exists a vector* p^* *such that* $p^* \geq 0$ *and*

$$p^{*\prime} y \leqq \lambda^* p^{*\prime} x, \qquad (x, y) \in T. \tag{17}$$

(*Clearly* (17) *holds with equality for the balanced growth pair* (x^*, y^*). *Economically* (17) *implies that no input-output pair makes a positive profit, a requirement that is in accord with the assumption of perfect competition.*)

Proof: Let

$$\lambda^* = \sup\{\lambda(x, y) \mid (x, y) \in T, x \geq 0\}. \tag{18}$$

Then we wish to show $0 < \lambda^* < \infty$. Since by assumption (A.4') there exists $(x^0, y^0) \in T$ with $y^0 > 0$,

$$\lambda^* \geqq \lambda(x^0, y^0) > 0.$$

Also if λ^* is not finite, then there exists a sequence $(x^\nu, y^\nu) \in T$ such that $y^\nu \geq 0$, $y^\nu \geq \lambda^\nu x^\nu$, and $\lim \lambda^\nu = \infty$. Normalizing y^ν such that $\sum_{i=1}^n y_i^\nu = 1$ and taking a limit point $\bar{y}$ of $\{y^\nu\}$, it follows that $(0, \bar{y}) \in T$ where $\bar{y} \geq 0$, thereby contradicting assumption (A.3). Thus, $0 < \lambda^* < \infty$, as we wished to prove. Since T is a closed cone, there exists a vector pair $(\tilde{x}, \tilde{y}) \in T$ with $\lambda^* = \lambda(\tilde{x}, \tilde{y})$ where λ^* is defined in (18). By assumption (A.2) we can find (x^*, y^*) satisfying (15) and (16), so part (i) of the theorem is proved.

To prove part (ii) of the theorem, we define a set $V \in E^n$ as follows:

$$V = \left\{ (y - \lambda^* x) \,|\, (x, y) \in T, \sum_{i=1}^n (x_i + y_i) \leq 1 \right\}. \tag{19}$$

Since T is a closed convex set, V is also a closed convex set. Also, by definition of λ^*, V does not overlap the positive orthant of E^n. Hence there exists a hyperplane through the origin which separates the positive orthant from V. (See Koopmans [14] or Karlin [12, Appendix B] for discussion of the separating hyperplane theorem.) Thus there exists a nonzero vector p^* such that

$$p^{*\prime}(y - \lambda^* x) \leq 0 \tag{20}$$

for all $(x, y) \in T$ and

$$p^{*\prime} z \geq 0 \qquad \text{for all} \qquad z > 0. \tag{21}$$

From (21) it follows that $p^* \geq 0$, and then (20) is the statement of part (ii) of the theorem. Hence the proof is complete.

7–5. The von Neumann Model

A special case of the Karlin model discussed in the preceding section is the well-known von Neumann model [35] in which the technology incorporates linear production functions. As in the previous model, it admits joint production and does not completely specify output decisions, so again the question of convergence of paths from specified initial conditions does not arise. What is demonstrated, as before, is the existence (and perhaps uniqueness) of a balanced growth path at a maximal rate. This result will be vital in later sections, particularly since some approaches to the turnpike theorem to be discussed in Chapter 10 rely on the von Neumann formulation of the problem. We shall therefore restate the results of the theorem in the original terms.

Let the production activities be finite in number and be indexed by j, $j = 1, \ldots, m$. Suppose that the operation of the jth activity at unit level requires an input $(a_{1j}, \ldots, a_{nj})$ of the n commodities and produces an output $(b_{1j}, \ldots, b_{nj})$. It is assumed that

(i) $a_{ij} \geq 0$ and $b_{ij} \geq 0$, $(i = 1, \ldots, n; j = 1, \ldots, m)$.
The transformation set T is now defined by

$$T = \{(x, y) \mid x \geq Az, y \leq Bz \quad \text{for some} \quad z \geq 0, \quad z = (z_1, \ldots, z_m)\}$$

where $A = (a_{ij})$ and $B = (b_{ij})$ are the matrices of input and output coefficients, respectively. (It may be noted that this specification of production possibilities, though less general than that just described, still admits possibilities of joint production, and is thus more general than the models to be discussed later.)

With this specification of technology, assumptions (A.1) and (A.2) are always satisfied. Assumption (A.3) is equivalent to (ii).

(ii) For any j there is at least one i such that $a_{ij} > 0$; that is, every activity uses some commodity as input. Assumption (A.4) is equivalent to (iii).

(iii) For any i there is at least one j such that $b_{ij} > 0$; that is, every commodity can be produced by some activity.

Thus, under these conditions the von Neumann theorem asserts that there exists an activity level z^* and a price level p^* such that

$$z^* \geq 0, \quad p^* \geq 0, \quad Bz^* \geq \lambda^* Az^*, \tag{22a}$$

$$p^* B \leq \lambda^* p^* A. \tag{22b}$$

Furthermore it can be shown (see [9], [12]) that if

$$b^i z^* > \lambda^* a^i z^*, \quad \text{then} \quad p_i^* = 0, \tag{22c}$$

and if

$$p^* b^j < \lambda^* p^* a^j, \quad \text{then} \quad z_j^* = 0, \tag{22d}$$

and that

$$p^* Bz^* > 0. \tag{22e}$$

In this model $(\lambda^* - 1)$ is both the maximal rate of balanced growth and the rate of interest, these being necessarily equal in equilibrium. Moreover, result (22a) says that the output of goods must increase at a rate at least equal to λ^*; relation (22b) states that no activity shows a positive profit; relation (22c) states that if any good is expanding at a rate greater than λ^*, i.e., if it is oversupplied, its price drops to zero; relation (22d) states that activities that show a negative profit will not be used; and relation (22e) states that something of value is produced.

There are several remarks to be made about these results.

(i) The equilibrium output vector x^* and the equilibrium price vector may contain zero components.

(ii) At the von Neumann prices and interest rate there may be pairs (x, y) other than (x^*, y^*), the von Neumann pair, that earn zero profits. The set of all pairs (x, y) that earn zero profits at the von Neumann prices and interest rate is the *von Neumann facet* (see McKenzie [18]).[11] The von Neumann facet, as well as the von Neumann ray, which consists of the pair (x^*, y^*), plays a crucial role in the establishment of the turnpike theorem to be discussed in Chapter 10. Furthermore, from (20) we see that the set of all $(x, y) \in T$ such that $p^{*'}(y - \lambda^* x) = 0$ forms the intersection of the support plane to T and the set T itself. A diagrammatic treatment of this situation is given by Koopmans [15].

(iii) The von Neumann growth rate λ^* is the rate of growth of the slowest-growing sector.

(iv) If the assumption of convexity in (A.1) is strengthened to *strict convexity*,[12] it follows that only one pair of activities makes zero profits at the von Neumann prices. In other words, the von Neumann facet reduces to the von Neumann ray.[13]

(v) Finally, we mention the concept of a *regular* model, which Gale [5] defines as one in which every optimal process (x, y) has $y > 0$. That is, for regular models every optimal process produces a positive amount of all goods. A sufficient condition for a model to be regular is that it be

---

[11]Note that we can have a von Neumann facet but still have a unique von Neumann ray. Output configurations lying on a von Neumann ray possess the following properties: (1) they permit expansion at the maximum balanced growth rate attainable by the economy, and (2) they earn zero profits at the von Neumann equilibrium prices and interest rate. Points on the facet possess only the latter property. However, we can also have more than one von Neumann ray, when more than one point on the facet in addition has property (1). In Hicks' terminology [7], any process satisfying (2) is said to be a "top process."

[12]In the present context the set T may be said to be strictly convex if for $(x_1, y_1) \in T$, $(x_2, y_2) \in T$, (with $(x_2, y_2) \neq \alpha(x_1, y_1)$ for any α), and $0 < \lambda < 1$, there is a number $\nu > 1$ such that

$$\{\lambda x_1 + (1 - \lambda)x_2, \nu[\lambda y_1 + (1 - \lambda)y_2]\} \in T.$$

[13] *Proof:* Suppose (x_1, y_1) and (x_2, y_2) both give zero profits; then $p^{*'}y_1 = \lambda^* p^{*'}x_1$ and $p^{*'}y_2 = \lambda^* p^{*'}x_2$. Therefore, $\{\lambda x_1 + (1 - \lambda)x_2, \nu[\lambda y_1 + (1 - \lambda)y_2]\} \in T$ for some $\nu > 1$ and with $0 < \lambda < 1$. Also, $p^{*'}[\lambda y_1 + (1 - \lambda)y_2] = \lambda^* p^{*'}[\lambda x_1 + (1 - \lambda)x_2]$. Therefore

$$p^{*'}\nu[\lambda y_1 + (1 - \lambda)y_2] > \lambda^* p^{*'}[\lambda x_1 + (1 - \lambda)x_2],$$

which contradicts the assertion that λ^* is the maximum balanced growth rate.

indecomposable,[14] which means in economic terms that no process in the model can sustain production unless every good in the economy is produced. This result will be relevant in McKenzie's development of the turnpike theorem, to be discussed in Chapter 10.

7–6. Extensions of the von Neumann Model

The von Neumann model discussed in the previous section deals with a closed model of production in which consumption is treated like any other input. Labor is assumed to be produced by the system and capable of indefinite expansion. Wages are at a subsistence level and all capitalists' income is immediately reinvested. This model has been generalized by Morishima [23, 25, 27, 28] in the following ways. He assumes:

(i) Labor grows at some finite rate and need not be produced within the system.
(ii) Workers' demand for consumption goods depends not only on wage income, but also on prices.
(iii) Capitalists consume a constant proportion of their income and their demand for consumption goods is responsive to price changes.

By allowing for consumers' choice and the existence of a primary factor in the von Neumann model, Morishima achieves an important generalization of the work just discussed. However, he is forced to assume that all capitalists have identical utility functions which are *strictly quasiconcave* and *quasi-homogeneous*.[15] This is restrictive as it implies that the capitalists' income elasticities of demand for all goods are unity. He also assumes all laborers have identical tastes and imposes the same restrictions on their utility function.

The technology is defined by a matrix of inputs A, of outputs B, and a column vector of labor inputs a_0. Morishima assumes:

Assumption (A.5): $A \geq 0$, $B \geq 0$.

Assumption (A.6): $a_0 > 0$.

Assumption (A.7): *Every column of B has at least one positive entry.*

The meaning of (A.5) is clear, and (A.6) asserts that labor is a necessary input into all processes. Assumption (A.7) ensures that every output can be

---

[14] See the definition of *indecomposable* in the Appendix.
[15] The definition of quasiconcavity was given on p. 10. A function $U(x)$ is also quasi-homogeneous if for all nonnegative vectors x_1 and x_2 and for all positive numbers λ, $U(x_1) \geq U(x_2)$ if and only if $U(\lambda x_1) \geq U(\lambda x_2)$.

produced. To proceed, the following notation is introduced:

$$r_0 = \text{rate of interest}$$
$$\lambda - 1 = \text{rate of growth of the economy}$$
$$g = \text{exogenously given rate of growth of labor}$$
$$w = \text{deflated wage rate}$$
$$p = \text{normalized price vector}$$
$$y = \text{normalized output vector}$$
$$c_r = \text{capitalists' marginal propensity to consume}$$
$$h^1(p) = \text{vector of capitalists' Engel coefficients}$$
$$h^2(p) = \text{vector of laborers' Engel coefficients}$$

With this notation we may obtain the following inequalities corresponding to (22a)–(22e):

$$p'B \le (1 + r_0)(p'A + wa_0) \tag{23a}$$

$$p'By = (1 + r_0)(p'A + wa_0)y \tag{23b}$$

$$By \ge \lambda[Ay + a_0 h^2(p)y] + r_0[p'Ay + wa_0 y]h^1(p) \tag{23c}$$

$$p'By = (\lambda + r_0 c_r)(p'A + wa_0)y \tag{23d}$$

$$p'By > 0 \tag{23e}$$

where $\lambda = 1 + g$.

The first inequality asserts that under perfect conditions no process can yield a rate of return in excess of the rate of interest. However, if the rate of return actually falls short of r_0, the process will not be operated. This implies the equality (23b). Inequality (23c) asserts that the supply of any good must not fall short of total demand, which consists of industrial demand, consumption demand by capitalists, and consumption demand by laborers. Equation (23d) says that if supply actually exceeds demand, the price of the good drops to zero. Inequality (23e) requires the value of output produced to be strictly positive. Finally, for balanced growth with full employment, the growth of labor must equal the growth of the economy, as indicated by $\lambda = 1 + g$.

An immediate consequence of (23b) and (23d) is that

$$\lambda - 1 = r_0(1 - c_r). \tag{24}$$

That is, the equilibrium rate of interest must equal the rate of growth divided by the capitalists' propensity to save. Note that if $c_r = 0$, as in the models of Section 7-5, then $\lambda = (1 + r_0)$, a result that was asserted before.

The proof of the theorem uses a fixed-point theorem to establish the existence of values p^*, x^*, and λ^* which satisfy the conditions of (23e). Substantial effort is required to ensure that the conditions for the application of the fixed-point theorem are satisfied. One approach is first to select a deflated wage rate w and then to determine the prices and interest rate that will permit the perfectly competitive economy to attain maximal balanced growth. This rate of growth need not equal g, the rate of population growth, so that full employment may not be maintained. The deflated wage rate w would then have to be adjusted until a solution is found for which $\lambda^* = 1 + g$. In fact, the rate of growth is a declining function of the deflated wage rate.

The steady growth path found by solving (23) is shown to have certain optimality properties. First, it implies a Pareto optimal distribution of consumable outputs among the capitalists and laborers. Second, the steady growth path is more efficient than a path that starts with steady growth but later departs from it. (The relationship of efficient paths that do not start with steady growth to the steady growth path is the core of the discussion of relative stability and turnpike theorems studied in Chapter 10.)

Further extensions by Morishima include a model in which the population growth rate g is a function of the deflated wage rate w such that g increases with w and is always positive. In this case it is possible that the real wage rate corresponding to the steady rate of growth may fall below subsistence level, so that in fact the balanced growth path may result in a stationary state or even balanced decay.

In the models so far considered the elements of A, B, and a_0 are technologically given constants. Morishima [28] has argued that the labor coefficients should not be regarded as technologically given, but should reflect the workers' welfare since the productivity of labor is intimately related to the well-being of the workers. Accordingly, the production process is broken down into two parts:

(i) The labor feeding process, and
(ii) The industrial production process.

Apart from the usual technological assumptions, Morishima postulates a law along Malthusian lines that states that the rate of population growth is greater than the smallest of the rates of growths of the outputs, comparing them at their highest feasible values. He also assumes in this model that workers cannot choose their consumption in accordance with some utility function, but instead are obliged to accept what is assigned to them. Under these circumstances Morishima proves the existence of a balanced growth path along which per capita output remains constant.

7-7. The Solow-Samuelson Model

In the previous sections we constructed alternative models of technology. In Sections 7-2 and 7-3 we described the smooth neoclassical technology with several sectors and the Leontief technology with alternative activities, respectively. Both these represented open technologies in which input of a primary factor and output of a final good appear. In Section 7-4 we moved to a closed model of production, and in Section 7-5 studied the von Neumann model, a special case of the general closed model. Section 7-6 sketched some possible extensions to the von Neumann model. All of these models represent only the supply or technological side of an economic system. They specify a set of technologically feasible growth paths, but they do not select any one growth path from the feasible set. In the following sections, we will consider ways to complete the model (somewhat artificially) so as to determine the allocation of factors in production and hence to determine a unique path of growth from given initial conditions.

One closed multisector model in which this allocation decision remains implicit only, but the growth path is determinate, is the Solow-Samuelson model [34]. This study provides a useful starting point in introducing the results that are the main focus of several models to be analyzed in more detail later.

The Solow-Samuelson model assumes that all internal allocation and optimization can be completely determined from knowledge of the stocks of factor endowments only, so that the results of these decisions may be described by functions in which only those total stocks appear as arguments. Then all outputs may be described by the equations

$$X_i(t + 1) = H^i[X_1(t), X_2(t), \ldots, X_n(t)], \quad (i = 1, \ldots, n), \tag{25}$$

and the model is completely self-contained and determinate. It can be noted that joint production is not excluded—indeed, since all stocks appear in each equation, the system is really a model of a single joint production process. The functions H^i are assumed to be continuous, homogeneous of degree one, and strictly increasing in each argument. Several questions may be asked concerning this model, just as they are asked about the other models in this book.

The first question refers to the existence and uniqueness of a balanced growth path. We say that a sequence $X(t)$ satisfying equations (25) is a *balanced growth path* or a *steady growth path* if for some $\lambda > 0$ we have

$$X(t + 1) = \lambda X(t) \qquad \text{for all} \quad t, \tag{26}$$

or, equivalently, if there is some positive vector X such that

$$\lambda X = H(X) \qquad \text{for all} \quad t. \tag{27}$$

Because of the homogeneity of H, we may equivalently seek a positive vector V such that

$$\lambda V = H(V) \tag{28}$$

where

$$\sum_{i=1}^{n} V_i = 1. \tag{29}$$

Consider the set of nonnegative vectors V whose components sum to one. This set is a closed simplex in E^n. On this set define the mapping

$$y = H(V) \Big/ \sum_{i=1}^{n} H^i(V). \tag{30}$$

Then clearly y is nonnegative and has components summing to unity. Moreover, the mapping is continuous. Hence we have a continuous mapping of the closed simplex into itself, and we may apply Brouwer's fixed-point theorem[16] to conclude that there is at least one fixed-point V^*. The vector V^* satisfies

$$V^* \sum_{i=1}^{n} H^i(V^*) = H(V^*) \tag{31}$$

and is therefore a solution to the problem just posed, with

$$\lambda = \sum_{i=1}^{n} H^i(V^*).$$

From the description of the function H we know that any solution V^*, which must be a nonzero vector because of (29), is strictly positive. Moreover, these same properties of H make it possible to show that both the growth rate λ and the vector V^* are unique.

The difference equation system (25) with prescribed initial conditions will determine a unique future for the model economy. If we consider the family of all time paths generated by the system (leaving the initial conditions open to choice), then we have just shown that there exists within this family a unique balanced growth path and a unique (and hence obviously maximal) rate of balanced growth. If the initial configuration is prescribed so that $X(0)$ is proportional to V^*, then the system begins and remains in balanced growth.

Since in this model there are no remaining allocation or optimization problems, the technology itself determines the unique feasible path from any prescribed initial configuration. Thus the second major question asked of this model concerns the properties of this actual growth path. In particular, it is of interest to know whether the actual growth path from arbitrarily specified initial conditions shows any tendency to converge to the unique

[16] See footnote 7.

balanced growth path derived earlier. Although it is not clear why we should expect this result, the answer for this model is affirmative. The "sausage-grinder" system (25) ensures that every time path, from any nonnegative initial values, converges to the balanced growth path in the following sense.

Definition: The vector $X(t)$ *converges relatively* to the vector $\overline{X}(t)$ if for all i

$$\lim_{t \to \infty} X_i(t)/\overline{X}_i(t) = x$$

where x is a constant that depends on initial conditions. The vector $\overline{X}(t)$ may be said to be *relatively stable in the small* if all vectors $X(t)$ in some neighborhood of $\overline{X}(t)$ converge relatively to $\overline{X}(t)$, and *relatively stable in the large* if all admissible vectors $X(t)$ converge relatively to $\overline{X}$.

Solow and Samuelson [34] demonstrate that the balanced growth solution $\overline{X}(t) = \lambda^t V^*$ just derived is, in fact, relatively stable in the large; that is, they show that for any solution to the system (25)

$$\lim_{t \to \infty} X_i(t)/\lambda^t V_i^* = x \tag{32}$$

for all i.

These results have been slightly extended by Morishima [25] to the case in which the function H^i need not be strictly monotonic, by Nikaido [30] to the more general case of resolvent equations, and by Fisher [4] to the case of nearly decomposable systems. We shall return to the Fisher contribution later in this chapter. But we now emphasize, as he did, that the relations (25), despite a superficial resemblance, are certainly not production functions. The arguments of each function are the same, namely the *total* endowments of the goods available. The functions describe the end result of a much larger system involving presumably, production functions, efficiency conditions, and demand or allocation decisions. To imagine that the resulting output configuration can be expressed in the form of equations (25) with constant returns to scale and strict monotonicity assumes a very simple economy indeed.

Nevertheless the discussion of the model is important in providing the concept of relative stability and an example of a descriptive model in which relative stability can be demonstrated.

We now turn to a second way in which a closed technology may be completed; this second case appends some rather specific demand considerations. The result is a closed dynamic model developed by Leontief [17].

7–8. The Closed Leontief Model

A closed Leontief technology can be obtained from the more general von Neumann model described in Section 7-5 by ruling out joint production and assuming a unique activity vector for the production of each good. Demand conditions based upon an accelerator structure, and an assumption that all capacity is always fully utilized, serve to determine a growth path generated within this technology.

We maintain the assumptions that there is no primary factor in the economy and no production of any consumption good; consequently we may continue to deal only with a vector of outputs which are used later as inputs. Leontief, however, wished to distinguish output of intermediate goods used as circulating capital from output of final goods used to augment productive capacity by adding to fixed capital. In order to maintain this distinction he postulated an underlying fixed capital stock represented by a vector K, say, and a capital/output matrix D such that

$$DY(t) = K(t) \tag{33}$$

indicates the requirements for fixed capacity in each production sector. The coefficient d_{ij} thus denotes the use of capital of type i required to produce a unit output of good j. Then the capacity required to support an output $Y(t + 1)$ is $DY(t + 1)$, and the increment to capacity required if the output $Y(t + 1)$ is to be feasible is therefore $I(t) = DY(t + 1) - DY(t)$. This is the investment that must take place in period t if there is to be adequate fixed capital in place during period $t + 1$. The output flow $Y(t)$ must include provision for this investment.

In addition, Leontief postulates a requirement for interindustry flows of intermediate goods, described by the matrix C, say. An element c_{ij} denotes the use of output i in producing good j. The columns of C therefore list the interindustry flows used in producing good j; the rows show the distribution of good i among users. The demand for intermediate goods to sustain an output $Y(t)$ is therefore $CY(t)$. Since the system is closed there is no final demand for output, so the output flow has to match the requirements for the two uses just enumerated. Hence we determine the difference equation

$$Y(t) = CY(t) + D[Y(t + 1) - Y(t)] \tag{34}$$

which output flows must satisfy.

We are thus interpreting the dynamic Leontief model as a transitional step bridging the gap between the models of the last few sections and the models in the next chapters. In the former the capital stock does not appear explicitly, and joint production permits us to work with the simple point-input point-output form.[17] In the latter, capital stocks appear explicitly and activity vectors are expressed in terms of allocations of factor stocks to sectors. The closed dynamic Leontief model obviously has capital stocks in the background to determine the output required for investment purposes, but after a simple substitution they are eliminated from the difference equations finally studied.

It is important to note also that we obtain a determinate difference equation system only because we assume that all capacity is exactly fully utilized. This assumption has important implications and will be assessed later. Finally, we shall see in our later models that the matrix C in fact is not independent of the matrix D.[18]

The closed dynamic Leontief model is for us a step toward the models in the next chapters. It is also important in its own right, however, and it has been the object of considerable study. We now turn to a discussion of one property that is central in much of our later discussion.

Rewriting equation (34) we find

$$DY(t + 1) = [I + D - C] Y(t)$$

and if D is nonsingular,[19] we may write

$$Y(t + 1) = D^{-1}[I + D - C]Y(t)$$

or

$$Y(t + 1) = [I + D^{-1}(I - C)]Y(t). \tag{35}$$

Two observations can be made about this system. First, it is capable of balanced growth if the matrix C satisfies Hawkins–Simons conditions.[20] The

[17] Since the notation is very general, we may equally well interpret the input-output pair (x, y) as the output flow x from the previous period available as input to produce the output flow y in the current period, or alternatively as the stock x left over from production in the previous period available to generate the stock y in the current period. In either case it is easy to include factor stocks carried over (in either augmented or depreciated form) from one period to the next. Bruno, Burmeister, and Sheshinski [1], p. 528–531, also observe that the formal properties of the capital model developed in the next chapter are preserved if interindustry flows of intermediate goods are introduced into the system.

[18] The argument, which will become clear in Chapter 8, is based on the fact that the flow matrix C should reflect depreciation of capital stocks due to use in production. This observation is present in Morishima [25], p. 95, and is slightly elaborated in the discussion of Bruno, Burmeister, and Sheshinski [1] cited above.

[19] If not, we may define new variables that are linear combinations of the old, reducing the order of the system until the transformed matrix D becomes nonsingular. We follow tradition and ignore this complication.

[20] See the Appendix. For simplicity we also assume that C is indecomposable.

second is that the balanced growth path need not be stable—indeed the presumption might be that it is not.

The proof of the first observation follows from the fact that the matrix $(I - C)^{-1}D$ will be positive, and therefore it will have a positive characteristic root ρ greater in modulus than any other root; the root ρ has an associated positive eigenvector.[21] Then $1/\rho$ is clearly a root of $D^{-1}(I - C)$, and the system (35) is therefore able to sustain a balanced growth path with all positive outputs and a rate of expansion $(1 + 1/\rho)$.

The stability is questionable because we know that all other characteristic roots of $(I - C)^{-1}D$ are bounded above in modulus by ρ, and hence all other characteristic roots λ_i of $D^{-1}(I - C)$ are bounded below by $1/\rho$. (This observation does not prove instability because it is the magnitude of $(1 + 1/\rho)$ in comparison to the magnitude of $(1 + \lambda_i)$ that determines stability.) If $(1 + 1/\rho)$ does not dominate all other values $(1 + \lambda_i)$ in magnitude, then the system must depart from the balanced growth path defined by the unique[22] positive eigenvector, and eventually some outputs must become negative.

In summary, there are several aspects of interest in this model. First, we know a balanced growth path exists. On the other hand, analysis of the growth path from specified initial conditions shows that it need not be stable; that is, the system need not converge toward the balanced growth path, but may diverge from it. Moreover, if the system is in fact unstable in this sense, then

---

[21] By assumption C is indecomposable and satisfies the Hawkins-Simons conditions, so that lemmas L.6 and L.5′ in the Appendix imply $(I - C)^{-1} > 0$. But since D is a nonnegative matrix with an inverse, det $D \neq 0$. Consequently, every row and column of D must contain at least one positive element and $(I - C)^{-1}D > 0$. Lemmas L.2′ and L.4′ (in the Appendix) complete the proof of the statement in the text.

[22] Actually, eigenvectors are uniquely only up to a scalar multiple. Thus, if ρ^* is a characteristic root an $n \times n$ matrix A with an associated eigenvector satisfying $Az^* = \rho^*z^*$, then for any scalar $\alpha > 0$, $z^{**} = \alpha z^*$ is also an eigenvector associated with ρ^*. It is precisely for this reason, of course, that we are only able to establish *relative stability*, with asymptotic uniqueness of *ratios* $z_i^*/z_1^* = z_i^{**}/z_1^{**}$ for any $\alpha > 0$ and all $i = 2, \ldots, n$.

Any other normalization rule suffices to assure uniqueness, and in particular the normalization

$$\sum_{i=1}^{n} z_i^* = 1$$

was used in Section 7-7. The exact logical equivalence of the two normalizations stated above is easily seen by writing (32) in the form

$$\lim_{t \to \infty} X_i(t) = x \lim_{t \to \infty} \lambda^t V_i^*, \qquad (i = 1, \ldots, n),$$

or

$$\lim_{t \to \infty} \frac{X_i(t)}{X_1(t)} = \frac{V_i^*}{V_1^*}, \qquad (i = 2, \ldots, n).$$

Finally, we remind the reader that our earlier models with one capital good also involved relative stability theorems since only the asymptotic ratio of capital to labor was uniquely determined.

there must be concern whether the requirement of nonnegativity in all variables can be preserved over all time. In general, it cannot. This problem, which Dorfman, Samuelson, and Solow [3] have labeled "causal indeterminacy" is severe. The problem is that there are no rules for the system to follow—there is no determinate future for the system—when it reaches the boundaries imposed by the nonnegativity constraints. One solution in such circumstances (see McManus [22]) is to let the system switch regimes and follow a different, but again determinate, set of rules. Dorfman, Samuelson, and Solow [3] on the other hand argue that the system was not legitimately complete in the first place because the set of feasible growth paths should be described by inequalities in the system (35), and they further argue that choice among these paths should be accomplished by an allocation rule (e.g., an optimizing procedure) of some kind, and not simply by an insistence on equalities everywhere. We return to this issue later, but now we will examine another aspect of the foregoing model.

7–9. The Dual Price System and Dual Stability

We have seen that the system (35) may or may not converge toward its balanced growth path, and if it does not, at some finite time some components of the output vector will become negative.

Solow [33] noted another aspect of this Leontief model when he studied the behavior of an associated system of prices. Admitting expectations of capital gains,[23] Solow developed the following price model which is dual to the output model and is interesting in itself. (Also, as Fisher [4] pointed out, the dual price model may plausibly satisfy the conditions of the Samuelson-Solow model described in Section 7-7, which means that relative stability results derived there may be relevant for situations of balanced price inflation even if not for balanced output growth.) Clearly the behavior of solutions to the dual price system is related very closely to the solutions of the quantity system. Indeed, Solow [33] conjectured that if the quantity system is stable, the price system must be unstable, and vice versa. The proof, sketched by Solow and developed by Jorgenson [10], is as follows.

The familiar argument about the determination of asset prices in perfect capital markets (when assets are held only for their earnings and do not have value in themselves) requires that capital gains be determined to bring the yield on all assets into equality. For if all capital goods did not earn the same yield (over any holding period), some capital goods would not be willingly held but would be offered in trade for alternative assets promising

[23] The explicit recognition of capital gains is crucial to the character of the resulting model.

a higher return. When prices are changing this return must include all expected capital gains. If forecasts of capital gains are perfectly accurate, then one has the equations

$$P'(t + 1)[I - C + D] = [1 + r_0(t)]P'(t)D \qquad (36)$$

which determine a row vector P of equilibrium asset prices in the model of Section 7-8. The rationale for these equations may be seen by observing that the jth equation reads

$$P_j(t + 1) - \sum_{i=1}^{n} P_i(t + 1)c_{ij} + \sum_{i=1}^{n} P_i(t + 1)d_{ij} = [1 + r_0(t)]\sum_{i=1}^{n} P_i(t)d_{ij}.$$

The right-hand side represents the value (principal plus interest) at time $t + 1$ of the funds necessary to purchase at time t the capital goods required to produce one unit of good j at time $t + 1$. The left-hand side represents the value at $t + 1$ of the output produced, less the direct cost incurred for circulating capital at the time of production $(t + 1)$, plus the value (reestimated at new prices) of the durable capital goods retained. Capital market equilibrium demands that the two values be equal.

Equation (36) may be rewritten

$$P(t + 1) = [1 + r_0(t)][I + (D^{-1})' (I - C)']^{-1}P(t). \qquad (37)$$

Comparing (37) with (35), it becomes clear that the characteristic roots for the price system are intimately related to those for the quantity system. We saw that the quantity system need not be stable; now we see that if it is not the reciprocal nature of the characteristic roots in (35) and (37) suggests that the price system is stable. This result was conjectured by Solow [33] and proved by Jorgenson [10]; we now state but do not prove Jorgenson's theorem.

> **Theorem 2 (Dual Stability Theorem):** *For systems of order greater than one, if the output system* (35) *is relatively stable in the large, then the price system* (37) *is relatively unstable in the large, and vice versa.*

Thus, the closed Leontief model leaves us with a very strong result on the dual stability features of the price-quantity systems taken together. Notice, though, that we might feel somewhat more at liberty to argue that initial prices are at our disposal than we would to argue that initial quantities are free. If initial prices and quantities are given historically, then the dual stability result just enunciated holds. If however, we imagine that initial prices are ours to set, then the result tells us that when the output system is stable there is only one choice of an initial price vector that will not eventually imply a negative value for at least one price.[24]

Finally, observe that this system is completely decoupled. Price and quantity systems run along side by side but never affect one another. Later results will lead us to believe that this feature is, in fact, one reflection of the issue which Dorfman, Samuelson, and Solow [3] raised, namely that this quantity system is an illegitimate representation of allocation decisions that should properly depend on price considerations. Like the closed Solow-Samuelson model with which this discussion began, the above output model lacks the internal optimizing and allocating that must form an integral part of any interesting economic system. Because there is no choice of production activities and full utilization is imposed, simple demand conditions instead suffice to determine an output path that might be unstable.

7–10. Summary

This chapter has sketched elements of a number of multisector models and has introduced major themes to be elaborated in the next two chapters. Without reviewing matters in detail, we may summarize the most important issues.

It is our goal to extend some of the analysis in previous chapters to the case where there are several sectors and distinct capital goods. A natural extension is to adopt the multisector neoclassical technology described in Section 7-2. While it is convenient to develop some preliminary results, however, we defer any discussion of that model until Chapter 9. Some other preliminary results are developed in discussion of the Leontief technology with alternative choice of production techniques; however, again we defer discussion until a later chapter (Chapter 8).

Both of the foregoing models are open, i.e., a primary factor and a consumption good both appear. In Section 7-4 we assume that neither a primary factor nor a consumption good appear, and thus we obtain a closed model of production. Once the technology is specified for such a model it is natural to ask whether the set of technologically feasible growth paths contains any balanced growth path, and further whether it contains a balanced growth path attaining the maximal rate of expansion. In addition, the uniqueness of the maximal balanced growth path is an issue.

---

[24] These observations may be illustrated in part by a phase diagram. Consider a case with the vectors Y and P both of order 2. Plot the ratio Y_2/Y_1 along the horizontal axis, and P_2/P_1 along the vertical, identifying the unique values y^* and p^* associated with the eigenvectors in each case. Then the dual stability theorem asserts that the motion of the system may be described by a phase diagram in which the point (y^*, p^*) is a saddlepoint equilibrium, and all trajectories are hyperbola-like arcs, with the lines $y = y^*$, $p = p^*$ serving as orthogonal separatrices.

In a study of the closed model of production (Section 7-4) and the von Neumann model (Section 7-5), we found that there exists a maximal balanced growth rate and a balanced growth path attaining this maximal rate. Moreover, we saw that associated with this maximal balanced growth path there is a price vector and an interest rate (equal to the rate of growth) at which all activities used yield zero profit.

Similar results are valid for less restrictive open von Neumann models, and in Section 7-6 we sketched some of these results without proof.

All the foregoing discussion relates to existence properties in models that determine only a technologically feasible set of growth paths. There are various ways in which these models can be completed to determine a unique feasible growth path from any starting point. Then we may still ask whether for a suitable choice of initial conditions there exists a balanced growth path; that is, whether the economy is capable of sustained balanced growth, and, further, whether this balanced growth path is stable. We introduced the definition of relative stability in order to have a stability concept appropriate to this last question.

The Solow-Samuelson sausage machine model represents one way to complete the system. It determines a unique growth path by assuming that all resource allocation decisions can be assumed solved and summarized in homogenous and strictly monotone functions entering directly into the accumulation equations. We found that this model is capable of sustained balanced growth, and we found that the unique balanced growth path is relatively stable in the large. From any given initial conditions the growth path tends toward the balanced growth proportions.

A second method to complete the system is to go to some version of the closed dynamic Leontief model. This structure determines a unique growth path by adding demand conditions derived from an accelerator mechanism and by insisting implicitly upon full utilization of all underlying factor stocks.[25] In this case we found again that the model is capable of sustained balanced growth, but there is no guarantee that the balanced growth path is relatively stable. If it is not, then the dynamic equations imply that eventually some outputs must become negative, and thus the adequacy of the whole model structure is called into question.

Adjoining a dual price system to the Leontief model we found a strong dual stability result: if the dual price system is stable, then the quantity system is unstable, and vice versa.

Neither of the foregoing devices for completing the system and selecting (from among the technologically feasible growth paths emanating from a

---

[25] As this description implies, the model is in many ways more akin to demand-oriented Harrod–Domar or multiplier-accelerator models than it is to our supply-oriented potential output models. Nevertheless, it is useful here in providing a convenient vehicle for introduction of dynamic properties that will recur later.

specified initial position) one unique path of accumulation is completely satisfactory. Proper treatment must make explicit the allocation decisions implicit in the Solow-Samuelson sausage grinder, and the next two chapters are directed to this task.

References

[1] BRUNO, M., E. BURMEISTER, and E. SHESHINSKI, "The Nature and Implications of the Reswitching of Techniques," *Quarterly Journal of Economics*, **LXXX**, *4* (November, 1966), pp. 526–553. Reprinted in *Readings in Mathematical Economics* (Peter Newman, Ed.), **II**, pp. 68–95. Baltimore: Johns Hopkins Press, 1968.

[2] CHAMPERNOWNE, D. G., "A Note on J. von Neumann's Article," *Review of Economic Studies*, **XIII** (1945), pp. 10–18.

[3] DORFMAN, R., P. A. SAMUELSON, and R. M. SOLOW, *Linear Programming and Economic Analysis*. New York: McGraw-Hill, 1958.

[4] FISHER, F. M. "Decomposability, Near Decomposability, and Balanced Price Change under Constant Returns to Scale," *Econometrica*, **31**, *1–2* (January–April, 1963), pp. 67–89.

[5] GALE, D., "The Closed Linear Model of Production," pp. 285–303, in *Linear Inequalities and Related Systems* (H. W. Kuhn and A. W. Tucker, Eds.). Princeton: Princeton University Press, 1956.

[6] HAHN, F. and R. C. O. MATTHEWS, "The Theory of Economic Growth: A Survey," *Economic Journal*, **LXXIV**, 296 (December, 1964), pp. 779–902.

[7] HICKS, J. R. "Prices and the Turnpike: (I) The Story of a Mare's Nest," *Review of Economic Studies*, **XXVIII**, *76* (February, 1961), pp. 77–88.

[8] — *Capital and Growth*. New York: Oxford University Press, 1965.

[9] HOWE, C. W., "An Alternative Proof of the Existence of General Equilibrium in a von Neumann Model," *Econometrica*, **28**, *3* (July, 1960), pp. 635–639.

[10] JORGENSON, D., "A Dual Stability Theorem," *Econometrica*, **28**, *4* (October, 1960), pp. 892–899.

[11] KAKUTANI, S., "A Generalization of Brouwer's Fixed Point Theorem," *Duke Mathematical Journal* (1941). Reprinted in *Readings in Mathematical Economics* (Peter Newman, Ed.), **II**, p. 33–35. Baltimore: Johns Hopkins Press, 1968.

[12] KARLIN, S., *Mathematical Methods and Theory in Games, Programming, and Economics*, **I**, **II**. Reading, Mass: Addison-Wesley, 1959.

[13] KEMENY, J. G., O. MORGENSTERN and G. L. THOMPSON, "A Generalization of the von Neumann Model of an Expanding Economy," *Econometrica*, **24**, *2* (April, 1956).

[14] KOOPMANS, T. C., *Three Essays on the State of the Economic Science*. New York: McGraw-Hill, 1957.

[15] — "Economic Growth at a Maximal Rate," *Quarterly Journal of Economics*, **LXXVIII**, *3* (August, 1964), pp. 355–394.

[16] LEFSCHETZ, S., *Introduction to Topology*. Princeton: Princeton University Press, 1949.

[17] LEONTIEF, W. W. *The Structure of the American Economy, 1919–1939*. New York: Oxford University Press, 1951.

[18] McKenzie, L. W., "Turnpike Theorems for a Generalized Leontief Model," *Econometrica*, **31**, *1–2* (January-April, 1963), pp. 165–180.

[19] — "The Turnpike Theorem of Morishima," *Review of Economic Studies*, **XXX**, *84* (October, 1963), pp. 169–176.

[20] — "The Dorfman-Samuelson-Solow Turnpike Theorem," *International Economic Review*, **4**, *1* (January, 1963), pp. 29–43.

[21] — "Maximal Paths in the von Neumann Model," paper presented at Boston meeting of Econometric Society (1963), abstract in *Econometrica*, **32**, *4* (October, 1964), p. 691.

[22] McManus, M., "Self-Contradiction in Leontief's Dynamic Model," *Yorkshire Bulletin of Economic and Social Research*, **9**, *1* (May, 1957), pp. 1–21.

[23] Morishima, M., "Economic Expansion and the Interest Rate in Generalized von Neumann Models," *Econometrica*, **XXVIII**, *2* (April, 1960), pp. 352–363.

[24] — "Proof of a Turnpike Theorem: The 'No Joint Production Case'," *Review of Economic Studies*, **XXVIII**, *76* (February, 1961), pp. 89–98.

[25] — *Equilibrium, Stability and Growth.* Oxford: Clarendon Press, 1964.

[26] — "On the Two Theorems of Growth Economics: A Mathematical Exercise," *Econometrica*, **33**, *4* (October, 1965), pp. 829–840.

[27] — "Theory of Growth: von Neumann Revolution," Technical Report No. 130, Institute for Mathematical Studies in the Social Sciences. Stanford, Calif.: Stanford University, 1965.

[28] — "Theory of Growth: Remodelling and Refinements," Technical Report No. 132, Institute for Mathematical Studies in the Social Sciences. Stanford, Calif.: Stanford University, 1965.

[29] Nikaido, H., *Convex Structures and Economic Theory*, New York: Academic Press, 1968.

[30] — "Balanced Growth in Multi-Sectoral Income Propagation under Autonomous Expenditure Schemes," *Review of Economic Studies*, **XXXI**, *85* (January, 1964), pp. 25–42.

[31] Robinson, Joan, *The Accumulation of Capital.* New York: St. Martin's Press, 1966.

[32] Samuelson, P. A., "Parable and Realism in Capital Theory: The Surrogate Production Function," *Review of Economic Studies*, **XXIX**, *80* (June, 1962), pp. 193–206.

[33] Solow, R. M., "Competitive Valuation in a Dynamic Input-Output System," *Econometrica*, **27**, *1* (January, 1959), pp. 30–53.

[34] — and P. A. Samuelson, "Balanced Growth under Constant Returns to Scale," *Econometrica*, **21**, *3* (July, 1953), pp. 412–424.

[35] von Neumann, J., "Über ein Ökonomisches Gleichungsystem und eine Verallgemeinerung des Brouwerschen Fixpunktsatzes," *Ergebnisse eines Mathematischen Seminars* (K. Menger, Ed.; G. Morgenstern, Trans. 1938). English translation: "A Model of General Economic Equilibrium," reprinted in *Readings in Mathematical Economics* (Peter Newman, Ed.), **II**, pp. 221–229. Baltimore: Johns Hopkins Press, 1968.

[36] Winter, S. G., "Some Properties of the Closed Linear Model of Production," *International Economic Review*, **6**, *2* (May, 1965), pp. 199–210.

Chapter 8 Leontief Models with Alternative Techniques

8–1. Introduction

The Leontief model with alternative techniques is described in Section 7-3. In this model the production functions are of the form

$$Y_j = \min\left[\frac{L_j}{a_{0j}(\mu_j)}, \frac{K_{1j}}{a_{1j}(\mu_j)}, \ldots, \frac{K_{nj}}{a_{nj}(\mu_j)}\right], \quad (j = 0, 1, \ldots, n). \qquad (1)$$

A selection of the index $\mu_j \in \{1, \ldots, m_j\}$ determines the activity vector $[a_{0j}(\mu_j), 0, a_{1j}(\mu_j), \ldots, a_{nj}(\mu_j)]$ for producing the jth good ($j = 0, 1, \ldots, n$). Consequently a selection of $n+1$ such indices for each good determines $n+1$ activity vectors, which together constitute a technique matrix. As noted in Chapter 7 there are

$$M = \prod_{j=0}^{n} m_j \qquad (2)$$

such matrices, and the set of all these comprises the *technology, book of blue prints*, or *spectrum of techniques* open to the economy.

We first consider simple cases (Sections 8-2 and 8-3) in which there is only one technique matrix available to the economy, and we restrict our attention to steady states in which prices remain constant over time. We assume that the money rate of interest is an exogenous (nonnegative) constant, and we insist on equilibrium in perfect capital markets under the assumption that foresight is perfect at least one period into the future. (In steady states with unchanging prices such a requirement is not unduly stringent.)

Given this setting, the basic economic issue is whether or not the economy is in fact viable, that is, productive enough to generate strictly positive prices in competitive equilibrium. The analysis of this question involves properties of nonnegative square matrices; these properties are quoted in the Appendix to this book, and we make extensive use of them in this chapter. In addition we find it convenient to analyze the same problem in a slightly more general form in which the entire vector of gross own-rates of return, rather than simply the money rate of interest r_0, is exogenous. (That is, we drop momentarily the requirement that all own-rates be constant and equal to a common value, and alternatively insist only that they all be constant.)

In Section 8-4 we admit alternative techniques in an analysis of the same questions. In this case, however, another issue arises, namely, what technique matrix will in fact be observed in a cost-minimizing competitive equilibrium? This crucial question, often called the question of "the choice of technique," is answered in Theorem 7. The familiar factor-price frontier and the non-substitution theorem follow immediately from our analysis. Section 8-5 is very similar in structure, except that there we seek conditions that ensure that all quantities are strictly positive in competitive equilibrium.

Reswitching of techniques is examined in Section 8-6, and "paradoxical" implications of this phenomenon highlight Section 8-7. Our analysis casts considerable doubt on the general validity of the so-called "neoclassical parable."

The concept of the social rate of return is introduced in Section 8-8. Section 8-9 sketches without proof some price-quantity duality relationships from which the familiar Golden Rule follows as a corollary. Finally, the dynamic behavior of the model is studied in Section 8-10, and we find that some of the dual instability features mentioned in Chapter 7 (in the context of a closed Leontief model) remain an important issue.

8–2. Equilibrium Prices with One Technique Matrix

We stipulate that there exists only one technique matrix, Technique α, and we simplify the notation by suppressing μ_j with the understanding that

$$a_{ij}(\mu_j) = a_{ij}, \qquad (i, j = 0, 1, \ldots, n), \tag{3}$$

are the input coefficients for Technique α.

Full employment requires satisfaction of the equalities

$$\sum_{j=0}^{n} K_{ij} = K_i, \qquad (i = 1, \ldots, n), \tag{4}$$

and

$$\sum_{j=0}^{n} L_j = L \tag{5}$$

where K_i is the total employment of the ith capital good and L is the total employment of labor. We introduce the following matrix notation:

$$Y = \begin{bmatrix} Y_0 \\ Y_1 \\ \vdots \\ Y_n \end{bmatrix}, \qquad a_0 = (a_{00}, a_{01}, \ldots, a_{0n}),$$

$$a = \begin{bmatrix} 0 & 0 & \cdots & 0 \\ a_{10} & a_{11} & \cdots & a_{1n} \\ \vdots & \vdots & & \vdots \\ a_{n0} & a_{n1} & \cdots & a_{nn} \end{bmatrix}, \qquad \text{and} \qquad K = \begin{bmatrix} 0 \\ K_1 \\ \vdots \\ K_n \end{bmatrix}.$$

Assuming that no factors are redundant in any individual production process, (4) and (5) may be expressed in the equivalent forms

$$a Y = K \tag{6}$$

and

$$a_0 Y = L, \tag{7}$$

respectively.

The production functions (1) need careful interpretation because we assume output requires inputs for a discrete time interval (one day, for example) or for one *period of production*. Various timing postulates are conceivable, but we adopt the following convention. The inputs employed *during the* tth production period ($t = 1, 2, \ldots$) are denoted by $K_{ij}(t)$ and $L_j(t)$, whereas the outputs (produced from these inputs) are not available for use until the beginning of period $t + 1$ and are denoted by $Y_j(t + 1)$. We also emphasize that the beginning of period $t + 1$ is the end of period t, so other standard notational conventions are equivalent to ours.

Furthermore, we assume that the jth capital good depreciates by a constant fraction δ_j during each production period.[1] Thus the total stock of the jth capital good available at the beginning of period $t + 1$ is

$$K_j(t + 1) = Y_j(t + 1) + (1 - \delta_j)K_j(t), \qquad (j = 1, \ldots, n). \tag{8}$$

---

[1] This assumption implies that the depreciation rate δ_j depends only on j and not on the particular sectors in which the jth capital good may be employed. In general depreciation rates and hence rental rates for the jth capital good may differ from sector to sector, a complication we wish to avoid. We also assume for convenience that all depreciation occurs at the end of the production period.

However, a more general model can be studied by similar methods (see, e.g., Burmeister and Sheshinski [4]) and consequently our assumptions do not substantially affect the main results.

We introduce the following notation and definitions.

$W_i(t)$ = the gross rental rate for the ith capital good paid at the end of period t, $(i = 1, \ldots, n)$

$W_0(t)$ = the nominal wage rate paid at the end of period t

$W(t) = [W_0(t), W_1(t), \ldots, W_n(t)]$

$P_i(t)$ = the price for one unit of the ith output at the beginning of period t, $(i = 0, 1, \ldots, n)$

$P(t) = [P_0(t), P_1(t), \ldots, P_n(t)]$

$W_i(t)/P_i(t) \equiv \rho_i(t)$ = the gross own-rate of return for the ith capital good, $(i = 1, \ldots, n)$

$\rho_i(t) - \delta_i \equiv r_i(t)$ = the net own-rate of return for the ith capital good

$r_0(t)$ = the money rate of interest or the profit rate

$$[\theta + \delta] = \begin{bmatrix} 1 & 0 & \cdots & 0 \\ 0 & \theta + \delta_1 & \cdots & 0 \\ \vdots & \vdots & & \vdots \\ 0 & 0 & \cdots & \theta + \delta_n \end{bmatrix} \quad \text{for any scalar } \theta$$

$$[\rho] = \begin{bmatrix} 1 & 0 & \cdots & 0 \\ 0 & \rho_1 & \cdots & 0 \\ \vdots & \vdots & \cdots & \vdots \\ 0 & 0 & \cdots & \rho_n \end{bmatrix}$$

Consider now an investor with one dollar at the beginning of period t. He can either (1) invest in the ith capital good thereby earning a profit equal to the net own-rate of return $r_i(t)$ plus any net capital gains that will arise if $P_i(t + 1) \neq P_i(t)$, or (2) invest in some underlying financial asset at the money rate of interest and earn a net profit $r_0(t)$. In competitive equilibrium the options (1) and (2) must yield equal returns,[2] i.e., the equations

$$r_i(t) + \frac{P_i(t + 1) - P_i(t)}{P_i(t)} = r_0(t), \quad (i = 1, \ldots, n), \tag{9}$$

must be satisfied. Since he can purchase $1/P_i(t)$ machines of type i with one dollar, the second term in (9) is equal to the net capital gains that will be earned if $P_i(t + 1) \neq P_i(t)$. Furthermore, it is easily seen that

$$r_i(t) = \frac{W_i(t) - P_i(t)\,\delta_i}{P_i(t)}. \tag{10}$$

[2] See Dorfman, Samuelson, and Solow [8], p. 318. It is important to realize that this argument assumes perfect certainty at least one period into the future.

The numerator of (10) is equal to the net money returns obtained by renting one machine of type i during period t and is also equal to the gross returns $W_i(t)$ minus the cost of maintaining (e.g., servicing) one machine. The latter cost is *assumed* equal[3] to $P_i(t)\delta_i$, and if the numerator of (10) is multiplied by $1/P_i(t)$ (the number of machines of type i that can be purchased with one dollar), we obtain the net own-rate of return $r_i(t)$.

Equation (9) reduces to

$$r_i = r_0, \qquad (i = 1, \ldots, n), \qquad (11)$$

if $W_i(t) = W_i$, $P_i(t) = P_i$, and $r_0(t) = r_0$ for all t. This special case is easy to understand because in competitive equilibrium the price of one machine must equal the value of future rentals discounted at the interest rate r_0. However, our depreciation assumption implies that one machine of type i becomes only $(1 - \delta_i)$ machines at the end of one period, $(1 - \delta_i)^2$ machines at the end of two periods, etc. Consequently, the equations

$$P_i = W_i \left[\frac{1}{1 + r_0} + \frac{1 - \delta_i}{(1 + r_0)^2} + \frac{(1 - \delta_i)^2}{(1 + r_0)^3} + \cdots \right], \qquad (i = 1, \ldots, n), \quad (12)$$

must be satisfied under our assumptions. However, if $r_0 > 0$ and $0 < \delta_i < 1$, (12) may be solved for

$$P_i = \frac{W_i}{r_0 + \delta_i}, \qquad (13)$$

which is equivalent to (11) (Exercise 1).

Thus we may expect that arbitrage in markets for capital goods will restrict rates of return, forcing the rate of return on each asset into equality with the rate $r_0(t)$, a money rate of interest assumed to be exogenously given. If $P(t)$, $W(t)$, and $r_0(t)$ are given, equations (9) and (10) would determine $P_i(t + 1)$, $i = 1, \ldots, n$. On the other hand, quite independently of capital market trading, unit costs of production also are expected to determine output prices, as the following paragraphs demonstrate.

In competitive equilibrium the value of output must equal the cost of production. The value of the jth output produced during period t is

$$P_j(t + 1) Y_j(t + 1),$$

[3] See footnote 1. It might be argued that $P_i(t + 1)\delta_i$ is an alternative measure of such costs, but our assumption is more convenient. In any event the two measures are equivalent when $P_i(t + 1) = P_i(t)$, the case we will study in most of this chapter.

whereas the cost, incurred at the end of period t, is

$$W_0(t)L_j(t) + \sum_{i=1}^{n} W_i(t)K_{ij}(t).$$

However, the timing of inputs and outputs necessitates the convention

$$a_{ij} = K_{ij}(t)/Y_j(t+1), \qquad (i = 1, \ldots, n; j = 0, 1, \ldots, n), \tag{14}$$

and

$$a_{0j} = L_j(t)/Y_j(t+1), \qquad (j = 0, 1, \ldots, n), \tag{15}$$

respectively. (Remember that we are still considering only Technique α.) Thus, in competitive equilibrium we have the following conditions:

$$P_j(t+1) = W_0(t)a_{0j} + \sum_{i=1}^{n} W_i(t)a_{ij}$$

$$= W_0(t)a_{0j} + \sum_{i=1}^{n} P_i(t)\rho_i(t)a_{ij}, \qquad (j = 0, 1, \ldots, n). \tag{16}$$

In matrix notation (16) is rewritten

$$P(t+1) = a_0 W_0(t) + P(t)\rho(t)a. \tag{17}$$

Our results may be summarized as follows. Consider Technique α and the corresponding matrix of input coefficients

$$\begin{bmatrix} a_0 \\ \cdots \\ a \end{bmatrix}.$$

For this given technique, we appear to have two independent conditions determining the prices $P(t+1)$ for the output of the tth period. The first, described in equation (16), relates to rentals for the use of the capital goods in production, and determines price as equal to the cost of production when rentals are given. Assuming that initial prices $P(t)$ are known, this same condition may be expressed as in equation (17), in terms of W_0 and own-rates $\rho_1, \ldots, \rho_n$ rather than rentals $W_1, \ldots, W_n$.

The second, described in equations (9) and (10), relates to trading on asset markets among owners of the capital goods. Taking the price of existing durable goods and the price of the flow output of new durable goods to be the same (an assumption that is tenable, strictly speaking, only under the hypothesis of exponential decay of all durable goods), and given a money rate of interest r_0, we may argue that $P_1(t + 1), \ldots, P_n(t + 1)$ are determined, once $P(t)$ is known, by the requirement of capital market equilibrium.

To insist that these two sets of conditions yield consistent results thus entails restrictions on the vector of rentals of own-rates taken as given in equation (17). In the last section of this chapter we combine equations (9) and (17), and study the development of prices over time. In the next section we turn to the special case in which prices are stationary, and study conditions ensuring that steady-state prices generated by equation (17) are positive when the vector ρ of gross own-rates is given and need not satisfy the restrictions (9).

8-3. Steady-State Equilibrium Prices with One Technique Matrix

For simplicity we will again consider Technique α and will restrict our attention to steady states in which all prices and rental rates remain constant over time, i.e., we consider only cases for which $P_i(t) = P_i$ and $W_i(t) = W_i$ for all t, $i = 0, 1, \ldots, n$. Consequently, the definitions of the gross and net own-rates of return imply immediately that they are also constant with $\rho_i(t) = \rho_i$ and $r_i(t) = r_i$, $i = 1, \ldots, n$. In addition, competitive equilibrium in the capital markets requires that all the net own-rates of return equal a common value r_0 which is "the" interest or profit rate. However, in order to apply our results in a different context we will ignore this restriction for the moment and allow the net own-rates of return to differ.

The issue, then, is whether or not the economy is capable of generating—i.e., is productive enough to generate—strictly positive equilibrium prices and quantities. If the question is to be meaningful we must assume that the technology contains at least one technique matrix, Technique α, for which prices are strictly positive when the net own-rates of return are all zero, [assumption (A.3)]. If this assumption were not satisfied, the economy would not be productive enough to generate strictly positive prices unless one or more net-own rates of return became negative, a case which we exclude as economically meaningless.

Assumptions A.1 and A.2 replace the stronger but more common assumption that the technique matrix is indecomposable. However, they serve the same objective, namely to insure that all equilibrium prices are strictly positive.

Our purpose at this point is fulfilled by considering only one *viable* (defined later in the text) technique, Technique α. Theorem 4 states our primary conclusion: when the ρ_i's satisfy the given inequalities, the matrix ρ is *feasible* (defined later in the text) and the competitive equilibrium price vector given by (20) is strictly positive.

Theorem 5 states a result that has received considerable attention in the literature, one to which we will return later in this chapter. We will establish that all equilibrium prices are determined only by the interest or profit rate r_0, where $r_i = r_0$ $(i = 1, \ldots, n)$, and that these prices are all strictly positive provided $0 \leq r_0 < r_0^*$; r_0^* is equal to the reciprocal of the dominant characteristic root of the matrix $a[I - \delta a]^{-1}$ (Theorems 1, 2, 3, and 4). Theorem 5 asserts further that $dp_i/dr_0 > 0$ $(i = 1, \ldots, n)$; moreover, the function $p_i(r_0)$ has a pole at $r_0 = r_0^*$, i.e., $\lim_{r_0 \to r_0^*} p(r_0) = +\infty$, whereas if r_0 exceeds r_0^*, one or more equilibrium prices will become nonpositive.

We now turn to proofs of these remarks, which are restated below as Theorems 1–5.

In view of our assumptions, equation (17) may be rewritten as

$$P = a_0 W_0 + P\rho a \tag{18}$$

or

$$p = a_0 + p\rho a, \tag{19}$$

where

$$p \equiv (P_0/W_0, P_1/W_0, \ldots, P_n/W_0)$$

is a vector of relative prices with the wage rate as *numeraire*. Provided that the matrix $[I - \rho a]^{-1}$ exists, (19) may be solved for

$$p = a_0[I - \rho a]^{-1}, \tag{20}$$

but this solution is economically meaningful only if prices are strictly positive $(p > 0)$. Therefore we seek sufficient conditions implying (1) $[I - \rho a]^{-1}$ exists, and (2) $p > 0$.

In the following proofs we make extensive use of a well-known lemma which we have stated in the Appendix. L.1, L.2, etc., refer to statements of this lemma. Likewise we adopt here the vector notation outlined in the Appendix.

We require the following assumptions.

Assumption (A.1): *Labor is required, either directly or indirectly, to produce every good.*

Assumption (A.2): *At least one capital good is needed to produce every good, and every capital good is required, directly or indirectly, to produce the consumption good.*

Definition: A technique matrix is *viable* if the price vector (20) is strictly positive when the net own-rates of return r_i satisfy $r_i = 0$, $i = 1, \ldots, n$.

Assumption (A.3): *The technology contains at least one viable technique matrix, which, without loss of generality, we designate as Technique α.*

We may now prove the following results.

Theorem 1 (Hicks[4]): *Let $\bar{r}$ be a nonnegative scalar. Then $[I - \bar{r}a - \delta a]^{-1}$ $\equiv [I - (\bar{r} + \delta)a]^{-1} \geq 0$ if and only if $\bar{r} < 1/\lambda^{**}$ where λ^{**} is the dominant characteristic root of the matrix $a[I - \delta a]^{-1}$.*

Proof: Since Technique α is viable by (A.3), $[I - (0 + \delta)a]^{-1} \geq 0$.[5] Therefore, L.5 implies that $1 = \lambda > \lambda^*$ where λ^* is the dominant characteristic root of the matrix δa. Furthermore,

$$[I - (\bar{r} + \delta)a] = \{I - \bar{r}a[I - \delta a]^{-1}\}[I - \delta a].$$

Thus, if $[I - (\bar{r} + \delta)a]^{-1}$ exists,

$$[I - (\bar{r} + \delta)a]^{-1} = [I - \delta a]^{-1}\{I - \bar{r}a[I - \delta a]^{-1}\}^{-1}.$$

Since $[I - \delta a]^{-1} \geq 0$, we require only that $\{I - \bar{r}a[I - \delta a]^{-1}\}^{-1} \geq 0$. Setting $\lambda = 1/\bar{r}$, we find the conclusion follows immediately from L.5 and L.6.   QED

Theorem 2: *Let $\bar{r} = \max_{i=1,\ldots,n}\{r_i\}$. Then $[I - (\bar{r} + \delta)a]^{-1} \geq 0$ implies $[I - \rho a]^{-1} \geq 0$.*

Proof:[6] Clearly

$$\bar{r} + \delta_i \geq r_i + \delta_i = \rho_i, \qquad i = 1, \ldots, n.$$

Therefore $(\bar{r} + \delta)a \geq \rho a$. Let $b = (\bar{r} + \delta)a$; the dominant characteristic root of b, λ_b^*, satisfies $0 \leq \lambda_b^* < 1$ by L.1 and L.5, whereas L.3 implies that the dominant characteristic root of ρa is no greater than λ_b^*.

---

[4] See Hicks [12], p. 314–319.

[5] Theorem 5 in the next chapter will justify this statement.

[6] The result is intuitively obvious since decreasing the input coefficients of a well-behaved Leontief model with positive prices must leave the system well behaved; see Dorfman, Samuelson, and Solow [8], p. 254.

Again, using L.5 with $\lambda = 1$ and now setting $b = \rho a$, we conclude that $[I - \rho a]^{-1} \geq 0$. QED

Definition: The matrix ρ is called *feasible* if the price vector (20) is strictly positive. (Since $\rho_i = r_i + \delta_i$, $i = 1, \ldots, n$, (A.3) implies that $\rho = \delta$ is feasible.) The scalar r_0 will also be called *feasible* if the matrix ρ is feasible when $r_i = r_0$, $i = 1, \ldots, n$.

Theorem 3:[7] ρ *is feasible if* $[I - \rho a]^{-1} \geq 0$.

Proof: Let $b = \rho a$ and $\lambda = 1$; then by L.7 we conclude that

$$[I - \rho a]^{-1} = I + (\rho a) + (\rho a)^2 + (\rho a)^3 + \ldots.$$

Thus,

$$p = a_0[I - \rho a]^{-1} = a_0 + a_0(\rho a) + a_0(\rho a)^2 + a_0(\rho a)^3 + \ldots.$$

If labor is directly required to produce good j and $a_{0j} > 0$, the conclusion $p_j > 0$ is immediate. If not, (A.1) implies that there exists an integer $m \leq n$ and at least one index h such that $a_{0h} A_{hj} > 0$ where $A \equiv a^m$; hence $p_j > 0$, $j = 1, \ldots, n$, as required.[8] QED

Theorem 4: *Let the elements of the matrix ρ satisfy the conditions*

$$\delta_i < \rho_i < 1/\lambda^{**} + \delta_i, \qquad (i = 1, \ldots, n),$$

where λ^{**} is defined as in Theorem 1; then ρ is feasible.

Proof: Exercise 2.

Theorem 5: *Let $\rho = r_0 + \delta$ be feasible where $r_i = r_0$, $i = 1, \ldots, n$. Then*

$$\frac{dp_i}{dr_0} > 0, \qquad (i = 1, \ldots, n).$$

Proof: Exercise 4.

---

[7] Theorem 5 in the next chapter proves the converse.
[8] This result is well-known; see, for example Dorfman, Samuelson and Solow [8], p. 253, or Bruno, Burmeister, and Sheshinski [7], p. 530.

Theorem 6: *Let ρ be feasible. Then*

$$\frac{\partial p_i}{\partial \rho_j} \geq 0, \qquad (i = 0, 1, \ldots, n; j = 1, \ldots, n)$$

with inequality holding if the jth capital good is required, either directly or indirectly, for the production of good i.

Proof: Exercise 5.

8–4. Steady-State Equilibrium Prices with Many Alternative Techniques

As already noted, the jth good can be produced by any one of m_j alternative activities, and consequently there are

$$M = \prod_{j=0}^{n} m_j$$

alternative technique matrices labeled Technique α, Technique β, etc. For notational convenience the input coefficients

$$a_{ij}(\mu_j) \qquad (i, j = 0, 1, \ldots, n)$$

will be denoted by

$$a_{ij}(\alpha), \qquad (i, j = 0, 1, \ldots, n)$$

when the indices μ_0, μ_1, $\ldots$, μ_n correspond to Technique α, etc.

Let the vector ρ be given exogenously. *What technique matrix will be employed in steady-state price equilibrium?* This is a crucial economic question—the "choice of technique"—and it will finally be answered by Theorem 7.

Of course the question is not even meaningful unless the given ρ is feasible for at least one technique matrix, which we will assume. If, in fact, the given ρ is feasible for only one technique matrix, our question is answered immediately: obviously, that unique technique will be employed. In general, however, the given ρ may be feasible for many alternative technique matrices, and we must determine which of these will be employed in cost-minimizing competitive equilibrium.

Suppose Technique α is used[9] and prices are

$$p(\alpha) = a_0(\alpha)[I - \rho a(\alpha)]^{-1}; \tag{21}$$

---

[9] By assumption the given ρ must be feasible when α is used.

suppose further that (1) the given ρ is also feasible if Technique β is employed, and (2) Techniques α and β are identical except for the nth activity vector. The prices $p_i(\alpha)$ may then be used to evaluate the cost of production for the nth commodity if the new activity is introduced,[10] and from (19) we see that this cost is equal to

$$a_{0n}(\beta) + \sum_{i=1}^{n} a_{in}(\beta)\rho_i \, p_i(\alpha). \tag{22}$$

Let the latter cost be strictly less than $p_n(\alpha)$; clearly the new activity for producing the nth commodity will be employed given our assumption of pure competition. Moreover, the price of the nth commodity must fall, and, consequently, so must the price of the ith good if $a_{ni}(\alpha) = a_{ni}(\beta) > 0$. And this process continues, i.e., if $a_{ni}(\alpha) = a_{ni}(\beta) > 0$ and $a_{ij}(\alpha) = a_{ij}(\beta) > 0$, then the price of the jth good falls below $p_j(\alpha)$. Eventually, when steady-state price equilibrium is attained, the new prices will be

$$p(\beta) = a_0(\beta)[I - \rho a(\beta)]^{-1}. \tag{23}$$

Thus

$$p(\beta) \leq p(\alpha),$$

where $p_i(\beta) < p_i(\alpha)$ if either $i = n$ or the nth good is required, directly or indirectly, for the production of the ith good.

The argument just described may be repeated for all sets of alternative activity vectors, i.e., for all alternative technique matrices for which the given ρ is feasible. We conclude that there exists a matrix of activity vectors, say Technique η, such that

(i) The given ρ is feasible for Technique η, and
(ii) The components of the equilibrium price vector are simultaneously minimized when Technique η is employed.

Moreover, it may be shown that the prices $p_i(\eta)$ are less than or equal to the equilibrium prices generated by any convex combination of matrices for which the given ρ is feasible (Exercise 6).

In the foregoing argument we assumed that the cost given by (22) was strictly less than the initial price $p_n(\alpha)$. In general, this need not be the case; there may be "ties" between two (or more) different technique matrices that generate the same equilibrium price vector for the given ρ. If this price vector is also minimal, either technique (or any convex combination of them) may be employed in equilibrium.

Our results are summarized in the following formal statement.

---

[10] This method of proof follows Levhari [16], pp. 101–102.

Theorem 7^{11}: *Let the matrix ρ be exogenous. Define the set of technique matrices*

$$S \equiv \{\alpha, \beta, \ldots, \eta, \ldots \mid \text{the given } \rho \text{ is feasible}\};$$

by assumption S is not empty. Among all the technique matrices belonging to S there exists at least one (let it be Technique η) such that the equilibrium prices $p_i(\eta)$, $i = 1, \ldots, n$, satisfy the inequality

$$p(\eta) \leqq a_0(\cdot) + p(\eta)\rho a(\cdot)$$

where $a(\cdot)$ designates any technique matrix (or any convex combination of technique matrices) belonging to S.[12]

Definition: A technique matrix that satisfies the conditions stated in Theorem 7 is termed *optimal for the exogenous ρ.*

Theorem 7 provides the answer to the question posed at the beginning of this section.

We now introduce the additional restrictions that have been ignored, namely (11). Rather than allow the entire matrix ρ to be exogenous, we now insist on the equalities

$$\rho_i - \delta_i = r_i = r_0, \qquad (i = 1, \ldots, n), \qquad \textbf{(24)}$$

and therefore equilibrium prices are functions only of the exogenous profit or interest rate r_0. The following results are a special case of Theorem 7 in which the additional restrictions (24) are satisfied; they are especially easy to understand because two-dimensional illustrations are possible.

Assume that Technique α is viable (A.3); thus, $\rho_i = \delta_i$ $(i = 1, \ldots, n)$ or $r_0 = 0$ is feasible when Technique α is employed. Let λ_α^* be the dominant characteristic root of the matrix $a(\alpha)[I - \delta a(\alpha)]^{-1}$. Applying Theorem 1, we conclude that r_0 is feasible (when Technique α is employed) if and only if

$$r_0 < \frac{1}{\lambda_\alpha^*} \equiv r_0^*(\alpha).$$

---

[11] This theorem is equivalent to Morishima's theorem 1 on p. 97 of [17] in the special case $\rho_i - \delta_i \equiv r_0, i = 1, \ldots, n$.

[12] Thus, in equilibrium, any other technique that is employed must generate a price vector equal to $p(\eta)$. In other words, for some given ρ, more than one technique matrix may be optimal (defined later), but in this case all such optimal techniques generate the same equilibrium prices.

A graph of $1/p_i \equiv W_0/P_i$ versus r_0 when Technique α is employed is plotted in Figure 28. This curve is called *the factor-price curve for Technique* α; by virtue of Theorem 5, it is downward-sloping with

$$d(W_0/P_i)/dr_0 < 0, \qquad (i = 0, 1, \ldots, n).$$

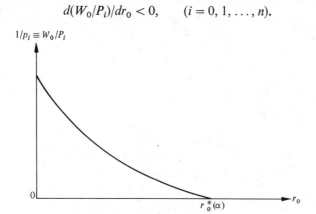

Figure 28.   *Factor-price curve for Technique α.*

Similarly we may find the factor-price curves for Techniques α, β, etc., where λ_β^* is the dominant characteristic root of the matrix $a(\beta)[I - \delta a(\beta)]^{-1}$ and $r_0^*(\beta) \equiv 1/\lambda_\beta^*$, etc. These curves are all downward sloping, but in general they may have any shape since the sign of the second derivative is ambiguous. Their outer-envelope is called *the economy's factor-price frontier.*[13]

Assume for simplicity that the economy's technology consists only of Techniques α, β, and γ. The corresponding factor-price curves and the economy's factor-price frontier are illustrated in Figure 29. Let the exogenously

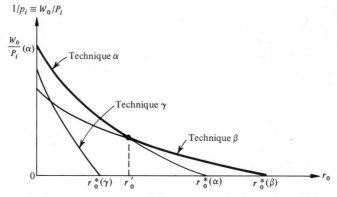

Figure 29.   *Factor-price curves for Techniques α, β, and γ. The economy's factor-price frontier, indicated by the heavy line, is the outer-envelope of these curves.*

[13] This concept was first introduced by Samuelson [28].

given profit or interest rate be $r_0 = 0$. From Theorem 7 we deduce that all prices $p_i \equiv P_i/W_0$ will be minimized in competitive steady-state equilibrium; equivalently, the real wage-rate in terms of any commodity as *numeraire*, W_0/P_i, will be maximized. We conclude, therefore, that in competitive steady-state equilibrium with $r_0 = 0$, Technique α is optimal and will be employed; thus the real wage-rate will equal $(W_0/P_i)(\alpha)^*$. As the exogenously given r_0 is increased above zero, competitive steady-state equilibrium is established at corresponding points on the factor-price curve for Technique α. Obviously the (equilibrium) real wage rate (in terms of any good as *numeraire*) decreases as the profit or interest rate increases.

When $r_0 = r_0'$, Techniques α and β are "tied", i.e., both techniques generate exactly the same prices in competitive steady-state equilibrium and both are optimal. When r_0 is increased above r_0', the economy "switches" from Technique α to Technique β since the latter technique now generates the lowest (equilibrium) prices and is optimal. A point such as r_0' is a *switching point*, a topic we shall return to in Section 8-6. When r_0 reaches $r_0^*(\beta)$, the real wage-rate (in terms of every good as *numeraire*) is equal to zero. Thus no profit or interest rate $r_0 \geq r_0^*(\beta)$ is feasible in this economy; with any rate of profit that high the technology is incapable of generating (is not productive enough to generate) both a positive nominal wage rate W_0 and positive (equilibrium) prices P_i, $i = 0, 1, \ldots, n$.

Finally, observe that although Technique γ is a technical option it would never be employed by an economy in competitive steady-state equilibrium since Technique α dominates Technique γ for all feasible r_0. The latter situation would arise, for example, if

$$a_{ij}(\alpha) < a_{ij}(\gamma), \qquad (i, j = 0, 1, \ldots, n).$$

All of the foregoing results regarding the determination of prices in competitive steady-state equilibrium have been derived without any reference to the final demands for the outputs $Y_0, Y_1, \ldots, Y_n$. Samuelson and others[14] have called this conclusion the *nonsubstitution theorem*, which is, in fact, a special case of Theorem 7 and may be stated as follows.

Theorem 8 (Nonsubstitution Theorem): *Let a feasible interest or profit rate r_0 be given exogenously. In competitive steady-state equilibrium the ratios of all prices are determined by the value of r_0 alone and are independent of the equilibrium quantities $Y_0, Y_1, \ldots, Y_n$. Moreover, the*

---

[14] See for example, Dorfman, Samuelson and Solow [8], Burmeister and Sheshinski [4], Morishima [17], Levhari [16], and Samuelson [25]. There are many other references to the same or similar theorems. Actually the original nonsubstitution theorem was developed for the special case $r_0 = 0$; Morishima refers to the more general result as a "dynamic nonsubstitution theorem."

real wage-rate in terms of every good as numeraire *is determined (maxi-mized)*[15] *by "the invisible hand of competition" and likewise depends only on the value of* r_0.

8–5. Steady-State Equilibrium Quantities

As discussed in Section 8-1, productive inputs during period t are denoted by $K_{ij}(t)$ and $L_j(t)$, $i = 1, \ldots, n$; $j = 0, 1, \ldots, n$. These inputs yield outputs $Y_j(t + 1)$ at the beginning of period $t + 1$, $j = 0, 1, \ldots, n$. Consequently, from equation (8) we obtain that the stock of the jth capital good available as a productive input during period $t + 1$ is

$$K_j(t + 1) = Y_j(t + 1) + K_j(t) - \delta_j K_j(t), \qquad (j = 1, \ldots, n). \qquad (25)$$

Again let the matrix ρ be exogenous and assume that Technique η is employed.[16] Full employment of capital and labor implies that by using (14) and (15), we may rewrite (6) and (7) as

$$a(\eta)Y(t + 1) = K(t) \qquad (26)$$

and

$$a_0(\eta)Y(t + 1) = L(t), \qquad (27)$$

respectively.

Equation (25) may be expressed in matrix notation, and after rearranging terms we obtain

$$Y(t + 1) = K(t + 1) - K(t) + \delta K(t) + C(t + 1) \qquad (28)$$

where $Y_0(t + 1)$ is consumption at the beginning of period $t + 1$ and $C(t + 1)$ is the column vector $[Y_0(t + 1), 0, \ldots, 0]$. Substituting (26) into (28) yields

$$Y(t + 1) = a(\eta)[Y(t + 2) - Y(t + 1)] + \delta a(\eta)Y(t + 1) + C(t + 1). \qquad (29)$$

---

[15] It is correct to say that the real wage-rate in terms of every good as *numeraire* is maximized if we adopt the interpretation that all excess profits (i.e., excess profits in the production of all goods $i = 0, 1, \ldots, n$) are nonnegative; however, if we adopt the alternative interpretation that all excess profits are nonpositive, then the real wage-rate is minimized. Of course in competitive equilibrium where all excess profits are zero, both interpretations are valid. These matters will be clarified in Section 8–6.

[16] See Theorem 7 in Section 8-4.

The difference equation (29) determines the time path of outputs when Technique η is employed.[17]

Suppose that the available labor supply grows according to the equation

$$L(t + 1) = (1 + g)L(t) \tag{30}$$

where $g \geqq 0$ is exogenous. The outputs at the beginning of period $t + 1$ per worker employed during period t are defined as

$$y_i(t + 1) \equiv Y_i(t + 1)/L(t), \qquad (i = 0, 1, \ldots, n). \tag{31}$$

We seek a steady-state quantity solution to our model for which

$$y_i(t + 1) = y_i(t) = y_i, \qquad (i = 0, 1, \ldots, n),$$

is constant for all t.

Substituting (31) into (29) and dividing by $L(t)$ we may derive

$$y(t + 1) = a(\eta)[(1 + g)y(t + 2) - y(t + 1)] + \delta a(\eta)y(t + 1) + c(t + 1) \tag{32}$$

(Exercise 7) where $c(t + 1)$ is the column vector $[y_0(t + 1), 0, \ldots, 0]$. Thus we want to find a strictly positive column vector $y = [y_0, y_1, \ldots, y_n]$ which is a solution to

$$y = a(\eta)[(1 + g)y - y] + \delta a(\eta)y + c. \tag{33}$$

Let λ_η^* be the dominant characteristic root of the matrix $a(\eta)[I - \delta a(\eta)]^{-1}$. If $g < 1/\lambda_\eta^*$, then $[I - (g + \delta)a(\eta)]^{-1} \geqq 0$ and (33) can be solved for

$$y = [I - (g + \delta)a(\eta)]^{-1}c > 0.[18] \tag{34}$$

Moreover, we see from (27) that $a_0(\eta)y = 1$, and therefore y_0 (and hence the vector c) can be calculated from

$$a_0(\eta)[I - (g + \delta)a(\eta)]^{-1}\begin{bmatrix} y_0 \\ 0 \\ \vdots \\ 0 \end{bmatrix} = 1. \tag{35}$$

---

[17] This assumption is a crucial simplification. It is satisfied provided that prices adjust instantaneously to their competitive steady-state equilibrium values and that only Technique η is optimal for the given p.

[18] See Theorem 1 in Section 8-3. The strict inequality $y > 0$ follows from (A.2) (Exercise 13).

This solution gives the value of per capita consumption in steady-state equilibrium, and (35) is called the *consumption possibility frontier*.[19]

Finally, suppose as before that r_0 rather than ρ is exogenous. We have already proved that an optimal technique matrix is determined uniquely (except for ties) by r_0. Thus, if we ignore values of r_0 for which more than one technique matrix is optimal, per capita consumption is a (single-valued) function of r_0 alone in steady-state equilibrium.

8–6. Reswitching of Techniques

In Section 8-3 we proved that in complete steady-state price equilibrium (with all the net own-rates of return equal to the profit or interest rate r_0), the technique matrix employed and hence the price vector $p = (P_0/W_0, P_1/W_0, \ldots, P_n/W_0)$ are both determined by the exogenous profit or interest rate r_0 alone. The concept of a switching point was briefly mentioned. We now define it precisely.

> **Definition:** A profit or interest rate r_0' is a *switching point* between any two techniques, e.g., between Techniques α and β, if there exists $\varepsilon > 0$ such that
> (i) Only Technique α is optimal for $r_0 \in (r_0' - \varepsilon, r_0')$,
> (ii) Both Techniques α and β are optimal for $r_0 = r_0'$, i.e., $p(\alpha) = p(\beta)$ when $r_0 = r_0'$, and
> (iii) Only Technique β is optimal for $r_0 \in (r_0', r_0' + \varepsilon)$.

Assumption (A.3) implies that Technique α is viable, or, equivalently, that $r_0 = 0$ is feasible when Technique α is employed. Assume further that (1) only Technique α is optimal for all r_0 satisfying

$$0 \leqq r_0 < r_0',$$

and (2) r_0' is a switching point between Techniques α and β.

It is clear that only Technique α will be employed (in equilibrium) if r_0 is strictly less than r_0', whereas only Technique β will be employed if r_0 exceeds

---

[19] For simplicity we assume one consumption good, so that the solution to (35) is a point on the positive real-number line. However, our results generalize immediately to the case in which all goods are consumed; the column vector $c = [c_0, c_1, \ldots, c_n]$ must replace $[y_0, 0, \ldots, 0]$ in (35), and the consumption possibility frontier becomes the equation of a hyperplane in the nonnegative orthant of $(n+1)$-dimensional space. Consequently the equilibrium output vector y depends upon the final demands for consumption goods. But once the economy selects any vector c that lies on the consumption possibility frontier, i.e., that satisfies (35), then the equilibrium vector y is determined by (34).

r'_0 by more than some small positive number. Moreover, if $r_0 = r'_0$, either Technique α or β (or any convex combination of them) can be employed. We ask the following question.

Does there exist any other profit or interest rate $\bar{r}_0 > r'_0$ such that only Technique α is optimal[20] when $r_0 = \bar{r}_0$? As the following demonstrates, in general the answer to this question may be "yes"; the situations illustrated in Figures 30 and 31 are possible. Observe that in both cases only Technique α is optimal for low interest or profit rates and is not optimal for intermediate interest or profit rates. But if the profit or interest rate is sufficiently high [although, of course, below $r_0^*(\alpha)$], again only Technique α is optimal. This phenomenon reflects the *reswitching of techniques*, defined more precisely as follows.

> ***Definition:*** Consider any technique matrix, e.g., Technique α, and three profit or interest rates satisfying the inequalities $0 < r_0^1 < r_0^2 < r_0^3 < r_0^*(\alpha)^{21}$.
> If
>
> (i) Only Technique α is optimal for $r_0 = r_0^1$,
> (ii) Technique α is not optimal for $r_0 = r_0^2$, and
> (iii) Only Technique α is optimal for $r_0 = r_0^3$, then the technology exhibits the *reswitching of techniques* and Technique α is said to *recur*.

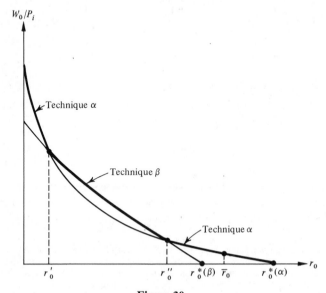

Figure 30

[20] Thus it is necessary (but not sufficient) that r_0 satisfy the inequality $\bar{r}_0 < r_0^*(\alpha)$, where, as before, $r_0^*(\alpha) \equiv 1/\lambda_\alpha^*$ and λ_α^* is the dominant characteristic root of the matrix $a(\alpha) [I - \delta a(\alpha)]^{-1}$.

[21] See the preceding footnote.

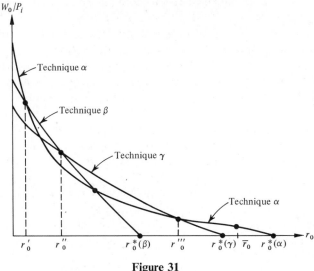

Figure 31

It should be emphasized that reswitching implies that an entire technique matrix recurs at different profit or interest rates. A related but separate issue is the recurrence at different profit or interest rates of a single activity vector. The latter phenomenon, which Joan Robinson has called[22] the "Ruth Cohen Curiosum," is obviously a necessary but not sufficient condition for reswitching.

A little reflection indicates why many authors find reswitching paradoxical. Consider an economy (with a given technology) in steady-state equilibrium at a high rate of interest. Suppose this economy abstains from consumption for a period of time, thereby enabling it to accumulate capital. In the spirit of Jevons, Böhm–Bawerk, Wicksell, and other neoclassical authors, we would expect the economy to approach a new steady state with a lower interest rate.[23] Moreover, we would expect that the new steady state would have more capital and that the technique matrix employed would be more roundabout or more mechanized.

Now imagine that the economy again abstains from consumption and that a third steady-state equilibrium with a still lower interest rate is attained. If reswitching has occurred the technique matrix employed in the third steady state will be the same as the one employed in the first. Consequently it is impossible to claim that an economy always employs (in steady-state equilibrium) more mechanized or more roundabout technique matrices at lower profit or interest rates. Likewise we would expect, in the neoclassical tradition,

---

[22] Robinson [20], p. 109.
[23] See, e.g., Samuelson [27], p. 568. In this discussion we ignore any stability problems that may arise during transitions from one steady-state equilibrium to another.

that if two economies having the same technology are both in steady-state equilibrium then the one with the lowest profit or interest rate will have the most capital. The existence of reswitching warns us however,, that such a statement has no economically meaningful interpretation.[24]

Because reswitching contradicts the intuition of neoclassical authors, it has been called paradoxical or perverse. In fact, however, it is not reswitching per se that is troublesome, but rather it is the foregoing implications as well as others to be discussed in Section 8-7 that are crucial for capital and growth theory. The possibility of reswitching has long been recognized by several authors,[25] but now a stronger conclusion can be stated: *Numerical examples conclusively prove that reswitching can occur, even in models satisfying very strong assumptions.*[26]

A posteriori reswitching is not surprising because switching points are positive roots of nth degree polynomials, and, as is well known, there may exist as many as n such roots. To see this fact consider a technology with two alternative technique matrices, α and β, and for simplicity again assume that only their nth activity vectors differ with[27]

$$
\begin{bmatrix}
a_{00}(\alpha) & a_{01}(\alpha) & \cdots & a_{0n}(\alpha) \\
\hline
0 & 0 & \cdots & 0 \\
a_{10}(\alpha) & a_{11}(\alpha) & \cdots & a_{1n}(\alpha) \\
\vdots & \vdots & & \vdots \\
a_{n0}(\alpha) & a_{n1}(\alpha) & \cdots & a_{nn}(\alpha)
\end{bmatrix}
-
\begin{bmatrix}
a_{00}(\beta) & a_{01}(\beta) & \cdots & a_{0n}(\beta) \\
\hline
0 & 0 & \cdots & 0 \\
a_{10}(\beta) & a_{11}(\beta) & \cdots & a_{1n}(\beta) \\
\vdots & \vdots & & \vdots \\
a_{n0}(\beta) & a_{n1}(\beta) & \cdots & a_{nn}(\beta)
\end{bmatrix}
=
$$

$$
\begin{bmatrix}
0 & 0 & \cdots & \Delta_0 \\
\hline
0 & 0 & \cdots & 0 \\
0 & 0 & \cdots & \Delta_1 \\
\vdots & \vdots & & \vdots \\
0 & 0 & \cdots & \Delta_n
\end{bmatrix}.
\tag{36}
$$

If there is any switching point between Techniques α and β, it is clear that the column vector $(\Delta_0, 0, \Delta_1 \ldots, \Delta_n) \neq (0, \ldots, 0)$ is neither semipositive nor seminegative (Exercise 8). Consequently we assume that this vector contains

[24] The vector of capital goods consistent with steady-state price and quantity equilibrium can be calculated from (35), (34), and (6). Clearly it depends only on the particular technique matrix employed. Thus, if reswitching occurs we may find exactly the same equilibrium vector of capital goods for widely different profit or interest rates.

[25] See, e.g., Robinson [20] and Morishima [17].

[26] See the articles in "Paradoxes in Capital Theory: A Symposium" [18]. In particular, the example on pp. 537–538 of Bruno, Burmeister, and Sheshinski [7] proves that reswitching can occur even if the alternative technique matrices are all indecomposable.

[27] For a more complete discussion see Bruno, Burmeister, and Sheshinski [7], pp. 538–546.

a mixture of positive, negative, and zero elements, and we wish to determine how many switching points may exist between Techniques α and β.

It is easy to show (Exercise 9) that if only Technique α is optimal[28] for $r_0 = r_0^1$, then

$$[a_0(\alpha) - a_0(\beta)] - p(\alpha)(r_0^1 + \delta)[a(\alpha) - a(\beta)] \leq 0, \tag{37}$$

which, of course, implies

$$p(\alpha) \leq p(\beta), \qquad r_0 = r_0^1. \tag{38}$$

It is well known that

$$[I - (r_0 + \delta)a(\alpha)]^{-1} = \frac{\text{Adj}[I - (r_0 + \delta)a(\alpha)]}{\det[I - (r_0 + \delta)a(\alpha)]},$$

and thus

$$p(\alpha) = a_0[I - (r_0 + \delta)a(\alpha)]^{-1} = \frac{a_0 \, \text{Adj}[I - (r_0 + \delta)a(\alpha)]}{\det[I - (r_0 + \delta)a(\alpha)]}. \tag{39}$$

Moreover, for any feasible value of r_0,

$$\det[I - (r_0 + \delta)a(\alpha)] > 0;$$

see L.6 in the Appendix to this book.

Define the vector function

$$G(r_0) = [G_0(r_0), G_1(r_0), \ldots, G_n(r_0)] \equiv \det[I - (r_0 + \delta)a(\alpha)][a_0(\alpha) - a_0(\beta)]$$
$$+ a_0 \, \text{Adj}[I - (r_0 + \delta)a(\alpha)](r_0 + \delta)[a(\alpha) - a(\beta)]. \tag{40}$$

Observing equations (37), (39), and (40), we conclude that

$$G(r_0^1) \leq 0.$$

However, $G_i(r_0)$, $i = 0, 1, \ldots, n$, is at most a polynomial of degree n (Exercise 10), and consequently it can have at most n positive roots. Our example has been constructed so that

$$G_i(r_0) \equiv 0, \qquad (i = 0, 1, \ldots, n - 1)$$

---

[28] In this discussion we consider only values of r_0 that are feasible when either technique is employed.

and

$$G_n(r_0^1) < 0.$$

Therefore, if r_0' is a switching point between Techniques α and β, we must have

$$G_n(r_0') = 0$$

and

$$G(r_0') = (0, \ldots, 0). \tag{41}$$

Also note that (41) holds if and only if $p(\alpha) = p(\beta)$ for $r_0 = r_0'$ (Exercise 11). Moreover, r_0' is a switching point if in addition

$$G_n(r_0' - \varepsilon) < 0 \qquad (\text{or} > 0)$$

and

$$G_n(r_0' + \varepsilon) > 0 \qquad (\text{or} < 0)$$

for some (small) positive number ε; equivalently, the number of switching points is equal to the number of times $G_n(r_0)$ *changes sign* over the domain of nonnegative r_0's that are feasible when either Technique α or β is employed. Clearly, $G_n(r_0)$ may have n roots in this domain, and therefore there may exist up to n switching points.

A more complete discussion of reswitching as well as sufficient conditions to exclude it have been given by Bruno, Burmeister, and Sheshinski.[29] However, their sufficient conditions are very unlikely to be satisfied in any realistic model, and the foregoing discussion suffices to establish the following general conclusion: *The recurrence of at least one technique matrix must not be considered exceptional.*

8–7. Steady-State Consumption Patterns

Let $a_{ij}(\cdot)$ designate the input coefficients corresponding to Technique $(\cdot)$. As is evident from Section 8-3, in steady-state quantity equilibrium the level of per capita consumption y_0 must satisfy

$$a_0(\cdot)[I - (g + \delta)a(\cdot)]^{-1}\begin{bmatrix} y_0 \\ 0 \\ \vdots \\ 0 \end{bmatrix} = 1 \tag{42}$$

[29] The interested reader is referred to Bruno, Burmeister, and Sheshinski [7], especially pp. 538–546.

when Technique $(\cdot)$ is employed. However, steady-state price equilibrium requires that Technique $(\cdot)$ be optimal and, except at switching points, usually only one technique matrix is optimal for any given value of the profit or interest rate r_0. We assume the latter is true[30] and also insist upon both steady-state price and quantity equilibrium.

Consequently the choice of Technique $(\cdot)$ and the level of per capita consumption are both uniquely determined for any given value of r_0 that is not a switching point. Let the switching points, all of which must lie on the factor-price frontier, be

$$r_0^1, r_0^2, \ldots, r_0^v,$$

where v is necessarily finite (see Exercise 12). Furthermore, let a_{ij}^* designate the unique choice of input coefficients determined for any $r_0 \neq r_0^i$, $i = 1, \ldots, v$, and define the vector function

$$\varphi(r_0) \equiv [\varphi_0(r_0), \varphi_1(r_0), \ldots, \varphi_n(r_0)] \equiv a_0^*[I - (g + \delta)a^*]^{-1},$$

$$r_0 \neq r_0^i, \quad i = 1, \ldots, v. \quad \textbf{(43)}$$

From (42) and (43) we conclude that $\varphi_0(r_0)y_0 = 1$, and we define the scalar function

$$c(r_0) \equiv y_0 = 1/\varphi_0(r_0), \qquad r_0 \neq r_0^i, \quad i = 1, \ldots, v.$$

Given any value of r_0 that is not a switching point, the function $c(r_0)$ determines the level of per capita consumption in steady-state price and quantity equilibrium.

We must now investigate under what circumstances the equilibrium price and quantity solutions are strictly positive and therefore economically meaningful. Define

$$1/\bar{\lambda} \equiv \max\{1/\lambda_\alpha^*, 1/\lambda_\beta^*, 1/\lambda_\gamma^*, \ldots\}$$

where $(\cdot) = \alpha, \beta, \gamma, \ldots$ is any viable[31] technique matrix and $\lambda^*(\cdot)$ is the dominant characteristic root of the matrix $a(\cdot)[I - \delta a(\cdot)]^{-1}$. Theorems 1 and 7 imply that strictly positive equilibrium prices are uniquely determined for any value of $r_0 \neq r_0^i$, $i = 1, \ldots, v$, satisfying

$$0 \leq r_0 < 1/\bar{\lambda}. \quad \textbf{(44)}$$

---

[30] Minor modifications in the following argument would enable us to dispense with this assumption. We also consider only $r_0 \geq 0$.

[31] The definition of "viable" is stated in Section 8-3. Note that only viable techniques can be observed in equilibrium if $r_0 \geq 0$.

Similarly, it is easily established[32] that $y > 0$ when Technique $(\cdot)$ is employed if and only if

$$g < 1/\lambda^*(\cdot). \tag{45}$$

Clearly, therefore, we must assume the inequality

$$g < 1/\bar{\lambda} \tag{46}$$

if any meaningful equilibrium exists. In other words, the economy is incapable of balanced growth if (46) is violated.

Combining the foregoing results, we conclude that $p > 0$ and $y > 0$ are uniquely determined if

$$0 \leqq g \leqq r_0 < 1/\bar{\lambda}, \, r_0 \neq r_0^i, \qquad i = 1, \ldots, v. \tag{47}$$

Now define the sets

$$U \equiv \{(\cdot) \mid g < 1/\lambda^*(\cdot)\}$$

and

$$T \equiv \{r_0 \mid (\text{i}) \, r_0 \geqq 0, \text{ and (ii) some technique matrix } \eta \in U \text{ is optimal for } r_0\}.$$

Further define

$$r_0^{\min} \equiv \inf_{r_0 \in T} \{r_0\}.$$

We have proved that $p > 0$ and $y > 0$ are uniquely determined if

$$0 \leqq r_0^{\min} < r_0 < 1/\bar{\lambda}, \qquad r_0 \neq r_0^i, \quad i = 1, \ldots, v. \tag{48}$$

It is important to realize that $r_0^{\min}$ need not be zero. For example, suppose that only Technique α is optimal for any r_0 satisfying

$$0 \leqq r_0 \leqq \bar{r}_0, \tag{49}$$

where $\bar{r}_0 < 1/\lambda_\alpha^*$. If, in addition, $g > 1/\lambda_\alpha^*$, then the equilibrium quantity vector y is not strictly positive for r_0 satisfying (49) because

$$[I - (g + \delta)a(\alpha)]^{-1} \not\geq 0,$$

although equilibrium prices are strictly positive.

---

[32] Refer to Exercise 13 and let $(\cdot)$ replace η in the proof

Consider now any given value of $r_0 = r_0^i$ which is a switching point, but assume

$$r_0^{\min} < r_0^i < 1/\bar{\lambda}.$$

Since r_0^i is a switching point, more than one technique is optimal and any convex combination of optimal techniques may be employed. Obviously, however, equilibrium prices and quantities are strictly positive (although they are not unique) because any convex combination of strictly positive numbers is strictly positive.

Our results are illustrated in Figure 32.

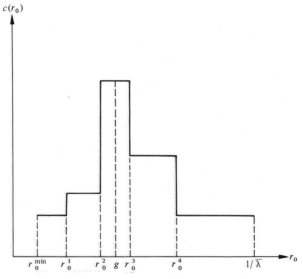

Figure 32

(i) $c(r_0) > 0$ for all r_0 satisfying

$$r_0^{\min} < r_0 < 1/\bar{\lambda},$$

although prices may be strictly positive even for $r_0 < r_0^{\min}$.

(ii) $c(r_0)$ is a (single-valued) function of r_0 except at switching points r_0^i, $i = 1, 2, 3, 4$.

(iii) At switching points $c(r_0^i)$ may assume any one of an infinity of values depending on which particular convex combination of optimal techniques is employed.

As we shall prove in Section 8-9, $c(r_0)$ attains a maximum when $r_0 = g$, and in the well-behaved examples $c(r_0)$ is nondecreasing for $r_0 \leqq g$ and non-increasing for $r_0 \geqq g$. (Such an example is illustrated in Figure 32.) Suppose, however, that the economy exhibits reswitching in the interval

$$g \leqq r_0 < 1/\bar{\lambda}.$$

The behavior shown in Figure 33 then results, and the statement $c(r_0)$ is

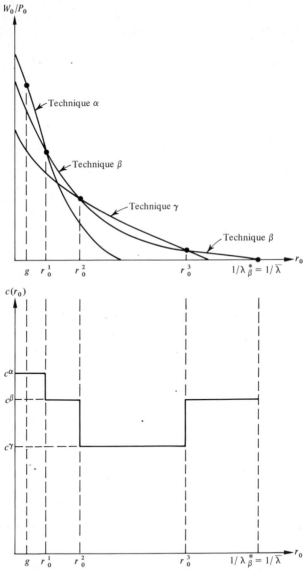

Figure 33

nonincreasing for $r_0 \geqq g$ is false. Likewise $c(r_0)$ is decreasing over some interval of r_0, $r_0 \leqq g$ if there is reswitching in the interval

$$r_0^{\min} < r_0 \leqq g.$$

The paradoxical nature of this result is perhaps best understood in the case $g = 0$. If two economies have identical technologies and both are in stationary-state[33] equilibrium, an economist following the neoclassical tradition[34] would predict that the economy with the lower interest or profit rate has the most capital, and, moreover, since capital is productive, he would predict that this economy enjoys a higher consumption level. *Reswitching demonstrates that such predictions are false.*

Although reswitching alerts us to the existence of paradoxical consumption patterns it is not a necessary condition. This fact is illustrated in Figure 34. Note that if $g = 0$ the height of the factor-price curve for Technique ($\cdot$) evaluated at $r_0 = 0$ is exactly equal to per capita consumption when Technique ($\cdot$) is employed (Exercise 14). If Technique α were not an option the economy would exhibit reswitching between Techniques β and γ; r_0' and r_0^2 would be the switching points on the factor-price frontier. However, the existence of Technique α eliminates the possibility of reswitching and no technique recurs, as shown in Figure 34. Nevertheless, *there is a paradoxical consumption pattern even in the absence of reswitching.* Clearly this result may be traced to the fact that reswitching would have occurred in the absence of Technique α.

In summary, reswitching in the interval $r_0^{\min} < r_0 \leqq g$ (or in the interval $g \leqq r_0 < 1/\bar{\lambda}$) is a sufficient but not necessary condition for paradoxical patterns of steady-state consumption. As we shall prove in the next chapter, reswitching is not present in models with neoclassical production functions,[35] but the possibility of paradoxical consumption patterns remains *if there is more than one kind of capital good in the economy.* Moreover, neither reswitching nor paradoxical behavior can occur in linear models *provided that there is only one kind of capital good* (Exercise 15).

We are led to the conclusion that the possibility of paradoxical behavior which conflicts with the neoclassical tradition is due to the existence of many (more than one), physically different kinds of capital goods.[36] The next chapter lends further support to this viewpoint.

---

[33] The steady states with $y_i \equiv Y_i/L$ constant are in fact stationary states with Y_i constant when $g \equiv \dot{L}/L = 0$.

[34] See the discussion in Section 8-6.

[35] In fact, a stronger theorem can be proved: If (1) at least one capital good is produced by a neoclassical production function, and (2) labor and each capital good is an input in one or more of the neoclassical production functions, then the possibility of reswitching is precluded. See Bruno, Burmeister, and Sheshinski [7] pp. 545–546.

[36] In interpreting traditional capital models such as wine aging, it should be remembered that ten-year-old wine is distinctly different from one-year-old wine. Who could disagree?

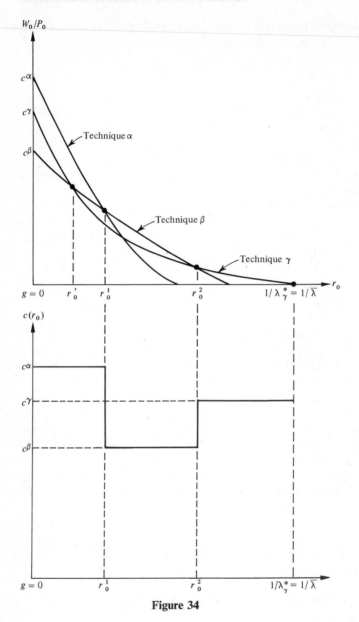

Figure 34

8–8. The Social Rate of Return

We have shown that steady-state quantity and price equilibrium is uniquely determined for any exogenous value of the profit or interest rate r_0 that (1) is not a switching point, and (2) satisfies the inequality $r_0^{\min} < r_0 < 1/\bar{\lambda}$. Thus, even when we restrict our attention to steady-state equilibria our model lacks enough equations to determine simultaneously all the variables, including r_0. This observation deserves closer attention.

Assume for simplicity that the technology consists only of Technique α. With the wage rate W_0 as *numeraire*, the matrix equation

$$p = a_0(\alpha) + p\rho a(\alpha) \tag{50}$$

expresses the competitive equilibrium condition that unit prices equal unit costs of production. Likewise,

$$a_0(\alpha)y = 1 \tag{51}$$

and

$$a(\alpha)y = k \tag{52}$$

are the equations that insure the full employment of labor and capital respectively, where the labor supply is normalized at unity. Finally, the steady-state restrictions $k_i(t + 1) = k_i(t) = k_i(i = 1, \ldots, n)$, necessitate the demand equations

$$y_i = (g + \delta_i)k_i$$

or

$$y = (g + \delta)k. \tag{53}$$

The equilibrium conditions (50)–(53) represent $3n + 2$ equations in $n + 1$ p_i's, $n + 1$ y_i's, n ρ_i's, and n k_i's. If we were to assume that the capital/labor ratios $k_1, \ldots, k_n$ are given exogenously, our system would reduce to $3n + 2$ equations in the same number of variables, and in principle there would be a solution. We will return to this point again in Section 8-10.

However, we have not allowed exogenous k_i's, but rather we have added the additional n equations

$$\rho_i - \delta_i = r_0, \qquad i = 1, \ldots, n, \tag{54}$$

that are implied by a steady-state price equilibrium in which $p_i(t + 1) = p_i(t) = p_i$. Accordingly, (50)–(54) are $4n + 2$ equilibrium conditions in $4n + 3$ variables. If r_0 is exogenous, we have proved earlier (Theorem 7) that a unique competitive equilibrium is determined even when there are many alternative techniques; the only restrictions are (1) r_0 is not a switching point (which is required for uniqueness), and (2) $r_0^{\min} < r_0 < 1/\bar{\lambda}$ (which is required for strictly positive prices and quantities).

What is the significance of the value r_0 by which we characterize alternative steady-states? One interpretation relates to the attractiveness of investment opportunities, in a very traditional way.

Consider an economy that has been in steady-state equilibrium with $c(t) = c$, constant for $t = -1, -2 \ldots$. Assume that in period 0 consumption is set to $c(0) < c$, thereby enabling the economy, through temporary reallocation of resources to production of durable goods, to achieve a consumption stream $c(t)$, $t = 1, 2, \ldots$. The *social rate of return to savings-investment* is defined as the positive root of the equation

$$\sum_{t=0}^{\infty} \frac{(c(t) - c)}{(1 + \gamma)^t} = 0,$$

provided this is unique. It is remarkable that in competitive steady-state equilibrium the exogenous r_0 equals the social rate of return to savings-investment so defined.[37] This result, which was proved by Solow [30], demonstrates that r_0 does have an economic interpretation even when it is exogenous and is not equal to the marginal product of capital.

Finally, if γ is the positive rate of time preference, we may insist on the equilibrium condition $r_0 = \gamma$ if capital markets are perfect. In this case, of course, the one degree of freedom is removed and a steady state is completely determined.

8–9. Duality Relationships and the Golden Rule

Hicks [12], Bruno [5], and Burmeister and Kuga [3] have explored the quantity-price duality relationships for the model discussed in this chapter.[38] We will outline briefly some of these results.

Let $h_i \, (i = 1, \ldots, n)$ designate the *gross rate of growth for the ith capital good*, where

$$K_i(t + 1) = (1 + h_i)K_i(t) - \delta_i K_i(t), \qquad (i = 1, \ldots, n).$$

We wish to determine the maximum attainable level of per capita consumption when the actual gross rates of growth in the economy equal (or possibly

---

[37] When there are multiple positive roots, it will still be true that in steady-state equilibrium one among these will be equal to the exogenous profit rate r_0, but the correct economic interpretation of this result is no longer as apparent. The phenomenon of re-switching demonstrates that we cannot exclude this possibility.

The reader who is interested in pursuing this concept is referred to Solow [29, 30]. Burmeister [2] considers some qualifications.

[38] Many of these results were anticipated by von Weizsäcker [34].

exceed) the exogenously assigned numbers $h_i \geq 0$, and we formulate the following problem. For notational simplicity the time indices t and $t + 1$ have been dropped, but the correct index is obvious from the context.[39]

(*) Primal Problem

Maximize

$$c = \sum_{\mu_o = 1}^{m_o} y_0(\mu_0) \tag{55}$$

subject to

$$\sum_{i=0}^{n} \sum_{\mu_i = 1}^{m_i} a_{0i}(\mu_i) y_i(\mu_i) \leq 1 \equiv L, \tag{56}$$

$$\sum_{i=0}^{n} \sum_{\mu_i = 1}^{m_i} a_{ji}(\mu_i) y_i(\mu_i) \leq k_j, \qquad (j = 1, \ldots, n), \tag{57}$$

$$\sum_{\mu_j = 1}^{m_j} y_j(\mu_j) \geq h_j k_j, \qquad (j = 1, \ldots, n), \tag{58}$$

$$y_j(\mu_j) \geq 0, \qquad (j = 0, 1, \ldots, n; \mu_j = 1, \ldots, m_j), \tag{59}$$

and

$$k_j \geq 0, \qquad (j = 1, \ldots, n). \tag{60}$$

The only additional notation is $y_j(\mu_j)$, denoting *the per capita output of the jth commodity from the μ_jth activity*[40] $(\mu_j = 1, \ldots, m_j; j = 0, 1, \ldots, n)$.

If (*) has optimal solutions for different assigned values of the vector h these optimal solutions define the function $c = E(h)$ which is called the *optimal transformation frontier*. Its interpretation is that when the gross rate of growth for the ith capital good must equal (or possibly exceed) the given value h_i $(i = 1, \ldots, n)$, then $c = E(h)$ is optimal in the sense that no higher level of per capita consumption is attainable without violating the growth-rate requirements.

We now turn to the dual valuation problem. Let the vector $\rho = (\rho_1, \ldots, \rho_n)$ be assigned exogenously. We wish to determine the minimum real wage rate

---

[39] For example, in our notation all outputs have the index $t + 1$.
[40] If activity μ_j is not employed, then the corresponding output is $y_j(\mu_j) \equiv 0$.

(in terms of the price of the consumption good P_0 as *numeraire*) when the actual gross own-rates of return in the economy satisfy

$$W_i/P_i \leqq \rho_i, \qquad i = 1, \ldots, n.$$

Setting $P_0 \equiv 1$, we formulate the following problem.[41]

(**) Dual Problem

Minimize

$$W_0 \tag{61}$$

subject to

$$a_{00}(\mu_0)W_0 + \sum_{j=1}^{n} a_{j0}(\mu_0)W_j \geqq 1 \equiv P_0, \qquad (\mu_0 = 1, \ldots, m_0), \tag{62}$$

$$a_{0i}(\mu_i)W_0 + \sum_{j=1}^{n} a_{ji}(\mu_i)W_j \geqq P_i, \qquad (i = 1, \ldots, n; \mu_i = 1, \ldots, m_i), \tag{63}$$

$$W_i \leqq \rho_i P_i, \qquad (i = 1, \ldots, n), \tag{64}$$

$$W_i \geqq 0, \qquad (i = 1, \ldots, n), \tag{65}$$

and

$$P_i \geqq 0, \qquad (i = 1, \ldots, n). \tag{66}$$

Note that (56) and (57) in the primal problem imply that factor requirements do not exceed supply; analogously, (62) and (63) in the dual problem imply that price does not exceed cost of production (no excess profits). *If we set* $\rho_i \equiv h_i$ $(i = 1, \ldots, n)$, *then* (*) *and* (**) *are dual problems in the standard terminology of linear programming theory.*[42]

As the following discussion indicates, Theorem 7 and the dual problem (**) are closely related. In order to facilitate a two-dimensional diagram, we assume $\rho_i - \delta_i = r_0$ $(i = 1, \ldots, n)$, and in Figure 35 we graph the factor-price curves for Techniques α and β, designated by $FPC(\alpha)$ and $FPC(\beta)$, respectively. Assume that only Technique β is employed, and consider any point in the strictly positive $(W_0/P_i) - r_0$ plane that lies below the curve $FPC(\beta)$; clearly excess profits are strictly positive for the production of the

---

[41] Again the timing indices are obvious from context, e.g., all output prices implicitly carry the index $t + 1$.
[42] See, for example, Gale [9].

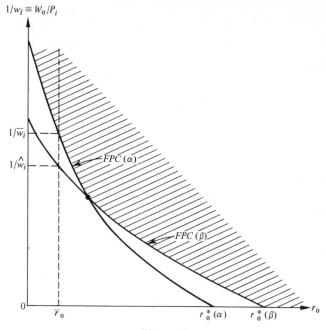

Figure 35

ith good.[43] Similarly, excess profits are strictly negative at all points above $FPC(\beta)$, whereas they are zero for all points on $FPC(\beta)$.

Now let $r_0 = \bar{r}_0$, and initially assume that only Technique β is employed. Suppose $W_0/P_i = 0$. The process of competition (described in the proof of Theorem 7) will raise the real wage rate in terms of every good as *numeraire* until eventually Technique β no longer generates positive profits. However, by employing Technique α instead of Technique β, positive profits again result and W/P_i continues to rise above $1/\hat{w}_i$. Competitive equilibrium is finally established at the point $(\bar{r}_0, 1/\overline{w}_i)$ on the curve $FPC(\alpha)$. At this point excess profits are all zero and the real wage rates in terms of every good as *numeraire* are simultaneously maximized.

Consider the dual problem (**) when $r_0 = \bar{r}_0$. Since excess profits for the production of every good must be nonpositive by (63) and (64), any feasible solution must lie on or above both $FPC(\alpha)$ and $FPC(\beta)$, which is the shaded region in Figure 35. Clearly the real wage rate W_0/P_0 is minimized at the point $(\bar{r}_0, 1/\overline{w}_i)$ when $r_0 = \bar{r}_0$ is assigned.

The preceding argument is easily generalized, and we reach the following

---

[43] The reader who doubts this statement should check his understanding of Theorem 7 and its derivation.

conclusion.[44] Let the given vector ρ be feasible for at least one technique matrix. The maximum real wage rate W_0/P_0 generated by Theorem 7 (under the restriction that excess profits for the production of goods 0, 1, ..., n are all nonnegative) is exactly equal to the minimum real wage rate W_0/P_0 which is the optimal feasible solution to the dual problem (**) (under the restriction that excess profits are all *nonpositive*).

Recall that the real factor-price frontier gives the equilibrium value of W_0/P_0 as a function of r_0.[45] However, our foregoing results show that W_0/P_0 is determined by the vector ρ even if $\rho_i - \delta_i \neq r_0$, and thus this concept may be generalized.

> **Definition:** If (**) has optimal solutions for different assigned values of the vector ρ, these optimal solutions define the function $W_0/P_0 = G(\rho)$ which is the *generalized real factor-price frontier*.[46]

Of course the assigned vector ρ must be restricted to some domain to insure that (**) has an optimal solution; however, we will ignore this problem and assume that ρ belongs to such a domain.[47]

Standard linear programming theorems applied to problems (*) and (**) yield the following theorem.

> **Theorem 9:** *The optimal transformation frontier and the generalized real factor-price frontier are mathematically identical, i.e., $c = E(h) = W_0/P_0 = G(\rho)$ for all $\rho = h$ restricted to a suitable domain.*[48]

Consider any case for which the optimal solutions to (*) and (**) satisfy (58) and (64) with equality. Setting $\rho = h$, we then find that $c = E(h) = W_0/P_0 = G(\rho)$ has the following simple economic characterization.

(i) $P_0 C = W_0 L$, i.e., all wage income is consumed, and
(ii) $P_i Y_i = W_i K_i$ ($i = 1, \ldots, n$), i.e., gross rentals on the ith capital good equal gross investment in the ith capital good.

---

[44] Also see footnote 15.
[45] Hicks [12] calls the same function the *wage curve*. The concept of the factor-price frontier has been developed further by Samuelson [25, 26], Morishima [17], and Bruno [5]. The reader is warned that a (generalized) factor-price frontier (which determines W_0/P_0 as a function of ρ independently of final demands) cannot be defined in a model with joint production such as von Neumann's [33]. There is an analogous frontier $W_0/P_0 = G(\rho)$ that gives the lowest real wage rate, but the actual equilibrium value of W_0/P_0 depends on the composition of output. See Samuelson [24, 28] and Burmeister and Kuga [3].
[46] Clearly there is a (generalized) nonsubstitution theorem analogous to Theorem 8.
[47] For example, the previous condition $0 \leq r_0 < 1/\bar{\lambda}$ is sufficient in the special case $\rho_i - \delta_i = r_0$, $i = 1, \ldots, n$. The interested reader is referred to Burmeister and Kuga [3].
[48] See Bruno [5] and Hicks [12]. Also see Burmeister and Kuga [3].

This result is immediate since

(i) Optimal solution to (*) and (**) must satisfy[49]

$$\frac{W_0}{P_0} = \frac{C}{L} \equiv \sum_{\mu_0 = 1}^{m_o} y_0(\mu_0),$$

and

(ii)

$$h_i = \frac{Y_i}{K_i} = \rho_i \equiv \frac{W_i}{P_i}, \qquad (i = 1, \ldots, n),$$

where

$$Y_i = L \sum_{\mu_i = 1}^{m_i} y_i(\mu_i).$$

Now let us apply some of these results to a familiar issue. An economy is on a *balanced growth path* when it is in complete steady-state price and quantity equilibrium with $k_i(t + 1) = k_i(t) = k_i$ $(i = 1, \ldots, n)$, $c(t + 1) = c(t) = c$, and $P_i(t + 1) = P_i(t) = P_i$ $(i = 0, 1, \ldots, n; t = 0, 1, \ldots)$. The familiar Golden Rule[50] states that the balanced growth path with the highest level of per capita consumption c is characterized by the condition $r_0 = g$, where $L(t + 1) = (1 + g)L(t)$. We now prove this result for our model.

Theorem 10 (Golden Rule): *Consider the model described in this chapter. Let $g \geq 0$ be exogenous and suppose the steady-state restrictions stated in the preceding paragraph must be satisfied. If $\rho_i - \delta_i = r_0 = g$ $(i = 1, \ldots, n)$, per capita consumption c is maximized.*

Proof: $k_i(t + 1) - k_i(t) = 0$ if and only if $h_i = g + \delta_i$ $(i = 1, \ldots, n; t = 0, 1, \ldots)$; $r_0 = g$ implies $\rho = h$, and the maximum level of per capita consumption is

$$c = E(h) = W_0/P_0 = G(\rho).$$

QED

It should be noted that $r_0 = g$ is a sufficient but not necessary condition for maximizing per capita consumption, a conclusion that is immediately evident

---

[49] See, e.g., Gale [9].
[50] See, e.g., Phelps [19] and the references therein.

from Figure 32. In fact, reswitching implies that even an inequality such as

$$g - M \leqq r_0 \leqq g + M \qquad \text{(for some fixed } M > 0)$$

cannot be a necessary and sufficient condition. However, $r_0 = g$ is a necessary and sufficient Golden Rule condition in a model with neoclassical production functions which we will discuss in the next chapter.

8–10. Dynamic Behavior

The early sections of this chapter examined the conditions under which an economy with a single technique matrix determines an economically meaningful steady-state equilibrium for a specified vector of own-rates of return on capital goods. Subsequently the choice of one technique from among alternatives was considered, and the problem of reswitching, the relations governing steady-state consumption, the social rate of return to saving, and certain price-quantity duality relationships were investigated. All comparisons, however, related to comparisons of one steady state with another. Transitional paths were not discussed, although equation (17) of Section 2 and equation (29) of Section 5 express difference equations describing the evolution of equilibrium prices and quantities, respectively. The first of these equations (shifted one time period) was

$$Y(t) = a(\eta)[Y(t + 1) - Y(t)] + \delta a(\eta) Y(t) + C(t) \qquad \textbf{(29)}$$

which may be rewritten

$$Y(t) = B[Y(t + 1) - Y(t)] + A Y(t) + C(t)$$

where we substitute $B = a(\eta)$ and $A = \delta a(\eta)$ in order to express the equation in more familiar form.[51]

Then we may express the difference equation as[52]

$$BY(t + 1) = [I + B - A]Y(t) - C(t)$$

---

[51] As we indicated in Chapter 7, our analysis of the model with explicit capital stocks thus leads to a conventional dynamic model, except that the standard flow matrix of interindustry requirements is seen to be simply a matrix of elements whose entries represent actual use of capital in each sector. If depreciation were dependent upon the sector in which the capital good is used, then employing a full (rather than diagonal) matrix δ we could represent all interindustry flows as δa.

[52] We note that in our system the matrix B is definitely singular, since it has a row of zeros, so some reduction of the system would be necessary to carry out the analysis described in Chapter 7. Such a reduction is always possible. See Jorgenson [13].

and we recognize precisely the open dynamic input-output model discussed, for example, by Dorfman, Samuelson, and Solow [8]. We need not repeat the analysis already undertaken in Chapter 7 in connection with the closed dynamic input-output model; all properties of the characteristic roots of the system remain valid, and only the particular solution to the difference equation is affected. Again the problem of causal indeterminacy discussed by Dorfman, Samuelson, and Solow [8] arises: if the system is not stable, it must (for general initial conditions) depart from its stable balanced growth path until eventually some outputs would be forced to become negative to conform to the difference equation prescribed. At this point the future motion of the system becomes indeterminate.

Similarly, the price equation may be written, after substituting from (9) into (17), in the form

$$P(t + 1) - W_0 a_0 - P(t + 1)\delta a + P(t + 1)a = (1 + r_0)P(t)a$$

or

$$P(t + 1)[I - A + B] = (1 + r_0)P(t)a + W_0 a_0 .$$

This equation, in which capital gains are taken into account, corresponds to the standard dual price system introduced by Solow [32].[53]

Again we observe the close link between the quantity system and the associated price system. Because the model is now open, however, with a consumption good (produced at some exogenously determined rate) appearing as an output and a primary factor (labor) appearing as an input, the strong dual stability result discussed in Chapter 7 cannot be guaranteed. Nevertheless the conditions under which the dual stability result will hold have been fully established by Jorgenson [13, 14], and there is a strong presumption that these conditions would generally be satisfied in practice.[54]

It is worth noting that the foregoing output equations and price equations form a completely decoupled system in which the development of prices has no effect on the growth of outputs, and vice versa. This property is a consequence of the assumption that excess capacity never appears and (equally crucially) that only one technique matrix is adopted all along the growth path. If changes of technique of the kind we have just discussed in comparing different steady states should occur along the actual growth path from specified initial conditions, then the system would cease to be

[53] It is easy to see that if expectations are static, so that no anticipation of capital gains is considered in establishing capital rentals in equation (9) or in the pricing of capital services, then the above price equation reduces to an alternative dual price model in which prices are fully determined at each instant by algebraic relations rather than through a difference equation system.

[54] See Jorgenson [13], p. 898.

decoupled. The technique matrix itself would depend upon prices, and the analysis becomes complex indeed.[55] In his review of Morishima's book [17], Jorgenson [14] discusses further unresolved issues arising in linear models of the kind discussed in this chapter.

Finally, let us again note that the foregoing models are intended to be descriptive only; they have no optimizing significance at all (apart from that implied by the cost minimization). The dual stability result implies that if initial prices and quantities are arbitrarily assigned, then generally one of the two difference equation systems converges to a balanced growth track, whereas the other diverges. With control over initial prices, however, such as we might have in a planning problem, it would be possible to select initial conditions to eliminate all unstable components in the solution to the price system. Thus, if the output system is initially stable, we may force both systems to follow a stable path. Of course if the economy has a mechanism for ensuring that only the unique initial price that stabilizes the system can be observed, then no central planning is required to force convergence of both systems to balanced growth. We shall see the same feature recur in Chapter 9 which deals with neoclassical models.

Exercises

1. Derive (13) from (12) under the stated assumptions.
2. Prove Theorem 4.
3. Under what conditions is $\rho = I$ feasible?
4. Prove Theorem 5.
5. Prove Theorem 6.
6. Let S be the set of technique matrices defined in Theorem 7, and assume that Technique η is optimal. Denote by p* the vector of equilibrium prices generated by any convex combination of technique matrices belonging to S and prove that $p(\eta) \leqq p^*$.
7. Derive equation (32).
8. Let $\Delta = (\Delta_0, 0, \Delta_1, \ldots, \Delta_n)$ be the column vector defined by (36). Show that there does not exist any switching point between Techniques α and β if either (1) $\Delta \geqq 0$, (2) $\Delta \leqq 0$, or (3) $\Delta = 0$.
9. Derive (37) and (38) given the assumptions stated in the text.
10. Prove that each component of the vector polynomial defined by (40) is of degree n at most.

---

[55] Morishima [17], pp. 94–105 considers this more general case in which a technique matrix is selected from a set of alternative techniques, but this selection may change over time as prices change. He takes capital gains or losses to be negligible and is thus able to establish the very strong result that the price system is stable.

11. Let Techniques α and β be the only alternatives and assume that r_0' is feasible when either is employed. Prove that $p(\alpha) = p(\beta)$ for $r_0 = r_0'$ if and only if

$$G(r_0') = (0, \ldots, 0),$$

where $G(r_0)$ is defined by (40).

12. Verify equation (42) under the stated assumptions.

13. (a) Prove that the solution to (34) satisfies the strict inequality $y > 0$ if and only if $g < 1/\lambda_\eta^*$.
    (b) Why is assumption (A.3) not a serious restriction?

14. Assume that only Technique ($\cdot$) is employed. Prove that per capita consumption is equal (in steady-state equilibrium) to the height of the factor-price curve W_0/P_0 for Technique ($\cdot$) evaluated at $r_0 = g$.

15. Prove that neither reswitching nor the paradoxical behavior illustrated in Figure 34 can occur if there is only one kind of capital good.

Answers and Hints

PROBLEM 1. $r_0 > 0$ and $0 < \delta_i < 1$ imply that $0 < (1 - \delta_i)/(1 + r_0) < 1$. Let $(1 - \delta_i)/(1 + r_0) = \theta$ and use $1 + \theta + \theta^2 + \cdots = 1/(1 - \theta)$, $-1 < \theta < 1$.

PROBLEM 2. Sufficiency is established by showing that the conditions of Theorems 1, 2, and 3 are satisfied.

PROBLEM 3. $[\lambda I - a]^{-1} \geq 0$ if and only if $\lambda > \lambda_a^*$ where λ_a^* is the dominant characteristic root of the matrix a (L.5). Therefore $[I - \rho a]^{-1} \geq 0$ for $\rho = I$ if and only if $\lambda^* < 1$.

PROBLEM 4. $p = a_0 + a_0(r_0 + \delta)a + a_0(r_0 + \delta)^2 a^2 + a_0(r_0 + \delta)^3 a^3 + \cdots$; then use the proof of Theorem 3 and (A.2).

PROBLEM 5. Use (A.2) and proceed as in Exercise 4.

PROBLEM 6. It suffices to consider the convex combination of Techniques η and α. Define

$$a_{ij}^* \equiv \xi a_{ij}(\eta) + (1 - \xi)a_{ij}(\alpha), \qquad (i, j = 0, \ldots, n)$$

where ξ is a scalar satisfying $0 < \xi < 1$. Derive

$$p^* = a_0^*[I - \rho a^*]^{-1}$$

and

$$p^*[I - \rho a^*] = a_0^* = \xi a_0(\eta) + (1 - \xi)a_0(\alpha).$$

Since Technique η is optimal, we may use $p(\eta)$ to calculate the cost of production if any other technique were employed, thereby obtaining the inequality

$$p(\eta) \leq a_0(\alpha) + p(\eta)\rho a(\alpha)$$

or

$$p(\eta)[I - \rho a(\alpha)] \leq a_0(\alpha).$$

Thus deduce that

$$p^*[I - \rho a^*] \geq \xi a_0(\eta) + (1 - \xi)p(\eta)[I - \rho a(\alpha)],$$

and show that the right-hand side equals

$$p(\eta)[I - \rho a^*].$$

Combine these results to obtain

$$p(\eta)[I - \rho a^*] \leq p^*[I - \rho a^*];$$

finally, show that $[I - \rho a^*]^{-1} \geq 0$ and thereby conclude that

$$p(\eta) \leq p^*.$$

PROBLEM 8.
(1) Show that Technique β dominates Technique α with $p(\beta) \leq p(\alpha)$.
(3) Show that $p(\beta) = p(\alpha)$ and use the definition of a switching point.

PROBLEM 9. Since only Technique α is optimal when $r_0 = r_0^1$, we have the inequality

$$p(\alpha) \leq a_0(\beta) + p(\alpha)(r_0^1 + \delta)a(\beta);$$

see Hint 6. But

$$p(\alpha) = a_0(\alpha) + p(\alpha)(r_0^1 + \delta)a(\alpha),$$

and substitution yields (37). By assumption r_0^1 is feasible when either Technique α or β is employed, and

$$p(\alpha) \leq p(\beta)$$

follows immediately because $[I - (r_0^1 + \delta)a(\beta)]^{-1} \geq 0$. As before, $p_i(\alpha) < p_i(\beta)$ if either $i = n$ or if good n is required, directly or indirectly, for the production of good i.

PROBLEM 10. Each element, except those in the first column, of the matrix Adj$[I - (r_0 + \delta)a(\alpha)]$ is a polynomial of degree $n - 1$ at most; likewise, det$[I - (r_0 + \delta)a(\alpha)]$ is a polynomial of degree n at most.

PROBLEM 11.

(i) Assume $p(\alpha) = p(\beta)$, $r_0 = r_0'$; then

$$p(\alpha) = a_0(\alpha) + p(\alpha)(r_0' + \delta)a(\alpha)$$
$$= a_0(\beta) + p(\alpha)(r_0' + \delta)a(\beta) = p(\beta)$$

or

$$[a_0(\alpha) - a_0(\beta)] + p(\alpha)(r_0' + \delta)[a(\alpha) - a(\beta)] = (0, \ldots, 0).$$

(ii) Assume $G(r_0') = (0, \ldots, 0)$; then

$$[a_0(\alpha) - a_0(\beta)] + p(\alpha)(r_0' + \delta)[a(\alpha) - a(\beta)] = (0, \ldots, 0),$$
$$a_0(\alpha) + p(\alpha)(r_0' + \delta)a(\alpha) - p(\alpha)(r_0' + \delta)a(\beta) = a_0(\beta),$$

and

$$p(\alpha)[I - (r_0' + \delta)a(\beta)] = a_0(\beta).$$

PROBLEM

13. (a) The row vector

$$a_0(\eta)[I - (g + \delta)a(\eta)]^{-1} > 0;$$

this fact is established by expanding $a_0(\eta)[I - (g + \delta)a(\eta)]^{-1}$ in a power series and using (A.1) (see the proof to Theorem 3). Consequently, $y_0 > 0$ follows from (35). Similarly, by expanding $[I - (g + \delta)a(\eta)]^{-1}$ in a power series and using (A.2), it can be proved that the elements of the first column of $[I - (g + \delta)a(\eta)]^{-1}$ are all strictly positive, and thus the conclusion $y > 0$ is implied by (34).

(b) First, very few if any goods can be produced by labor only. Second, any capital good that is not required either directly or indirectly to produce the consumption good could be dropped from the system without affecting consumption.

PROBLEM 14. $c = 1/\varphi_0(r_0)$ where $\varphi(r_0) \equiv a_0(\cdot)[I - (g + \delta)a(\cdot)]^{-1}$. But the factor-price curve for Technique $(\cdot)$ is derived from

$$p(\cdot) \equiv \left[\frac{P_0}{W_0}(\cdot), \frac{P_1}{W_0}(\cdot), \ldots, \frac{P_n}{W_0}(\cdot) \right]$$
$$= a_0(\cdot)[I - (r_0 + \delta)a(\cdot)]^{-1}.$$

PROBLEM 15. The polynomials $G_i(r_0)$ defined by (40) are of degree one at most. Therefore any two factor-price curves have at most one intersection.

References

[1] ANDO, A., F. M. FISHER, and H. A. SIMON, *Essays on the Structure of Social Science Models.* Cambridge, Mass.: MIT Press, 1963.

[2] BURMEISTER, E., "The Social Rate of Return in a Linear Model," *Weltwirtshaftliches Archiv*, Band 101, Heft 2, 1968.

[3] — and K. KUGA, "The Factor-Price Frontier, Duality and Joint Production," *Review of Economic Studies*, XXXVII, *109* (January, 1970).

[4] — and E. SHESHINSKI, "A Nonsubstitution Theorem in a Model with Fixed Capital," *Southern Economic Journal*, XXXV, *3* (January, 1969), pp. 273–276.

[5] BRUNO, M., "Fundamental Duality Relations in the Pure Theory of Capital and Growth," *Review of Economic Studies*, XXXVI, *105* (January, 1969), pp. 39–53.

[6] — E. BURMEISTER, and E. SHESHINSKI, "The Badly Behaved Production Function: Comment," *The Quarterly Journal of Economics*, LXXXII, *3* (August, 1968), pp. 524–525.

[7] — "The Nature and Implications of the Reswitching of Techniques," *Quarterly Journal of Economics*, LXXX, *4* (November, 1966) pp. 526–554.

[8] DORFMAN, R., P. A. SAMUELSON, and R. M. SOLOW, *Linear Programming and Economic Analysis.* New York: McGraw-Hill, 1958.

[9] GALE, D., *Theory of Linear Economic Models.* New York: McGraw-Hill, 1960.

[10] GANTMACHER, F. R., *The Theory of Matrices.* New York: Chelsea, 1960.

[11] HAWKINS, D., and H. A. SIMON, "Note: Some Conditions of Macroeconomic Stability," *Econometrica*, 17, *3–4* (July-October, 1949), pp. 245–248.

[12] HICKS, J. R., *Capital and Growth.* New York: Oxford University Press, 1965.

[13] JORGENSON, D. W., "A Dual Stability Theorem," *Econometrica*, 28, *4* (October, 1960), pp. 892–899.

[14] — "Linear Models of Economic Growth," *International Economic Review*, 9, *1* (February, 1968), pp. 1–13.

[15] — "The Structure of Multi-Sector Dynamic Models," *International Economic Review*, 2, *3* (September, 1961), pp. 276–293.

[16] LEVHARI, D., "A Nonsubstitution Theorem and Switching of Techniques," *Quarterly Journal of Economics*, LXXIX *1* (February, 1965), pp. 98–105.

[17] MORISHIMA, M., *Equilibrium, Stability, and Growth.* Oxford: Clarendon Press 1964.

[18] "Paradoxes in Capital Theory: A Symposium," *Quarterly Journal of Economics* LXXX, *4* (November, 1966), pp. 503–583.

[19] PHELPS, E., *Golden Rules of Economic Growth.* New York: W. W. Norton,, 1966.

[20] ROBINSON, JOAN, *The Accumulation of Capital.* New York: St. Martin's Press, 1966.

[21] — *Essays in the Theory of Economic Growth.* New York: St. Martin's Press, 1962.

[22] — and K. A. NAQVI, "The Badly Behaved Production Function," *The Quarterly Journal of Economics*, LXXXI, *4* (November, 1967), pp. 579–591.

[23] SAMUELSON, P. A., "Abstract of Theorem Concerning Substitutability in Open Leontief Models," in *Activity Analysis of Production and Allocation* (T. C. Koopmans, Ed.). New York: Wiley, 1951, pp. 142–146.

[24] — "The Fundamental Singularity Theorem for Non-Joint Production," *International Economic Review*, **7**, *1* (January, 1966), pp. 34–41.

[25] — "A New Theorem on Nonsubstitution," pp. 407–423, in *Money, Growth, and Methodology and other Essays in Honor of Johan Åkerman* (H. E. Hegeland, Ed.). Lund: CWK Gleerup, 1961.

[26] — "Parable and Realism in Capital Theory: The Surrogate Production Function," *Review of Economic Studies*, **XXIX**, *80* (June, 1962), pp. 193–206.

[27] — "A Summing Up," *Quarterly Journal of Economics*, **LXXX**, *4* (November, 1966), pp. 568–583.

[28] — "Wages and Interest: A Modern Dissection of Marxian Economic Models," *American Economic Review*, **XLVII**, *6* (December, 1957), pp. 884–912.

[29] SOLOW, R. M., *Capital Theory and the Rate of Return*. Amsterdam: North-Holland, 1963.

[30] — "The Interest Rate and Transition Between Techniques," in *Socialism, Capitalism and Economic Growth* (C. H. Feinstein, Ed.). New York: Cambridge University Press, 1967, pp. 30–39.

[31] — "On the Structure of Linear Models," *Econometrica*, **20**. *1* (January, 1952), pp. 29–46.

[32] — "Competitive Valuation in a Dynamic Input-Output System," *Econometrica*, **27**, *1* (January, 1959), pp. 30–53.

[33] VON NEUMANN, J., "Über ein Ökonomisches Gleichungssystem und eine Verallgemeinerung des Brouwerschen Fixpunktsatzes," *Ergebnisse eines Mathematischen Seminars*. English Translation: "A Model of General Economic Equilibrium," *Review of Economic Studies*, **XIII** (1945), pp. 1–9.

[34] VON WEIZSÄCKER, C. C., "Bemerkungen zu einem 'Symposium' über Wachstumstheorie und Produktionsfunktionen," *Kyklos*, **XVI** (1963), pp. 438–457.

Chapter 9 Neoclassical

Multisector Models without

Joint Production

9–1. Introduction

This chapter deals with the same basic economic issues as did the last, except that we assume the smooth neoclassical technology described in Section 7-2. The production functions in this case have the form

$$Y_j = F^j(L_j, K_{1j}, \ldots, K_{nj}), \qquad (j = 0, 1, \ldots, n). \tag{1}$$

By the homogeneity property we may write (1)

$$1 = F^j(a_{0j}, a_{1j}, \ldots, a_{nj}), \qquad (j = 0, 1, \ldots, n), \tag{2}$$

where

$$a_{0j} \equiv L_j/Y_j, \qquad (j = 0, 1, \ldots, n), \tag{3}$$

$$a_{ij} \equiv K_{ij}/Y_j, \qquad (i = 1, \ldots, n; j = 0, 1, \ldots, n). \tag{4}$$

Any activity vector $(a_{0j}, 0, a_{1j}, \ldots, a_{nj})$ satisfying (2) is technically feasible, and the neoclassical properties of F^j imply that there is an infinite number of such vectors. Consequently, one interpretation of this neoclassical model is that there exists an infinite number of alternative Leontief matrices of the type studied in the last chapter such that the set of feasible activity vectors satisfying $F^j(a_{0j}, a_{1j}, \ldots, a_{nj}) \geq 1$ is strictly convex for any $j = 0, 1, \ldots, n$.[1]

[1] This interpretation illustrates that it is not sufficient simply to have an infinite number of techniques; in addition the feasible activity vectors must yield smooth neoclassical isoquant contour surfaces.

Important assumptions[2] will again be:

>**Assumption (A.1):** *Labor is required, either directly or indirectly, to produce every good.*

>**Assumption (A.2):** (1) *At least two factors of production are required to produce every good.* (2) *Every capital good is required, either directly or indirectly, to produce the consumption good.*

In addition we assume, as we have previously, that all factors of production are fully employed.

In Section 9-2 we investigate the conditions that ensure that when a vector of gross own-rates of return is exogenously specified the resulting competitively determined prices are all strictly positive. This analysis yields several results used later in the chapter. Moreover, it is easy to see that reswitching of techniques, as defined in the preceding chapter, cannot occur in this model with a neoclassical technology. We conclude Section 9-2 with the observation that the nonsubstitution theorem remains valid in this context, but give an example to illustrate that it is essential to exclude joint production to preserve this result.

Section 9-3 is devoted to a study of the output configuration in steady-state competitive equilibrium and to conditions that ensure that all outputs are strictly positive. An intriguing feature of this discussion is the observation that although reswitching is impossible the paradoxical consumption behavior referred to previously apparently cannot be excluded in general. We therefore seek conditions adequate to rule out this paradoxical behavior, and we are led in the process to a rather natural definition of capital deepening when there exist many capital goods. A numerical example demonstrates that paradoxical movements in the implied measure of capital value may occur in the absence of paradoxical consumption behavior.

Price-quantity duality relations, analogous to those stated in the last chapter, are discussed in Section 9-4; again the Golden Rule is an immediate corollary. We also state a somewhat stronger duality relationship that remains valid even in models admitting joint production. Finally, in Section 9-5 we return to certain familiar dual instability features arising in this dynamic neoclassical model.

The notation in this chapter generally follows that introduced in Chapters 7 and 8. Thus, for example, the price vector p and the vector w of factor rental rates, both in terms of the wage rate as numeraire, are respectively

$$p \equiv (P_0/W_0, P_1/W_0, \ldots P_n/W_0), \qquad w \equiv (1, W_1/W_0, \ldots W_n/W_0).$$

The input matrix a was defined on page 230.

---

[2] As in Chapter 8, these assumptions ensure that equilibrium prices and quantities are all strictly positive.

In one important respect our notation differs from that earlier. In this chapter we wish to refer to the n-vector ρ of gross own-rates of return, and also to the diagonal matrix ρ having the $(n + 1)$-vector $(1, \rho)$ as its main diagonal. Generally the context will make it obvious which interpretation is intended; where confusion is possible, we shall use the bold face letter $\boldsymbol{\rho}$ to refer to the $(n + 1) \times (n + 1)$ diagonal matrix.

9–2. Determination of Equilibrium Prices

Below we will show that equilibrium prices are uniquely determined if an admissible vector ρ of gross own-rates of return is assigned exogenously. The necessity for restrictions on the vector ρ may be seen from the following example.

Assume that the production function for the first capital good is of the CES form

$$Y_1 = F^1(L_1, K_{11})$$
$$= [\beta K_{11}^{(\sigma_1 - 1)/\sigma_1} + (1 - \beta)L_1^{(\sigma_1 - 1)/\sigma_1}]^{\sigma_1/(\sigma_1 - 1)}, \quad 0 < \beta < 1. \tag{5}$$

Since we insist on an equilibrium without any inequalities, the equation

$$\rho_1 \equiv W_1/P_1 = \partial F^1/\partial K_{11} \tag{6}$$

must be satisfied. However, the range of $\partial F^1/\partial K_{11}$ is restricted by

$$0 \leq \partial F^1/\partial K_{11} \leq \beta^{\sigma_1/(\sigma_1 - 1)} \quad \text{if} \quad \sigma_1 < 1 \tag{7}$$

and

$$\beta^{\sigma_1/(\sigma_1 - 1)} \leq \partial F^1/\partial K_{11} \leq \infty \quad \text{if} \quad \sigma_1 > 1. \tag{8}$$

Consequently (6) can be satisfied with equality only if the exogenously assigned value of ρ_1 is restricted to the open interval

$$(0, \beta^{\sigma_1/(\sigma_1 - 1)}) \quad \text{if} \quad \sigma_1 < 1$$

or

$$(\beta^{\sigma_1/(\sigma_1 - 1)}, \infty) \quad \text{if} \quad \sigma_1 > 1.$$

We now turn to an analogous result which is generally valid, namely if the vector ρ belongs to some admissible set Γ, corresponding equilibrium prices are determined.

Definition: Let E^n denote the set of real vectors $x = (x_1, \ldots, x_n)$ in n-dimensional Euclidean space. The *strictly positive orthant of E^n* is the set

$$\Omega = \{x \mid x \in E^n \quad \text{and} \quad x > 0\}.$$

Theorem 1[3]: *Assume* (A.1) *and* (A.2) *are always satisfied. There exists a nonempty set* $\Gamma \subset \Omega$ *such that a positive equilibrium price vector*

$$p = G(\rho) > 0$$

is uniquely determined for all $\rho \in \Gamma$.

Corollary 1.1: *Let* $\rho_i = \alpha$, $i = 1, \ldots, n$. *There exists a nonempty interval* $(0, \bar{\alpha})$ *such that a positive equilibrium price vector*

$$p = G(\alpha, \ldots, \alpha) > 0$$

is uniquely determined for all $\alpha \in (0, \bar{\alpha})$.

Assumption (A.3): *The depreciation rates* $\delta_1, \ldots, \delta_n$ *are all positive but are sufficiently small that* $\bar{\alpha} - \delta_i > 0$, $i = 1, \ldots, n$. *Thus,*

$$r_0^* \equiv \bar{\alpha} - \max_{i=1, \ldots, n} \delta_i > 0.$$

Corollary 1.2: *Let* $r_0 = \rho_i - \delta_i$, $i = 1, \ldots, n$. *There exists a number* $r_0^* > 0$ [*defined in* (A.3)] *such that a positive equilibrium price vector*

$$p = g(r_0) > 0$$

is uniquely determined for all $r_0 \in [0, r_0^*)$.

---

[3] Theorem 1 is analogous to Theorem 7 on p. 240 of Chapter 8, and the restriction $\rho \in \Gamma$ is similar to the requirement that all ρ_i are less than the upper bound $1/\bar{\lambda}$ defined on p. 251. The result is intuitively plausible, for this neoclassical model may be viewed as a limiting case of the linear model in Chapter 8 where now the set S (defined in Theorem 7 on p. 240) contains an infinite number technique matrices that satisfy certain regularity conditions.

Burmeister and Kuga [6] provide a direct proof of Theorem 1 which does not involve a contradiction of known results for linear models, and the interested reader is referred to their paper. Corollary 1.1 may be proved by similar methods with ρ_i replaced by α, $i = 1$, $\ldots, n$. Moreover, it is crucial to note that $\alpha \in (0, \bar{\alpha})$ is not inconsistent with equation (8) because $\sigma_1 > 1$ is ruled out by (A.1).

Corollary 1.2 is a special case of 1.1 when (A.3) is satisfied, and it is equivalent to Morishima's Theorem 1 [20], p. 66 and [21], p. 76. Assumption (A.3) serves to insure that every equilibrium price and rental rate is strictly positive for all r_0 satisfying $0 \leq r_0 < r_0^*$.

Definition: Any vector $\rho \in \Gamma$ or any number $r_0 \in [0, r_0^*)$ is termed *admissible* or *feasible*.

We now present several additional results needed later.

Theorem 2: *Let $\rho \in \Gamma$ be assigned. The activity vectors $(a_{0j}, 0, a_{1j}, \ldots, a_{nj})$, $j = 0, 1, \ldots, n$, are all uniquely determined.*

Proof: In equilibrium the a_{ij}'s are functions of the vector w. But, as ρ is given, $p = G(\rho)$ is unique, and since $w_i = p_i \rho_i$, the conclusion is immediate.   QED

Corollary 2.1: *Let $r_0 \in [0, r_0^*)$ be assigned. All activity vectors are uniquely determined, and we will write*

$$a_{ij} = a_{ij}(r_0), \qquad i, j = 0, 1, \ldots, n.$$

Theorem 3: *Consider $\rho \in \Gamma$ and define $B = [b_{ij}] \equiv [I - \rho a]^{-1}$.*

$$\left(\frac{\partial p_0}{\partial \rho_i}, \frac{\partial p_1}{\partial \rho_i}, \ldots, \frac{\partial p_n}{\partial \rho_i} \right) = (p_i a_{i0}, p_i a_{i1}, \ldots, p_i a_{in}) B \geq 0$$

or

$$\frac{\partial p_j}{\partial \rho_i} = p_i \sum_{h=0}^{n} a_{ih} b_{hj} \geq 0, \qquad (j = 0, 1, \ldots, n; i = 1, \ldots, n) \qquad (9)$$

with strict inequality holding if and only if the ith capital good is required, either directly or indirectly, for the production of good j.

Proof:[4]

$$a_0 [I - \rho a]^{-1} = a_0 B = (p_0, p_1, \ldots, p_n) \qquad (10)$$

where B is semipositive for all $\rho \in \Gamma$.[5] (A.1) implies that for all $j = 0$, $1, \ldots, n$, there is at least one i for which $a_{0i} > 0$ and $b_{ij} > 0$, ensuring that all prices p_i are strictly positive. By total differentiation we obtain

$$dp_j = \sum_{i=1}^{n} C_i^j (\rho_i \, dp_i + p_i \, d\rho_i) \qquad (11)$$

---

[4] See Burmeister and Kuga [6].
[5] See Theorem 4.

where

$$C_i^j \equiv \frac{\partial C^j}{\partial (W_i/W_0)} = a_{ij}.^6$$

The latter equations are written in matrix notation as

$$dp = (dp)\rho a + p(d\rho)a \qquad (12)$$

and may be solved for

$$dp = p(d\rho)aB. \qquad (13)$$

Observe that Theorem 3 is analogous to Theorem 6 in Chapter 8. It remains true that $\partial p_j/\partial \rho_i$ is strictly positive if and only if there exists at least one index h such that a_{ih} and b_{hj} are both positive; equivalently, $\partial p_j/\partial \rho_i > 0$ if and only if the ith capital good is required, either directly or indirectly, for the production of good j.[7]   QED

Corollary 3.1

$$\partial p_0/\partial \rho_i > 0, \qquad i = 1, \dots, n.$$

Proof: The conclusion is implied by Theorem 3 and (A.2).   QED

Corollary 3.2: *Consider any* $r_0 \in (0, r_0^*)$;

$$dp/dr_0 = g'(r_0) > 0. \qquad (14)$$

Proof: The conclusion follows immediately from Theorem 3 and (A.2).   QED

Corollary 3.3: *Consider any* $r_0 \in (0, r_0^*)$; *then*

$$w_i'(r_0) > 0, \qquad (i = 1, \dots, n) \qquad (15)$$

Proof: The result follows immediately from $w_i = p_i(r_0 + \delta_i)$, $i = 1, \dots, n$, Corollary 1.2, and Corollary 3.2.   QED

---

[6] See Samuelson [27]. $C^j(W_1/W_0, \dots, W_n/W_0)$ is the unit cost function (in terms of the wage rate W_0 as numeraire) for the jth good.
[7] See Exercise 5 in Chapter 8.

Corollary 3.4[8]:

$$a'_0(r_0) + wa'(r_0) \equiv 0. \tag{16}$$

Proof: Differentiating (2) gives

$$\sum_{i=0}^{n} F_i^j a'_{ij}(r_0) \equiv 0.$$

Substituting the static efficiency conditions $F_i^j = W_i/P_j$ and using $W_0/P_j > 0$ $(i = 1, \ldots, n; j = 0, 1, \ldots, n)$, we obtain

$$a'_{0j}(r_0) + \sum_{i=1}^{n} w_i a'_{ij}(r_0) \equiv 0, \qquad j = 0, 1, \ldots, n,$$

as required. QED

Theorem 4: *Consider any assigned vector $\rho \in \Gamma$, and let a be the corresponding matrix of equilibrium input coefficients; then*

$$[I - \rho a]^{-1} \geq 0. \tag{17}$$

Proof: Since $\rho \in \Gamma$, Theorem 1 implies that in equilibrium $p > 0$ is unique. As derived in Chapter 8, the equilibrium conditions that prices equal unit costs are expressed as

$$p = a_0 + p\rho a$$

or

$$p[I - \rho a] = a_0,$$

and $a_0 \geq 0$ by (A.1). Define $b \equiv \rho a$,

$$d \equiv \begin{bmatrix} p_0 & 0 & \cdots & 0 \\ 0 & p_1 & \ddots & \vdots \\ \vdots & \ddots & \ddots & 0 \\ 0 & \cdots & 0 & p_n \end{bmatrix},$$

$b^* \equiv dbd^{-1}$, and $b_0^* \equiv a_0 d^{-1}$, and assume b is written in the canonical

---

[8] See Theorem V in Burmeister and Dobell [4], pp. 22–23. Corollary 3.4 is essentially a development of the usual envelope theorems. See, e.g., Samuelson [25], p. 69.

form described in L.9.[9] The price-cost equations may then be rewritten as

$$(1, 1, \ldots, 1)[I - b^*] = b_0^*.$$

In view of assumption (A.1) it is clear that the column sums of b^* satisfy the sufficiency conditions stated in L.9, and therefore L.10 implies that the characteristic roots of b are all less than one in modulus. Finally, applying L.5 we conclude that

$$[I - b]^{-1} \equiv [I - \rho a]^{-1} \geq 0. \qquad \text{QED} \quad \textbf{(18)}$$

Theorem 5: *Reswitching of techniques as defined in Chapter 8 is impossible.*

Proof: Assumptions (A.1) and (A.2) imply that there exist some indices i and j for which $a_{0j} > 0$ and $a_{ij} > 0$. For any such choice of indices, the equation

$$\frac{F_i^j(a_{0j}, a_{1j}, \ldots, \bar{a}_{nj})}{F_o^j(a_{0j}, a_{1j}, \ldots, a_{nj})} = \frac{W_i/P_j}{W_0/P_j} = \frac{W_i}{W_0} = w_i(r_0) \qquad \textbf{(19)}$$

must be satisfied. Reswitching necessitates $a_{ij}(r_0') = a_{ij}(r_0'')$ ($i, j = 0, 1, \ldots, n$) for $r_0' \neq r_0''$. Corollary 3.3 implies that $w_i(r_0') \neq w_i(r_0'')$ if $r_0' \neq r_0''$, and thus reswitching contradicts the foregoing equilibrium condition.

QED

It is important to realize that our definition of reswitching requires that an entire matrix of input coefficients $\left[\dfrac{a_0}{a} \right]$ be adopted at two distinct values of r_0. Reswitching in a different sense can occur in neoclassical models, as the following simple example illustrates. Suppose a single output can be produced by capital and labor using either of the neoclassical production functions

$$Y = F(K, L)$$

or

$$Y = G(K, L).$$

Assuming that the unit isoquants are as pictured in Figure 36, we deduce that the function F will be employed for all values of the wage/rentals ratio $\omega \in (\omega_2, +\infty)$, G will be employed for all $\omega \in (\omega_1, \omega_2)$, but F will again be

[9] See the Appendix for L.1–L.10.

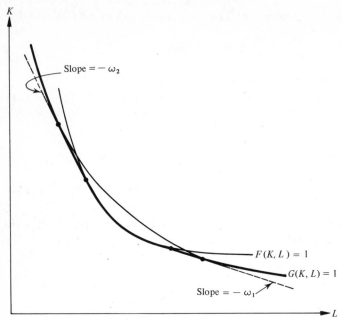

Figure 36

employed for all $\omega \in (0, \omega_1)$. The latter behavior may be called *reswitching*, and ω_1 and ω_2 may be identified as *switching points*. However, reswitching by our definition does not occur because the input coefficients L/Y and K/Y can never recur for two distinct values of ω. Moreover, we have assumed that the jth good can be produced only by one neoclassical production function F^j. Of course the functions F and G in this example could be combined into a single production function

$$Y = H(K, L);$$

but, as indicated in Figure 36, the relevant unit isoquant $H(K, L) = 1$ would then contain two straight-line segments, which implies that H is not neoclassical.

We conclude this section with the observation that the nonsubstitution theorem (Theorem 8 in Chapter 8) remains valid in this neoclassical model. Indeed, it should be obvious that the nonsubstitution result is a general feature of any economic model having (1) one primary (nonproduced) factor, in this case labor, and (2) no joint production.[10]

The necessity of (2) can be seen from the following simple example of

[10] Morishima [20], pp. 67–69 has questioned the relevance of nonsubstitution theorems, observing that it is not realistic to assume that the profit or interest rate r_0 is exogenous.

Samuelson [30].[11] Let the joint production function for an economy consisting of a single sector (which produces a single consumption good Y_0 and new capital goods Y_1) be

$$Y_0^2 + Y_1^2 = 2K_1 L, \tag{20}$$

and assume the depreciation rate $\delta_1 = 0$. A firm in competitive equilibrium seeks to maximize profits at given prices, and we form the constrained maximization problem

$$\Phi(Y_0, Y_1, K_1, L) = P_0 Y_0 + P_1 Y_1 - W_0 L - W_1 K_1$$
$$- \lambda(Y_0^2 + Y_1^2 - 2K_1 L) - \mu(Y_0 + Y_1 + K_1 + L - 1) \tag{21}$$

where we now use the normalization $Y_0 + Y_1 + K_1 + L \equiv 1$ rather than $L \equiv 1$. Differentiating (21) to obtain necessary maximization conditions and solving, we may derive the equilibrium condition

$$(P_0 - \mu)^2 + (P_1 - \mu)^2 - 2(W_0 + \mu)(W_1 + \mu) = 0 \tag{22}$$

(Exercise 5). However, since (normalized) profits are equal to

$$\mu = P_0 Y_0 + P_1 Y_1 - W_0 L - W_1 K_1$$

(Exercise 6), we see that μ must equal zero in competitive equilibrium, and hence (22) is rewritten

$$(P_0)^2 + (P_1)^2 = 2W_0 W_1$$

or

$$\frac{W_0}{P_0} = \frac{1}{2}\left[\frac{1 + (P_1/P_0)^2}{(W_1/P_0)}\right] = \frac{1}{2}\left[\frac{1 + (P_1/P_0)^2}{(P_1/P_0)}\right]\frac{1}{(W_1/P_1)} = \frac{x}{2\rho_1} \tag{23}$$

where

$$x \equiv \left[\frac{1 + (P_1/P_0)^2}{(P_1/P_0)}\right]. \tag{24}$$

(As before, $\rho_1 \equiv W_1/P_1 = r_0 + \delta_1 = r_0$.)

---

[11] Also see Samuelson [26, 28] and Burmeister and Kuga [7].

Now assume $\bar{\rho}_1 = \bar{r}_0 > 0$ is assigned exogenously. It is not true that the equilibrium real wage rate W_0/P_0 is determined since (23) cannot be written in the form

$$\frac{W_0}{P_0} = \frac{1}{G^0(\rho_1)};$$

the equilibrium value of W_0/P_0 is a function of both ρ_1 and the relative price P_1/P_0, as shown by (23). Moreover, the unique minimum value of (24) on the domain $P_1/P_0 > 0$ is $x = 2$ (Exercise 7), and thus any real wage rate satisfying the inequality

$$W_0/P_0 \geqq 1/\bar{\rho}_1 \tag{25}$$

is consistent with competitive equilibrium for some value of $P_1/P_0 > 0$. Since $P_1/P_0 = Y_1/Y_0$ in competitive equilibrium (Exercise 6), the nonsubstitution statement—given $\bar{\rho}_1$ the equilibrium value of W_0/P_0 is determined independently of final demand Y_1/Y_0—is false for this joint-production example.

However, we may define a *minimal real wage rate frontier* as

$$W_0/P_0 = 1/\rho_1, \qquad \rho_1 > 0; \tag{26}$$

(26) is satisfied for a given $\rho_1 > 0$ if and only if

$$\frac{Y_1}{K_1} = \frac{\dot{K}_1}{K_1} = \rho_1 = r_0 \tag{27}$$

(Exercise 8). We will discuss this result again in Section 9-4.

9–3. Steady-State Quantity Behavior

In addition to the steady-state price restrictions $\dot{p}_i = 0$ $(i = 0, 1, \ldots, n)$, we now impose the conditions

$$y_i = (g + \delta_i)k_i, \qquad (i = 1, \ldots, n), \tag{28}$$

which imply that $\dot{k}_i = 0$ $(i = 1, \ldots, n)$. As in Chapter 8, the output vector is

$$y = \begin{bmatrix} y_0 \\ y_1 \\ \vdots \\ y_n \end{bmatrix}$$

where y_0 denotes per capita consumption, and thus (28) may be rewritten

$$y = (g + \delta)k + c \tag{29}$$

with

$$c \equiv \begin{bmatrix} y_0 \\ 0 \\ \vdots \\ 0 \end{bmatrix}.$$

Full employment of capital and labor necessitates

$$k = ay \tag{30}$$

and

$$a_0 y = 1, \tag{31}$$

respectively. Substituting (30) into (29) yields

$$y = (g + \delta)ay + c$$

or

$$[I - (g + \delta)a]y = c. \tag{32}$$

We wish to solve (32) for a strictly positive quantity vector y, and the following assumption is needed.

Assumption (A.4): (1) The exogenous growth rate of labor satisfies the inequality $0 < g < r_0^*$, and (2) there exists a number $r_0^{\min}$ such that

$$0 \leqq r_0^{\min} < g < r_0^*$$

and the matrix $(g + \delta)a(r_0)$ has characteristic roots that are all less than one in modulus for any assigned value of $r_0 \in (r_0^{\min}, r_0^*) \equiv R$.

Although $g = 0$ is excluded by (A.4), that case can be handled separately without difficulty. Moreover, assumption (A.4) is less restrictive than it may appear because the characteristic roots of $(g + \delta)a(r_0)$ are all less than one in modulus for any assigned value of $r_0 \in [g, r_0^*)$ (see Exercise 9). We now prove the desired result.

Theorem 6: *Consider any assigned value of $r_0 \in R$. A corresponding steady-state equilibrium is uniquely determined with per capita consumption $y_0 > 0$ and the quantity vector*

$$y = [I - (g + \delta)a]^{-1}c > 0.$$

Proof: Corollary 2.1 implies that the vector a_0 and the matrix a are both uniquely determined for any assigned $r_0 \in R \subset [0, r_0^*)$. From (A.4) and L.5 (see page 244) we conclude that $[I - (g + \delta)a]^{-1} \geq 0$, whereas (A.2) implies that the first column of the latter matrix is strictly positive (Exercise 10). Define the vector

$$\varphi(r_0) \equiv a_0[I - (g + \delta)a]^{-1}.$$

(A.1) implies that $\varphi_0(r_0) > 0$, and thus the conclusion $y_0 = 1/\varphi_0(r_0) > 0$ follows from

$$a_0 y = a_0[I - (g + \delta)a]^{-1}c = 1$$

(see Exercise 11); accordingly, $y > 0$.   QED

We can therefore consider per capita consumption as a function of the interest rate alone, having, in effect, used the equilibrium conditions to substitute for all other variables. Thus we write $c = c(r_0)$, $r_0 \in R$. This function has a global maximum where the rate of interest equals the rate of growth of labor, as the following proves. If, moreover, it has no other relative maximum, then we call it *well-behaved*. Conversely, we shall say that the model shows *paradoxical behavior* if the function $c(r_0)$ has a regular relative maximum elsewhere than at $r_0 = g$, so that there is some range of interest rates in which per capita consumption increases even while the gap $|r_0 - g|$ increases.[12] We seek conditions that are adequate to rule out the latter case in a neoclassical model. (We have not seen a numerical example of a model with smooth production functions in which this kind of paradoxical behavior can occur. But, as Samuelson has pointed out to us, the fact that it can occur in linear models having isoquants that can be approximated as closely as desired by smooth production functions suggests that it also occurs in smooth technologies satisfying every neoclassical assumption.[13])

---

[12] See Section 8-6 for a discussion of paradoxical behavior in linear multisector models. Figures 37 and 38 illustrate the issue for this neoclassical model.

[13] Solow [38], pp. 37–38, states: "... in a technology with smoothly diminishing returns to variable proportions ..., it is not possible for a whole technique to 'recur', but it is possible for steady state consumption per head to be an increasing function of the steady state interest rate for some range or ranges " (when $g = 0$).

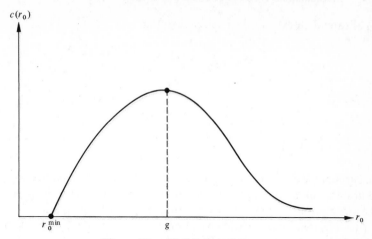

Figure 37.   *Well-Behaved Case*

Solow [37] has shown that the Golden Rule notion can be trivially extended to models in which there are many capital goods and a single consumption good. Static efficiency conditions lead to a transformation function of the form

$$c = T(y_1, \ldots, y_n; k_1, \ldots, k_n, 1) \tag{33}$$

which, upon substitution of the steady-state requirements, becomes

$$c = T[(g + \delta_1)k_1, \ldots, (g + \delta_n)k_n; k_1, \ldots, k_n, 1]. \tag{34}$$

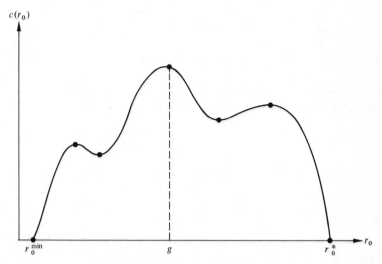

Figure 38.   *Paradoxical-Behavior Case*

Optimal capital stocks are then selected so that

$$\frac{\partial c}{\partial k_i} = T_i(g + \delta_i) + T_{n+i} = 0 \tag{35}$$

which implies

$$g + \delta_i = \frac{-T_{n+i}}{T_i} = \frac{-W_i/P_0}{-P_i/P_0} = \frac{w_i}{p_i} = r_i + \delta_i, \qquad i = 1, \ldots, n. \tag{36}$$

Thus, sustainable consumption is at a global maximum when all net own-rates of return are equal, and equal to the rate of growth of labor. Standard concavity assumptions assure sufficiency of this Golden Rule condition. We use the latter observation as a starting point to learn something about the behavior of consumption along the locus of points in the input space where all own-rates of return are equal to a common value r_0. On this locus c and k_i are functions of r_0 alone.

Theorem 7:

$$\frac{dc}{dr_0} \equiv c'(r_0) = (r_0 - g)\sum_{i=1}^{n} \frac{p_i}{p_0} \frac{dk_i}{dr_0} \equiv (r_0 - g)\sum_{i=1}^{n} \frac{p_i}{p_0} k_i'(r_0) \tag{37}$$

Proof: Differentiating (31) with respect to r_0 and using Corollary 3.4,[14] we find

$$a_0 y' - wa'y = 0$$

or

$$p\{[I - (r_0 + \delta)a]y' - (r_0 + \delta)a'y\} = p[y' - (r_0 + \delta)ay' - (r_0 + \delta)a'y] = 0.$$

But $k' = ay' + a'y$ from (30), whereas $y' = (g + \delta)k' + c'$ from (29); consequently,

$$p[c' + (g + \delta)k' - (r_0 + \delta)k'] = 0$$

or

$$pc' = (r_0 - g)pk'$$

which is (37) in vector notation.   QED

---

[14] A quicker but less direct proof may be based on the transformation function: $c(r_0) = T[(g + \delta_1)k_1(r_0), \ldots, (g + \delta_n)k_n(r_0); k_1(r_0), \ldots, k_n(r_0), 1]$. Thus, $c'(r_0) = \sum_{i=1}^{n}[T_i(g + \delta_i) + T_{n+i}]k_i'(r_0) = (r_0 - g)\sum_{i=1}^{n}(p_i/p_0)k_i'(r_0)$ since $T_i = -p_i/p_0$ and $T_{n+i} = w_i/p_0 = p_i(r_0 + \delta_i)/p_0$ in steady states with $\dot{p}_i = 0$.

Corollary 7.1: *At*

$$r_0 = g, \quad \sum_{i=1}^{n} p_i k_i'(r_0) \leq 0. \tag{38}$$

Proof: Since c has a global maximum at $r_0 = g$, it must certainly have a maximum when confined to the locus of efficient steady states. Hence, $c''(r_0) \leq 0$ at $r_0 = g$.

$$c''(r_0) = \sum_{i=1}^{n} \frac{p_i}{p_0} k_i'(r_0) + (r_0 - g) \frac{d}{dr_0} \left[\sum_{i=1}^{n} \frac{p_i}{p_0} k_i'(r_0) \right]$$

$$= \sum_{i=1}^{n} \frac{p_i}{p_0} k_i'(r_0) \quad \text{at} \quad r_0 = g.$$

QED

Since $p_0 > 0$, $\sum_{i=1}^{n} p_i k_i'(r_0) \leq 0$ at $r_0 = g$.

Corollary 7.2: *Any other stationary point of $c(r_0)$ must occur at a value of r_0 such that*

$$\sum_{i=1}^{n} p_i k_i'(r_0) = 0. \tag{39}$$

Hence, if $\sum_{i=1}^{n} p_i k_i' \leq 0$, then

$$\text{sign } c'(r_0) = \text{sign}(g - r_0),$$

except at possible stationary points of $c(r_0)$ which are not relative maxima or minima. That is, there is no paradoxical behavior if and only if

$$\sum_{i=1}^{n} p_i k_i'(r_0) \leq 0$$

for all $r_0 \in R$.

Thus, as we might expect, the paradoxical behavior question is tightly tied to capital valuation considerations. The value of per capita capital increments

$$\sum_{i=1}^{n} p_i k_i'(r_0)$$

is strictly negative in a neighborhood of $r_0 = g$. If, however, this expression becomes positive for some $r_0 \in R$, the paradoxical behavior discussed earlier exists.

We now develop some further conditions that are clearly satisfied by the one-capital model, and we use this observation to suggest some sufficient conditions appropriate to a model with many capital goods.

We shall write the term $\sum_{i=1}^{n} p_i k_i'(r)$ in vector notation as $pk'(r_0)$. We wish to derive conditions sufficient to imply that this expression is nonpositive for all $r_0 \in R$.

From (29) and (30) we have

$$k = ay = a[(g + \delta)k + c];$$

hence,

$$k'(r_0) = a[(g + \delta)k'(r_0) + c'(r_0)] + a'(r_0)y. \qquad (40)$$

Since

$$\det[I - a(g + \delta)] = \det[I - (g + \delta)a] \neq 0 \qquad \text{for} \qquad r_0 \in R,$$

(40) may be solved for

$$k'(r_0) = [I - a(g + \delta)]^{-1}[ac'(r_0) + a'(r_0)y].$$

Theorem 8: *The expression $pk'(r_0) < 0$ for all $r_0 \in R$ if the expression*

$$p[I - a(g + \delta)]^{-1}a'(r_0)y < 0 \qquad (41)$$

for all $r_0 \in R$.

Proof: These two conditions coincide at $r_0 = g$ where $c'(r_0) = 0$ and $pk'(r_0) < 0$. Hence, it suffices to show that the two expressions can change sign only if they do so together. It is clear that if $pk'(r_0) = 0$, then also $c'(r_0) = 0$ (where, it will be recalled, c' represents a column vector), and hence the two expressions coincide and both are zero. Thus we have proved sufficiency: if $p[I - a(g + \delta)]^{-1} a'(r_0)y < 0$ for all $r_0 \in R$, then $pk'(r_0)$ cannot change sign, and it must also remain negative (and hence nonpositive) for all $r_0 \in R$.

Corollary 8.1: *If $a'(r_0)$ is a seminegative matrix, i.e., if*

$$a'(r_0) \leq 0 \qquad \text{for all} \qquad r_0 \in R,$$

then

$$pk'(r_0) < 0 \qquad \text{for all} \qquad r_0 \in R.$$

Proof: Since $[I - a(r)(g + \delta)] = (g + \delta)^{-1}[I - (g + \delta)a(r_0)](g + \delta)$ where $(g + \delta)$ is a diagonal matrix with positive entries on the diagonal, our assumptions imply that $p[I - a(r_0)(g + \delta)]^{-1}$ is strictly positive for all $r_0 \in R$. Hence, since y is positive, if $a'(r_0) \leq 0$, then $a'(r_0)y \leq 0$, and

$$p[I - a(r_0)(g + \delta)]^{-1}a'(r_0)y < 0,$$

as required.   QED

For well-behaved models having only one capital good, Corollary 8.1 immediately implies the conclusion that sign $c'(r_0) = \text{sign}\ (g - r_0)$.[15] For if we now consider such a model with only one capital good (so that $n = 1$), then clearly

$$da_{0j}/dw_1 > 0, \qquad j = 1, 2,$$

and

$$da_{1j}/dw_1 < 0, \qquad j = 1, 2,$$

as illustrated in Figure 39. Since $w_1'(r_0) > 0$ by Corollary 3.3, we have established that $a'(r_0) \leq 0$.

A generalization of this result is possible, as seen in Corollary 8.2.

Corollary 8.2: *If* (1) $a_{0j} > 0, j = 0, 1, \ldots, n,$ *and* (2) *if for all j,* $a_{ij} = 0$ *except for exactly one value of i, then* $a'(r_0) \leq 0$ *and sign* $c'(r_0) = sign$ $(g - r_0)$.

In other words, if every good is produced by labor and only one kind of capital (though different goods may be produced by different capital goods), then there is no paradoxical behavior. The proof follows immediately from the Corollaries 8.1 and 7.2.

The paradox in question is more complex than might be anticipated; we find even the usually well-behaved Cobb–Douglas example yields less than the perfect regularity we would like in order to ensure the complete validity of the neoclassical parables. Although we have found neither a proof that paradoxical behavior cannot occur in a Cobb–Douglas world, nor an example in which it does, we have found examples in which

(i) Some capital/labor ratios rise whereas others fall (with changes in r_0), so that there is no unambiguous *capital deepening* in physical terms, and

[15] This result has been obtained previously for a two-sector model. See Burmeister [2], pp. 153–154.

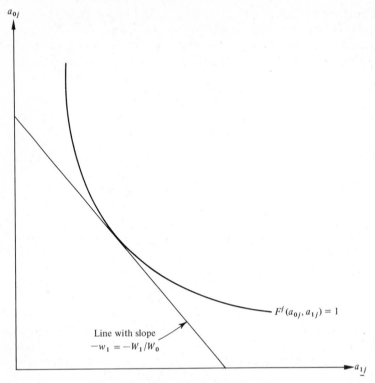

Figure 39. *The One-Capital Good Case*

(ii) The value of per capita capital is lower for lower values of r_0 (on either side of the Golden Rule point), so that there is no capital deepening in value terms as r_0 falls.

Table 2 gives some steady-state configurations for selected values of r_0 using the production functions $Y_1 = L_1^{0.75} K_{11}^{0.25}$, $Y_2 = L_2^{0.25} K_{22}^{0.75}$, and $C = Y_0 = L_0^{0.33} K_{10}^{0.33} K_{20}^{0.33}$ with depreciation rates $\delta_1 = 1.0$, $\delta_2 = 0.0$, and a labor growth rate $g = 0.5$. This table shows that there is a range of interest rates over which one capital/labor ratio $k_1(r_0)$ rises with increasing r_0. This is not surprising. Since the second capital good serves equally well in the production of the consumption good but is more durable (has lower depreciation rate) and is also itself produced by relatively capital intensive means, we expect that it will be adopted to a greater extent as the interest rate falls. Hence, as the rate of interest rises from 0.40 to 0.70, the economy substitutes capital good 1 for capital good 2 to such an extent that the per capita stock of capital good 1 increases despite the rise in interest rate. Thus it is clear that the possibilities of substitution between capital goods of different types and durability prohibits any hope that in well-behaved models

TABLE 2

r_0	$c(r_0)$	$k_1'(r_0)$	$k_2'(r_0)$	$pk'(r_0)$
0.40	0.1515	0.2121	-25.2884	-14.8431
0.45	0.2436	0.0465	$-\ 5.1313$	$-\ 4.3220$
0.50	0.2581	0.0177	$-\ 1.9059$	$-\ 2.2160$
0.55	0.2516	0.0078	$-\ 0.8941$	$-\ 1.39$
0.60	0.2385	0.0032	$-\ 0.4786$	$-\ 0.9721$
0.65	0.2239	0.0009	$-\ 0.2796$	$-\ 0.7257$
0.70	0.2094	-0.0004	$-\ 0.1740$	$-\ 0.5670$
0.75	0.1957	-0.0012	$-\ 0.1137$	$-\ 0.4579$
$\vdots$	$\vdots$	$\vdots$	$\vdots$	$\vdots$
1.00	0.1429	-0.0024	$-\ 0.0216$	$-\ 0.2108$
$\vdots$	$\vdots$	$\vdots$	$\vdots$	$\vdots$
1.50	0.0869	-0.0020	$-\ 0.0025$	$-\ 0.0848$
$\vdots$	$\vdots$	$\vdots$	$\vdots$	$\vdots$
2.00	0.0595	-0.0015	$-\ 0.0006$	$-\ 0.0475$
$\vdots$	$\vdots$	$\vdots$	$\vdots$	$\vdots$
3.00	0.0338	-0.0009	$-\ 0.0001$	$-\ 0.0220$
$\vdots$	$\vdots$	$\vdots$	$\vdots$	$\vdots$
4.00	0.0222	-0.0006	$-\ 0.0000$	$-\ 0.0129$

all per capita capital stocks will move in the same direction across alternative steady states. (The value of the increment to per capita capital stocks nevertheless remains negative in all of the Cobb–Douglas examples we have calculated.)

Table 3 gives some steady-state configurations computed for selected values of r_0 using the system of production functions $Y_1 = L_1^{0.6} K_{11}^{0.2} K_{21}^{0.2}$, $Y_2 = K_{12}^{0.5} K_{22}^{0.5}$, and $C = Y_0 = K_{10}^{0.1} K_{20}^{0.9}$ with depreciation rates $\delta_1 = 2$, $\delta_2 = 0$, and a labor growth rate of $g = 0.5$.

From this table it is seen that the value $V = \sum_{i=1}^{n} p_i k_i$ of steady state per capita capital stocks (evaluated at equilibrium prices) rises uniformly as r_0 rises, destroying any hope that in simple cases the value of per capita capital might support an interpretation of capital deepening analogous to the results in the one-capital case.

It is interesting that most of our results generalize immediately to the case of many consumption goods. Suppose that there are $m - n$ goods that are consumed only, so that the indices $n + 1, n + 2, \ldots, m$ designate consumption goods, whereas the indices $1, \ldots, n$ continue to designate capital goods. By adding a suitable number of zeros we can make the relevant vectors and matrices all $(1 \times m)$, $(m \times 1)$, or $(m \times m)$ and can easily derive the following:

$$\sum_{i=n+1}^{m} p_i c_i'(r_0) = (r_0 - g) \sum_{i=1}^{n} p_i k_i'(r_0)$$

TABLE 3

r_0	$c(r_0)$	$V(r_0)$	$pk'(r_0)$
0.32	0.001	5.517	−0.312
0.34	0.011	5.527	−0.295
0.36	0.018	5.537	−0.280
0.38	0.023	5.546	−0.267
0.40	0.027	5.556	−0.255
0.42	0.029	5.565	−0·244
0.44	0.031	5.574	−0.234
0.46	0.0316	5.583	−0.225
0.48	0.0318	5.591	−0.217
0.50	0.0322	5.600	−0.210
0.52	0.0321	5.609	−0.203
0.54	0.0318	5.617	−0.196
0.56	0.0313	5.625	−0.190
0.58	0.0307	5.633	−0.185
0.60	0.030	5.641	−0.179
⋮	⋮	⋮	⋮
1.00	0.017	5.779	−0.118
1.10	0.014	5.807	−0.110
1.20	0.013	5.833	−0.102
1.30	0.011	5.857	−0.096
1.40	0.010	5.882	−0.091
1.50	0.008	5.905	−0.086
⋮	⋮	⋮	⋮
2.00	0.005	6.000	−0.069

and

$$\sum_{i=n+1}^{m} p_i c_i = \left[(r_0 - g) \sum_{i=1}^{n} p_i k_i \right] + 1. \tag{42}$$

Of course, if the $m - n$ consumption goods are always consumed in exactly the same proportions, then we can define a *composite consumption good* by

$$c = \alpha_{n+1} c_{n+1} + \cdots + \alpha_m c_m$$

for nonnegative constants $\alpha_{n+1}, \ldots, \alpha_m$.

Assume on the contrary that the proportions in which consumption goods are selected do change with relative prices. However, assume that there exists a homothetic utility function $U(c_{n+1}, \ldots, c_m)$ that is maximized. In the latter case all of our previous results generalize with U now playing the role of the single consumption good. In particular, we may prove the following theorem.

Theorem 9: *The utility function U may be taken to satisfy*

$$\frac{U}{\lambda} = \sum_{i=n+1}^{m} p_i c_i,$$

and then

$$\frac{U'(r_0)}{\lambda} = \sum_{i=n+1}^{m} p_i c_i'(r_0) = (r_0 - g) \sum_{i=1}^{n} p_i k_i'(r_0), \qquad \lambda > 0.$$

Proof: Since U is homothetic by assumption, we lose no information regarding the *ordinal* ranking of per capita consumption vectors by assuming U is homogeneous of degree one. Applying Euler's theorem and using the conditions

$$U_i \equiv \frac{\partial U}{\partial c_i} = \lambda p_i, \qquad i = n + 1, \ldots, m,$$

(which are necessary for utility maximization by individual price takers), we obtain the required result simply by differentiating $U(C_{n+1}, \ldots, C_m)$ and substituting the foregoing equilibrium conditions.[16]   QED

This observation points up a rather interesting feature of this steady-state model—namely that the prices p_i do not correctly reflect the transformation curve along which the community moves across steady states, except if $r_0 = g$. Thus, identical individuals maximizing with respect to their personal budget constraints fall short of the maximum attainable utility, unless $r_0 = g$.

Specifically we observe that the consumption possibility frontier for the community is

$$a_0(r_0)[I - (g + \delta)a(r_0)]^{-1}c = 1, \tag{43}$$

while we have $p = a_0(r_0)[I - (r + \delta)a(r_0)]^{-1}$, and hence individuals acting according to prices p select a point on the consumption possibility frontier where indifference curves are not tangent to that frontier. Only if $r_0 = g$ do prices correctly reflect the slopes of the consumption possibility frontier, and hence only if $r_0 = g$ is there no utility loss.[17]

---

[16] Maximizing U subject to the steady-state constraints we of course find the condition $r_0 = g$ directly. As usual, λ is the marginal utility of expenditure on consumption goods. Given our homothety assumption, λ is a function only of prices and hence of r_0 in steady states.

[17] Of course the steady-state requirement is very strong, and *a priori* there is no reason why an economy should commit itself to this restriction. The issue will become clearer in Chapter 11 where we consider a growth path that optimizes a welfare function over a specified time horizon.

Our theorem thus says that the steady-state utility attainable by identical individual price takers will or will not show paradoxical behavior according to whether pk' is or is not nonpositive. The theorem does not say anything about the behavior of the maximum attainable steady-state utility.

The outcome of this section may be quickly summarized.

(i) There is an issue of paradoxical behavior in models with several capital goods even when all production functions are neoclassical. But the issue is not reswitching, which certainly cannot occur in neoclassical models.

(ii) When we consider comparisons only between alternative steady states while ignoring transitions, Wicksell effects and revaluations of capital apparently are not relevant to the question of whether or not the function $c(r_0)$, giving steady-state per capita consumption as a function of the common own-rate of interest, may show paradoxical behavior. This question rests solely on what happens to the *value*, at equilibrium prices, *of increments to per capita capital stocks pk'*, which is always nonpositive for well-behaved examples.

(iii) Thus it is natural to expect that if use of one capital good is tightly tied to the use of other capital goods, then substitution between capital goods of different durability or type will not be sufficient to destroy the usual capital deepening features of one-capital good models.

9–4. Price-Quantity Duality Relationships

The price-quantity duality relationships stated in Section 8-9 generalize to the neoclassical model discussed in this chapter. The results are obtained by the use of nonlinear concave programming, and we omit the difficult proofs of the theorems in this section.[18]

Consider the neoclassical technology examined in this chapter, and assume that the gross rates of growth are assigned exogenously. We wish to determine the maximum level of per capita consumption when the actual gross rates in the economy equal (or possibly exceed) an assigned vector $h = (h_1, \ldots, h_n)$, and we formulate the following problem.

(*) Primal Problem

Maximize

$$c = F^0(L_0, K_{10}, \ldots, K_{n0}) \tag{44}$$

---

[18] Karlin [15] contains an excellent mathematical discussion of nonlinear concave programming. The interested reader is referred to Burmeister and Kuga [7] for a proof of the analogous theorems in a linear joint-production model of the von Neumann type.

subject to

$$\sum_{i=0}^{n} L_i \leqq L \equiv 1,$$

$$\sum_{j=0}^{n} K_{ij} \leqq K_i, \qquad (i = 1, \ldots, n),$$

$$F^i(L_i, K_{1i}, \ldots, K_{ni}) - h_i K_i \geqq 0, \qquad (i = 1, \ldots, n),$$

$$L_i \geqq 0, \qquad (i = 0, 1, \ldots, n),$$

$$K_i \geqq 0, \qquad (i = 1, \ldots, n),$$

$$\qquad (45)$$

and

$$K_{ij} \geqq 0, \qquad (i = 1, \ldots, n; j = 0, 1, \ldots, n).$$

We now define the unit cost functions by

$$C^i(W_0, W_1, \ldots, W_n) \equiv$$

$$\inf\left\{\left(W_0 L_i + \sum_{j=1}^{n} K_{ji} W_j\right) \mid F^i(L_i, K_{1i}, \ldots, K_{ni}) \geqq 1\right\}, \qquad (i = 0, 1, \ldots, n),$$

and the following dual problem determines the minimum real wage rate (in terms of the price of the consumption good as *numeraire*) when the actual gross own-rates of return satisfy

$$W_i/P_i \leqq \rho_i, \qquad (i = 1, \ldots, n),$$

for an exogenously assigned vector $\rho = (\rho_1, \ldots, \rho_n)$.

(**) Dual Problem

Minimize

$$W_0 \qquad\qquad (46)$$

subject to

$$C^0(W_0, W_1, \ldots, W_n) \geqq P_0 \equiv 1,$$

$$C^i(W_0, W_1, \ldots, W_n) \geqq P_i, \qquad (i = 1, \ldots, n),$$

$$W_i - \rho_i P_i \leqq 0, \qquad (i = 1, \ldots, n),$$

$$W_i \geqq 0, \qquad (i = 0, 1, \ldots, n), \qquad (47)$$

and

$$P_i \geqq 0, \qquad (i = 1, \ldots, n).$$

As in Chapter 8, if (*) has optimal solutions for different vectors h these optimal solutions define the function $c = E(h)$ and determine the *optimal transformation frontier*; likewise if (**) has optimal solutions for different values of the vector ρ, these optimal solutions define the function $W_0/P_0 = H(\rho)$ and determine the *generalized real factor-price frontier*. The following theorem states the fundamental price-quantity duality relationship.

Theorem 10: *The optimal transformation frontier and the generalized real-factor price frontier are mathematically identical,*[19] *i.e.,*

$$c = E(h) = W_0/P_0 = H(\rho)$$

for all $\rho = h$ restricted to a suitable domain.

It is well known that the maximum maintainable level of per capita consumption c is achieved when all the net own-rates of return satisfy

$$r_0 = r_i \equiv \rho_i - \delta_i = g \equiv \dot{L}/L, \qquad (i = 1, \ldots, n);$$

the latter is the Golden Rule condition discussed in Section 9-3. The previous theorem, however, demonstrates that the question of maintenance may be ignored, i.e., we may discard the restrictions

$$h_i = g + \delta_i, \qquad (i = 1, \ldots, n),$$

which imply $\dot{k}_i = 0$ $(i = 1, \ldots, n)$. Thus the Golden Rule is merely a special case of the following theorem.

Theorem 11: *Consider any exogenous vector h belonging to a suitable domain. In a competitive neoclassical economy satisfying (45) the maximum level of per capita consumption is achieved if and only if $\rho = h$.*

It should be stressed that the latter theorem is purely static, and in general it would not be optimal to keep h (the vector of growth rates) fixed over time. We will turn to the question of dynamic efficiency in Chapters 10 and 11.

It is interesting that the price-quantity duality relationships are valid even in nonlinear neoclassical models with joint production such as Nikaido's [22].[20] However, the duality relationship is

$$E(h) = \max c = \min W_0/P_0 = H(\rho)$$

---

[19] The proof of this theorem requires additional assumptions, namely that suitably defined Lagrangian functions for (*) and (**) must satisfy the Slater [34] condition.

[20] Likewise these duality relationships are valid for linear joint-production models; see Burmeister and Kuga [7].

for exogenously assigned $\rho = h$ belonging to a suitable domain. In models without joint production we have already stated (Theorem 1) that the equilibrium price vector

$$p = G(\rho)$$

is uniquely determined for all $\rho \in \Gamma$, and in competitive equilibrium

$$1/p_0 = W_0/P_0 = 1/G^0(\rho) = H(\rho).$$

No such statement can be made for joint-production models because equilibrium prices P_i/W_0 $(i = 0, 1, \ldots, n)$ are not uniquely determined if only the vector ρ is assigned.

Suppose, however, we consider a joint-production model and an exogenous vector ρ. Of all the possible competitive equilibria corresponding to this ρ, the one with the minimum real wage rate is the competitive equilibrium solution with the growth rates $h_i = \rho_i$ $(i = 1, \ldots, n)$. Conversely, if h is exogenous, the maximum value of c is consistent with the competitive equilibrium solution having

$$W_0/P_0 = H(\rho)$$

for $\rho = h$ (see Exercise 12).[21] We conclude, therefore, that the results obtained for the simple joint-production example in Section 9-2 are simply a special case of a very general theorem.

9–5. A Sketch of Dynamic Considerations

Given the static equilibrium configuration just determined, steady-state factor allocations, sector outputs, wages, and rentals are all determined up to an exogenous scalar r_0 representing the interest or profit rate. Now we wish to extend some of this analysis to development paths that do not begin in steady-state growth, and we wish to examine some properties of the resulting dynamic model.

In outline we will argue that in the simplest descriptive model of neoclassical growth with competitive equilibrium there remains really only one

---

[21] This statement may be proved by considering the transformation schedule

$$c = T(h_1 k_1, \ldots, h_n k_n; k_1, \ldots, k_n, 1).$$

Assume h is given; maximization of c with respect to the parameters $k_1, \ldots, k_n$ necessitates the conditions $\partial c/\partial k_i = T_i h_i + T_{n+i} = 0$, $i = 1, \ldots, n$. Thus, in competitive equilibrium where $T_i = -P_i/P_0$ and $T_{n+i} = W_i/P_0$ we have $h_i = W_i/P_i \equiv \rho_i$ $(i = 1, \ldots, n)$. Applying Theorem 11, we conclude that $E(h) = \max c = \min W_0/P_0 = H(\rho)$ with $\rho = h$.

degree of freedom, which is the allocation of output between consumption and investment, or, in other words, the outcome of saving and investment decisions. The allocation of consumption expenditure among consumer goods (if more than one exist) is determined in the usual way by the static utility maximization decision of the consumer. The allocation of total investment expenditure among new capital goods (for which there are no explicit flow demand functions) is implicitly determined by portfolio decisions intended to maximize the value of the portfolio held; these decisions require that assets be held only if they offer the maximum available rate of return.[22] Such requirements serve to determine (together with initial conditions) prices for each asset, and these prices, taken as given by suppliers, determine outputs of each capital good. Thus the only remaining issue is the allocation of output between the two major categories—consumption and investment. One saving relation or one investment-saving equilibrium condition suffices to close the system.

Looking more specifically at a condition of equilibrium between realized investment and desired saving, we might find that this condition determines, in effect, the instantaneous yield at which saving desires are brought into balance with the realized rate of increase in wealth. Whether saving desires are generated by an arbitrary rule, or by an approximation reducing the lifetime allocation problem to a simple trade-off between present consumption and wealth (as in Walras' construct of perpetual net income), or by a sophisticated optimization of some lifetime integral criterion, this condition should determine the behavior of the model over time.[23]

To sketch the analysis of the model, we take equations (1)–(4) as given, and we assume full employment of all factors at all times. Hence we may write

$$\sum_{i=0}^{n} K_{ij} = K_i, \qquad (i = 0, 1, \ldots, n). \tag{48}$$

(For notational convenience we now denote the primary factor labor by the index zero, i.e., $K_0 \equiv L$.) These full employment conditions lead to the equations

$$\sum_{j=0}^{n} a_{ij} Y_j = K_i, \qquad (i = 0, 1, \ldots, n), \tag{49}$$

analogous to (30), but expressed in original rather than per capita units.

---

[22] Implicitly we assume perfect myopic foresight, and we ignore all complications introduced by uncertainty.

[23] In particular, if the presence of money in the system enables central authorities to peg the competitive yield on assets, it seems possible that the whole evolution of the system might thereby be controlled. This conjecture remains unsettled.

Adding the usual two further economic conditions for static equilibrium in terms of the consumption good price P_0 as *numeraire*, we obtain[24]

$$w_i = p_j F_i^j(a_{0j}, a_{1j}, \ldots, a_{nj}), \qquad (i = 0, 1, \ldots, n; j = 0, 1, \ldots, n), \quad \text{(50)}$$

and

$$p_j = \sum_{i=0}^{n} w_i a_{ij}, \qquad (j = 0, 1, \ldots, n). \tag{51}$$

We introduce the following matrix and vector notation (where $K_0 \equiv L$):[25]

$$A \equiv [a_{ij}] \equiv \begin{bmatrix} a_{00} & a_{01} & \cdots & a_{0n} \\ a_{10} & a_{11} & \cdots & a_{1n} \\ \vdots & \vdots & & \vdots \\ a_{n0} & a_{n1} & \cdots & a_{nn} \end{bmatrix};$$

$$k \equiv \begin{bmatrix} 1 \\ k_1 \\ \vdots \\ k_n \end{bmatrix} \equiv \begin{bmatrix} K_0/K_0 \\ K_1/K_0 \\ \vdots \\ K_n/K_0 \end{bmatrix}; \qquad y \equiv \begin{bmatrix} y_0 \\ y_1 \\ \vdots \\ y_n \end{bmatrix} \equiv \begin{bmatrix} Y_0/K_0 \\ Y_1/K_0 \\ \vdots \\ Y_n/K_0 \end{bmatrix};$$

$$w \equiv (w_0, w_1, \ldots, w_n) \equiv (W_0/P_0, W_1/P_0, \ldots, W_n/P_0);$$

and

$$p \equiv (1, p_1, \ldots, p_n) \equiv (P_0/P_0, P_1/P_0, \ldots, P_n/P_0).$$

We may now express (49) and (51) in the equivalent forms

$$Ay = k \tag{52}$$

and

$$wA = p, \tag{53}$$

respectively, where the matrix A itself is a function of the vector w.

---

[24] In the previous sections of this chapter all factor and output prices were measured in terms of the wage rate W_0 as *numeraire*. Now, however, it is most convenient to measure all factor and output prices in terms of the consumption good price P_0 as *numeraire*. Accordingly, throughout this section the vectors w and p denote $w \equiv (w_0, w_1, \ldots, w_n) \equiv (W_0/P_0, W_1/P_0, \ldots, W_n/P_0)$ and $p \equiv (1, p_1, \ldots, p_n) \equiv (P_0/P_0, P_1/P_0, \ldots, P_n/P_0)$. The reader is cautioned to keep this notational distinction in mind.

[25] See the preceding footnote. The reader should also note that the matrix A differs from the matrix a used in previous sections of this chapter.

Equations (52) and (53) express the static competitive equilibrium configuration of the model. Assuming the endowment vector k and the price vector p to be given, in general these equations may determine the output vector y and the rentals vector w as functions of k and p.

However, serious problems concerning the existence and uniqueness of such solutions (for which all our equations hold with equality) arise even in simple examples. The source of the difficulty is easy to find. Given an endowment vector k, there exists a production possibility frontier

$$Y_0 = T(Y_1, \ldots, Y_n; K_0, K_1, \ldots, K_n);$$

the function T is homogeneous of degree one and thus may be written

$$y_0 = T(y_1, \ldots, y_n; 1, k_1, \ldots, k_n).$$

Competitive equilibrium consistent with equations (50) necessitates the further conditions

$$T_i \equiv \partial T / \partial Y_i = -P_i/P_0 \equiv -p_i, \, (i = 1, \ldots, n);$$

however, T_i is homogeneous of degree zero and hence depends only on per capita quantities, i.e., in equilibrium we have

$$T_i = T_i(y_1, \ldots, y_n; 1, k_1, \ldots, k_n) = -p_i, \, (i = 1, \ldots, n).$$

Consequently when both k and p are given the hyperplane defined by the price vector must be tangent to the production possibility frontier T, which defines a convex (but not necessarily strictly convex) set of points in the space $(y_0, y_1, \ldots, y_n)$. Even if this set is strictly convex, an interior solution may not exist for some values of the vector p. This fact is clearly illustrated in Figure 40a and 40b for the case $n = 1$.

Given an endowment vector $k = (1, k_1)$, the production possibility frontier $y_0 = T(y_1; 1, k_1)$ defines a concave curve in the space (y_0, y_1). If in addition a price vector $p = (1, p_1)$ is given, competitive equilibrium with equality holding for every equation requires an interior tangency condition at a point such as E' in Figure 40a. Thus, given (k_1, p_1'), the equilibrium quantities $y_0(k_1, p_1')$ and $y_1(k_1, p_1')$ are uniquely determined.

Suppose, however, we are given the same endowment vector k and a price vector $(1, p_1'')$. As illustrated in Figure 40b, no tangency point exists and we are forced to consider a corner solution at the point E''. But all our equations can no longer hold with equality.

Finally, note that nonuniqueness results if the production possibility frontier is a straight line and the given price vector has exactly the same

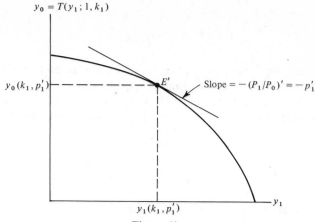

Figure 40a

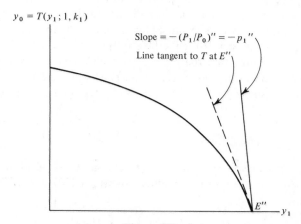

Figure 40b

slope as that line. Similar difficulties arise when $n > 1$, and under such circumstances, the dynamic behavior of the model becomes very complex indeed. An analysis of these complications would distract from our objectives in this section, and therefore we will assume that we may always (i.e., at all times along the growth path) find functions

$$y_i = y_i(k, p), \qquad (i = 0, 1, \ldots, n),$$

representing interior competitive equilibrium solutions (such as illustrated in Figure 40a). Given the solutions $y_i = y_i(k, p)$, we find that

$$\frac{\partial T}{\partial K_i} \equiv \frac{\partial T}{\partial K_i}(k, p) = W_i/P_0 \equiv w_i, \qquad (i = 0, 1, \ldots, n),$$

and we may write

$$w_i = w_i(k, p), \qquad (i = 0, 1, \ldots, n).$$

In summary, we assume that, given vectors k and p, we may always solve for unique equilibrium vectors y and w.

Further, we assume, as usual, that each of the produced assets entering the endowment vector depreciates at an exponential rate and that $\dot{L}/L \equiv \dot{K}_0/K_0 \equiv g$. Thus, the accumulation equations for this system are of the familiar form

$$\dot{k}_i = y_i(k, p) - (g + \delta_i)k_i, \qquad (i = 1, \ldots, n). \tag{54}$$

We note that if a price path $p(t)$ is somehow specified, the differential equation system is fully determined and would be expected, given an initial endowment vector, to yield the growth path $k(t)$ followed by the model economy. In such a case the growth path would display static efficiency at all times, and, further, it would satisfy all requirements for static equilibrium given asset stocks and prices for the flow output of capital goods.

But in fact we know that the price path is not arbitrary in a competitive economy with perfect capital markets and short-run perfect (myopic) foresight. Rather we expect an ideal competitive system to realize equations of the form

$$\dot{p}_i/p_i + w_i/p_i - \delta_i = r_0(t), \qquad (i = 1, \ldots, n), \tag{55}$$

where $r_0(t)$ denotes some common instantaneous yield on all assets, as yet undetermined. Now we bring together equations (54) and (55) and write them as

$$\dot{k}_i = y_i(k, p) - (g + \delta_i)k_i, \qquad (i = 1, \ldots, n), \tag{56}$$

and

$$\dot{p}_i = -w_i(k, p) + [r_0(t) + \delta_i]p_i, \qquad (i = 1, \ldots, n), \tag{57}$$

or, substituting from (52) and (53), in the more compact form[26]

$$\dot{k} = [A^{-1} - (g + \delta)]k, \qquad k(0) = \bar{k}, \tag{58}$$

and

$$\dot{p} = p[-A^{-1} + (r_0 + \delta)], \qquad p(0) = \bar{p}. \tag{59}$$

---

[26] We also assume that A^{-1} exists; otherwise a reduction of the system is required. This is cumbersome, but involves no issue of substance.

(Because of the normalization rules $k_0 \equiv p_0 \equiv 1$, the first entries of each vector equation should be ignored.) If a single time path $r_0(t)$ were specified, and if initial conditions for both prices and endowments were given, then we expect that this system would yield a solution path $\{k(t), p(t)\}$ describing the evolution of the competitive economy. The only difficulty in this interpretation attaches to the notion of imposing a value $r_0(t)$ on the common instantaneous asset yield at each point in time. There is no difficulty in ensuring that some common interest or profit rate r_0 is realized, of course; capital market trading assures this result under our assumptions. The question is how we should assign the values $r_0(t)$ that up to now have been simply exogenously given. Properties of the growth path would presumably depend rather crucially on the nature of the imposed path $r_0(t)$.

In fact, of course, in a competitive economy such a condition need not be imposed from outside. Rather, it is expected that since asset prices determine the output of investment goods (and hence the rate of investment in the economy), the yield on assets and the consequent price changes would be determined by the interaction of saving and investment desires in the community. Realized per capita net investment is a function of the endowments vector k, the price vector p, and the yield r_0. If, in addition, we postulate a rule determining desired per capita saving, we may solve for the common asset yield endogenously and hence close the system.

As in Chapter 6 we will impose a flow equilibrium condition $\dot{V} = S$ where $\dot{V}$ is the realized change in the real value of capital (wealth) and S is desired saving. In addition we take as a desired saving hypothesis the assumption that the propensities to save from three components of an income stream— capital gains, net rentals, and wages—are given constants s_c, s_r, and s_w, respectively, and we then obtain

$$S = s_c \sum_{i=1}^{n} \dot{p}_i K_i + s_r \sum_{i=1}^{n} (w_i K_i - \delta_i p_i K_i) + s_w w_0 K_0.$$

Thus the equilibrium condition $\dot{V} = S$ is

$$\dot{V} = \frac{d}{dt}\left(\sum_{i=1}^{n} p_i K_i\right) = \sum_{i=1}^{n} \dot{p}_i K_i + \sum_{i=1}^{n} p_i \dot{K}_i = S$$

and using (55) the latter may be written

$$\dot{V} = r_0 \sum_{i=1}^{n} p_i K_i + (w_0 K_0 - Y_0) = r_0 V + (w_0 K_0 - Y_0) = S.$$

In general this equilibrium condition may be solved for r_0. For example, in the special case where $0 \leqq s_r = s_c < 1$ and $s_w = 0$, we may solve explicitly for

$$r_0 = \frac{\sum_{i=1}^{n} (w_i K_i - p_i Y_i)}{(1 - s_c) \sum_{i=1}^{n} p_i K_i} = \frac{Y_0 - w_0 K_0}{(1 - s_c) V};$$

or, in per capita terms we have

$$r_0 = (y_0 - w_0)/(1 - s_c)v$$

where $v \equiv V/K_0$ is the real per capita value of wealth.

The system thus becomes autonomous under this savings hypothesis, and it is possible to consider qualitative analysis of the evolution of the system from assigned initial conditions. In particular, stability properties of the growth path are of interest.

Stability

Observed saving behavior in a descriptive system with perfect capital markets may cause unstable development whenever history gives us initial conditions on both prices and stocks. Hahn [13] has illustrated this result in a model with log-linear production functions. What we must ask then, is whether in general a competitive system with capital market conditions satisfied is unstable in the sense that with arbitrary assignment of initial prices and endowments it will diverge from balanced growth. We will argue that the answer may hinge on saving hypotheses and generalized factor intensity conditions stemming from technological relations. The following discussion, although it does not rigorously demonstrate this conclusion, is intended to support that argument.

As before, we write the differential equations system as

$$\dot{k}_i = y_i - (g + \delta_i)k_i, \qquad (i = 1, \ldots, n), \tag{56}$$

and

$$\dot{p}_i = -w_i + (r_0 + \delta_i)p_i, \qquad (i = 1, \ldots, n), \tag{57}$$

which can be interpreted as the last n equations in each of the vector equations

$$k = [A^{-1} - (g + \delta)]k \tag{58}$$

and

$$\dot{p} = p[-A^{-1} + (r_0 + \delta)] \tag{59}$$

with initial conditions $k(0) = \bar{k}$ and $p(0) = \bar{p}$. We find that a dual stability feature would be immediate if A were a constant matrix and r_0 were equal to g.[27] In that case, if the characteristic roots of the k equation all have negative real parts, then the characteristic roots of the $\dot{p}$ equations all have positive real parts, and conversely. Hence, when the yield r_0 is constant, then so long as the matrix A is not so sensitive to changes in endowments k or prices p that changes in the matrix itself dominate the direct effects, the dual stability of the system is assured. If, however, the yield expression r_0 is not constant the system becomes more complex and (local) stability may be possible. (The global stability or instability of the system with A or r_0 changing is, of course, more difficult to establish.)

The local stability of the system

$$\dot{k} = g(k, p)$$

and

$$\dot{p} = h(k, p)$$

near an equilibrium point (k^*, p^*) depends on the characteristic roots of the matrix

$$J^* = \begin{bmatrix} \dfrac{\partial \dot{k}_i}{\partial k_j} & \dfrac{\partial \dot{k}_i}{\partial p_j} \\[3mm] \dfrac{\partial \dot{p}_i}{\partial k_j} & \dfrac{\partial \dot{p}_i}{\partial p_j} \end{bmatrix}$$

evaluated at the equilibrium point. The entries of this matrix J^* depend in turn upon (1) generalized capital intensity conditions implicit in the matrix A derived from (52) and (53), and (2) the behavior of $r_0(t)$. The latter reflects in part the saving hypotheses adopted to close the system. The problem is thus to determine whether there are plausible saving hypotheses and capital intensity conditions stringent enough to ensure stability in the foregoing system. Intuition and the analogy with the Solow-Jorgenson dual stability result discussed in the previous chapter suggest that both price and quantity stability is unlikely. Complete results, however, are as yet unavailable.[28]

---

[27] If savings behavior is such that the interest or profit rate $r_0(t)$ is at all times equal to a constant rate of time preference $\gamma > 0$, then equations (56) and (57) have the same form as those resulting from optimizing models discussed in Chapter 11. In this case, therefore, we should anticipate a saddlepoint equilibrium. (The matrix $[\theta + \delta]$ for any scalar θ is defined on p. 231.)

[28] A related interesting question is whether a well-chosen dynamic monetary policy could have the effect of stabilizing the system by controlling the time path of the yield $r_0(t)$. Such indirect controls are of interest in the models of Chapter 6.

Hahn [13] analyzed a model in which the results seem clear. His investigation of a descriptive model suggests that its unique balanced growth path is a saddlepoint equilibrium. In a descriptive growth model we may expect to have initial capital stocks and initial asset prices assigned at historically given values, and consequently the model must in general diverge from the balanced growth equilibrium path. (If the descriptive model has some market mechanism for selecting appropriate initial prices, however, or if the model is really a planning model with initial prices open to choice, then the formal instability feature need never be realized on any observed growth path.)

Both Shell–Stiglitz [33] and Burmeister, Dobell, and Kuga [5] have discussed the dual instability or saddlepoint property just described. However, we defer discussion of these results to Chapter 11. It suffices here to mention that Shell–Stiglitz impose perfect foresight into the indefinite future, whereas Burmeister, Dobell, and Kuga impose a strong saving hypothesis that ignores capital gains. Both approaches, for entirely different reasons, serve to circumvent instability.

The main feature in this brief sketch of the dynamics of the model with neoclassical technology is that the technique matrix depends explicitly upon prices, so that the complete (k, p) vector is required to determine momentary equilibrium. The price and quantity equations become interlinked, and the earlier dual stability results are likely to appear in modified form. Little more can be said at this time; the question is a subject of current research.

9–6. Concluding Remarks and Summary

As anticipated in Chapter 4, neoclassical growth models with many heterogeneous capital goods are very difficult to analyze completely and rigorously. They do, however, represent an obvious advance beyond simple one- or two-sector models involving a single real capital good, and they do permit a more sophisticated discussion of portfolio choice, capital market trading conditions, and other important features of a general equilibrium system.

We have achieved a fairly complete understanding of steady-state behavior, although conditions adequate to exclude paradoxical behavior are still lacking. It has been shown that equilibrium prices are uniquely determined for assigned (admissible) values of the own-rates of return, and thus most of the theorems proved in Chapter 8 for a linear multisector model have been generalized to the neoclassical case in which the variable input coefficients are determined by relative factor prices (rental/wage rates). In particular, the price-quantity duality relationships stated in Chapter 8 for linear multisector models are also valid in models with neoclassical production functions.

It is important to note that the growth path defined by the neoclassical technology together with capital market equilibrium conditions contains only one degree of freedom, related to the determination of the instantaneous yield on all assets. In the next chapter we will see that in a normative, rather than a descriptive, model the capital market equilibrium conditions emerge as necessary conditions for efficient capital accumulation. And in Chapter 11 we will see that by adding an explicit intertemporal social welfare function to the weak requirement that a growth path be efficient, we remove the last degree of freedom, forcing the yield on assets to be equal to the implied rate of social time preference at all times.

Exercises

1. Derive equation (11).

2. Why is the production function $Y = H(K, L)$ defined on page 280 not neo-classical?

3. Derive the cost function corresponding to the CES production function (5).

4. Assume

$$Y_1 = F^1(L_1, K_{11}) = [K_{11}^{(\sigma_1 - 1)/\sigma_1} + L_1^{(\sigma_1 - 1)/\sigma_1}]^{\sigma_1/(\sigma_1 - 1)}$$

and $\sigma_1 > 1$. Prove that there exists a function

$$p_1 = G^1(\rho_1) > 0 \qquad \text{if} \qquad \rho_1 \in (1, +\infty).$$

5. Derive the necessary conditions for the constrained maximization problem defined by (21), and derive (22) from these conditions.

6. Consider the problem in Exercise 5 and show that

$$\mu = P_0 Y_0 + P_1 Y_1 - W_0 L - W_1 K_1;$$

then derive the equilibrium condition $P_1/P_0 = Y_1/Y_0$ when $\mu = 0$.

7. Consider the function

$$x = \left[\frac{1 + (P_1/P_0)^2}{(P_1/P_0)} \right]$$

for $P_1/P_0 > 0$. Show that x has a unique minimum $x = 2$ when $P_1/P_0 = 1$.

8. Again consider the problem in Exercise 5. Let $\rho_1 > 0$ be assigned exogenously, and show that in equilibrium (26) holds if and only if (27) holds.

9. Prove that the characteristic roots of the matrix $(g + \delta)a(r_0)$ are all less than one in modulus for any assigned value of $r_0 \in [g, r_0^*)$.

10. Consider any fixed $r_0 \in R$. Prove that the first column of $[I - (g + \delta)a]^{-1}$ is strictly positive.

11. Define the vector

$$\varphi(r_0) \equiv a_0[I - (g + \delta)a]^{-1}, \qquad r_0 \in R,$$

and prove that $\varphi_0(r_0) > 0$.

12. Consider the joint-production example described in Section 9-2 with

$$(Y_0)^2 + (Y_1)^2 = 2K_1 L$$

or

$$c^2 + h^2 k^2 = 2k$$

where $c \equiv Y_0/L$, $k \equiv K_1/L$, and $h \equiv \dot{K}/K$. Let $h > 0$ be exogenous, and maximize c with respect to the parameter k. Prove that your answer corresponds to competitive equilibrium with $h = \rho_1$.

13. Derive equations (56).

14. Derive equations (57).

Answers and Hints

PROBLEM 5. The condition (22) is derived from $\partial \Phi/\partial Y_0 = 0$, $\partial \Phi/\partial Y_1 = 0$, $\partial \Phi/\partial K_1 = 0$, and $\partial \Phi/\partial L = 0$.

PROBLEM 8. Assume (26) holds. Deduce from Exercise 5 that

$$\frac{W_0}{P_0} = \frac{K_1}{Y_0} = \frac{1}{\rho_1}$$

when $\mu = 0$. Exercises 6 and 7 imply that (26) holds if and only if

$$P_1/P_0 = Y_1/Y_0 = 1;$$

therefore, $Y_0 = Y_1$ and

$$\frac{Y_0}{K_1} = \frac{Y_1}{K_1} = \rho_1 .$$

References

[1] ALLEN, R. G. D., *Mathematical Analysis for Economists*. London: Macmillan, 1937.

[2] BURMEISTER, E., "The Existence of Golden Ages and Stability in the Two-Sector Model," *Quarterly Journal of Economics*, **LXXXI**, *1* (February, 1967), pp. 146–154.

[3] — and R. DOBELL, "Disembodied Technological Change with Several Factors," *Journal of Economic Theory*, **1**, *1* (June, 1969), pp. 1–8.

[4] — and R. DOBELL, "Steady State Behavior of Neoclassical Models with Many Capital Goods," paper presented at the Econometric Society Meeting, December, 1967. Discussion Paper No. 72, Department of Economics, University of Pennsylvania. Abstract in *Econometrica*, **36**, *5* (1968), pp. 124–25.

[5] — R. DOBELL, and K. KUGA, "A Note on the Global Stability of a Simple Growth Model with Many Capital Goods," *The Quarterly Journal of Economics*, **LXXXII**, *4* (November, 1968), pp. 657–665.

[6] — and K. KUGA, "The Factor-Price Frontier in a Neoclassical Multi-Sector Model," forthcoming in the *International Economic Review*.

[7] —, and K. KUGA, "The Factor-Price Frontier, Duality and Joint Production," *Review of Economic Studies*, **XXXVII**, *109* (January, 1970).

[8] — and E. SHESHINSKI, "A Nonsubstitution Theorem in a Model with Fixed Capital," *The Southern Economic Journal*, **XXXV**, *3* (January, 1969), pp. 273–276.

[9] DORFMAN, R., P. A. SAMUELSON, and R. M. SOLOW, *Linear Programming and Economic Analysis*. New York: McGraw-Hill, 1958.

[10] FISHER, F. M., "Choice of Units, Column Sums, and Stability in Linear Dynamic Systems with Nonnegative Square Matrices," *Econometrica*, **33**, *2* (April, 1965), pp. 445–450.

[11] — "An Alternative Proof and Extension of Solow's Theorem on Nonnegative Square Matrices," *Econometrica*, **30**, *2* (April, 1962), pp. 349–350.

[12] GORMAN, W. M., "Production Functions in which the Elasticities of Substitution Stand in Fixed Proportion to Each Other," *Review of Economic Studies*, **XXXII**, *91* (July, 1965), pp. 217–224.

[13] HAHN, F. H., "Equilibrium Dynamics with Heterogeneous Capital Goods," *The Quarterly Journal of Economics*, **LXXX**, *4* (November, 1966), pp. 633–646.

[14] — "On Warranted Growth Paths," *Review of Economic Studies*, **XXXV**, *102* (April, 1968), pp. 175–184.

[15] KARLIN, S., *Mathematical Methods and Theory in Games, Programming and Economics*, **I, II**. Reading, Mass.: Addison-Wesley, 1959.

[16] KURZ, M., "The General Instability of a Class of Competitive Growth Processes," *Review of Economic Studies*, **XXXV**, *102* (April, 1968), pp. 155–174.

[17] McFADDEN, D., "Further Results on C.E.S. Production Functions," *Review of Economic Studies*, **XXX**, *83* (June, 1963), pp. 73–83.

[18] McKENZIE, L., "Matrices with Dominant Diagonals and Economic Theory," pp. 47–62, in *Mathematical Methods in the Social Sciences*, 1959 (K. Arrow, S. Karlin, and P. Suppes, Eds.). Stanford, Calif.: Stanford University Press, 1960.

[19] — "The Inversion of Cost Functions: A Counter-Example," *International Economic Review*, **8**, *3* (October, 1967), pp. 271–278.

[20] MORISHIMA, M., *Equilibrium, Stability, and Growth.* Oxford: Clarendon Press, 1964.

[21] — and Y. MURATA, "An Input-Output System Involving Non-Transferable Goods," *Econometrica*, **36**, *1* (January, 1968), pp.71–92.

[22] NIKAIDO, H., "Note on the General Economic Equilibrium for Non-Linear Production Functions," *Econometrica*, **22**, *1* (January, 1954), pp. 49–53.

[23] PEARCE, I., "More about Factor Price Equilization," *International Economic Review*, **8**, *3* (October, 1967), pp. 235–270.

[24] SAMUELSON, P. A., "Some Aspects of the Pure Theory of Capital," *Quarterly Journal of Economics*, **LI** (May, 1937), pp. 469–496.

[25] — *Foundations of Economic Analysis.* Cambridge: Harvard University Press, 1947.

[26] — "Abstract of a Theorem Concerning Substitutability in Open Leontief Models," pp. 142–146, in *Activity Analysis of Production and Allocation* (T. C. Koopmans, Ed.). New York: Wiley, 1951.

[27] — "Prices of Factors and Goods in General Equilibrium," *Review of Economic Studies*, **XXI**, *54* (1953–54), pp. 1–14.

[28] — "Wages and Interest: A Modern Dissection of Marxian Economic Models," *American Economic Review*, **XLVII**, *6* (December, 1957), pp. 884–912.

[29] — "Efficient Paths of Capital Accumulation in Terms of The Calculus of Variations," pp. 77–88, in *Mathematical Methods in the Social Sciences, 1959* (K. Arrow, S. Karlin, and P. Suppes, Eds.). Stanford: Stanford University Press, 1960.

[30] — "The Fundamental Singularity Theorem for Non-Joint Production," *International Economic Review*, **7**, *1* (January, 1966), pp. 34–41.

[31] — "Summary on Factor-Price Equilization," *International Economic Review*, **8**, *3* (October, 1967), pp. 286–295.

[32] — "Indeterminacy of Development in a Heterogeneous-Capital Model with Constant Savings Propensity," in *Essays on the Theory of Optimal Economic Growth* (K. Shell, Ed.). Cambridge, Mass.: MIT Press, 1967, pp. 219–231.

[33] SHELL, K., and J. E. STIGLITZ, "The Allocation of Investment in a Dynamic Economy," *The Quarterly Journal of Economics*, **LXXXI**, *4* (November, 1967), pp. 592–609.

[34] SLATER, M., "Lagrange Multipliers Revisited " (mimeo.), November, 1950.

[35] SOLOW, R. M., "On the Structure of Linear Models," *Econometrica*, **20**, *1* (January, 1952), pp. 29–46.

[36] — "A Contribution to the Theory of Economic Growth," *The Quarterly Journal of Economics*, **LXX**, *1* (February, 1956), pp. 65–94.

[37] — "Comment on the Production Function Symposium," *Review of Economic Studies*, **XXIX**, *80* (June, 1962), pp. 255–257.

[38] — "The Interest Rate and Transition Between Techniques," pp. 30–39 in *Socialism, Capitalism and Economic Growth* (C. H. Feinstein, Ed.). New York: Cambridge University Press, 1967.

Chapter 10 Turnpike Theorems

and Efficient Economic Growth

(by STEPHEN J. TURNOVSKY)

10–1. Introduction

The models that have been discussed so far are all strictly descriptive; they indicate how an economy will grow under various assumptions pertaining to its structure and institutions. Nothing has been said to suggest that the resulting growth paths will be in any way optimal or even desirable. In this and the following chapter we therefore turn our attention to normative models and study the development of economic systems over time when assumptions concerning optimizing behavior replace our earlier conditions on price formation. That is, we retain all the previous technological specifications but drop institutional assumptions concerning price determination and the necessity of full utilization of all factors. Our grounds for doing so are that these latter conditions do not reflect physical constraints on the production possibilities open to the system and therefore need not be taken into account in a pure normative problem.

In this chapter we first adopt a criterion that is a generalization of the standard notion of static Pareto optimality to the intertemporal case. This criterion, known as the *efficiency criterion*, ignores consumption flows realized along the growth path and evaluates alternative paths on the basis of terminal capital stocks alone. Specifically, a path is said to be *efficient* in the foregoing sense if it yields a terminal capital stock vector that is not dominated by a capital stock vector attained on any other feasible path.[1] Later in this chapter we specialize the criterion somewhat and assume that the goal of the community is to maximize a criterion function (or bequest

[1] See the definition of *vector dominance* in the Appendix.

311

function), denoting the utility attached to the vector of terminal capital stocks.

Chapter 11 imposes a stronger optimality criterion in which the objective is to maximize a functional defined on a stream of consumption utilities (possibly discounted) given over some specified planning period. This latter objective is much stronger in the sense that it involves intertemporal comparisons of consumptions by means of some cardinal social welfare function. It is also stronger in the sense that the efficiency conditions that emerge as optimizing conditions from this chapter are also (as we would expect) necessary conditions for an optimal consumption utility maximizing path, although the reverse is not true.

Most of the models in the present chapter are extensions of the closed model of production introduced in Chapter 7. In this model there are no primary factors of production; instead all goods are produced within the system. Consumption may be ignored, or treated as a simple input (into the production of labor as a productive factor). Moreover, the behavior of efficient growth paths will be seen to be intimately related to the von Neumann path of maximal balanced growth that was discussed in Chapter 7. We will consider the problem for both infinite and finite time horizons, although we treat the latter case in more detail.

In the case of an infinite horizon, the main result, discussed in Section 10-2, is that any efficient path must converge to the von Neumann balanced growth path. Analysis of paths that are efficient over a finite horizon leads to *final state* turnpike theorems. The main purpose of this chapter is to give an exposition of these theorems and to survey some of the relevant literature. The aim is to give a fairly complete development of the logic, indicating the role played by different assumptions but omitting the details of many proofs.

More explicitly, the turnpike conjecture, first expressed by Dorfman, Samuelson, and Solow [7], claims that given a constant technology, specified consumption paths, a historically given initial capital stock, and the objective of maximizing the size of a capital stock having a specified structure at some future date, then the efficient growth path (that is, the path that realizes this objective) will run close to the von Neumann path of fastest proportional growth for most of the planning period. It must be stressed that the turnpike theorem is concerned with very long-run (but finite) programs of growth and, as we shall demonstrate presently, the proportion of time spent near the von Neumann ray (the turnpike) increases with the length of the planning period. Furthermore, in keeping with the von Neumann models the turnpike theorem deals with a closed consumptionless economy; or, rather, consumption is treated not as an end in itself but only as an input into processes that have labor as outputs.

Two features characterize a turnpike result.

(i) Motion of the optimal path toward some maximal-rate steady growth path, and

(ii) A tendency of the optimal path to spend an increasing proportion of the time near the path as the length of the planning period increases.

In the next chapter it will be found that a similar turnpike property holds for all paths that are consumption-optimal over some finite horizon. There it will be shown that under quite general conditions (but in the absence of time discounting) all such paths arch toward that steady-state growth path that yields the highest sustainable consumption per capita, spending an increasing proportion of the time in the neighborhood of that Golden Rule path as the horizon lengthens.

10–2. Efficient Growth in Infinite Time Horizons

In Chapter 7 the notion of relative stability was defined and the Solow-Samuelson result was demonstrated, namely that, under appropriate conditions regarding the technology (particularly the homogeneity property), a closed system starting from any arbitrary positive initial position tends to the balanced growth path [40]. This original relative stability theorem was not concerned with studying the intertemporal efficiency of either the balanced growth path or of any path that ultimately converges to the balanced growth path. Indeed, no question of efficiency or optimality can arise, since the model of Chapter 7 determines a unique feasible path from specified initial conditions. The issue of efficiency can only arise in models that admit more than one feasible growth path. This problem of efficiency is examined in the present section. We begin with the following definition of intertemporal efficiency.[2]

> **Definition:** A time sequence of successive transformations (x_1, y_1), $(x_2, y_2), \ldots, (x_n, y_n)$ is called a *feasible* path of order N if $(x_i, y_i) \in T$ and $x_{i+1} = y_i$. We can denote this by writing $(x_1, y_N) \in T^{(N)}$ or $\{x_n\}_{n=0}^{N} \in T^{(N)}$. A feasible path is then said to be *efficient* of order N if there is no other feasible path $(x_1, \hat{y}_N) \in T^{(N)}$ such that $\hat{y}_N \geq y_N$.[3]

With this definition we can prove the following two lemmas originally proved by Dorfman, Samuelson, and Solow [7]. Following the original authors (and for the sake of expositional ease), we will restrict ourselves to the two-commodity case, although the results can be easily generalized to n goods.

> **Lemma 1:** *A necessary condition for intertemporal efficiency of a given growth path is that the marginal rate of substitution between any two*

---

[2] The notation for this chapter was introduced in Chapter 7.
[3] The concept of efficiency was first used in an intertemporal context by Debreu [5] and Malinvaud [17].

goods regarded as outputs of the previous period must equal their marginal rate of substitution as inputs for the next period.

Proof: Suppose that we have initial stocks K_{10}, K_{20}, and consumption in each period is C_{it}, $i = 1, 2, t = 0, \ldots, T$; the terminal stock of good 1 is prescribed as K_{1T}. In each period production possibilities are described by the transformation functions

$$F(K_{1t} + C_{1t}, K_{1, t-1}, K_{2, t-1}) = C_{2t} + K_{2t}, \qquad (t = 1, \ldots, T). \quad \textbf{(1)}$$

The problem of efficient growth is then to maximize the terminal output of the remaining commodity $K_{2T} + C_{2T}$, subject to the constraints given by (1). This problem can be reformulated as one of maximizing the Lagrangean expression

$$F(K_{1T} + C_{1T}, K_{1, T-1}, K_{2, T-1})$$
$$+ \sum_{t=1}^{T-1} \mu_t[F(K_{1t} + C_{1t}, K_{1, t-1}, K_{2, t-1}) - K_{2t} - C_{2t}]$$

where μ_t are the Lagrange multipliers. Differentiating with respect to K_{1t} and K_{2t}, equating the derivatives to zero, and eliminating the Lagrange multipliers, leads to the following optimality conditions:

$$\frac{\partial F(K_{1t} + C_{1t}, K_{1, t-1}, K_{2, t-1})}{\partial K_{1t}} = -\frac{\dfrac{\partial F(K_{1, t+1} + C_{1, t+1}, K_{1t}, K_{2t})}{\partial K_{1t}}}{\dfrac{\partial F(K_{1, t+1} + C_{1, t+1}, K_{1t}, K_{2t})}{\partial K_{2t}}},$$
$$(t = 1, \ldots, T). \quad \textbf{(2)}$$

This establishes the lemma.

We may then prove the following lemma for a closed consumptionless economy.

Lemma 2: *The only efficient balanced growth path is the von Neumann path of balanced growth at a maximal rate.*

Proof: The technological production possibilities for a closed consumptionless economy are described by

$$K_{2, t+1} = F(K_{1, t+1}, K_{1t}, K_{2t}) \quad \textbf{(3)}$$

where F is assumed to be homogeneous of degree one. The conditions for intertemporally efficient growth in such an economy are given by equations (2) written as

$$F_2(K_{1,t+1}, K_{1t}, K_{2t}) + F_3(K_{1,t+1}, K_{1t}, K_{2t}) \cdot F_1(K_{1t}, K_{1,t-1}, K_{2,t-1}) = 0,$$

$$(t = 0, \ldots, T - 1).$$

Consider a balanced growth path along which the capital stock configuration is given by $K_1/K_2 = k$ and where both sectors grow at a constant rate λ. Since F is homogeneous of degree one, dividing (3) by K_{1t} gives

$$\frac{K_{2,t+1}}{K_{1,t+1}} \cdot \frac{K_{1,t+1}}{K_{1t}} = F\left(\frac{K_{1,t+1}}{K_{1t}}, 1, \frac{K_{2t}}{K_{1t}}\right).$$

which may be written more compactly as

$$k\lambda = F(\lambda, 1, k). \tag{4}$$

Equation (4) will be satisfied by any balanced growth path. In particular, the configuration k which yields the maximum balanced growth rate is obtained by differentiating (4) with respect to k and setting $d\lambda/dk = 0$. Thus we derive

$$\lambda = F_3(\lambda, 1, k), \tag{5}$$

and, since second-order conditions are satisfied, equations (4) and (5) are the conditions that must be satisfied to ensure maximal balanced growth. Moreover, from the homogeneity of F, Euler's theorem implies that

$$F = F_1\lambda + F_2 + F_3k,$$

and using equations (4) and (5) this equation reduces to

$$F_1F_3 + F_2 = 0,$$

which are exactly the intertemporal efficiency conditions as stated before.

Thus the maximal balanced growth path is efficient, and, moreover, it is the only balanced growth path to have this property.[4]

---

[4] Morishima [28] also establishes the intertemporal efficiency of the balanced growth path for a more general model that includes consumption and a constant exogenous rate of labor force growth. However, he also shows in another model that permits consumption and endogenous population growth [29] that the balanced growth path need no longer be intertemporally efficient.

Of course there may be other nonbalanced efficient growth paths that begin from the same initial point. However, all such paths that are efficient for infinite time horizons must converge to the von Neumann growth path. This proposition was first proved by Furuya and Inada [10] using a closed linear model of the type described in Chapter 7.[5] In addition to assumptions (A.1)–(A.4) of Chapter 7, the authors require two additional rather strong assumptions to establish their result.

Assumption (A.1) (Strong Súperaddivity): *For* $(x_1, y_1) \in T$, $(x_2, y_2) \in T$, $x_1 \cdot \neq \alpha x_2$ *there exists a process* $(x_1 + x_2, y) \in T$ *such that* $y \geq y_1 + y_2$; *then T is said to be* strongly superadditive.

Assumption (A.2) (Primitivity): *For* $x_0 \geq 0$ *there is some finite t such that* $y_t > 0.$[6]

Economically (A.2) means that if initial stocks include some goods in positive quantities, then in a finite time it is possible to produce all goods in positive amounts.

The primitivity assumption plays the same role in the development of the theorem as the assumption of strict monotonicity plays in the Solow-Samuelson relative stability theorem, and at first sight may seem very restrictive. It implies that if one good is available in positive amounts at some initial time, then after some finite time period everything will be producible in positive amounts. The main significance of assuming primitivity is that it excludes cyclic production where goods can be grouped into disjoint batches x_i such that goods from batch i can produce goods in batch $i + 1$ only. It is convenient to exclude this case because with a cyclic technology there need no longer be any tendency for an efficient path to converge to the von Neumann ray. Instead, convergence may be replaced by nondamped oscillatory motion about the ray. This problem also arises in discussions of turnpike theorems and these cyclic exceptions will be considered in greater detail in connection with these theorems.

Strong superadditivity ensures uniqueness of the maximum balanced growth ray. Moreover, strong superadditivity is necessary to establish the existence of a strictly positive price vector such that at these prices the unique maximum balanced growth path makes zero profits and all other paths make strict losses.[7] This result is necessary in order to establish the crucial theorem of Furuya and Inada that asserts that if the maximum growth ray is unique, all intertemporally efficient paths of infinite order converge relatively to the

---

[5] Also see Fisher [9] for a correction to Furuya and Inada's paper.

[6] See the definition of a *primitive matrix* given in Section 10-7 and in the Appendix.

[7] This is Theorem II in Furuya and Inada [10]. Their proof is not valid and has been corrected by Fisher [9].

unique ray. Convergence is proved by applying the method developed by Radner [31] in his proof of the turnpike theorem which we will discuss in greater detail later. Here we will just mention that the method involves comparing value sums for an efficient path with any feasible path and proving that the number of points on the efficient path whose distance from the maximum growth rate exceeds some $\varepsilon > 0$ is finite.

We turn now to the pricing implications for efficient growth paths of infinite duration. It is a well-known theorem of static welfare economics that for any economy in which the technology and preference sets are convex, then to each efficient allocation of resources there corresponds a set of non-negative prices that would be equilibrium prices for a competitive economy. Furthermore, at these efficiency prices the value of final output is maximized. The converse result also holds: in such an economy every competitive equilibrium is also efficient (see Dorfman, Samuelson, and Solow [7]). This theorem generalizes readily to efficient paths of finite duration, since the same goods in different periods can be treated simply as different goods and the classical theorem may be applied (see Debreu [5] and Chapter 1).

The problem of extending these results to efficient paths over an infinite horizon was first investigated by Malinvaud [17, 18] and has since been given further attention by Radner [33] and McFadden [19]. Malinvaud obtained the following results for an economy in which production is de-centralized, taking place in a number of individual firms (denoted by subscripts k) each with their own technology.

(i) For each efficient time path of infinite order there is a nonnegative sequence of price vectors $p = (p_1, p_2, \ldots p_t, \ldots)$ such that for all T the expression

$$p_1 y_1 + \sum_{t=1}^{T-1} (p_{t+1} y_{t+1} - p_t x_t) - p_T x_T$$

is maximized. This expression is simply the total present value of final output produced until time T, and, as in the static case, it is maximized by the efficiency price vectors.

(ii) A sufficient condition for a path of infinite order to be efficient is that there exist a positive sequence of prices p such that
(a) For all T, k

$$p_1 y_{1k} + \sum_{t=1}^{T-1} (p_{t+1} y_{t+1, k} - p_t x_{tk}) - p_T x_{Tk}$$

is a maximum, where x_{tk}, y_{tk} are the vectors of inputs and outputs respectively of the kth firm in year t.

(b) $$p_T x_T \to 0 \qquad \text{as} \qquad T \to \infty.$$

Condition (a) asserts that each firm must maximize the present value of its final output, whereas (b) says that the present value of the stock of·inputs remaining at time T must tend to zero as T becomes infinite. The reason for requiring (b) is that although any intertemporally efficient allocation can be found for any given price structure over some finite time period T, say, it is quite possible that the stock of inputs that remain at the end of that finite period may prove to be inefficient for the remaining infinite time period that extends beyond T. This fact cannot be detected during the period preceding T but only after, and the second condition serves to eliminate this possibility.

10–3. The Turnpike Theorems

We move now from studying the behavior of paths which are efficient over an infinite planning horizon to studying the properties of paths which begin from some specified initial conditions and are efficient over some specified finite time interval. These paths have given rise to the celebrated turnpike theorem. This states that if the planning period is very long, the efficient capital accumulation program behaves as follows: (1) The system first invests so as to alter its capital structure toward the von Neumann balanced growth proportions. (2) When it has come sufficiently close to this configuration, it spends most of the time growing at the steady-state maximal rate. (3) As the end of the planning period approaches, the path bends away from the von Neumann path and investment takes place in such a way as to alter the capital structure to the desired capital proportions. In this sense the von Neumann path acts like a turnpike, and, moreover, the longer the planning period the greater the proportion of time spent in the neighborhood of the turnpike. This is more or less the form in which the turnpike theorem was first conjectured by Dorfman, Samuelson, and Solow [7], although their sketch of a proof was later seen to be faulty. Since then an extensive literature has developed and valid proofs have been obtained using a variety of techniques. We will distinguish three broad types of turnpike theorems (exclusive of the consumption turnpike theorem to be discussed in Chapter 11) in accordance with the analytical methods used in the respective proofs.

(i) Radner-type,
(ii) Morishima-type, and
(iii) Samuelson-type.

In very general terms the differences are as follows: theorems of type (i) use set-theoretic methods to obtain convergence to the von Neumann output ray and furthermore define convergence in terms of the angular distance between two vectors. Theorems of type (ii) first obtain convergence of the price ray to the von Neumann price ray and then, using this result, obtain convergence of the output ray to the von Neumann output ray. Moreover, type (ii) theorems employ the notion of convergence used by Solow and Samuelson in their relative stability theorem. Both these classes work with discrete time intervals and make no statements concerning the smoothness of the production set. They are also globally valid, i.e., they hold for efficient paths regardless of the location of the initial point. Type (iii) theorems deal with smooth production functions that are homogeneous of the first degree. Samuelson's version of the theorem was proved, using the calculus of variations, for continuous time, and a completely analogous proof has been given for discrete time. However, the derivation of type (iii) theorems depends upon linear approximations that hold only in a neighborhood of the maximum growth ray. Additional argument is necessary to obtain global conclusions.

10–4. Radner-Type Turnpike Theorems

We will begin by expounding in detail the turnpike theorem as first proved by Radner [31]. This version has been chosen for expositional purposes because it is the most basic of the type (i) theorems. It is also mathematically the simplest and most elegant theorem, although as we shall see it is not the most powerful.

Radner's theorem deals with the closed model of production discussed in Chapter 7. Of the assumptions (A.1)–(A.4) of Chapter 7, Radner drops the requirement of convexity of the production set T in (A.1) and substitutes assumption (A.1'). He retains assumption (A.3) but does not explicitly require assumptions (A.2) and (A.4) of Chapter 7. However, he does assume the existence of a unique von Neumann balanced growth pair and growth rate, and this itself implicitly assumes conditions at least as strong as the other two assumptions.

Radner focuses attention upon the final state and defines a utility function $U(x_N)$ in terms of the commodities of the final state. He then poses the problem of finding sequences that maximize $U(x_N)$, given N, the length of the planning period and x_0, the initial commodity vector. Such a sequence is called U-optimal, and it can be seen that the preference among feasible sequences depends only upon comparisons among the terminal states of such sequences.[8] Two further assumptions are made about the utility function U.

---

[8] Koopmans [16] proves Radner's theorem for the case in which the utility function is linear and of the form $p^{*\prime}x_N$ where p^* represents the vector of von Neumann prices. These values he calls *the von Neumann value of the commodities*, and the optimum path is then defined as the one which maximizes this value.

Assumption (A.3): $U \geq 0$ *and is continuous on the commodity space, and there exists an x such that* $U(x) > 0$.

Assumption (A.4): *U is homogeneous of degree one.*

Under certain conditions, including uniqueness of the von Neumann ray, all U-optimal sequences must be close to the von Neumann ray, except possibly for a finite number of periods, and this number is independent of the length of the sequence. To make the notion of *closeness* precise, Radner defines the distance between two vectors in terms of the angle between them. The symbol $d(x, y)$ denoting the distance between two vectors x and y is defined as follows:

$$d(x, y) = \left| \frac{x}{|x|} - \frac{y}{|y|} \right| \qquad \text{where} \qquad |x| = (x'x)^{1/2}. \tag{6}$$

We will also define $\{x \mid d(x, x^*) < \varepsilon\}$ to be an *ε-neighborhood of x^*.*

We are now in a position to state in formal terms the Radner turnpike theorem. Under assumptions (A.1') and (A.3) of Chapter 7 and (A.3) and (A.4) of this chapter, if

(i) $x^*, \lambda^* - 1, p^*$ are the von Neumann balanced growth path, growth rate, and equilibrium price system, respectively;

(ii) $p^*(y - \lambda^* x) < 0$ for all $(x, y) \in T$ not proportional to $(x^*, \lambda^* x^*)$;

(iii) There is a number $M > 0$ such that for all commodity vectors x, $U(x) \leq Mp^* x$;

(iv) An initial commodity x_0 is given such that for some number $L > 0$, $(x_0, Lx^*) \in T$; and

(v) $U(x^*) > 0$;

then for any $\varepsilon > 0$ there is a number S such that, for any N and any U-optimal sequence $\{x_n\}_{n=0}^{N}$, the number of periods in which $d(x_n, x^*) \geq \varepsilon$ does not exceed S. It is important to note that S is independent of the length N of the sequence.

In words Radner's theorem asserts the following. Suppose we nominate a neighborhood of the von Neumann ray, inside of which the output ray will be considered to be *close* to the balanced growth output configuration. Then, having decided on this degree of closeness, we can find a number S that is a finite upper bound to the number of time periods that an optimum path can lie outside the neighborhood. Furthermore—and this is the crux of the theorem—S is *independent* of N, the length of the planning period, so that as the length of the period increases the fraction of time spent in this prescribed neighborhood increases toward unity. This result holds for any prescribed neighborhood. It is true that if an exceedingly short period N were proposed then S might exceed N, in which case the theorem would be trivial. But since the turnpike theorem is concerned with very long-run growth problems this possibility can be excluded. Obviously if N is sufficiently large, it must certainly exceed S.

Radner's theorem does not tell us how to get to the turnpike, but asserts a criterion that must be satisfied by paths if they are to be optimal. Thus, if a path stays outside the prescribed neighborhood for more than S periods it cannot be optimal, so that we know a more efficient path exists. This approach in fact is the key to the method of proof developed by Radner and used by other writers.

Before proving the theorem we must first establish Radner's lemma.

Lemma 3: *Assuming* (A.1′) *and* (A.3) *of Chapter 7 and conditions* (i) *and* (ii)′ *just given, then for any* $\varepsilon > 0$ *there exists a* $\delta > 0$ *such that for any* $(x, y) \in T$ *for which* $d(x, x^*) \geq \varepsilon$ *it follows that* $p^{*\prime}y \leq (\lambda^* - \delta)p^{*\prime}x$. *(Essentially this lemma asserts that the value loss incurred by being away from the von Neumann ray cannot be less than a given fraction of the value of the inputs.)*

Proof: The set $T_1 = \{y \mid (x, y) \in T, |x| = 1\}$ is bounded. For if not, there is a sequence (x_k, y_k) such that $|x_k| = 1$ and $|y_k| \to \infty$. Then the sequence $(x_k/|y_k|, y_k/|y_k|)$, $k = 1, 2, \ldots$, being bounded in T, has a limit point $(0, \bar{y})$ in T, with $|\bar{y}| = 1$, which contradicts assumption (A.3) of Chapter 7. Now suppose there is an $\varepsilon > 0$ and a sequence (x_k, y_k) in T such that

$$p^{*\prime}x_k > 0, \quad d(x_k, x^*) \geq \varepsilon, \quad \text{and} \quad \frac{p^{*\prime}y_k}{p^{*\prime}x_k} \to \lambda^*.$$

Normalizing, we may take $|x_k| = 1$, $k = 1, 2, \ldots$. Hence the sequence (x_k, y_k) is bounded and has a limit point $(\bar{x}, \bar{y})$. Since the sequence $p^{*\prime}x_k$ is also bounded, it follows that

$$\frac{p^{*\prime}y_k}{p^{*\prime}x_k'} \to \frac{p^{*\prime}\bar{y}}{p^{*\prime}\bar{x}} = \lambda^* \quad \text{or} \quad p^*(\bar{y} - \lambda^*\bar{x}) = 0. \tag{7}$$

But this statement, together with the fact that $(\bar{x}, \bar{y})$ cannot be proportional to (x^*, λ^*x^*), contradicts condition (ii) and hence establishes the lemma.

Proof of the Turnpike Theorem: Define a feasible sequence $\{\tilde{x}_n\}_{n=0}^{N}$ by

$$\tilde{x}_0 = x_0, \qquad \tilde{x}_1 = Lx^*,$$

and

$$\tilde{x}_n = L\lambda^{*n-1}x^*, \qquad (n = 1, \ldots, N).$$

The strategy of the proof is to show that the sequence $\{\tilde{x}_n\}_{n=0}^{N}$ is better than any sequence that departs too far for too long from the von Neuman ray, even though $(\tilde{x}_n)$ may not itself be U-optimal.

Consider any $\varepsilon > 0$ and any sequence $\{x_n\}_{n=0}^{N}$ that is feasible given x_0. For any period n for which $d(x_n, x^*) \geq \varepsilon$, it follows from the lemma that

$$p^{*\prime}x_{n+1} \leq (\lambda^* - \delta)p^{*\prime}x_n \qquad \text{where} \qquad \delta > 0. \tag{8}$$

It also follows from the definition of a von Neumann equilibrium that for all n

$$p^{*\prime}x_{n+1} \leq \lambda^* p^{*\prime}x_n. \tag{9}$$

Suppose that $d(x_n, x^*) \geq \varepsilon$ for P periods. Then from (8) and (9) it follows that

$$p^{*\prime}x_N \leq (\lambda^* - \delta)^P(\lambda^*)^{N-P}p^{*\prime}x_0, \tag{10}$$

and therefore from condition (iii) we obtain

$$U(x_N) \leq M(\lambda^* - \delta)^P(\lambda^*)^{N-P}p^{*\prime}x_0. \tag{11}$$

By definition of the path and the homogeneity of U,

$$U(\tilde{x}_N) = U(L\lambda^{*N-1}x^*) = L\lambda^{*N-1}U(x^*) > 0. \tag{12}$$

Dividing these last two equations, we obtain

$$\frac{U(x_N)}{U(\tilde{x}_N)} \leq \frac{M(\lambda^* - \delta)^P\lambda^{*N-P}p^{*\prime}x_0}{L\lambda^{*N-1}U(x^*)}$$

$$\leq \frac{M\lambda^* p^{*\prime}x_0}{LU(x^*)}\left(\frac{\lambda^* - \delta}{\lambda^*}\right)^P$$

$$= C\left(\frac{\lambda^* - \delta}{\lambda^*}\right)^P \qquad \text{where} \qquad C = \frac{M\lambda^* p^{*\prime}x_0}{LU(x^*)}. \tag{13}$$

Hence, for $\{x_n\}_{n=0}^N$ to be optimal we require

$$C\left(\frac{\lambda^* - \delta}{\lambda^*}\right)^P \geq 1$$

or

$$P \leq \frac{\log C}{\log\left[\dfrac{\lambda^*}{\lambda^* - \delta}\right]}. \tag{14}$$

The proof is completed by taking

$$S = \max\left[1, \frac{\log C}{\log\left[\dfrac{\lambda^*}{\lambda^* - \delta}\right]}\right] \tag{15}$$

This number S gives the maximum number of periods that any efficient path can remain at a distance exceeding ε from the von Neumann ray, and S is independent of the planning period N.

Before concluding this discussion of Radner's theorem, we should make several observations. In the first place the theorem depends crucially on the assumption that all activities other than von Neumann activities make a loss at the von Neumann prices. This condition will be satisfied if the transformation set T is strictly convex, except on rays through the origin. Hence, Radner's result applies to a technology that is strongly superadditive. However, it is not applicable to the technology treated by von Neumann himself, which was not required to be strictly convex. Second, condition (iii) will be satisfied if $p^* > 0$. Condition (iv) is concerned with the problem of the accessibility of the turnpike and is clearly very important. The question arises whether or not we can, given our initial endowment, in fact reach the von Neumann path. Consider a situation in which the von Neumann activity includes a certain commodity at a positive level, but where this commodity is not included in our initial endowment. Furthermore, suppose that this commodity cannot be produced by any activity. This, of course, amounts to a rejection of assumption (A.4′) of Chapter 7, which, however, Radner did not use explicitly. In this case the von Neumann ray would be inaccessible. Condition (iv) asserts explicitly that given the initial capital structure we can attain the von Neumann configuration. Given the disposability assumption (A.3) of Chapter 7, if x_0 has positive amounts of those commodities for which x^* is positive, this condition is fulfilled. Also it should be observed that as it stands, (iv) states that we can reach the maximum balanced growth ray in one period. This can be weakened to the requirement that there be some feasible sequence that enables the von Neumann ray to be reached from the initial endowment in some finite period.

The greatest weakness of Radner's theorem, however, is that the proof does not exclude the possibility that the periods spent by the optimal path in the ε-neighborhood of the turnpike are not consecutive. In other words, there may be repeated entry and re-entry into the neighborhood of the turnpike. All the theorem asserts is that an efficient path will spend no more than S periods at a distance $d(x, x^*) \geq \varepsilon$ from the von Neumann equilibrium path. It does not inform us at what stage of the sequence these points occur.

Radner's theorem has been the take-off point for further developments of turnpike theorems. In particular, subsequent theorems have strengthened his theorem in two respects. McKenzie [20] has extended the theorem to the case where the von Neumann facet need not be a unique ray as was assumed before. Also, Nikaido [30] has proved (with the help of additional assumptions) that the periods spent by the path outside the ε-neighborhood of the von Neumann ray do in fact occur either at the beginning or at the end of the path (or both).

Additional assumptions imposed by Nikaido follow.

Assumption (A.5): *For any* $x \geq 0$ *there is some* y *such that* $(x, y) \in T$, $y \geq 0$. *That is, goods can be combined as inputs in any proportion to produce some nonnegative output.*

Assumption (A.6): $x^* > 0$. *That is, the von Neumann ray is generated by a positive vector.*

Assumption (A.7): *The preference indicator* $U(x)$ *is such that* $x > y \geq 0$ *implies* $U(x) > U(y)$.

That is, (A.7) implies there is no saturation level for utility. We will delay a consideration of the plausibility of these assumptions until Section 10-9. Under these slightly more stringent assumptions a stronger version of the turnpike theorem can be stated. In formal terms it can be expressed as follows.

Theorem: *For any* $\varepsilon > 0$ *there is a number* M *such that for any programming span* N *and any* U-*optimal sequence* $\{x_n\}_{n=0}^{N}$ *with* x_0 *given, we have*

$$\left| \frac{x_n}{|x_n|} - \frac{x^*}{|x^*|} \right| < \varepsilon \qquad for \qquad M \leq n \leq N - M. \tag{16}$$

Thus, any U-optimal sequence lies entirely within the ε-neighborhood of the maximum balanced growth path in all periods extending from M to $N - M$.

In essence Nikaido's theorem involves applying Radner's theorem to the following subpath of the original optimal path. From Radner's theorem we know that the optimal path is outside the ε-neighborhood of x^*, the von Neumann ray, for at most S periods. Nikaido assigns the subscripts r and s to the *first* and *last* steps that lie within the ε-neighborhood of x^*. Now he considers the inputs x_r to the rth step, and the outputs y_s of the sth step as the initial and final points (corresponding to x_1 and x_N of Radner's theorem). The only difference in this case is that the points x_r and y_s already lie within the ε-neighborhood of the von Neumann ray x^*. Since $x^* > 0$, for small enough ε it can be shown by a continuity argument that x_r and y_s have positive components. This fact, together with the disposability assumption [actually a little stronger than (A.5)], enables a comparison path similar to that used by Radner to be constructed. An application of Radner's methodology to this maximum subpath and the comparison path shows that the number of periods the subpath can be outside the ε-neighborhood of the von Neumann ray between the rth and the sth step is, in fact, zero. The theorem is finally established using assumption (A.5) instead of assuming disposability. It follows therefore that the periods spent by the path outside the ε-neighborhood of the maximum balanced growth ray must occur at either end of the path.

The other generalization of Radner's result is McKenzie's theorem [20], in which a technology set T that gives rise to a von Neumann facet is considered. McKenzie deals with a Leontief model with capital goods and alternative activity vectors.[9] There are n goods and consequently n industries, although each industry has the choice of several activities. As the activities are altered, the coefficients of the input-output matrix change. Stocks of commodities existing at the end of one period are regarded as being converted by production into stocks during the next period. In the model the transformation set T is the set $(-x_t, x_{t+1})$ which satisfies

$$\begin{pmatrix} I - A + B \\ -B \end{pmatrix} z_{t+1} \geqq \begin{pmatrix} x_{t+1} \\ -x_t \end{pmatrix} \tag{17}$$

for some $z_{t+1} \geqq 0$. The matrix A represents the consumption of goods used in production during the period, whereas B represents the transfer of stocks from one period to the next—entries of both matrices being measured relative to unit activity levels. Since there are n industries, both A and B are $n \times n$

---

[9] Since McKenzie does not permit joint production, it is in one sense less general than Radner's result. Morishima [28] has proved a more general theorem in which a polyhedral technology permitting joint products and giving rise to a von Neumann facet is considered. The proof is similar in strategy to McKenzie's.

matrices, although they will change as the chosen activity vectors vary. The vector z_{t+1} indicates the level of production of these n industries during period $t + 1$, whereas x_t represents the level of stocks available at the end of period t. The first of the two inequalities of (17) relates the level of production to stocks available at the end of the period. More precisely, it states that the total output less the output necessary to sustain current production, together with the quantity of stocks transferred during the period, cannot be less than the total quantity of goods available at the end of the period. The second inequality asserts that the quantity of stocks transferred during the period cannot exceed the amount of stocks available initially. Furthermore, the inequality (17) can be interpreted as saying that disposal can occur without cost. (Note that the negative sign has been introduced since it conveniently permits both sets of inequalities to be expresesd more concisely.) We define D_j to be the set of (a_j, b_j) that can appear together in the jth process, where a_j and b_j are the jth column of A and B respectively. Therefore,

$$\begin{pmatrix} 1 - a_j + b_j \\ - b_j \end{pmatrix} \tag{18}$$

is an input-output combination that is possible for the industry which produces the jth good. McKenzie then makes three assumptions about the technology.

Assumption (A.8): *The set D_j is compact (i.e., bounded and closed), convex, and nonempty.*

Assumption (A.9): $b_j \geq a_j \geq 0$ *for* $(a_j, b_j) \in D_j$.

Assumption (A.10): *There are* $(a_j, b_j) \in D_j$ $(j = 1, \ldots, n)$ *such that* $[I - A]$ *has a dominant diagonal.*[10] *Moreover,* $[I - A]z \geq 0$ *for some* $z \geq 0$ *implies that B is indecomposable.*

In economic terms, if $[I - A]$ has a dominant diagonal, then at any level of activity the output of each industry exceeds the inputs (valued at some common denominator) from all industries (including itself) necessary to sustain that level of activity. If the vector of intensity levels for the n industries is denoted by z, then $[I - A]z$ represents the vector of net outputs of each industry, i.e., the output after all interindustry flows have been provided for. The second part of assumption (A.10) then asserts the following: suppose

---

[10] An $n \times n$ matrix $A = [a_{ij}]$ is said to have a dominant diagonal if $|a_{jj}| > \sum\limits_{\substack{i=1 \\ i \neq j}}^{n} |a_{ij}|$ for each j, where in this context $|a_{ij}|$ denotes the absolute value of a_{ij}. (See McKenzie [20]. A slightly more general definition is given in L.8 of the Appendix.)

for some nonzero intensity level (i.e., an intensity level at which at least one industry is operating at a positive level), the net output of at least one industry is positive. Then the transfer of stocks of any sector is dependent either directly or indirectly on the intensity level of all industries (see Section 10-9 and the Appendix for further explanation of indecomposability).

The first step in McKenzie's argument is the establishment of strictly positive von Neumann output and price vectors. Assumption (A.10) suffices to show that the model is *regular*[11] (see Gale [11]), which implies the existence of a strictly positive equilibrium output ray, and this in turn permits the existence of the strictly positive price ray to be proved. The next stage is to prove the convergence of efficient paths to the von Neumann facet. The convergence is obtained by a modification of Radner's argument, where in this instance distance between the path and the facet is defined as the minimum distance from the path to any vector in the facet.[12] We may note that strict positivity of the von Neumann price and output ray is not necessary to obtain convergence to the facet, as McKenzie shows in [23]. In order to obtain uniqueness of the von Neumann ray, assumptions (A.8) and (A.10) are strengthened to the following.

Assumption (A.8′): *The set D_j is compact, relatively strictly convex,*[13] *and nonempty.*

Assumption (A.10′): *There are $(a_j, b_j) \in D_j$ $(j = 1, \ldots, n)$ such that $[I - A]$ has a dominant diagonal. Moreover, $[I - A]z \geq 0$ for some $z \geq 0$ implies that B is indecomposable and nonsingular.*

The uniqueness and strict positivity of the von Neumann ray and prices enable the set $(-x_t, x_{t+1})$ belonging to the facet to be expressed by the difference equation

$$\{I + [I - A]B^{-1}\}^{-1}x_{t+1} = x_t \tag{19}$$

or

$$x_{t+1} = \{I + [I - A]B^{-1}\}x_t, \tag{20}$$

where A and B describe the processes which generate the unique von Neumann ray. If a path lies on the facet for N periods, it can be expressed by this

---

[11] A model is defined to be *regular* if for every optimal process $(x, y), y > 0$. That is, for a regular model every optimal process produces a positive amount of all goods. A sufficient condition for a model to be regular is that it be indecomposable.

[12] That is if we denote the facet by F, then $d(x, F)$—the distance from a vector to the facet—is defined to be inf $d(x, y)$ where $y \in F$.

[13] A set contained in $2n$-Euclidean space is *relatively strictly convex* if it is strictly convex in the smallest subspace containing it; see McKenzie [23].

equation for $t = 0, \ldots, N - 1$. In order to ensure that solutions of this equation with $x_t \geq 0$ will converge to the von Neumann ray, an additional assumption must be made. This requirement is of a purely mathematical nature and asserts the following.

Assumption (A.11): $\{I + [I - A]B^{-1}\}$ *is nonsingular. Also, if* λ *is a characteristic root of* $\{I + [I - A]B^{-1}\}$ *and if* $|\lambda| = \lambda^*$, *then* $\lambda = \lambda^*$ *where* λ^* *is the rate of maximum balanced growth.*

Assumption (A.11) is the primitivity condition,[14] which, as we have already remarked, rules out cyclic, undamped motion.

Thus having proved the convergence of an optimum path to the facet, McKenzie then shows that any vector in the facet satisfies the difference equation (20), and for some proportion of the plan period this vector must lie in an ε-neighborhood of the von Neumann ray. He then shows that the optimum path must lie near one of these paths in the facet. From this he concludes that the optimum path must stay near the von Neumann ray for a period not less than some minimum value.

Two extensions of McKenzie's theorem have since appeared. The first is a theorem by Drandakis [8] that considers an economy in which production is decentralized. As Drandakis shows, even if each production unit has a strictly convex production cone it does not follow that the aggregate production set will have this property, which all the theorems discussed so far have required. With assumptions (A.1)–(A.4) of Chapter 7, (A.4) of the present chapter, and using Radner's approach, Drandakis proves the convergence of efficient paths to the von Neumann facet, providing the total value of the initial stocks at the initial associated efficiency prices is positive. Convergence of any efficient path on the facet to the von Neumann ray is proved following McKenzie's proof. However, additional assumptions concerning the nature of the input and output matrices and their characteristic roots are required to achieve the result.

The second paper is by Tsukui [41] who modifies McKenzie's technology by relaxing assumption (A.8) and assuming instead that each industry has a polyhedral technology. Apart from this alteration he adopts a set of assumptions equivalent (but not identical) to those of McKenzie and derives the same result. Finally, he proves a dual theorem by showing similar turnpike behavior about the von Neumann price ray of the shadow prices of the efficient path.

[14] See the definition of a *primitive matrix* given in Section 10-7 and in the Appendix.

10–5. Morishima-Type Turnpike Theorems

Morishima's turnpike theorem [25] is proved along somewhat different lines from those we have been considering.[15] Like McKenzie he deals with a Leontief model in which an industry i can choose between m_i different activities for producing good i. The total set of activities can be denoted by an $n \times m$ matrix A where

$$A = \begin{bmatrix} a_{11}(1) \cdots a_{11}(m_1) & a_{12}(1) \cdots a_{12}(m_2) \cdots a_{1n}(1) \cdots a_{1n}(m_n) \\ \vdots \qquad \vdots & \vdots \qquad \vdots \qquad \vdots \qquad \vdots \\ a_{n1}(1) \cdots a_{n1}(m_1) & a_{n2}(1) \cdots a_{n2}(m_2) \cdots a_{nn}(1) \cdots a_{nn}(m_n) \end{bmatrix}$$

and where $m = \Sigma \, m_i$ and n is number of commodities. A typical element of the matrix A, $a_{ij}(\mu_j)$, designates the amount of output of sector i required to produce a unit of output in sector j when the latter sector adopts the technique μ_j. Since there is no joint supply, the matrix of output coefficients may be written

$$B = \begin{bmatrix} 1 \cdots 1 & 0 \cdots 0 \cdots 0 \cdots 0 \\ 0 \cdots 0 & 1 \cdots 1 \cdots 0 \cdots 0 \\ \vdots \quad \vdots & \vdots \quad \vdots \quad \vdots \quad \vdots \\ 0 \cdots 0 & 0 \cdots 0 \cdots 1 \cdots 1 \end{bmatrix}.$$

The s_ith activity of industry i is defined by $a_{si} = [a_{1i}(s_i), \ldots, a_{ni}(s_i)]$. If each industry selects a single activity from among those available to it there are $m_1 \times m_2 \times \cdots \times m_n$ possible sets of activities that could be adopted by the economy. Any $n \times n$ matrix A_σ, which represents a particular set of activities adopted, is nonnegative and therefore has a characteristic root h_σ that is nonnegative and not less in absolute value than any other root. (See [6] and the Appendix.) In particular, let A_ε be an activity set such that $h_\varepsilon \leq h_\sigma$, and let the column and row eigenvectors of A_ε, associated with h_ε, be x_ε and P_ε respectively.[16]

Assumption (A.12): A_ε is indecomposable.[17]

Assumption (A.13): A_ε is unique.

Let $A_\varepsilon = (a_{\varepsilon 1}, \ldots, a_{\varepsilon n})$ and let $x_{\varepsilon i}$ be the ith component of x_ε. Let Y_ε be an m-dimensional column vector such that its s_ith component is $x_{\varepsilon i}$ when $s_i = \varepsilon_i$

[15] A companion paper to Morishima's has been written by Hicks [14].
[16] This implies $P_\varepsilon A_\varepsilon = h_\varepsilon P_\varepsilon$, $A_\varepsilon x_\varepsilon = h_\varepsilon x_\varepsilon$.
[17] See the Appendix for a definition of an indecomposable matrix.

and zero otherwise. Morishima then shows that h_ε, Y_ε, and P_ε satisfy the inequalities

$$P_\varepsilon B \leq \frac{1}{h_\varepsilon} P_\varepsilon A,$$

$$P_\varepsilon BY = \frac{1}{h_\varepsilon} P_\varepsilon AY_\varepsilon,$$

$$BY_\varepsilon \geq \frac{1}{h_\varepsilon} AY_\varepsilon,$$

(21)

and

$$P_\varepsilon BY_\varepsilon > 0.$$

Since $h_\varepsilon \leq h_\sigma$, we may identify $h_\varepsilon^{-1} - 1$, x_ε, and P_ε as the von Neumann growth rate, output ray, and price ray respectively. Because the technology is not strictly convex, assumption (A.13) is necessary to ensure uniqueness of the von Neumann ray.

Morishima sets up his statement of the turnpike theorem as a primal and dual linear programming problem, the primal determining the course of the outputs of an efficient path, and the dual determining the course of the imputed prices corresponding to the efficient path of outputs.

Let $Y(t)$ be a vector of intensities at time t (m-dimensional), and let $X(0)$ be an initial stock vector (n-dimensional). In this linear programming format a sequence $Y(1), \ldots, Y(T)$ of intensity vectors is called feasible given $X(0)$ if

$$Y(t) \geq 0, \quad (t = 1, \ldots, T),$$

$$AY(1) \leq X(0),$$

and

(22)

$$AY(t + 1) \leq BY(t), \quad (t = 1, \ldots, T - 1).$$

Furthermore, if $\hat{x}$ is a given stock structure at time T (i.e. $\Sigma \hat{x}_i = 1$), and if q is defined as $\min_i[x_i(T)/\hat{x}_i]$ where $x_i(T)$ is the ith component of $BY(T)$, then

$$q\hat{x} \leq BY(T).$$

A feasible path is said to be efficient if there is no other feasible path $Y'(1), \ldots,$ $Y'(T)$ such that $q' > q$. This definition is completely analogous to the one given before for the more general technology. An efficient path of outputs starting from $x(0)$ and reaching $\hat{x}$ is obtained by solving the linear program. The primal problem is to maximize $h_\varepsilon^T q$ such that

$$AY(1) \leq X(0); \qquad AY(t+1) \leq BY(t), \quad (t = 1, \ldots, T-1);$$

$$q\hat{x} \leq BY(T); \qquad \text{and} \qquad Y(t) \geq 0, \quad q \geq 0.$$

The dual problem is to minimize $P(0)x(0)$ such that

$$P(t)A \geq P(t+1)B, \quad (t = 0, \ldots, T-1);$$

$$P(T)\hat{x} \geq h_\varepsilon^T; \qquad \text{and} \qquad P(t) \geq 0, \quad (t = 0, \ldots, T).$$

Two further assumptions are introduced.

Assumption (A.14): *A_ε is primitive.*[18]

Assumption (A.15): *For each good there is at least one industry j that uses i indispensably.*

Having set up this analytical machinery, the proof proceeds in the following manner. First it is shown that if there are no zero outputs in the final period (i.e., $\hat{x} > 0$), assumption (A.15) ensures that there are no zero outputs in any period. Hence, each commodity i is always produced by some process s_i of the ith industry. Therefore, using the duality theorem of linear programming, costs must equal prices throughout the period.[19] Of course we must remember that each industry had a choice of activities for the manufacture of a given commodity, so this result asserts that (1) of these activities at least one makes zero profits, and (2) in fact this is the minimum cost activity for the firm.

The next stage involves taking the configuration for the whole economy which results when each industry operates its minimum cost activity. Explicitly, if for industry i we denote $P(t)a_{Li} = \min[P(t)a_{1i}, \ldots, P(t)a_{mi}]$ and let $A_t = [a_{L1}, \ldots, a_{Ln}]$ be the configuration for the whole economy, then

$$P(t+1) = P(t)A_t \leq P(t)A_\sigma \tag{23}$$

where A_σ is any other configuration of activities.

Morishima then proves that any price path starting from an arbitrary nonnegative price $P(0)$ and satisfying equation (23) eventually approaches

[18] The definition of a primitive matrix is given in Section 10-7 and in the Appendix.
[19] That is, the solution to the dual program satisfies its constraints with equality.

the von Neumann price ray. In other words, any path of prices that yields zero profits will converge to the equilibrium price ray. The proof follows lines similar to the Solow–Samuelson proof for relative stability of balanced growth paths (see Chapter 7) and relies on assumptions (A.12) and (A.13) to obtain the convergence.

The result of this lemma can be stated in more formal terms as follows. Let N be a prescribed neighborhood of the von Neumann price ray, and let $P[t, P(0)]$ be the path satisfying (23) and starting from $P(0)$. For $P(0) \geq 0$ there exists a finite integer $t[P(0), N]$ such that for all integers $t \geq t[P(0), N]$, the path $P[t, P(0)]$ remains within N. Let $\bar{t}$ be the smallest of such integers. This gives the time required for $P[t, P(0)]$ to come into the neighborhood N.

By an argument relying primarily on continuity properties, this result can be strengthened to establish the uniform convergence of the path for points within a given neighborhood of a prescribed point. In the previous lemma the value of $\bar{t}$ varied with the initial point of the path. In this strengthened lemma it is shown that given a prescribed point, P^+ say, there is a neighborhood of P^+ such that any path starting in this neighborhood will remain within the neighborhood N after a time t^*. In this instance t^* is *independent* of the actual starting point, though it does depend on the point P^+. In this sense the convergence is said to be uniform.

Boundedness of the initial imputed prices together with the uniform convergence of the price paths enables a finite time, T_* say, to be determined such that (1) T_* is independent of the length of the programming period, and (2) after time T_* the sequence of prices starting from any initial price $P(0)$ and satisfying (23), will lie within the prescribed neighborhood of the von Neumann price ray.

Thus far the proof of the theorem has succeeded in establishing the convergence of the price path satisfying (23) to the von Neumann ray. We also know that the solution to the dual linear program, which are the prices associated with an efficient path of outputs, satisfies the equation (23). Hence it follows that the path of prices, associated with an efficient output path, converges to the von Neumann price ray. In order to focus on the output path itself, the duality theorem of linear programming is invoked. Before applying this theorem, however, let us make some observations. In the first place it can be shown that $P_\varepsilon A_\varepsilon < P_\varepsilon A_\zeta$ where A_ζ is a set of activities that contains none of the von Neumann activities. By continuity, Morishima then shows that this inequality holds for any P belonging to the prescribed neighborhood of P_ε, the von Neumann price ray. He also shows that for any P in this neighborhood of the von Neumann price ray, the von Neumann activities themselves satisfy the equation (23). Combining this result with the last it then follows that for P in the neighborhood of P_ε, the constraints of the dual linear program are satisfied with strict inequality for activities other than those of the von Neumann ray. Now applying the dual theorem of linear programming, these activities will be operated at zero level in the time interval $(T_* + 1, T)$. In other words, after some finite time T_* an efficient path will adopt the same activities as on the von Neumann ray. Hence, over the time interval $(T_* + 1, T)$, the constraints of the primal problem can be written as $A_\varepsilon X(t + 1) \leqq X(t)$, where $X(t)$ is an n-dimensional vector with elements corresponding to the von Neumann activities. Moreover, the equilibrium price vector P_ε is strictly positive, so again applying continuity in the small neighborhood of P_ε, P is also strictly positive. Hence, P is strictly positive for the time interval (T_*, T). Therefore, using the duality theorem once again we can express the constraints of the primal problem as equalities:

$$A_\varepsilon X(t + 1) = X(t), \qquad (t = T_* + 1, , \ldots, T - 1),$$
$$X(T) = q_T \hat{x} > 0. \tag{24}$$

Suppose we write

$$X(t) = q_T W(T - t), \qquad (t = T_* + 1, \ldots, T). \tag{25}$$

Therefore,

$$A_\varepsilon W(s - 1) = W(s), \qquad (s = 1, \ldots, T - T_* - 1), \tag{26}$$

where $W(0) = \hat{x}$.

Again the assumptions of primitivity and indecomposability enable the same argument used to prove convergence of the price rays to be applied here. Hence there is some finite integer, S say, such that $s > S$ implies that $W(s)$ is within a prescribed neighborhood of the maximum balanced growth ray. Therefore, when T is sufficiently large the solution to (26) will remain within this neighborhood for all s in $(S, T - T_* - 1)$. Thus, $X(t)$, the efficient path, will remain within the prescribed neighborhood of the von Neumann maximum balanced growth ray for all t in the interval $(T_* + 1, T - S)$. Finally, we may observe as $T \to \infty$, the proportion of time spent in this neighborhood tends to unity.

This completes the outline of Morishima's turnpike theorem. It differs quite substantially from the type-(i) theorems in its approach. Convergence to the equilibrium price ray is first established and then is used together with the duality theorem of linear programming to obtain the convergence of the activities path to the von Neumann activity vector for all but a finite number of periods. The precise convergence obtained by Morishima is, of course, due to the fact that he has specified a technology that enables him to employ linear programming results, and it is well known that convergence to optimal solutions in linear programming occurs by finite jumps. Consequently, when the price vector becomes sufficiently close to the von Neumann price ray, the activities jump to the optimal solution for that price configuration, namely the von Neumann activity vector.

We have seen how the assumption of indecomposability and uniqueness of the von Neumann activity set are essential to obtaining unique von Neumann price and output rays. Assumption (A.12) also ensures a strictly positive price ray that is necessary for the application of the dual linear programming theorem in the final stages of the proof. Finally, we have also indicated that the assumption of primitivity of the von Neumann activity set is crucial in obtaining the convergence of the price and output vectors. The exceptions to the turnpike theorem that occur when this last condition is not satisfied will be dealt with presently. Morishima's theorem is global, but it does exclude joint production.

McKenzie [21] has generalized this theorem by altering two assumptions.

(i) Still dealing with a finite number of goods, he replaces the assumption that the number of activities be finite by the assumption that the normalized set of activities form a compact set, although there are still n goods being produced.

(ii) The theorem applies uniformly to all efficient paths regardless of whether the final stocks are positive, as Morishima stipulated.

However, McKenzie still retains the assumption of no joint production. Although linear programming techniques are no longer available to him, his general approach is very similar to Morishima's, and he obtains essentially the same result.

Recently Inada [15] has made an effort to unify the characteristics of the Radner [31], McKenzie [20], and Morishima [25] turnpike theorems. He postulates a mathematical condition with little economic meaning that is sufficient to yield a turnpike theorem. He also shows that the three theorems satisfy this mathematical condition—Radner's and Morishima's doing so trivially. Hence the three theorems may be interpreted as providing economically meaningful conditions that suffice to secure the basic mathematical property. But as long as this mathematical property cannot be given any economic interpretation, as he himself admits, the generalized theorem is of little economic significance. Of course, if we could give this more general mathematical condition an economic interpretation, we would obtain a more general turnpike theorem. Inada requires our assumptions (A.1'), (A.2), and (A.3) of Chapter 7, and in addition he assumes the existence of a unique, strictly positive, maximum balanced growth path and an associated strictly positive price configuration. To outline the theorem we must also introduce some further terminology.

(i) $(x, y) \in T$ is *value preserving* if $\lambda^* p^* x = p^* y$ where p^* as usual denotes the equilibrium price vector.

(ii) An ε-feasible path is a feasible path of some order which starts at a point not in the ε-neighborhood of the maximum balanced growth ray.

The technology is said to satisfy the condition of *uniform convergence of the value preserving paths* if any feasible and value preserving path $(x_0, \ldots, x_t)$ lies inside the ε-neighborhood of the maximum balanced growth ray, except for a certain number of periods $\bar{\imath}$, that depends on the magnitude of ε but not on the starting point and the course of the path. With this terminology, the generalized turnpike theorem can now be stated.

Theorem: *If the technology satisfies the condition of uniform convergence of the value preserving paths, the intertemporally efficient path of order N, which starts from a certain point, cannot stay outside the ε-neighborhood of the von Neumann output ray for more than a certain percentage of the whole period, and this percentage tends to zero as N tends to infinity.*

The significance of this theorem can be seen readily. In the first place, a value preserving path of any order is intertemporally efficient, although the converse is not necessarily true.[20] The condition of uniform convergence of the value preserving paths is a property pertaining to a subset of the set of all intertemporally efficient paths. Turnpike theorems relate to the set of intertemporally efficient paths starting from a given point and this forms another subset of the set of all intertemporally efficient paths. The theorem then asserts that properties pertaining to the second subset can be deduced from those pertaining to the first subset.

It is possible to show the relationship of Radner's, McKenzie's and Morishima's theorems to this more generalized theorem and show the uniform convergence of the value preserving paths in each case. We shall not demonstrate the uniform convergence here, but merely indicate that the respective value preserving paths of the three theorems are given by $[p^{*\prime} y^* - \lambda^* p^{*\prime} x^*]$, equation (20), and equation (24), respectively.

[20] *Proof:* Let $(x_0, x_1, \ldots, x_n)$ and $(x_0, \tilde{x}_1, \ldots, \tilde{x}_n)$ be any feasible and value preserving paths respectively, starting from a point x_0. We know that $p^{*\prime} \tilde{x}_0 = (1/\lambda^*) p^{*\prime} \tilde{x}_1 = (1/\lambda^*)^n p^{*\prime} \tilde{x}_n$. We also know that p^* is defined so that $p^{*\prime}(y - \lambda^* x) \leqq 0$ for $(x, y) \in T$; therefore $p^{*\prime} x_0 \geqq \lambda^*) p^{*\prime} x_1 \geqq \ldots \geqq (1/\lambda^*)^n p^{*\prime} x_n$. If $x_n > \tilde{x}_n$, then $(1/\lambda^*)^n p^{*\prime} \tilde{x}_n > (1/\lambda^*)^n p^{*\prime} x_n$ since $(1/\lambda^*) p^* > 0$. Therefore, $(1/\lambda^*)^n p^{*\prime} x_n > p^{*\prime} x_0$, which is a contradiction. Hence $\tilde{x}_n \geqq x_n$, and the value preserving path is efficient.

10-6. Samuelson-Type Turnpike Theorems

Let us now consider the optimal path when the production functions are smooth, so that appropriate derivates exist. For the sake of expositional consistency we will formulate the problem using discrete time, although Samuelson [34] originally solved the problem in the continuous-time case. Thus our formulation bears closer resemblance to a subsequent paper by McKenzie [22], which restates the Samuelson theorem using discrete time.[21] Formally the two approaches are very similar, and since the continuous-time approach may be derived from the analysis in Chapter 11, it is useful to give the alternative formulation here.

Suppose $[K_{1,t-1}, K_{2,t-1}, \ldots, K_{n,t-1}]$ represents the magnitude of the capital stocks of n commodities at time $t-1$ and that

$$[\Delta K_{1t}, \Delta K_{2t}, \ldots, \Delta K_{nt}]$$

represents the amount of net investment occurring between time $t-1$ and time t. Also, let $[C_{1t}, C_{2t}, \ldots, C_{nt}]$ be the consumption flows of the n commodities during the time interval $(t-1, t)$.

Consider the production possibility frontier expressed in the following form:

$$\Delta K_{1t} = F[K_{1,t-1}, \ldots, K_{n,t-1}, \Delta K_{2t} + C_{2t}, \ldots, \Delta K_{nt} + C_{nt}] - C_{1t},$$
$$(t = 1, \ldots, T) \quad (27)$$

where we assume F is homogeneous of degree one and T denotes the terminal time. Since we are concerned with a closed economy, we shall let all the consumption flows be zero and restate equation (27) as

$$\Delta K_{1t} + F[K_{1,t-1}, \ldots, K_{n,t-1}, \Delta K_{2t}, \ldots, \Delta K_{nt}], \quad (t = 1, \ldots, T). \quad (28)$$

Furthermore, following neoclassical tradition, we shall assume that

$$\frac{\partial F}{\partial K_i} > 0, \quad (i = 1 \ldots n); \qquad \frac{\partial F}{\partial \Delta K_i} < 0, \quad (i = 2, \ldots, n); \qquad (29)$$

---

[21] Actually the original Dorfman, Samuelson, Solow conjecture [7] was formulated in terms of discrete time.

and

$$
\begin{bmatrix}
\dfrac{\partial^2 F}{\partial K_i\,\partial K_j} & \dfrac{\partial^2 F}{\partial K_i\,\partial \Delta K_j} \\[2em]
\dfrac{\partial^2 F}{\partial \Delta K_i\,\partial K_j} & \dfrac{\partial^2 F}{\partial \Delta K_i\,\partial \Delta K_j}
\end{bmatrix},\quad (i,j = 2, \ldots, n),
$$

is negative semi-definite of rank $(2n - 3)$. In economic terms, the first set of conditions means that all stocks have a positive marginal productivity in producing commodity one; the second set means that if net investment increases in any other commodity it must be correspondingly reduced in commodity one; the negative definiteness of the matrix implies diminishing marginal productivity conditions. Suppose that initially at time 0, $K_i = K_{i0}$, $(i = 1, \ldots, n)$, and that at the final time T, $K_i = K_{iT} > 0$, $(i = 2, \ldots, n)$. The efficient path between t_0 and t_1 is the one which maximizes $\sum_{t=0}^{T} \Delta K_{1t}$ subject to the constraints of the production function.

Analytically the problem can be expressed as that of selecting the values K_{it} for $i = 1, \ldots, n$, and $t = 1, \ldots, (T-1)$ so as to maximize:

$$
\sum_{t=1}^{T} \Delta K_{it} + \sum_{t=1}^{T} \mu_t[f(K_{1,\,t-1}, \ldots, K_{n,\,t-1}, \Delta K_{2t}, \ldots, \Delta K_{nt}) - \Delta K_{1t}] \tag{30}
$$

where μ_t are the Lagrange multipliers. Differentiation with respect to the K_{it} yields first-order conditions that can be written as follows.

$$
-\mu_t + \mu_{t+1}\left[\frac{\partial F}{\partial K_{1t}} + 1\right] = 0 \tag{31a}
$$

and

$$
\mu_t\,\frac{\partial F}{\partial \Delta K_{it}} + \mu_{t+1}\left[\frac{\partial F}{\partial K_{it}} - \frac{\partial F}{\partial \Delta K_{i,\,t+1}}\right] = 0, \quad (i = 2 \ldots n). \tag{31b}
$$

Eliminating μ_t and μ_{t+1} results in the following set of equations:

$$
\frac{\partial F}{\partial \Delta K_{i,\,t+1}} - \frac{\partial F}{\partial \Delta K_{it}} = \frac{\partial F}{\partial K_{it}} + \frac{\partial F}{\partial K_{it}} \cdot \frac{\partial F}{\partial \Delta K_{it}}, \quad (i = 2, \ldots, n), \tag{32}
$$

which together with the accumulation equations (28) consitute the *dynamic efficiency conditions*. As Samuelson has indicated, these efficiency conditions can readily be given an economic interpretation. Letting p_{it} denote the price ratio of the ith flow good in terms of the first good as *numeraire*, then

$p_{it} = -\partial\Delta K_{1t}/\partial\Delta K_{it} = -\partial F/\partial\Delta K_{it}$. Furthermore, the own-rate of interest for each commodity, which shows the increase of the flow of commodity i resulting from an increase in the stock of commodity i, is given by $r_{it} = \partial\Delta K_{it}/\partial K_{it} = -(\partial F/\partial K_{it})/(\partial F/\partial\Delta K_{it})$ for each t. With this notation, the efficiency conditions can be rewritten in the form:

$$r_{1t} = r_{it} + \frac{\Delta p_{i,t+1}}{p_{it}}, \tag{33}$$

and this is the equilibrium condition that must hold among the various own-rates of interest (see Chapters 8, 9, and 11).

On a balanced growth path, $\Delta K_{it}/K_{it} = (\lambda-1)$, $(i = 1, \ldots, n)$. Hence, substituting into (28) we obtain

$$\Delta K_1 = F(K_1, \ldots, K_n, (\lambda-1)K_2, \ldots, (\lambda-1)K_n) \tag{34}$$

where λ is the balanced growth factor and (34) holds for all t.

It can be shown that this equation can be solved explicitly for λ and that λ achieves a unique maximum, which is, of course, the von Neumann maximum balanced growth factor λ^*.[22] Again it can be shown that this von Neumann path satisfies the efficiency conditions and that it is the only balanced growth path to do so.

In order to determine the behavior of efficient paths in the neighborhood of the equilibrium balanced growth path, the procedure is to consider small variations of the motions of the efficient paths about the von Neumann ray. We know that all efficient paths (and in particular the von Neumann ray) satisfy equations (32). The approximation to the motion of an efficient path in the neighborhood of the maximum balanced growth path is obtained by expanding the equations of (32) in a Taylor's series about the equilibrium point and approximating this development by the linear terms of the series. The resulting motion can then be shown to be such that at first the efficient paths approach the von Neumann ray, but as time increases they tend to veer away from the ray in the direction of the final desired capital stock structure.

The argument can be stated more explicitly in the case of two goods. In this instance it can be shown that the motion of efficient paths in the neighborhood of the maximal balanced growth path can be described by a difference equation of the form[23]

$$K_{2,t+2} - K_2^* + 2b(K_{2,t+1} - K_2^*) + K_{2t} - K_2^* = 0 \tag{35}$$

[22] The uniqueness is ensured by the strict inequality conditions (29) imposed upon the production possibility function, along with the stated rank condition on the Hessian matrix of F.

[23] A detailed discussion of the reciprocal characteristic root property of discrete time maximization problems is given by Samuelson [38].

where K_{2t}, K_2^* denote the *proportions* of good 2 to good 1 on the efficient growth path and maximal balanced growth path, respectively, while b is a constant, the value of which depends upon the function F and its various partial and cross-partial derivatives evaluated on the von Neumann ray. Since all commodities grow at a constant rate on the ray, K_2^* is constant. The solution to this equation is of the form

$$K_{2t} - K_2^* = A(\lambda_1)^t + B\left(\frac{1}{\lambda_1}\right)^t \qquad (36)$$

where A and B are constants determined by the initial and final conditions imposed upon the capital structure and λ_1 is given by

$$\lambda_1 = -b + \sqrt{b^2 - 1}.$$

The solution describing the motion of efficient paths has two components. For values of t near zero the second term dominates, whereas if t tends to infinity, the first term assumes the dominant role. Irrespective of the values of A and B, the motion of efficient paths described in equation (36) is of the following form. Starting from the initial point the second term dominates and as t increases, K tends towards the equilibrium level K_2^*. Then as t increases further, the first component dominates and eventually causes the motion of K_2 to veer away from K_2^* toward the final stock configuration. This type of motion is referred to as catenary motion, and it should be remarked that once the initial and final values of K are determined the speed of the motion depends on the value of the constant b. Whether the efficient paths actually cross the von Neumann path or remain on one side depends on the sign of the constants A and B, and this in turn depends on the initial and final capital stock structures. If initially K_2 is less that K_2^*, and at the end of the period K_2 exceeds K_2^*, then clearly the efficient path will have to cross the von Neumann ray at some point. (This case corresponds to $A > 0$ and $B < 0$.) The four possible types of motion of efficient paths about the equilibrium balanced growth path are shown in Figure 41, assuming that $\lambda_1 > 1$.

With certain modifications this argument generalizes to the case of n goods where a similar catenary motion will result. In this case it can be shown that the linearization yields a difference equation that can be written in the form

$$A(K_{t+2} - K^*) + B(K_{t+1} - K^*) + A'(K_t - K^*) = 0$$

where A is a matrix, B is a symmetric matrix, and K_t, and K^* are vectors of capital stocks normalized by the first good (see McKenzie [22]). Equations of this kind can be shown to have characteristic roots that come in reciprocal pairs so that if λ is a characteristic root then so must be $1/\lambda$ (see McKenzie

[22], Samuelson [38]). So long as $\lambda \neq 1$, catenary motion of the kind we have been describing will result. However, if $\lambda = 1$, then the solution K_t will trace out undamped sinusoidal motion about K^*. This is the cyclic exception to the turnpike theorem which we will discuss in the next section. McKenzie excludes this possibility by simply assuming that the characteristic roots of the matrix describing the motion must have an absolute value different from unity. (See McKenzie [22] p. 38, assumption 5.)

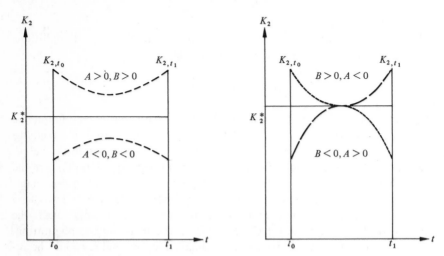

Figure 41. *Possible motions of efficient paths about the equilibrium balanced growth path.*

Finally, it should be emphasized that this version of the turnpike theorem holds only locally; that is, it holds for efficient paths that commence from points that lie in the neighborhood of the von Neumann ray. It does not hold for paths starting from any point because in deriving the equation describing the motion of efficient paths about the equilibrium terms of higher order than the first are ignored in the Taylor expansion. This may be a valid enough approximation for points that lie near the equilibrium, but for more distant points these higher order terms can no longer be treated as negligible, and this invalidates the linearization. However, additional argument may suffice to prove a similar global result; see, e.g. Samuelson [35].

10–7. Exceptions to the Turnpike Theorem

Frequent reference has been made to the case in which the efficient path does not converge to the von Neumann path but instead oscillates about it.

This has been referred to as the cyclic exception, and a sufficient condition to exclude this situation has been to assume that the technology is primitive. The assumption of primitivity can be expressed in two ways.

(i) A technology is said to be primitive if, after a finite number of periods every commodity is produced in positive quantities.
(ii) A matrix A (describing an indecomposable technology) is imprimitive (cyclic) if it can be transformed by permutation into the form

$$\begin{bmatrix} 0 & B_1 & 0 & \cdots & 0 \\ 0 & 0 & B_2 & \cdots & 0 \\ \vdots & \vdots & \vdots & & \vdots \\ 0 & 0 & 0 & \cdots & B_{n-1} \\ B_n & 0 & 0 & \cdots & 0 \end{bmatrix}$$

where B_i are submatrices.

In economic terms this means that the goods being produced can be divided into n disjoint groups such that the commodities of group i produce only those of group $i + 1$. Otherwise a matrix is said to be primitive (acyclic). Clearly any cyclic matrix is necessarily indecomposable, although the converse need not hold. In fact if a matrix A is primitive then there exists a number $n > 0$ such that $A^n > 0$ (see [6]). In other words, when the matrix is primitive, after some finite number of periods all goods will be produced and we obtain the assertion of (i) for the case when the technology is described by an input-output matrix.

The essential problem involved with a cyclic technology matrix can be most conveniently understood by considering its characteristic roots. Suppose we have a dynamic system described by the equation

$$Ax_{t+1} = x_t. \tag{37}$$

The condition for convergence of this system is that all the characteristic roots of A^{-1} are less than unity in absolute value. Note that a system such as this is precisely that described by the difference equation (19) in McKenzie's and by (23) and (24) in Morishima's theorems. If, however, an indecomposable matrix A is also cyclic, then applying a theorem proved by Debreu and Herstein [6] we know that A has at least two characteristic roots of absolute value 1, one of them being 1 and the other not. The other root(s) whose absolute value is unity—whether equal to minus one, or a pair of complex conjugate roots whose absolute value is one—will cause the system described by the equation to oscillate, and furthermore these oscillations do not dampen.

Hence, unless cyclic motion is excluded the optimal path will exhibit undamp-ed motion about the von Neumann equilibrium growth path, in which case the turnpike theorem does not hold.

Morishima [26] has studied the Radner–Nikaido theorem for a cyclic technology set. For each process (x, y) he partitions the commodities into n disjoint subgroups so that the commodities of group i produce only those of group $i + 1$. Both Radner's and Nikaido's theorems are based on the assumption that the von Neumann ray is unique and hence they apply to the case in which the production set is strongly superadditive. Morishima relaxes this assumption to the extent of permitting strong superadditivity to exist between two processes with common products in a given group. More precisely, if two processes (x_1, y_1) and (x_2, y_2) have at least one commodity in common in their jth subgroup, then there exists a process $(x_1 + x_2, y_3)$ such that $y_3 \geq y_1 + y_2$. If (x_1, y_1) and (x_2, y_2) have no commodity in common in their jth subgroup, then he assumes that the processes can be operated additively so that $(x_1 + x_2, y_1 + y_2) \in T$. Finally he modifies assumption (A.7) to

> **Assumption (A.16):** *The preference indicator $U(x)$ is such that $x \geq y \geq 0$ implies $U(x) > U(y)$.*

Following the Radner–Nikaido approach, Morishima shows that in general the optimal path oscillates with period n around the von Neumann ray. If $n = 1$ so that the technology is in fact primitive, the theorem reduces to the turnpike theorem. Alternatively, if the economy is endowed initially with capital stocks of certain specified proportions, even if $n > 1$ the optimal path may converge—but only in a very special case.

Before leaving these cyclic exceptions brief mention should be made of yet another paper by Morishima [27] in which weakened forms of the turnpike and relative stability theorems are obtained. The assumptions necessary for the theorem are

(i) assumption (A.1′) of Chapter 7,
(ii) assumption (A.2) of Chapter 7,
(iii) assumption (A.3) of Chapter 7,
(iv) assumption (A.1) of this chapter, modified slightly to permit $y = y_1 + y_2$, and
(v) the existence of a unique, strictly positive von Neumann output ray.

Under these conditions the theorems then assert that even if the system is imprimitive, the path traced out by the *averages* of the outputs of each of the commodities over the whole period must lie in the neighborhood of the von

Neumann ray for most of the planning period if it is finite, or else converge to it in the case of an infinite horizon. Accordingly, these theorems have been named mean turnpike and mean relative stability theorems, respectively. More precisely stated, the averaging process is as follows: at the end of the first period the output of that period is taken as a point on the path; at the end of the second period the average of the output of the first two periods is taken as a further point; at the end of the third period the average of the output of the first three periods is taken, and so forth until the end of the planning period is reached. If the optimal path has exhibited cyclical motion about the equilibrium path, the deviations tend to cancel out by this averaging process, thus enabling the theorem to be established.

Recently a further difficulty regarding convergence to the turnpike has been discussed by Winter [43]. The problem arises when the quantity of some commodity can increase indefinitely at a faster rate than the von Neumann equilibrium and can thus become infinitely large relative to the results obtained by a von Neumann ray. Suppose also that the utility function being maximized depends on this commodity; then the optimal path need not converge to the von Neumann ray. But if the von Neumann price vector is strictly positive it is impossible for the quantity of any commodity to increase indefinitely relative to the expansion at the von Neumann ray. If it did, inequality (17) of Chapter 7 ultimately would be violated. Thus the problem reduces to the possibility of some commodity having a zero price at the von Neumann equilibrium.

In any case, Winter shows that the growth factor λ^* associated with the von Neumann growth path is the maximum *geometric* growth factor at which any commodity can increase indefinitely in an infinite sequence. Expressed in another way, we can say that no commodity can tend to infinity relative to the von Neumann growth factor at an exponential rate. However, the existence of technologies satisfying assumptions (A.1)–(A.4) of Chapter 7 can be established in which the quantity of some commodity does tend to infinity relative to the von Neumann growth factor, but at an order of infinity lower than an exponential increase. On such paths the turnpike theorem need not hold if the utility depends on the commodity that is increasing relative to the equilibrium growth path at this less than exponential rate. By adding further conditions, however, this possibility also can be excluded so that the turnpike theorem will hold again.[24] It is only in Radner's proof that this possibility of unbounded growth of certain commodities is serious, for he does not stipulate a strictly positive price vector which excludes the possibility.

---

[24] The precise condition sufficient to obtain boundedness relative to the von Neumann path is that $\lambda_1 < \lambda^*$ where λ_1 is the maximum balanced growth factor of the subgroup of commodities whose prices are zero in the equilibrium price vector p^*.

10–8. Consumption-Turnpike Theorem and its Relationship to Final State Turnpike Theorems

The problem of determining the optimal path[25] for an economy in which the objective is to maximize the utility functional of consumption over some time period, subject to given initial and final capital stocks, will be studied at length in Chapter 11. It will be seen that these consumption-optimal paths also give rise to turnpike behavior, and it is of some interest to relate the turnpike emerging from these models to those resulting from efficient growth. Unlike the models we have been considering in this chapter, most of these are aggregate models in which labor is a primary resource that grows at some exogenously given rate. By an argument similar to that outlined in Section 10–6, provided there is no time discounting, the capital stock k on the optimal path of these models can be shown to exhibit catenary behavior about the Golden Rule level of capital stock k^* (see Samuelson [35]). Again the catenary motion implies that commencing with a given capital stock k_0 the optimal growth path of capital stock arches towards the Golden Rule level capital stock k^*, which acts as the turnpike, and then finally veers away towards the final capital stock k_T.[26] It can be shown also that as the time interval increases the proportion of the time *spent in the neighborhood* of the turnpike increases.[27]

Another aggregate model is used by Atsumi [1] in establishing the consumption turnpike theorem along lines used by Radner. He uses a two-good model in which one commodity is a pure consumption good, whereas the other is a pure capital good. Production takes place under constant returns to scale. Utility is taken to be a function of per capita consumption, and he examines the path that maximizes the sum over time of undiscounted utility. It is found that the balanced growth path yielding the maximum per capita consumption is efficient and is the only balanced growth path to be so. Using Radner's lemma, Atsumi proves two theorems. The first states that any utility maximizing path starting with positive initial capital converges to the maximal balanced growth ray. The second is a turnpike result and says that if the final stock is given and less than some critical value, there is a number c, independent of the length of the planning horizon T, which is an upper limit to the number of periods that an optimal path can be outside a prescribed neighborhood of the maximum balanced growth ray. The critical value is the largest value of the capital/labor ratio for which a balanced growth path exists.

Radner [32] has explored in great detail the implications of different criteria for the path of optimal growth. He deals with an n commodity

[25] The reader is advised that he may find it useful to reread this section after he has studied Chapter 11.

[26] Note that if utility is discounted the Modified Golden Rule level of capital stock becomes the turnpike (see, e.g., Cass [3]).

[27] The consumption turnpike theorem can be generalized to n variables.

multi-sector economy and formulates four criteria, two of which correspond
to those we have been considering here. These are

(i) Maximize the total discounted welfare, $U = \sum_{t=1}^{T} \gamma^{t-1} U_t(K)$ given $K(0)$,
where K is a vector of stocks of the commodity, U_t is the utility of period
t, and γ is the discount factor.
(ii) Maximize the final period utility $U_T(K_T)$ given $K(0)$ and $K(T)$.

He assumes that production is "fully regular," meaning that the production
set has constant returns to scale, is primitive, and is indecomposable. In order
to achieve more explicit results he also assumes a Cobb–Douglas production
function for each sector. Finally, he also considers two situations: the first
in which primary resources are present and necessary for production, the
second in which they are absent from the economy. The long-run behavior
of the optimal growth path is found to depend crucially on whichever of these
two situations prevails.

Radner's results are too numerous to be reported in detail here; nevertheless,
we can refer to some of those more directly relevant to our discussion.
According to criterion (i), if there are no primary resources the optimal path
grows proportionately in the long run at a rate depending on γ and the
relative long-run proportions are independent of the initial stock $K(0)$. It
is also shown that as γ, the discount factor, tends to one the optimal path
tends to the path of fastest proportional growth (the von Neumann ray).
If primary resources are present, each produced commodity grows asymptotically at a constant rate independent of γ. The growth factors (one plus
the growth rate) of the commodities are weighted geometric means of the
growth factors of the primary resources and may vary from one commodity
to another. However, if there are constant returns to scale and if all primary
resources grow at the same rate, long-run proportional growth follows.
With the second criterion and no primary resources, for large T the optimal
path behaves approximately as the limit as $\gamma \to 1$ of the optimal path according to criterion (i). Hence when there are no primary resources present and
the discount factor equals unity, the paths optimal to criterion (i) and
criterion (ii) both tend to the von Neumann ray. When there are primary
resources growing at a constant rate, the solution of (ii) does not correspond
to a solution of (i) for any value of $\gamma \leq 1$.

Radner's paper throws considerable light on the sensitivity of the optimal
path to the criterion adopted. It can also help us relate the consumption
turnpike to the von Neumann ray. In the consumption turnpike theorem
labor is a primary resource and therefore the path optimal with respect to a
utility function defined over the path tends to a balanced growth path along
which all outputs grow at the same rate as labor. In the final state turnpike
theorem, however, there are no primary resources and the optimal path
tends to the von Neumann ray as we have seen. Along this ray the rate of
growth is determined by the rate of growth of the slowest growing sector,

provided the economy is indecomposable. Hence, only if the growth rate of labor sets the von Neumann rate will the rates of growth along the two turnpikes be identical. Furthermore, Radner's results imply that in this case there is no reason to expect that the output configurations along the two turnpikes will coincide. In making these comparisons it should be borne in mind that Radner's results have been obtained for the very special case of Cobb–Douglas production functions. However, if the two turnpikes are not identical in this case they will certainly not be for more general technologies.

Recently this problem of determining the optimal path that maximizes the sum of a utility stream over time for a multisector economy has been given further treatment by a number of authors (see, e.g., Atsumi [2], Gale [12], McKenzie [24], Samuelson [36, 37, 38], Tsukui [42]). Gale, assuming an infinite planning horizon and a constant exogenous labor growth rate, shows that any path that maximizes a strictly concave utility function defined on the stocks of inputs and outputs will converge to an activity vector of inputs and outputs that grows at the labor growth rate. Recently this result has been generalized somewhat by McKenzie [24]. Atsumi [2], also assuming an infinite planning horizon, studies a closed model of production in which part of the output is withdrawn from the system for consumption purposes. He defines the concept of an efficient steady-state accumulation program and establishes conditions for a steady-state program to be efficient. Then, defining the criterion of optimality to be the maximization of a discounted sum of consumption utilities, he proves that such an optimal path must tend to that particular efficient steady-state program along which the rate of growth is given by

$$g^\alpha = \frac{1}{\lambda^* \gamma}$$

where

g = growth factor of the economy,
α = elasticity of the marginal utility, assumed constant for all goods,
γ = discount factor, assumed to be less than one, and
λ^* = von Neumann growth factor.

Tsukui considers a finite time horizon and a von Neumann technology with a constant growing labor force. Requiring slightly more stringent assumptions, he shows that the optimal consumption path will display catenary motion about a consumption vector along which the consumptions of all goods grow at the labor growth rate. He also shows that the optimal output path will similarly arch around the von Neumann turnpike which also grows at the same rate.

There is no need to give further discussion of these works here, and for details the reader should consult the original papers. Finally, passing reference should also be made to recent work by Samuelson [36] in which he studies the optimality properties of a similar model by converting the problem into a von Neumann model in which labor is produced within the system. This transformation is performed by treating consumption as a necessary input into the supply of labor, thereby deriving a closed " pseudo-von Neumann model." The turnpike for this latter model is known to have catenary properties, thus implying catenary motion for the optimal path of the original model.

10–9. Summary

We have completed our brief survey of the standard turnpike theorems and the related problems of efficient economic growth. Before concluding, however, it is desirable to review some of the assumptions on which these theorems have been based. The logical starting point is the von Neumann · model described in Chapter 7, since this model forms the basis for the turnpike analysis of the present chapter.[28]

Without doubt the least tenable feature of the von Neumann model is that it is a closed model of production and does not permit consumption as an end in itself. The whole motivation of such an economy is to accumulate, keeping consumption at a minimum subsistence level at which the supply of labor is perfectly elastic. That this is not entirely realistic is obvious. In the model there is no place for consumers' choice; prices, interest, and output are determined purely by supply conditions. In fact, the best characterization of the von Neumann model and closed models in general is that they focus attention on those parts of the price, interest, and output determining mechanism that depend on the technological supply conditions alone. Since the model is concerned with very long-run equilibrium, and since in the very long run there is some justification for claiming that supply conditions essentially determine prices and outputs, the model may not appear as untenable as at first sight. In Chapter 7 we indicated generalizations of the von Neumann model to include consumption, but with few exceptions these extensions have not been carried over to the turnpike theorems.[29]

---

[28] For a detailed criticism of the von Neumann model, see Champernowne [4].

[29] Two exceptions appear in a paper by Morishima [29]. The first is a weak theorem that shows that all paths efficient with respect to the final state converge in the sense that the average output per man—discounted at the von Neumann growth factor λ^*—over T periods for each good approximates the per capita output as $T \to \infty$. Formally, if ℓ is number of laborers and x^*/ℓ^* is per capita output on the von Neumann ray we have

$$\frac{x_j(1)/\lambda^* + x_j(2)/\lambda^{*2} + \cdots + x_j(T)/\lambda^{*T}}{\ell(1)/\lambda^* + \ell(2)/\lambda^{*2} + \cdots + \ell(T)/\lambda^{*T}} = \frac{x^*}{\ell^*}, \qquad (j = 1, \ldots, n).$$

If the assumption of strong superadditivity—not used in the proof of the weak theorem—is added, the strong turnpike theorem (i.e., the convergence of each $x_j(t)/\ell(t) \to x^*/\ell^*$) is obtained. The other theorems prove similar weak convergence when the criterion is the utility of a discounted average of consumption and the discounted average of the number of workers. Again strong superadditivity yields the strong turnpike result.

Tsukui [42] also includes consumption in his turnpike theorem where the objective is to maximize an undiscounted sum of consumption utilities.

Another questionable assumption implicit in the closed model is the existence of unlimited amounts of factors of production. In equilibrium, all outputs, including factors of production, are assumed to grow at a steady maximal rate. Clearly this assumption causes difficulties in the case of factors of production such as land which may be relatively fixed in supply. However, if indecomposability of the system is assumed, the rate of expansion is determined by the good whose supply can be expanded least rapidly, so if land is a scarce factor its slow rate of expansion may set a limit to the growth rate of the economy.

We turn now to the explicit assumptions (A.1)–(A.4) of Chapter 7 which, it should be recalled, are somewhat more general than those required in von Neumann's original paper, although they are still rather restrictive. In the original model there were a finite number of commodities produced by a finite number of processes. In the more general model the number of commodities is still restricted to a finite number, but an infinite number of processes is permitted. The assumption of a constant number of goods being produced over time is itself unrealistic, for innovations invariably give rise to new commodities.[30] This problem could be circumvented by considering sectors rather than goods, since the new commodities could always be classified into some sector. Convexity, implying that any weighted average of two sets of inputs is feasible, is also a fairly stringent requirement, whereas any disposal of excess goods is unlikely to be completely costless. On the other hand, the impossibility of producing something from nothing and the assumption that every commodity can be produced from some set of outputs can be accepted more readily. We should also remember that the system deals with perfect competition, excluding the possibility of positive (excess) profits.

The assumptions we have just discussed are the most general which suffice to prove the existence of a maximal balanced growth path, and since the existence of such a growth path must be established before any turnpike result can be achieved they are therefore also necessary for the proof of the turnpike theorem. However, in addition to the existence of the maximal balanced growth path, the turnpike theorem requires that such a path is unique. By specifying that the transformation set be strictly convex, except on rays through the origin, the required property of uniqueness is ensured. (Rays through the origin must be excluded because of constant returns to scale, i.e., if $(x, y) \in T$, then $(\alpha x, \alpha y) \in T$ for all $\alpha > 0$.)

It has already been observed that Radner's assumptions (essentially those we have been discussing) need only to be moderately strengthened to ensure the strong turnpike theorem in which the optimal path remains within the neighborhood of the von Neumann ray except possibly for a finite number of

---

[30] For a discussion of this problem see Morishima [26].

periods that occur either at the beginning or at the end of the planning period. Recalling assumptions (A.5)–(A.7) of the present chapter we observe that the assumption that something can be produced whatever the initial endowment (A.3) is in fact weaker than the costless disposability assumption necessary for the establishment of the von Neumann theorem, but it is not assumed explicitly by Radner. Also, for certain technologies the requirement that the von Neumann ray be strictly positive, implying that every commodity be produced, is likely to be satisfied, particularly if the technology is indecomposable.

Primitivity is a property somewhat similar to indecomposability, and we have already discussed in some detail its significance in turnpike theory. Here we note one further interpretation suggested by Morishima ([26], p. 162). As mentioned before, a technology is imprimitive if it can be divided into a number, say k, of subgroups s, such that the commodities of group i produce only those of group $(i + 1)$. This means that after k periods the commodities of group i would be used to produce only the commodities of that same group i. Thus, if we view the k time periods as being one new time period, then over this composite time interval the economy would be *decomposable*, even though in any one or all of the k subperiods the technology may be *indecomposable*. Hence the significance of the assumption of primitivity is that it eliminates this possibility of independence among sectors over multitime periods.

Let us recapitulate briefly some of the main results presented in this chapter. We have been concerned with efficient growth paths for both infinite and finite time horizons. In the former case we discussed the result that in a closed economy any efficient path must converge to the balanced growth path. In the case of a finite time horizon, efficient paths were shown to give rise to "turnpike behavior." In other words, such paths were shown to arch about the balanced growth path and three such kinds of turnpike theorems—as well as some exceptions—were studied. Some of the most interesting results that emerge are the *dynamic efficiency conditions* that must be satisfied along any intertemporally efficient path. In the absence of any uncertainty, these conditions, derived from purely technological considerations, are identical to competitive equilibrium conditions in capital markets (see Chapter 8). Provided individuals behave so as to maximize their current net profits and equate returns at the margin, then the capital stock of the economy will follow an efficient growth path. Finally, we have indicated briefly some links between the final state turnpike theorems of the present chapter and the turnpike behavior that results from optimal growth paths in which the objective is to maximize some functional defined on consumption utilities over time. We shall return to this latter question in the next chapter.

References

[1] ATSUMI, H., "Neo-Classical Growth and the Efficient Program of Capital Accumulation," *Review of Economic Studies*, **XXXII**, *90* (April, 1965), pp. 127–136.

[2] —"The Efficient Capital Program for Maintainable Utility Level," *Review of Economic Studies*, **XXXVI** *107* (July, 1969), pp. 263–287.

[3] CASS, D., "Optimum Growth in an Aggregative Model of Capital Accumulation," *Review of Economic Studies*, **XXXII**, *91* (July, 1965), pp. 233–240.

[4] CHAMPERNOWNE, D. G., "A Note on J. von Neumann's Article," *Review of Economic Studies*, **XIII** (1945), pp. 10–18.

[5] DEBREU, G., "The Coefficient of Resource Utilization," *Econometrica*, **19**, *3* (July, 1951), pp. 273–292.

[6] — and I. N. HERSTEIN, "Nonnegative Square Matrices," *Econometrica*, **21**, *4* (October, 1953), pp. 597–607.

[7] DORFMAN, R., P. A. SAMUELSON, and R. M. SOLOW, *Linear Programming and Economic Analysis*. New York: McGraw-Hill, 1958.

[8] DRANDAKIS, E. M., "On Efficient Accumulation Paths in the Closed Production Model," *Econometrica*, **34**, *2* (April, 1966), pp. 331–346.

[9] FISHER, F., "Balanced Growth and Intertemporal Efficiency in Capital Accumulation: Comment," *International Economic Review*, **4**, *2* (May, 1963), pp. 232–234.

[10] FURUYA, H., and K. INADA, "Balanced Growth in Intertemporal Efficiency in Capital Accumulation," *International Economic Review*, **3**, *1* (January, 1962), pp. 94–107.

[11] GALE, D., "The Closed Linear Model of Production," in *Linear Inequalities and Related Systems* (H. W. Kuhn and A. W. Tucker, Eds.). Princeton: Princeton University Press, 1956, pp. 285–303.

[12] — "On Optimal Development in a Multi-Sector Economy," *Review of Economic Studies*, **XXXIV**, *97* (January, 1967), pp. 1–18.

[13] HAHN, F. H., "Equilibrium Dynamics with Heterogeneous Capital Goods," *Quarterly Journal of Economics*, **LXXX**, *4* (November, 1966), pp. 633–646.

[14] HICKS, J. R., "Prices and the Turnpike: (I) The Story of a Mare's Nest," *Review of Economic Studies*, **XXVIII**, *76* (February, 1961), pp. 77–88.

[15] INADA, K., "Some Structural Characteristics of Turnpike Theorems," *Review of Economic Studies*, **XXXI**, *85* (January, 1964), pp. 43–58.

[16] KOOPMANS, T. C., "Economic Growth at a Maximal Rate," *Quarterly Journal of Economics*, **LXXVIII**, *3* (August, 1964), pp. 355–394.

[17] MALINVAUD, E., "Efficient Capital Accumulation and Efficient Allocation of Resources," *Econometrica*, **21**, *2* (April, 1953), pp. 233–268.

[18] — "Efficient Capital Accumulation: A Corrigendum," *Econometrica*, **30**, *3* (July, 1962), pp. 570–573.

[19] McFADDEN, D., "On Malinvaud Prices," Working Paper No. 123, Center for Research in Management Science, University of California, Berkeley (1965).

[20] McKENZIE, L. W., "Turnpike Theorems for a Generalized Leontief Model," *Econometrica*, **31**, *1–2* (January-April, 1963), pp. 165–180.

[21] — "Turnpike Theorem of Morishima," *Review of Economic Studies*, **XXX**, *84* (October, 1963), pp. 169–176.

[22] — "The Dorfman-Samuelson-Solow Turnpike Theorem," *International Economic Review*, **4**, *1* (January, 1963), pp. 29–43.

[23] — "Maximal Paths in the von Neumann Model," paper presented at Boston meeting of Econometric Society (1963), abstract in *Econometrica*, **32**, *4* (October, 1964), p. 691.

[24] — "Accumulation Programs of Maximum Utility and the von Neumann Facet," in *Value, Capital, and Growth* (J. N. Wolfe, Ed.). Chicago: Aldine, 1968, pp. 353–383.

[25] MORISHIMA, M., "Proof of a Turnpike Theorem: The 'No Joint Production Case'," *Review of Economic Studies*, **XXVIII**, *76* (February, 1961), pp. 89–98.

[26] — *Equilibrium, Stability, and Growth*. Oxford: Clarendon Press, 1964.

[27] — "On the Two Theorems of Growth Economics: A Mathematical Exercise," *Econometrica*, **33**, *4* (October, 1965), pp. 829–840.

[28] — "Theory of Growth: von Neumann Revolution," Technical Report No. 130, Institute for Mathematical Studies in the Social Sciences, Stanford University Press, 1964.

[29] — "Theory of Growth: Remodelling and Refinements," Technical Report No. 132, Institute for Mathematical Studies in the Social Sciences, Stanford University Press, 1964.

[30] NIKAIDO, H., "Persistence of Continual Growth Near the von Neumann Ray: A Strong Version of the Radner Turnpike Theorem," *Econometrica*, **32**, *1–2* (January-April, 1964), pp. 151–162.

[31] RADNER, R., "Paths of Economic Growth That are Optimal with Regard Only to Final States: A Turnpike Theorem," *Review of Economic Studies*, **XXVIII**, *76* (January, 1961), pp. 98–104.

[32] — "Optimal Growth in a Linear-Logarithmic Economy," *International Economic Review*, **7**, *1* (January, 1966), pp. 1–33.

[33] — "Efficiency Prices for Infinite Horizon Production Programmes," *Review of Economic Studies*, **XXXIV**, *97* (January, 1967), pp, 51–66.

[34] SAMUELSON, P. A., "Efficient Paths of Capital Accumulation in Terms of the Calculus of Variations," in *Mathematical Methods in the Social Sciences, 1959* (K. J. Arrow, S. Karlin, and P. Suppes, Eds.). Stanford, Calif.: Stanford University Press, 1960, pp. 77–88.

[35] — "A Catenary Turnpike Theorem involving Consumption and the Golden Rule," *American Economic Review*, **LV**, *3* (June, 1965), pp. 486–496.

[36] — "Indeterminacy of Development in a Heterogeneous-Capital Model with Constant Saving Propensity," in *Essays on the Theory of Optimal Economic Growth* (K. Shell, Ed.). Cambridge, Mass.: MIT Press, 1967, pp. 219–232.

[37] — "The Two-Part Golden Rule Deduced as the Asymptotic Turnpike of Catenary Motions," *Western Economic Journal*, **VI**, *2* (March, 1968), pp. 85–89.

[38] — "Reciprocal Characteristic Root Property of Discrete-Time Maxima," *Western Economic Journal*, **VI**, *2* (March, 1968), pp. 90–93.

[39] SHELL, K., and J. E. STIGLITZ, "The Allocation of Investment in a Dynamic Economy," *Quarterly Journal of Economics*, **LXXXI**, *4* (November, 1967), pp. 592–609.

[40] SOLOW, R. M., and P. A. SAMUELSON, "Balanced Growth under Constant Returns to Scale," *Econometrica*, **21**, *3* (July, 1953), pp. 412–424.

[41] TSUKUI, J., "Turnpike Theorem in a Generalized Dynamic Input-Output System," *Econometrica*, **34**, *2* (April, 1966), pp. 396–407.

[42] — "The Consumption and the Output Turnpike Theorems in a von Neumann Type of Model: A Finite Term Problem," *Review of Economic Studies*, **XXXIV**, *97* (January, 1967), pp. 85–93.

[43] WINTER, S. G., "Some Properties of the Closed Linear Model of Production," *International Economic Review*, **6**, *2* (May, 1965), pp. 199–210.

Chapter 11 Optimal Economic Growth

11–1. Introduction

In Chapters 2–9 we studied the evolution of a competitive system in momentary equilibrium at all times, under the assumption that aggregate saving is determined by some simple rule involving only present quantities. In Chapters 8 and 9 we permitted the composition of investment to depend upon prices, as we must do to reflect the behavior of perfect capital markets in which old and new capital goods may be traded, and the reactions of suppliers to the prices so set. But we constrained the total of investment to satisfy some simple aggregate saving rule.

Since saving is the result of a conscious decision, however, it is natural to ask what is a rational saving policy, and how the evolution of the economy would proceed if saving were determined according to such a policy. The most satisfying approach to this question might be to adopt, for each individual, a criterion that reflects consumption over a lifetime (including perhaps a terminal bequest at the end of it), and to permit each individual to determine his saving policy in the light of that criterion.[1] Then we would ask whether such life-cycle saving is consistent, given the age structure of the population, with balanced growth, and whether it is consistent with Phelps-Koopmans efficiency[2] or desirable on some other criterion.[3] Such an approach still would be essentially descriptive: it postulates that the economic system is best described by a model that contains life-cycle saving by individuals and net

---

[1] A study carried out by Tobin [98] suggests that observed saving behavior in the United States could be accounted for by such life-cycle motives. We studied a highly simplified version of such a model in Chapter 2.

[2] This notion of dynamic efficiency was defined in Chapter 2.

[3] We could also ask whether there are general instruments of economic policy that might be employed to influence these individual decisions. We will return to this point briefly later.

worth maximization by investors holding portfolios of capital goods; the descriptive model thus contains individual optimization among its components and the resulting necessary conditions for optimality of individual decisions serve to close the system. Of course the implied aggregate saving behavior may satisfy no simple rules, and it may also fail to satisfy possible criteria for social welfare, as Diamond's model [26] discussed in Chapter 2 demonstrated.

In this chapter we deal with a less ambitious question, an issue that may be interpreted as normative rather than descriptive. We ask how much the community ought to save, in the aggregate, in order to realize a maximum to some criterion of social welfare. Such a question takes us into a discussion of optimal economic growth, outlining how the economy might evolve ideally if it were possible to influence saving decisions by centrally determined social policy, rather than predicting how the economy must evolve when an arbitrary saving rule is prescribed.

The first steps in study of this issue were already taken in the previous chapter, of course. There we dealt with a rather weak criterion of optimality, but one commanding wide acceptance. We defined a path to be *efficient* if it could not be dominated by any other feasible path, and we sought to characterize the class of efficient growth paths in various models. Now in the present chapter we wish to study methods for selecting from the class of efficient paths that path which yields a maximum to a more specific criterion of social welfare. We will see that we may interpret the criterion of efficiency as prescribing the required composition of saving and investment, whereas the explicit social welfare function is necessary to determine the scale of aggregate saving and investment. The efficiency criterion of the last chapter reflects technological possibilities that determine the appropriate composition of saving, whereas explicit consideration of social time preferences and attitudes toward redistribution of consumption over time is required to establish the actual level of saving appropriate to particular circumstances.

11–2. One-Factor Case

The Model

To begin our analysis of optimal capital accumulation, let us consider a simple one-factor, one-sector technology based on a single production function

$$Q = F(K), \tag{1}$$

describing a stream of output produced by the services of a single produced asset and allocated either to consumption or to further accumulation of asset stocks. Thus the national income identity may be written (assuming that realized and potential output coincide)

$$Q = C + I = F(K), \qquad (2)$$

and production possibilities at any instant may be represented by the familiar linear transformation curve displayed in Figure 42. The accumulation equation

$$\dot{K}(t) = I(t) - \delta K(t), \quad K(0) = K_0 \text{ (an initial point to be prescribed)}, \qquad (3)$$

incorporating the tractable assumption of exponential depreciation, completes the system.

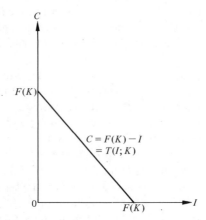

Figure 42.   *Production possibility frontier for the one-sector economy.*

If imposed demand conditions suffice to pick out a point on this transformation curve at each instant, then the whole future of the economy is determined from a given starting point. Until now we have studied the consequences of various arbitrary rules for determining the composition of output in this fashion; now we would like to derive these rules from some more fundamental considerations of social welfare.

Imagine, for example, that a new central government is elected for a term of T years on a platform which promises to "determine economic policy in such a way as to realize the maximum attainable value of the social welfare criterion

$$J = \int_0^T U[C(t)] \exp(-\gamma t) \, dt \qquad (4)$$

(where U is a specified, well-behaved utility function[4] and γ a fixed discount rate) subject to initial capital and labor stocks K_0 and L_0, and to the pledge that terminal capital stocks will not be less than a value K_T." Assume, since the voters approved the proposal, that this criterion accurately reflects desires of the community in general.[5] How is the promise to be implemented?

We observed before that the only issue in this fully employed one-sector economy is to determine the composition of output at each instant. Let us first develop a rather plausible—but not rigorous—argument suggesting how this determination might be made. Afterwards we will verify the general validity of the argument.

Introduction of Asset Price and Decomposition to Static Problem

On economic grounds, perhaps the first consideration to come to mind is that the physical transformation curve displayed in Figure 42 does not really reflect the trade-offs most relevant to a community whose preferences can be described by a utility function $U(C)$. The important decision the community faces at each moment is to trade increased current utility flow against increased investment flow; consumption is relevant only as it relates to utility. Thus, the relevant transformation curve is that displayed in Figure 43, in which the function

$$U = U[F(K) - I] = M(I; K)$$

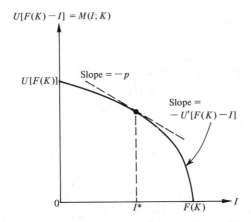

Figure 43. *Transformation curve relating utility and investment.*

[4] By "well-behaved" we mean that the function is strictly concave, monotone increasing in C, with a second derivative defined everywhere, and such that

$$\lim_{c \to 0} U'(C) = \infty.$$

[5] Of course there are substantial reservations about whether any acceptable meaning can be assigned to such an assertion, as Arrow [5] and others have demonstrated. We overlook these difficulties.

is plotted. In Figure 44 the slope of this transformation curve is graphed, emphasizing that (by assumption) the marginal utility of consumption becomes infinite as consumption tends to zero and approaches a positive lower bound as consumption increases to absorb all of output.

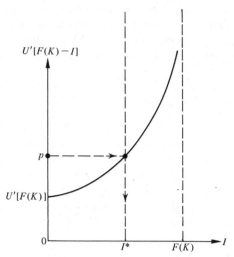

Figure 44. *Marginal utility curve as a function of investment rate.*

Now suppose that we knew what value to put upon an increase in the rate of investment. (We have a difficulty here, in knowing what units to use to specify values. Since the consumption good usually serves as numeraire, our transformation from consumption to utility has the effect of eliminating the natural unit of measurement, and we are forced to measure value in the same units in which the utility function is measured. This unpalatable fact highlights for us the artificiality involved in assuming that there exists a utility function suitable to the role we have assigned it.[6] For our purposes we can ignore this issue and treat all prices as composites containing both the usual price and the marginal utility of income.) Given such a valuation p we can suggest a plausible rule for determining the composition of output, namely

(i) If $U'(C) > p$ and $C < F(K)$, then C should be increased, whereas if $U'(C) > p$ and $C = F(K)$, then no improvement is possible.
(ii) If $U'(C) < p$, then C should be decreased. **(5)**
(iii) If $U'(C) = p$, then no improvement is possible.

[6] It should be emphasized, for example, that rankings assigned by the welfare criterion J in (4) are not invariant under strictly increasing transformations of the instantaneous utility function U; thus, we cannot avoid the strong assumption that $U(C)$ is a suitable cardinal measure of utility. (Of course strictly increasing transformations of J itself preserve rankings.)

More familiarly, we are arguing that the composition of output should be so determined as to bring the marginal utility of consumption into equality with the social value of an increment in investment, or if this equality cannot be achieved, then the entire output flow should be consumed. (The absence of a corresponding boundary case with investment of all output is, of course, due solely to our assumption that the marginal utility increases without bound as consumption falls to zero.) Thus we are arguing that if the true social value of an increase in investment were known, the composition of output could be determined by a very conventional calculation—indeed, by precisely the rule that the value of output (evaluated in utility units at the imposed relative price) should be a maximum. This rule gives the usual tangency condition shown in Figure 43. In still other words, we may treat $U'(C)$ as the supply price of a unit of investment which measures the utility loss due to an increment in the rate of investment. Treating p as the demand price of a unit of investment, our rule is simply that as long as the demand price exceeds the supply price, the output of investment goods should increase, constraints permitting, whereas if the demand price falls short of supply price, output should contract. (As before, we are assuming this adjustment to be carried out instantaneously so that this product market is always in equilibrium. Figure 44 thus portrays this market and its equilibrium output.)

Determination of the Asset Price

Faced with the need for a perfect asset price that correctly reflects the value to the community of an increase in investment, we might appeal to asset valuation based on the present value of all future rentals on the grounds that this measure is the best estimate of the value of the increment to output made possible by the marginal machine. This reasoning suggests that the asset price ought to be

$$p(t) = \int_t^T R(\tau)\exp[-(\delta + \gamma)(\tau - t)] \, d\tau + p_T \exp[-(\delta + \gamma)(T - t)] \qquad (6)$$

where $R(\tau)$ is the value of the marginal product of capital at time τ, p_T is the (unknown) "scrap" value of the asset at the terminal time T, and the exponential decay factor reflects both time discount and physical deterioration.[7] Assuming that an interior solution to the problem of output composition is always found,[8] then the imputed rental $R(\tau)$ can be estimated by

$$R(\tau) = U'[C(\tau)]F'[K(\tau)]. \qquad (7)$$

[7] Thus we are implicitly assuming that the instantaneous money rate of interest (r_0) is always equal to the social rate of time preference γ imposed in (4).

[8] If this assumption does not hold, then the value of the marginal output flow could not be assumed, as it is here, independent of its allocation between additional consumption or investment.

Differentiating the expression for $p(t)$ with respect to t and substituting for $R(\tau)$, we find

$$\dot{p}(t) = -U'[C(t)]F'[K(t)] + \gamma p + \delta p \tag{8}$$

with terminal condition

$$p(T) = p_T. \tag{9}$$

If this decomposition based on plausible but not rigorous economic reasoning is correct, we may summarize the computational issue in the following differential equation problem

$$\dot{K} = I - \delta K, \qquad\qquad\qquad K(0) = K_0$$
$$\dot{p} = -U'[F(K) - I]F'(K) + (\gamma + \delta)p, \qquad p(T) = p_T \tag{10}$$

where I satisfies

$$U'[F(K) - I] \geq p, \qquad (U' - p)I = 0.$$

The task of the planning agency is two-fold:

(i) To select a value for p_T that ensures adequate terminal capital, and
(ii) To solve the differential equation (two-point boundary value) problem (10) for the assigned value of p_T.

The agency could present the solution in a number of different ways. It could, first of all, simply solve for $I(t)$ as a function of time. Such a so-called *open loop* control determines the investment rate for the entire plan period and thus determines the capital stock and output flows throughout the entire plan period. The community need never know that asset prices p had been computed. Alternatively, the agency could publish the price $p(t)$, and then the short-run output composition rule (5) would determine I as a function $I(p, K)$. Finally, the agency could synthesize a *feedback* control, solving for a function $I(K)$ displaying investment as a function of the capital stock at each instant. This true *saving policy* again is conceived to be implemented by central control.

We may note in passing that if we sought a decentralized mechanism for implementing the feedback policy discussed before, we would introduce precisely the asset price p such that individual decision makers would be led to adopt the policy $I(p, K)$—that is, precisely the asset price p computed before. We will return to implications of this observation later.

Still placing our faith in the validity of the reasoning thus far, we can analyze the nature of the accumulation process and of the optimal saving policy. We do this by looking more closely at the implications of the differential equation problem to which we reduced the planning problem.

Qualitative Analysis of Differential Equations System

The final version of the planning problem was formulated as in (10), (where p_T is to be chosen), and in addition we require

$$U'[F(K) - I] \geq p; \qquad (U' - p)I = 0,$$

$$I \geq 0, \qquad K \geq 0, \qquad \text{and} \qquad p \geq 0.$$

Let us consider the possibility of an equilibrium state $\dot{K} = \dot{p} = 0$. Such an equilibrium would require

$$I = \delta K > 0 \qquad \text{if} \qquad K > 0$$

and

$$p = \frac{U'[F(K) - \delta K]F'(K)}{(\gamma + \delta)} \tag{11}$$

$$= \frac{pF'(K)}{\gamma + \delta} \qquad \text{if} \qquad K > 0.$$

Thus, if there is to be any positive equilibrium solution, it can only be at a value K^* such that

$$F'(K^*) - \delta = \gamma; \tag{12}$$

that is, at a capital stock such that the own-rate of return net of depreciation is equal to the imposed rate of time preference γ. At this capital stock a constant equilibrium price

$$p^* = U'[F(K^*) - \delta K^*] \tag{13}$$

is determined.[9]

---

[9] The point $(0, \infty)$ is also a possible equilibrium state for the system. For $K = 0, p < \infty$, we have $\dot{p} = -\infty$, and the nonnegativity constraint $p \geq 0$ becomes binding, at which point the differential equation for p fails to hold.

In addition, motion up the vertical line $K = \bar{K}$ toward an equilibrium at $(\bar{K}, \infty)$ is also consistent with the equations (10). Motion along the horizontal axis $p = 0$ is not. We therefore confine our discussion throughout the following to the interior of the region bounded by $K = 0, K = \bar{K}, p = 0$.

Turning to trajectories with changing prices and stocks, it is helpful to determine the locus of points on which one or other of the variables is momentarily constant. For the case in which there is equality between what we may call the demand price p and the supply price $U'(C)$ of the investment good, we may write the price equation either as

$$\frac{\dot{p}}{p} = -[F'(K) - (\gamma + \delta)]$$

or as

$$\frac{\dot{U}'}{U'} = -[F'(K) - (\gamma + \delta)],$$

the latter equation eliminating all reference to the price p. From the former equation we conclude that $\dot{p}$ is zero only on the locus of points

$$K = K^*$$

in the (K, p) plane.

Inverting the side condition

$$U'[F(K) - I] = p$$

we obtain

$$I = -U'^{-1}(p) + F(K),$$

and observing that the condition

$$\dot{K} = 0$$

requires

$$I = \delta K,$$

we may conclude that $\dot{K}$ is zero only on the locus of points $N(p, K)$ satisfying

$$F(K) - \delta K = U'^{-1}(p). \tag{14}$$

Figure 45 illustrates a graphical determination of the shape of this curve.

With the additional information just developed, we may plot a phase

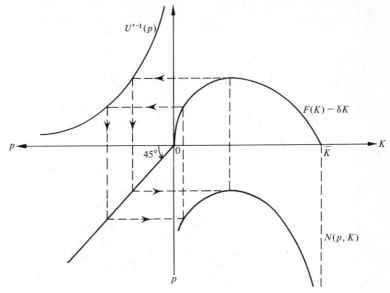

Figure 45.   *Graphical determination of the curve* $U'^{-1}(p) = F(K) - \delta K$.

diagram for the system as in Figure 46. From this diagram we may determine what the value of p_T must be to ensure satisfaction of the pledge that $K(T) \geqq K_T$, and thus may characterize the accumulation path to be followed.[10] For the choice of initial and terminal values illustrated, for example, and assuming that the trajectory never enters the shaded region where production is specialized to consumption, the optimal path is indicated by the heavily drawn arc $p_0 - p_T$.

It might happen that capital is initially so plentiful that all output can be consumed. In this case we must deal explicitly with the boundary case $I = 0$. The system equations under these circumstances become

$$\dot{K} = -\delta K$$
$$\dot{p} = -U'[F(K)]F'(K) + (\gamma + \delta)p \tag{15}$$

with appropriate boundary conditions. Trajectories for this system are indicated in the shaded region only, which is the only region in which the

[10] If the value prescribed for K_T is very small, then the attempt to finish the plan period with $K(T)$ exactly equal to K_T could force the economy to forego desirable capital accumulation earlier in the planning period. In this case it is plausible to expect that we would wish to formulate a flexible terminal condition to satisfy $K(T) \geqq K_T$; namely, that $p(T)[K(T) - K_T] = 0$. Thus the optimal policy will terminate with excess capital only if the demand price for that capital is zero.

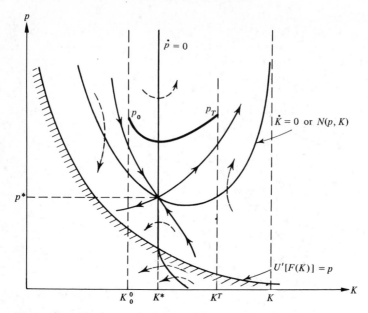

Figure 46. *Phase portrait for the planning problem of Section* 11-2.

boundary case applies. One possible sequence of events, then, is that capital is so plentiful initially that all output may be consumed. In this situation capital decumulates, and the price for investment goods rises, ultimately to equal the marginal utility of consumption if all output is consumed. At this point the system switches into its interior mode, with output divided between consumption and investment. Thereafter the system may continue to follow a path with rising price for investment and gradually slowing rate of capital decumulation. (Of course nothing we have said so far guarantees that only one such switch point will occur; this question is studied in detail by Arrow [4].)

The time required to traverse the distance between fixed initial and terminal values K_0 and K_T can be expected to increase as trajectories enter smaller neighborhoods of the fixed point (K^*, p^*), near which the velocity of the system point is very low. Thus, in other words, we see that as the plan period becomes longer the system tends to spend an increasing proportion of the period in the vicinity of the particular value K^*. Further, we might conjecture that if the problem remains meaningful even as the plan period becomes infinitely long, then the economy would tend asymptotically to this stationary point (K^*, p^*). This conjecture will be developed more fully and verified later.

This simple example has occupied rather a lot of space, but if our original argument as to the decomposition can be taken as correct, we have a fairly complete solution to the question of the optimal saving policy. The techniques of analysis illustrated in this example are of general application and are widely used in optimal planning models. Before turning to the complications introduced by consideration of labor force and population growth, we must now justify more formally the economic argument we have just developed.

Solution by Calculus of Variations

We wish now to establish more rigorously the results of the economic argument we have just given. Returning to the problem as originally posed, we recall that the mandate to the planning agency was to maximize

$$J = \int_0^T U(C)\exp(-\gamma t)\, dt$$

subject to

$$\dot{K} = I - \delta K = F(K) - C - \delta K,$$

and

$$
\begin{aligned}
K(0) &= K_0, &&\text{a prescribed constant,} \\
K(T) &\geq K_T, &&\text{also a prescribed constant.}^{11}
\end{aligned}
$$

Substituting for C in the integrand function yields

$$J = \int_0^T U[F(K) - \dot{K} - \delta K]\exp(-\gamma t)\, dt, \qquad \textbf{(16)}$$

to be maximized subject to the given end conditions and to the requirement that neither consumption nor investment (nor the capital stock itself) be negative. Leaving this nonnegativity constraint aside for later check, we may view the problem as a conventional question in the calculus of variations. (Several texts provide excellent discussion of this topic: one of the classic references is Bliss [12]; Akhiezer [1] and Gelfand and Fomin [39] both provide comprehensive accounts; and Dreyfus [32] surveys results without providing proofs.)

Before beginning to calculate, we must ensure that the problem is meaningful and consider more precisely what policies should be regarded as admissible. In the first place, there is little point in going further if the criterion function can be made infinite by any of a number of policies. This possibility is ruled out, however, by the assumption that the utility function U itself is

---

[11] For the moment we will assume that the end condition $K(T) = K_T$ is imposed with strict equality required.

bounded above, so that the integral J is surely also bounded above. (Indeed, for a discount rate γ strictly greater than zero, the assumption that U is bounded above ensures that J remains bounded above even as the terminal time T approaches infinity.) Let us make this assumption for the moment.[12]

Second, let us take the class of admissible policies to be the set of all functions $C(t)$ defined on the interval $[0, T]$ and continuous at all except perhaps a finite number of points at which finite discontinuities occur. Thus, the class of admissible accumulation paths is the class of paths $K(t)$ defined and continuous on $[0, T]$ and having a continuous derivative at all except perhaps a finite number of points in the interval.

To be complete, we ought to verify that the criterion J does indeed attain its least upper bound on this set. Such a proof of existence of a solution to the maximizing problem is possible, but we will postpone the question.

Accepting that the problem is mathematically meaningful, let us turn to identifying an optimal policy. Just as in ordinary calculus problems, the first step in locating an extremum is to screen out points that might yield a solution from points that definitely cannot. In ordinary calculus, this test is carried out by requiring that the first derivative equal zero, since otherwise a small perturbation of the candidate point would improve the value of the criterion. Similarly, a fundamental result of the calculus of variations is that unless the so-called *Euler-Lagrange equation* is satisfied by a particular candidate policy, a slight (admissible) variation in that policy would improve the value of the functional J. (See Gelfand and Fomin [39], Chapter 1.) Thus, a first necessary condition that an accumulation path be optimal is that along that path the Euler-Lagrange equation (or sometimes simply *Euler equation*)

$$\frac{\partial L(K, \dot{K}, t)}{\partial K} = \frac{d}{dt} \frac{\partial L(K, \dot{K}, t)}{\partial \dot{K}}, \qquad (17)$$

where the function L represents the integrand function $U[F(K) - \dot{K} - \delta K]e^{-\gamma t}$, be satisfied. This equation is a second-order differential equation in the function $K(t)$ and must, of course, be satisfied at each instant t in the interval $[0, T]$ except perhaps at points where $\dot{K}$ is undefined because of a discontinuity in $C(t)$.[13] The equation also requires two boundary conditions to determine completely the solution function $K(t)$; these are obtained from the boundary conditions of the maximization problem.

For the example at hand, then, we know that a first necessary condition that a policy be optimal is that it satisfy the differential equation

[12] It has been shown that if this assumption is violated, some version of the St. Petersburg paradox can always be constructed.

[13] Weierstrass-Erdmann corner conditions or the Euler-Lagrange equations in integrated form demand that K remain continuous across such discontinuities. See Akhiezer [1].

$$\frac{\partial}{\partial K} U[F(K) - \dot{K} - \delta K]\exp(-\gamma t) = \frac{d}{dt}\left\{\frac{\partial}{\partial \dot{K}} U[F(K) - \dot{K} - \delta K]\exp(-\gamma t)\right\},$$

$$(18)$$

or, carrying out the differentiation,

$$U'(C)[F'(K) - (\gamma + \delta)] = -\dot{U}'(C) = -U''(C)[\{F'(K) - \delta\}\dot{K} - \ddot{K}] \quad (19)$$

where C represents the expression $F(K) - \dot{K} - \delta K$.

Examining this differential equation, we note that the coefficient attached to the highest derivative is $U''(C)$—or, more generally, is the expression $L_{\dot{K}\dot{K}}(K, \dot{K}, t)$ where L again denotes the integrand function. This suggests, correctly, that we must require $U''(C) \neq 0$ in order to ensure that the solution to the Euler-Lagrange equation is well defined and can, in principle, be solved locally.[14] Further, the *Legendre necessary condition* for a maximum requires, in analogy to ordinary calculus, that this same expression $L_{\dot{K}\dot{K}}$ should be nonpositive at all points along the trajectory defined by the Euler equation. Both the two foregoing requirements are met by our assumption of diminishing marginal utility which ensures

$$U''(C) < 0 \quad \text{for} \quad 0 \leqq C < \infty. \quad (20)$$

It is not true, as we might also have hoped by analogy with ordinary calculus, that some simple strengthening of the Legendre necessary condition provides a sufficient condition for a maximum. Indeed, sufficiency proofs in the calculus of variations are usually troublesome, and in order to avoid distracting from our main theme we will not consider them explicitly at this point.

Along with the necessary condition

$$-\frac{\dot{U}'(C)}{U'(C)} = F'(K) - (\gamma + \delta) \quad (21)$$

derived before, we might write the technological relation

$$\dot{K} = F(K) - \delta K - C \quad (22)$$

explicitly, rather than employing this condition to substitute for C in the Euler-Lagrange equation. This procedure has the effect of casting the

---

[14] Global solution of the two-point boundary value problem is more difficult to ensure. See, for example, Bernstein's theorem as cited in Gelfand and Fomin [39] or Akhiezer [1].

Euler-Lagrange condition as two first-order equations instead of a single second-order equation. The same two boundary conditions continue to apply. Clearly it is only a relabeling of variables to introduce

$$p = U'(C) \tag{23}$$

and write the system

$$\dot{p} = -p[F'(K) - (\gamma + \delta)], \qquad \dot{K} = F(K) - \delta K - C(p) \tag{24}$$

where $C(p)$ is defined by the relation (23). This system is then identical to that previously analyzed provided that the boundary case on page 361 can be ignored. We see, therefore, that analysis of the planning problem by calculus of variations leads to a first necessary condition—the Euler-Lagrange equation—which can be written in the same form as we obtained earlier by strictly economic argument. The calculus of variations procedure, legitimate only when constraints on the choice of functions C or I may safely be ignored, thus supports the economic reasoning outlined before. Moreover, the introduction of the new variable p corresponds closely to a traditional procedure in applied mathematics—one with strikingly direct economic interpretation. To this question we turn in the next section.

The Canonical Form

Rewriting a problem in an equivalent but apparently different form frequently is not only convenient, but also helpful in suggesting further useful development. Such is particularly true of the Legendre transformation (quite distinct from Legendre necessary conditions) alluded to in the closing lines of the previous section. For the problem at hand, which was to find the path yielding a maximum to

$$J = \int_0^T U[F(K) - \dot{K} - \delta K]\exp(-\gamma t)\, dt,$$

subject to fixed end points K_0 and K_T, the Legendre transformation calls for the introduction of a new variable q defined by[15]

$$q = U'[F(K) - \dot{K} - \delta K]\exp(-\gamma t), \tag{25}$$

and requires that we solve this system to obtain $\dot{K}$ as a function of the variables

---

[15] Actually, the usual canonical form would entail an inessential sign change in which one defines $\tilde{q} = -U'(C)\exp(-\gamma t)$ and $\tilde{H} = -U(C)\exp(-\gamma t) + \tilde{q}\dot{K}$. To permit more natural economic interpretation of the procedure, it is convenient to change signs as we have done.

t, K, and q. (This solution may be obtained, at least locally, provided the Jacobian determinant $L_{\dot{K}\dot{K}}$—in the present case just the scalar function $U''(C) \exp(-\gamma t)$—is nonzero. This condition is guaranteed from our previous discussion.)

Thereupon setting

$$\bar{H} = U[F(K) - \dot{K} - \delta K]\exp(-\gamma t) + q\dot{K} \tag{26}$$

where the solution $\dot{K}(t, K, q)$ is substituted, we have an expression that can be interpreted as having t, K, and q as independent variables. Differentiating with respect to q, keeping in mind that $\dot{K}$ is itself now treated as a function of q, we find

$$\frac{\partial \bar{H}}{\partial q} = U'[F(K) - \dot{K} - \delta K]\exp(-\gamma t)\left(\frac{-\partial \dot{K}}{\partial q}\right) + \dot{K} + q\frac{\partial \dot{K}}{\partial q} \tag{27}$$

$$= \dot{K}$$

because of the relation (25) defining q. Moreover, differentiating (26) directly we obtain

$$\frac{\partial \bar{H}}{\partial K} = U'[F(K) - \dot{K} - \delta K]\exp(-\gamma t)[F'(K) - \delta]$$

$$+ U'[F(K) - \dot{K} - \delta K]\exp(-\gamma t)\left(-\frac{\partial \dot{K}}{\partial K}\right) + q\frac{\partial \dot{K}}{\partial K} \tag{28}$$

$$= U'[F(K) - \dot{K} - \delta K]\exp(-\gamma t)[F'(K) - \delta].$$

On the other hand, differentiating (25) with respect to t yields

$$\dot{q} = \dot{U}'[F(K) - \dot{K} - \delta K]\exp(-\gamma t) - \gamma \exp(-\gamma t)U'[F(K) - \dot{K} - \delta K].$$

If the Euler-Lagrange equation (19) is satisfied, then we may rewrite the foregoing to yield

$$\dot{q} = -U'[F(K) - \dot{K} - \delta K]\exp(-\gamma t)[F'(K) - \delta].$$

Comparing this result with (28), we conclude

$$\dot{q} = -\frac{\partial \bar{H}}{\partial K}$$

if and only if the Euler-Lagrange equation is satisfied. Thus, the conditions defining an optimal policy may be written in the equivalent form

$$\bar{H} = U[F(K) - \dot{K}(t, K, q) - \delta K]\exp(-\gamma t) + q\dot{K}(t, K, q)$$

$$\dot{K} = \frac{\partial \bar{H}}{\partial q} \tag{29}$$

$$\dot{q} = -\frac{\partial \bar{H}}{\partial K} = -U'[F(K) - \dot{K} - \delta K]\exp(-\gamma t)[F'(K) - \delta].$$

For convenience we may go one step further, introducing $p = q \exp(\gamma t)$ and $H = \bar{H} \exp(\gamma t)$. (These adjustments simply have the effect of transforming values to undiscounted or current units.) Then also

$$\dot{p} = \dot{q} \exp(\gamma t) + \gamma q \exp(\gamma t)$$

$$= -U'[F(K) - \dot{K} - \delta K][F'(K) - \delta] + \gamma p = -\frac{\partial H}{\partial K} + \gamma p,$$

so

$$\dot{p} = -p[F'(K) - (\gamma + \delta)] \quad \text{and} \quad \dot{K} = \frac{\partial H}{\partial p}. \tag{30}$$

These canonical equations describing the solution path, and equivalent to the system derived before, have the advantage of reducing the Euler-Lagrange condition to a first-order system directly involving economically natural variables.

There is a further point. Let us recall our hypothesis as to the shape of U and our agreement to postpone consideration of possible constraints on the choice of C, I, or $\dot{K}$, acting as if such constraints were never binding. Under these conditions, we could define p not by the relation

$$p = U'[F(K) - \dot{K} - \delta K],$$

as we did before, but by the equivalent condition that

$$H(p, K, t) = \max_{I} U[F(K) - I] + p(I - \delta K); \tag{31}$$

that is, we define p by the condition that I be selected at all times to maximize H. Thus, when there are no binding constraints on I so that only interior maxima are encountered in this "static" maximization problem, we may write the first necessary condition for a maximum to the social welfare function as follows: Let

$$H = U[F(K) - I] + p(I - \delta K).$$

Then to be optimal an admissible path $K(t)$ must satisfy

$$\dot{K} = \frac{\partial H}{\partial p}$$

where   (32)

$$\dot{p} = -\frac{\partial H}{\partial K} + \gamma p$$

and I is so selected as to maximize H at each instant. That is, on an optimal path I is selected to ensure that the condition

$$p = U'[F(K) - \dot{K} - \delta K]$$

holds identically in $[0, T]$.

The form of H deserves further comment. We may interpret H as the utility of the consumption flow optimally determined at each instant, plus the value of net investment evaluated at prices reflecting marginal utility. It is, in other words, the value of net national product measured in the units employed in the criterion function. Our rule thus says that the composition of output must be chosen at each moment so that this value of net national product is as great as possible, taking the capital stock K and the price p to be fixed.

Finally, then, we may argue that an economic system satisfies the first necessary condition for an optimal policy if it

(i) Satisfies the static efficiency conditions that select an optimal composition of output for fixed price p and capital stock K;

(ii) Satisfies the dynamic efficiency condition that forces the asset price p to change over time in such a way that the capital good always yields a net rate of return equal to the imposed social rate of time preference γ; and

(iii) Satisfies the condition of long-run foresight that establishes the terminal price p_T (or the initial price $p(0)$) at precisely the level that ensures the required terminal capital stock.

If the rate of capital accumulation were not bounded above or below, these plausible conditions would complete the determination of the optimal path.

(There would, of course, remain a significant problem of actually computing that path.) But obviously we must recognize that neither consumption nor gross investment can be negative in a closed economy. We must therefore recognize that the rate of capital accumulation is bounded both above and below, and hence output might at some prices be specialized entirely to consumption. (We have ruled out the case that output be specialized entirely to investment by our assumption that $U'(C)$ tends to infinity as C approaches zero.) If specialization occurs, the equivalence of the conditions

$$p = U'[F(K) - \dot{K} - \delta K]$$

and

$$H = \max_{I} U[F(K) - I] + p(I - \delta K),$$

on which the preceding discussion depended, no longer holds. The next section employs the method of Pontryagin in solving our sample problem, illustrating that this method simply drops the first of the two foregoing conditions and retains the second. The method thus formulates the conditions that hold when the first-order condition for an interior maximum fails and substitutes the usual corner conditions for a boundary maximum. In a very direct sense, therefore, we may think of the maximum principle on which Pontryagin's method is based as being simply the "Kuhn-Tucker" type generalization[16] of the traditional canonical form to the case in which the "static" maximum is attained on a boundary rather than at an interior point of the output space.

Let us recapitulate the discussion to this point. We began with the problem of selecting a saving plan that attains the maximum to a specified social welfare criterion, and then of describing the optimal accumulation path that results. There are two kinds of inequality constraints to be respected, one on the consumption and investment flows and the other on the terminal capital stock.

Economic reasoning suggested that the problem could be solved by the introduction of a shadow price for the capital good. Given this price indicating the value of an additional flow output of machines, the composition of output could be determined, subject to the nonnegativity constraints on all flows. The evolution of the price over time was dictated by the valuation relationship determining the rate of capital gain required at each instant in order to persuade the community to hold the available stock of capital. And the terminal price was determined by the requirement that the constraint on

---

[16] By this expression we mean the general necessary conditions for the solution to a nonlinear programming problem or a nonlinear constrained optimization problem. See Kuhn and Tucker [57] or Arrow and Enthoven [6].

terminal capital stock should be met. Thus, in this method we fix the terminal value of capital, and all earlier values are derived from that benchmark. The price system may then be thought of as flowing backward from terminal valuations, whereas the quantity system flows forward from given initial stocks. The contrast with the results of Chapters 8 and 9 thus centers on the need for sufficient foresight to fix a terminal valuation rather than simply accepting historically given initial prices.

In this way economic reasoning suggests a complete solution to the problem posed. More formally, we examined a solution to the problem (in the absence of nonnegativity constraints and taking a fixed terminal capital stock) obtained by calculus of variations. This analysis led to the Euler-Lagrange equation as a necessary condition for a path to be optimal.

We then observed that the same condition could be rewritten by introducing a Legendre transformation (25) and passing to a canonical form (29). This is simply a notational change and yields conditions equivalent to the earlier Euler-Lagrange equation. We noted that in the absence of nonnegativity constraints the transformation could be introduced indirectly by insisting upon selection of the composition of output (choice of the instrument variable I) so as to maximize the value of the Hamiltonian expression H at each time t. This modification led to (32), a third equivalent way to rewrite the Euler-Lagrange conditions derived from calculus of variations.

When nonnegativity constraints are binding, the requirement (31) that the Hamiltonian H be a maximum at all times ceases to be equivalent to the introduction of the Legendre transformation. Arguing by analogy with Kuhn-Tucker conditions for constrained maximization, we suggested that we should retain the requirement (31) that the Hamiltonian H be a maximum, drop the equation (25) expressing the Legendre transformation, and determine the variable p by the equations (32) and terminal conditions. The justification for this jump lies in Pontryagin's maximum principle. We will not prove the necessity of these conditions for optimality, but will be content with the foregoing justification. Later we will demonstrate sufficiency for a class of cases of interest in economics. A more careful statement of the maximum principle itself is given under the next heading.

The Maximum Principle

In discussion of the maximum principle it is convenient to develop some further terminology. In particular, it is useful to define the gross saving rate

$$s = I/F(K), \tag{33}$$

and to observe that the nonnegativity of both C and I implies

$$0 \leqq s \leqq 1 \tag{34}$$

for all $t \in [0, T]$. This variable $s(t)$ is referred to as a *control*, or *control variable*, and the interval $[0, 1]$ as the *control region* for our problem; the relation $s \in [0, 1]$ is thus called a *control constraint*. The variable K, whose evolution is described by the *system equation*

$$\dot{K} = sF(K) - \delta K \tag{35}$$

is referred to as a *state variable*; a nonnegativity constraint $K \geqq 0$ would then be a *state constraint*, or *state-space constraint*.[17]

We may view our planning problem as that of selecting a piecewise continuous control $s(t)$ satisfying the control constraint (34) and yielding the maximum value attained by the criterion functional J over the class of trajectories corresponding to such controls. Given the discussion of the preceding sections it will come as no surprise that the first necessary condition that a policy—that is, a choice of control $s(t)$—be optimal may be written as follows. Let

$$H = U[(1 - s)F(K)] + p[sF(K) - \delta K]; \tag{36}$$

then a necessary condition that an admissible control $s(t)$ be optimal is that there exist a continuous function $p(t)$ satisfying

$$\dot{p} = -\frac{\partial H}{\partial K} + \gamma p \tag{37}$$

and such that for fixed K and p, H is a maximum with respect to s.

Thus it is clear that if for all t the maximum of H is attained at a value s in the interior of the interval $[0, 1]$, then the system reduces exactly to that studied before. The new possibility introduced is that the condition

$$p = U'(C)$$

may fail to hold at any interior point and the boundary condition

$$s = 0$$

must therefore be substituted in its place. The optimal policy and the motion of the system are still fully determined, but there arises the problem of determining the times of transition (if any) from one phase (with $s = 0$) to the other (with $0 < s < 1$). As we shall see in considering the worked example of the next section, the continuity of the function p and the satisfaction of boundary conditions must determine such transition times.

---

[17] This terminology and the general state-space approach to control problems is discussed in Athans and Falb [8] or Bryson and Ho [14].

Now that the constraints on the system have been introduced explicitly, it is desirable to indicate a direct proof that satisfaction of the conditions just enunciated is sufficient to ensure that a policy is optimal. For this purpose we state Theorem 1.

Theorem 1: *Let a piecewise continuous function $s^*(t)$ be selected such that $0 \leq s^*(t) \leq 1$ and such that the corresponding trajectory $K(t)$ satisfies*

$$K(0) = K_0 \qquad and \qquad K(T) = K_T$$

where K_0 and K_T are prescribed constants. A necessary and sufficient condition that the criterion J attain at s^* its maximum value over the class of all admissible functions satisfying the foregoing requirements is that there exist a continuous function $p(t)$ such that for all t

$$H = U[(1 - s)F(K)] + p[sF(K) - \delta K] \tag{38}$$

attains its maximum at s^* and p satisfies $\dot{p} = -\partial H/\partial K + \gamma p$.

The proof of this theorem is sketched in the Hints to Exercises 7 and 8.

At this point we may summarize our results. We introduced an optimization problem involving a simple decision as to capital accumulation and sketched an economic argument about conditions to be fulfilled along an optimal path. This argument led to a system of two differential equations with a side condition. We then turned to more precise analysis, developing the Euler-Lagrange equation in the calculus of variations, and we found that this condition can itself be written as a second-order differential equation or as a system of two first-order equations. Transforming this condition to so-called canonical form we could assign a direct economic interpretation to the canonical variables K, p, and H, and the introduction of the canonical variable p could be interpreted as arising from the unconstrained maximization of H with respect to gross investment I. Recognizing constraints on this maximization, we were led to introduce possible boundary solutions as described in the more general maximum principle and thus to formulate a system in which transitions between interior and boundary phases had to be permitted. Contemplation of the simple economic optimization problem thus leads to a rather characteristic differential equation structure to be analyzed. Further details of this structure will be considered after a specific example has been developed in the next section for purposes of illustration.

A Worked Example

To illustrate the comments made in previous sections, let us sketch the solution to one example of our planning problem. For this purpose, consider the particular utility function

$$U(C) = \frac{1}{1-v}[C - \bar{C}]^{1-v}, \qquad C \geq \bar{C}, \tag{39}$$

where $\bar{C}$ is a positive constant and v is a positive constant less than unity. Then we note that $U'(C) = [C - \bar{C}]^{-v}$, so that as C approaches $\bar{C}$ (from above), $U'(C)$ approaches infinity. Thus $\bar{C}$ acts as a lower bound on admissible consumption levels.

As a description of production conditions, let us in this example assume that capital does not depreciate, and take the linear production function

$$F(K) = bK \qquad \text{for} \qquad K \geq 0; \tag{40}$$

as a social welfare criterion let us take

$$J[C] = \frac{1}{1-v}\int_0^T [C - \bar{C}]^{1-v}\exp(-\gamma t)\,dt \tag{41}$$

where b and γ are positive constants. For reasons that will become clear we will also assume that the parameters of the problem satisfy

$$b(1 - v) < \gamma < b. \tag{42}$$

Thus our sample problem requires us to maximize

$$J[C] = \frac{1}{1-v}\int_0^T [C - \bar{C}]^{1-v}\exp(-\gamma t)\,dt$$

subject to $\dot{K} + C = bK$, $K(0) = K_0$, and $K(T) = K_T$.

The Euler-Lagrange equation for this problem may be easily derived; it is

$$v\ddot{K} + (b - \gamma + vb)\dot{K} + b(b - \gamma)K = (b - \gamma)\bar{C}. \tag{43}$$

A particular solution to this differential equation is seen to be $K(t) = \bar{K} = \bar{C}/b$. The homogeneous part of equation (43) has the form

$$\ddot{K} - \left(\frac{b-\gamma}{v} + b\right)\dot{K} + b\left(\frac{b-\gamma}{v}\right)K = 0;$$

thus the roots of the characteristic equation are clearly b and $(b - \gamma)/v$. Hence the general solution to the Euler-Lagrange equation has the form

$$K(t) = A_1 \exp(bt) + A_2 \exp(\beta t) + \bar{C}/b$$

where β denotes the root $(b - \gamma)/v$. Applying the boundary conditions to determine the constants, we find A_1 and A_2 are given by

$$[\exp(bT) - \exp(\beta T)]A_1 = K_T - K_0 \exp(\beta T) - \frac{\bar{C}}{b}[1 - \exp(\beta T)]$$

$$[\exp(bT) - \exp(\beta T)]A_2 = \exp(bT)K_0 - K_T + \frac{\bar{C}}{b}[1 - \exp(bT)].$$

Thus we have

$$K(t) = \exp(bt)\left[\frac{(K_T - \bar{K}) - (K_0 - \bar{K})\exp(\beta T)}{\exp(bT) - \exp(\beta T)}\right]$$

$$+ \exp(\beta t)\left[\frac{\exp(bT)(K_0 - \bar{K}) - (K_T - \bar{K})}{\exp(bT) - \exp(\beta T)}\right] + \bar{K}. \tag{44}$$

Let $S(t) = K(t) - \bar{K}$; $S_0 = K_0 - \bar{K}$, $S_T = K_T - \bar{K}$. Then the solution may be written

$$S(t) = \frac{[S_T - S_0 \exp(\beta T)]\exp(bt) + [\exp(bT)S_0 - S_T]\exp(\beta t)}{\exp(bT) - \exp(\beta T)}. \tag{45}$$

What does this imply about the path $C(t)$? We find by straight-forward calculation that

$$C(t) - \bar{C} = [b - \beta]A_2 \exp(\beta t). \tag{46}$$

We have already assumed that $b > \beta = (b - \gamma)/v$; hence, if A_2 is positive, which means

$$S_T < \exp(bT)S_0,$$

then the optimal path just derived entails consumption in excess of the subsistence level $\bar{C}$ at all times throughout the interval $[0, T]$. Further, if A_1 also is positive, which it is if

$$S_0 \exp(\beta T) < S_T,$$

then the investment rate $\dot{K}$ is always positive also. Thus we conclude that, given the restriction

$$b(1 - v) < \gamma$$

on the parameter values assumed, if the prescribed terminal value satisfies

$$S_0 \exp(\beta T) < S_T < S_0 \exp(bT), \tag{47}$$

then the solution to the Euler-Lagrange equation is an accumulation path on which both consumption and investment are always positive. Exercise 11 asks that the reader prove that this path does in fact yield the unique optimum to the problem posed.

Terminal Conditions

Throughout our discussion to this point we have assumed that the terminal time T and the terminal capital stock K_T are specified. Clearly, however, this specification is a very arbitrary matter; we worry about the implications of such an arbitrary choice. There are at least two questions to consider: First, do changes in arbitrarily specified terminal dates or terminal stocks make any significant difference in the computed optimal consumption policies? And second, if the optimal policy is in fact sensitive to these choices, is there no way that the analysis can guide the selection of arbitrary values, or perhaps avoid the necessity for their selection altogether? In this section we will look at the question of sensitivity in the specific example just discussed, and we discuss one approach that brings the determination of terminal conditions explicitly into the analysis. In the next section we approach the same issue differently.

Given the results of the foregoing calculations, it is quite simple to compute the sensitivity of oversubsistence consumption $C(t) - \bar{C}$ to a change in the terminal oversubsistence capital stock S_T. Indeed, we have

$$\frac{\partial[C(t) - \bar{C}]}{\partial S_T} / [C(t) - \bar{C}] = \frac{\partial A_2}{\partial S_T} / A_2 = -1/[\exp(bT)S_0 - S_T], \tag{48}$$

so that the corresponding elasticity measure is $-1/[\exp(bT)S_0/S_T - 1]$. Now, if the oversubsistence capital stock is very small initially, as might be the case for a less developed country, then a relatively small rate of growth in total capital $K(t)$ over the period may entail a large increase in oversubsistence capital $K(t) - \bar{K}$. That is, the likely values for S_T may be close to the upper bound $\exp(bT)S_0$. Under these circumstances we see that the level of oversubsistence consumption may be extremely sensitive to the specification of targets on the terminal capital stock. How, then, can we get away from the need for arbitrary specification of these targets?

One approach is to incorporate the determination of the appropriate target into the analysis by leaving the end point free. Exercise 12 asks the reader to show that in a standard variational problem with a free end point the Euler-

Lagrange equation must be augmented by a further condition, the so-called *natural boundary condition*. Unfortunately, for our present purposes this additional condition leads to inadmissible results, signaling that our formulation of the problem with free end points is inadequate in some respect. Specifically, Exercise 12 shows that the natural boundary condition

$$U'(bK - \dot{K}) \mid_{t=T} = 0 \qquad (49)$$

is derived for our sample problem. For finite K this condition clearly can hold only if we require decumulation of capital at an infinite rate, i.e.,

$$\dot{K} = -\infty,$$

at the terminal time, and this behavior is clearly inadmissible.

The economic reason for the result is obvious: since capital has no value beyond the terminal time T, whereas consumption may be enjoyed right up to the terminal time, the optimal policy must include "eating" of the entire capital stock just before the terminal time. Mathematically there is no solution to the Euler-Lagrange equation in the class of admissible functions $K(t)$; economically there is simply no legitimate policy to meet the demands of an ill-posed problem.

If this is the source of the difficulty, however, we have at hand the means to avoid it. Let us continue to leave the terminal capital stock unspecified, to be determined by the analysis, but let us incorporate the constraint that capital once in place cannot be unbolted and eaten. Thus, reduction of the capital stock cannot yield consumption except to the extent that maintenance and replacement are deferred. To incorporate this plausible constraint requires that we add explicitly the further condition $T \geq 0$ (or, since there is no depreciation, $\dot{K} \geq 0$) so that the problem now reads: maximize

$$J = \frac{1}{1-v} \int_0^T [C - \bar{C}]^{1-v} \exp(-\gamma t) \, dt$$

subject to

$$\dot{K} + C = bK, \qquad \dot{K} \geq 0,$$

and

$$K(0) = K_0, \quad K(T) \geq 0.$$

We have now dropped all restriction on the terminal capital stock, except the restriction that it not be negative. Now the set of admissible functions is constrained in a way that makes a solution on a boundary of the set a real possibility. Output may now quite possibly be specialized at a corner of the production possibility frontier where gross investment is zero. In such a case, we argued before, it is natural to expect the conditions for static optimality to include certain Kuhn-Tucker type corner conditions, and one convenient method for handling these additional conditions, as was described before, is to introduce a canonical form and a maximum principle.

The present problem may easily be formulated in control theory terms. We introduce a control σ, denote oversubsistence consumption by $X(t) = C(t) - \bar{C}$, and continue to denote oversubsistence capital stock by

$$S(t) = K(t) - \bar{K}.$$

Letting $\sigma = \dot{S}/bS$, the problem is to maximize

$$J = \frac{1}{1 - v} \int_0^T X^{1-v} \exp(-\gamma t) \, dt, \tag{50}$$

subject to

$$\dot{S} = \sigma bS, \quad S(0) = S_0, \quad X = (1 - \sigma)bS, \quad \text{and} \quad 0 \leq \sigma \leq 1,$$

where the terminal capital stock is not to be restricted except by a non-negativity requirement that is, in any case, guaranteed by the problem specification. Exercise 13 asks the reader to verify the following result: A necessary condition that a saving policy $\sigma(t)$ and the associated accumulation path $S(t)$ yield a maximum to the criterion J, subject to all the specified constraints, is that there exist a continuous function $q(t)$ defined on $[0, T]$ and such that, defining $\bar{H} = [(1 - \sigma)bS]^{1-v} \exp(-\gamma t)/(1 - v) + q\sigma bS$,

(i) $\dot{q} = -\partial \bar{H}/\partial S$,
(ii) For q and S specified at each instant t, the value of σ yields the maximum of $\bar{H}$ over admissible choices of σ, and
(iii) $q(T) = 0$.

Developing a solution to this particular problem will illustrate procedures in fairly wide use, so we will go through the argument in some detail here. As a first step we place the system in equivalent but slightly more convenient form by introducing a rescaled variable

$$p = q \exp(\gamma t)$$

and setting

$$H = \frac{1}{1 - v} [(1 - \sigma)bS]^{1-v} + p\sigma bS = \exp(\gamma t)\bar{H}.$$

In terms of these rescaled variables, the previous three conditions read

(i) $\qquad \dot{p} = \dot{q}\exp(\gamma t) + \gamma q\exp(\gamma t) = -\exp(\gamma t)\dfrac{\partial \bar{H}}{\partial S} + \gamma p$

$$= -\frac{\partial H}{\partial S} + \gamma p,$$

(ii) At any instant, with p and S specified, the value of σ yields the maximum of H over all admissible choices of σ, and

(iii) $p(T) = 0$.

Thus we seek our optimal policy by solving the differential equation system

$$\dot{S} = \sigma b S, \qquad S(0) = S_0 ,$$

$$\dot{p} = \gamma p - \frac{\partial H}{\partial S}, \qquad p(T) = 0, \tag{51}$$

where

$$H = \frac{1}{1-v}[(1-\sigma)bS]^{1-v} + p\sigma bS,$$

and where σ is determined by the side condition that

$$H = \max \frac{1}{1-v}[(1-\sigma)bS]^{1-v} + p\sigma bS, \qquad 0 \leq \sigma \leq 1.$$

Looking first at the determination of σ, it is clear that there are only two cases to be analyzed. We have

$$\frac{\partial H}{\partial \sigma} = -[(1-\sigma)bS]^{-v}bS + pbS \tag{52}$$

$$= bS\{p - [(1-\sigma)bS]^{-v}\}.$$

For fixed S and p, either there is exactly one value of σ in the interior of the interval $[0, 1]$ at which $\partial H/\partial \sigma = 0$, or else $\partial H/\partial \sigma$ is negative everywhere, so that the maximum of H is attained at $\sigma = 0$. In either case it is easy to derive the behavior of the system.

Case (a): $0 < \sigma < 1$ with $\partial H/\partial \sigma = 0$ at an interior point. The equations in this case are

(i) $p = [(1 - \sigma)bS]^{-v}$,   which yields $\sigma(S, p)$,

(ii) $\dot{S} = \sigma(S, p)bS$,   and

(iii) $\dot{p} = \gamma p - [(1 - \sigma)bS]^{-v}(1 - \sigma)b - p\sigma b = (\gamma - b)p$.

Let us denote by t_1 the time at which the system starts in case (a). Then equation (iii) yields a solution

(iv) $p(t) = \exp[(\gamma - b)(t - t_1)]p(t_1)$.

From equation (i), $p > 0$ for all $S < \infty$. The system cannot enter case (a) with $p = 0$, nor can $p = 0$ be attained in case (a). Assuming $p(t_1)$ and $S(t_1)$ to be known, the trajectory of the system in case (a) is completely determined.

Indeed, the path of the system may then be described by

$$X(t) = C(t) - \bar{C} = p(t_1)^{-1/v} \exp[\beta(t - t_1)]$$

$$\dot{S} = bS - p(t_1)^{-1/v} \exp[\beta(t - t_1)] \qquad \text{where} \qquad \beta = (\gamma - b)/v.$$

Case (b): The boundary case with $\sigma = 0$. The equations of the system become simply

$$(i) \quad \dot{S} = 0 \quad \text{and} \quad (ii) \quad \dot{p} = [bS]^{-v}b + \gamma p. \tag{53}$$

Since S is constant in this case, the foregoing equation yields

$$p(t) = E \exp(\gamma t) + \frac{[bS]^{-v}b}{\gamma} \tag{54}$$

where E is a constant to be determined.

Now we need consider only the possible switches from one case to the other. We know that $p = [(1 - \sigma)bS^{-v}$ in case (a), whereas $p \leq [bS]^{-v}$ in case (b). Further, we know that $\dot{p} < 0$ in case (a), and, letting t_2 be the time of entry into case (b) from case (a), we know that at $t = t_2$

$$p(t_2) = [bS]^{-v}.$$

Hence, at t_2,

$$\dot{p}(t_2) = -[bS]^{-v}b + \gamma[bS]^{-v} < 0.$$

Since S remains constant in case (b), we conclude that if the system switches from case (a) to case (b) at $t = t_2$, it can never switch back to case (a). Moreover, the same argument shows that we cannot switch from case (b) to case (a) at all. Hence, we have only three possible policies to consider.

(i) The system starts and remains in case (a).
(ii) The system starts and remains in case (b).
(iii) The system starts in case (a) and switches to case (b).

Policy (a) can be ruled out immediately by the terminal condition $p(T) = 0$, since we have seen that this condition cannot be realized in case (a). Therefore we know that the optimal policy must terminate in case (b). We may therefore integrate backwards from the terminal condition $p(T) = 0$ to find, from equation (54),

$$p(t)|_{t=T} = E \exp(\gamma T) + [bS]^{-v} \frac{b}{\gamma}$$

which implies

$$E = -[bS]^{-v} \frac{b}{\gamma} \exp(-\gamma T)$$

and hence

$$p(t) = [bS]^{-v} \frac{b}{\gamma} \{1 - \exp[-\gamma(T - t)]\}. \tag{55}$$

This equation completely determines $p(t)$ throughout case (b), terminating at $t = T$. Along this path, of course, $\sigma = 0$ and $S = S(t_2)$, the value at the time of entry to case (b). So long as $p(t)$ given by (55) continues to satisfy $p < [bS]^{-v}$, we have to remain in case (b). Thus we can calculate the time of transition to case (b) by the requirement that $p(t)$ must be continuous at t_2. Thus,

$$p(t_2^+) = [bS(t_2)]^{-v} \frac{b}{\gamma} \{1 - \exp[-\gamma(T - t_2)]\} = [(1 - \sigma)bS]^{-v}|_{\sigma=0} = p(t_2^-),$$
$$\tag{56}$$

where the right-hand side describes the value p must have in case (a) just before the time of transition, and the left-hand side describes the value p must have in case (b) just after the time of transition in order to satisfy the terminal condition $p(T) = 0$. From this equation we find t_2 must satisfy

$$\frac{b}{\gamma} \{1 - \exp[-\gamma(T - t_2)]\} = 1. \tag{57}$$

Hence we conclude that if t_2 so calculated is less than zero, the optimal policy is $\sigma(t) = 0$ for $0 \leq t \leq T$, with an associated path

$$S(t) \equiv S(0) = S_0 \qquad \text{for} \qquad 0 \leq t \leq T$$

and $\qquad\qquad\qquad\qquad\qquad\qquad\qquad\qquad\qquad\qquad\qquad\qquad$ **(58)**

$$p(t) = [bS_0]^{-v} \frac{b}{\gamma} \{1 - \exp[-\gamma(T - t)]\}.$$

If, on the other hand, t_2 so calculated is positive, then the optimal policy is to follow case (a) for $0 \leq t \leq t_2$, and follow case (b) for $t_2 \leq t \leq T$.

It should be carefully noted that all this calculation brings us to a conclusion that is very plausible on economic grounds. The criterion (57) is obviously sensible as a criterion for the time at which investment in new equipment should be discontinued, for the expression on the left-hand side is simply the present value of rentals of b per year, discounted at rate γ, continuing for $T - t_2$ years. (By the terms of our problem, a machine is discarded at time T without scrap value.) Hence, t_2 is established as the time at which the present value of a machine just equals its cost (unity). (Notice that there is actually a factor U' representing marginal utility canceled from both sides of the equation (57). For $t < t_2$, when (57) fails to hold, it is precisely the rising opportunity cost of a machine in terms of foregone utility that results in its cost being brought into balance with its present value.)

Thus our optimal policy may be summarized, for a time horizon T sufficiently long to warrant any investment at all, by the rule that initially the rate of investment should be set so as to equalize the demand price p and the supply price or opportunity cost $U'(C)$. As the demand price p falls, this will entail a rising proportion of output directed to consumption. Eventually, at some time $t_2 < T$, the proportion of output going to investment will fall to zero, and the system will click into case (b). Thereafter the system will refuse to add to the capital stock at all on the simple grounds that the resources devoted to machines cannot be recovered except as machine services, and the time remaining before the terminal date is too short to permit the value of machine services realized to match the cost. Although the mathematics is cumbersome, the conclusion is compelling on economic grounds alone.

To conclude this section, let us use this result to interpret our previous discussion of end conditions. Suppose that following this just-derived rule leads to a path $K(t)$ as shown in Figure 47. Suppose also that we imposed an end condition

$$K(T) = K_T$$

on the problem where K_T is precisely the value that emerges from our optimal

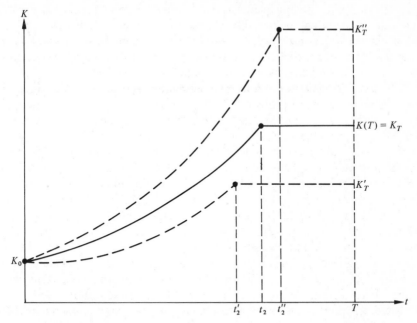

Figure 47.   *Optimal accumulation paths under alternative end conditions.*

policy with free end point; then we know that $p(T) = 0$. In order to realize a terminal capital greater than K_T, say K_T'', we would expect to require a higher price in order to induce greater capital accumulation, whereas to satisfy with exact equality a condition

$$K(T) = K_T' < K_T$$

we should require a lower price to be assigned to capital. Thus we see, contrary to our first reaction, that assigning a very low terminal capital stock as an end condition to be realized exactly may in fact harm the economy, the reason being that such an end condition prohibits capital accumulation that would have been desirable within the plan period. This welfare loss due to a forced shortage of capital is signaled by the appearance of a negative price $p(T)$. The adoption of an inequality constraint as a terminal condition avoids the difficulty, whereas if there were no constraint on the rate of decumulation of capital the problem would never arise in the first place.

11–3. The Ramsey Problem

A number of separate issues have to be considered in studying optimal economic growth. In the preceding section we analyzed the solution to the problem of optimal saving in a one-good economy with stationary population and a finite planning horizon. Characterization of the solution was found to be straightforward once suitable values for the terminal capital stock were specified, and we concluded the section with some discussion of the effect of different choices for the value of the terminal stock.

We saw that the data given to the community include the initial stock of capital and the production possibilities at each moment of the planning period. If, in addition, a saving policy $s(t)$ or a consumption policy $C(t)$ were prescribed throughout the plan, the evolution of the economy would be described completely by a single first-order differential equation subject to the given initial condition. If, however, a more general preference ordering based on some integral criterion function defined over consumption paths is prescribed, from which an optimal saving policy is to be determined, then the analysis leads to a second-order differential equation and we must find a second boundary condition. In general there is no natural way to prescribe this boundary condition at a finite terminal date.

A conventional approach to analyzing a higher order differential equation is to convert it into an equivalent system of first-order equations. This procedure is convenient, particularly in the presence of constraints on the admissible solutions. For planning problems of the type considered in the previous section we saw that there was a very natural translation to an equivalent first-order system. The transformation involved introducing a price variable that acts as the demand price, or social value, of the capital good. Unfortunately the introduction of this auxiliary variable, although it simplified the analysis in some respects, did not provide any natural specification for the remaining boundary condition. Because valuations intrinsically reflect future events—because the value of a machine now depends unavoidably on the value of its services in the future and on its market value at future dates—there is still no natural way to assign terminal prices (or initial prices) without somehow expressing the community's preferences regarding consumption beyond the plan period as compared to consumption within the plan period.

The mathematical problem, then, is that when we convert our second-order Euler equation into an equivalent first-order system, we find ourselves lacking one boundary condition. And this is but a mechanical reflection of a basic economic issue: since prices—asset valuations—sweep backward rather than forward in time, we always need information on prices beyond the horizon in order to close the system. So far as asset price determination is concerned, we are always in the shadow of future events.

Since there exists no natural stopping time and no natural valuation at any finite stopping time, perhaps a better mathematical model of the community's decision problem is to imagine planning for the entire future—that is, to imagine planning over an infinite horizon. It may be that we have no need to be so ambitious; nevertheless, the results obtained from the study of the limiting case, the approximation based on the assumption of an infinite horizon, may better reflect the economic issues at stake than any arbitrary finite-term problem with unavoidably arbitrary terminal targets or terminal valuations. At any rate, the possibility deserves consideration.

Indeed, Ramsey, in his remarkable paper published in 1928 [78] on the question "How much should a nation save?", adopted without discussion a criterion based on consumption over an infinite horizon. The purpose of this section is to consider his influential analysis of this topic.[18]

We may think of this problem as the limiting case of a sequence of problems, each with specified time horizon, as the length of the plan period increases without limit. There are some technical difficulties that have to be kept in mind.

In the first place, since the criterion functional in the limiting case is an improper integral, there arises the question of whether the performance index we are attempting to maximize is in fact bounded above. If not, if the criterion functional assumes arbitrarily large values for a whole class of possible accumulation paths, we have no way to choose between different paths. So long as consumption and utility remain finite for finite capital stocks, this issue would not arise in any finite-horizon problem.

Secondly, although it does arise in the problems we have discussed before, the question of whether there exists any optimal path may be more difficult to decide when the planning period is unbounded. That is, even if the criterion functional is bounded above, it is more difficult to know that the maximum value is actually attained at some admissible path.

A third question is to determine whether there is for the infinite horizon problem any natural terminal condition restricting capital valuations. It is really for the purpose of obtaining such a condition that we are looking to this limiting case. Finally, we may investigate the asymptotic behavior of the optimal paths, asking whether there are any interesting characteristics revealed by the sequence of solutions obtained as the length of the planning horizon increases.

We assume, therefore, as before, that the technology of the community may be described by a production function

$$Q = F(K),$$

[18] We will deviate from Ramsey's discussion in ignoring possible choices between leisure and income; that is, we will ignore the labor supply function and assume that labor is offered inelastically at whatever wage rate prevails. It is an easy matter to extend the model to determine an appropriate rate of labor input, as it would be to handle other variables that can be altered instantaneously (discontinuously if necessary) so as to be always at their optimal value.

a national income identity

$$Q = C + I,$$

and an accumulation equation

$$\dot{K} = I - \delta K, \qquad K(0) = K_0.$$

The preferences of the community may be expressed by an instantaneous utility function $U(C)$ assumed to be concave and bounded above, and by a social welfare function

$$J = \int_0^\infty U[C(t)] \exp(-\gamma t)\, dt.$$

Since the utility function U is assumed to be bounded above, it is clear that the presence of a positive rate of time preference γ guarantees that the improper integral J is also bounded above. However, Ramsey, a distinguished philosopher, suggested that the apparent presence of positive time preference reflected a weakness of the imagination—an imperfect telescopic faculty— and could hardly be appropriate for rational social planners analyzing, on behalf of the community, the intergenerational allocation of consumption. If this outlook is adopted, then we have to face the problem that the social welfare criterion J no longer provides a ranking that can discriminate among different paths. A great many consumption policies, among which a planner (or a citizen) might be able to express clear preference, would all be assigned the value $J = +\infty$ by the criterion function adopted. Ramsey therefore proposes an alternative criterion: the community should determine its saving policy so as to minimize the integral of deviations from the upper bound on the utility function. Now there are two types of saturation that might result in a maximum to $U(C)$. There might be saturation in consumption itself, which involves the existence of some finite value C^* such that

$$U(C^*) = \sup_{C \geq 0} U(C)$$

and thus

$$U'(C) = 0 \quad \text{for} \quad C \geq C^*.$$

Or there might be capital saturation, which involves an upper bound on output, and hence on consumption. Defining $\bar{K}$ by

$$F(\bar{K}) = \delta \bar{K},$$

we see that any solution $\psi(t; K_0)$ to the differential equation $\dot{K} = I - \delta K$ with $K_0 \leq \overline{K}$ satisfies

$$\psi(t; K_0) \leq \overline{K} \qquad \text{for all } t,$$

and, hence,

$$C(t) \leq F(\overline{K}) \qquad \text{for all } t \ [19].$$

Actually we might wish to adopt a different notion of capital saturation by considering net national product rather than gross. In the present case, Q must be considered gross national product since one component of Q is gross investment, I. Then net national product is

$$Q - \delta K = F(K) - \delta K$$

and we can say capital saturation occurs at the point where additional units of capital, after provision for replacement, make no contribution to net output. Then, defining $\hat{K}$ by

$$F'(\hat{K}) = \delta,$$

$\hat{K}$ is the saturation level of the capital stock. Unfortunately, however, this definition of capital saturation does not provide a binding upper bound on consumption or utility at any particular time unless it is agreed that consumption can never exceed net national product; that is, that replacement investment must always be made. Such a rule, though, ought to come *ex post*, not *ex cathedra*.

Indeed, rules will be derived for this kind of capital saturation case in the next section. Here we simplify the discussion by assuming consumption saturation such that

$$C^* = F(K^*) \qquad \text{for some} \qquad K^* < \overline{K}.$$

We define a *Bliss point B* by

$$B = U(C^*) = \sup_{0 \leq C} U(C).$$

Then, following Ramsey, we propose that the community select a saving policy that *minimizes* the expression

$$J = \int_0^\infty [B - U(C)] \, dt$$

[19] If $K_0 > \overline{K}$, we have to determine a policy to run down capital in excess of the maximum sustainable level $\overline{K}$, but $F(K_0)$ then provides a bound on output.

subject to the technological constraint

$$C = F(K) - \dot{K} - \delta K, \qquad K(0) = K_0.$$

Now it is clear that some constant saving policy can be constructed that will permit attainment of $C = C^*$ at a finite time and hence will render J finite. Therefore, by inspection of J it is clear that a necessary condition for any policy being optimal is that

$$\lim_{t \to \infty} U(C) = B,$$

since any policy for which the integral J does not converge cannot be optimal.[20]

The analysis of the problem is little different from that developed before. We set

$$J = \int_0^\infty \{B - U[F(K) - \dot{K} - \delta K]\} \, dt,$$

and the Euler equation becomes simply

$$-U'(C)[F'(K) - \delta] = \dot{U}'(C),$$

which, being of the special form in which time does not appear explicitly, may be immediately integrated to yield the first integral

$$B - U = \alpha + \dot{K} U'(C)$$

where α is a constant to be evaluated. Knowing that along the optimal path $U(C) \to B$ and $U'(C) \to 0$ as $t \to \infty$, and assuming that $\dot{K}$ remains finite, we can conclude that $\alpha = 0$. This yields the first-order differential equation

$$\dot{K} U'(C) = B - U(C), \qquad K(0) = K_0,$$

characterizing the optimal policy. (Notice that the characterization is not really as convenient as it looks, since upon substituting for C to obtain an explicit equation we find the rule to be

$$\dot{K} U'[F(K) - \dot{K} - \delta K] = B - U[F(K) - \dot{K} - \delta K],$$

[20] This conclusion depends upon the fact that B is the upper bound in this consumption saturation case. Since $U(C)$ cannot exceed B, any consumption policy $C(t)$ that fails to converge to C^* must cause the integral J to diverge and hence can be ruled out.

which could be quite cumbersome to solve. Nevertheless, it is an explicit characterization of the optimal path in the problem posed.)

This rule is known as Ramsey's rule. The good Lord Keynes is reported by Ramsey [78] to have suggested an intuitive justification, along the following rather standard lines, for the rule.

How should an economist rationalize this result? Consider the problem of whether or not to increment the flow rate of investment by an amount h for an interval Δt. The resulting utility loss (analogous to a capital cost) may be approximated by the expression

$$h \frac{\partial U}{\partial C} \Delta t = hU'(C) \Delta t.$$

On the other hand, the benefits from the increment to the capital stock arise from the increased output made possible over the future. The increment to the capital stock is approximately $h\Delta t$; the increment to output made possible (net of replacement) is approximately $h\Delta t[F'(K) - \delta]$; the utility gain resulting is approximately $h\Delta t[F'(K) - \delta]U'(C)$. If we integrate this utility gain to measure the present value of the incremental flows, we find

$$\int_t^T h \, \Delta t[F'(K) - \delta]U'(C) \, dt + p(T)$$

where $p(T)$ denotes the value to be assigned to the increment of capital at time T. Equating the capital cost with the present value of the increased benefit flow made possible, we find that investment at any moment should be increased until

$$hU'(C) \Delta t = \int_t^T h \, \Delta t[F'(K) - \delta]U'(C) \, d\tau + p(T).$$

Differentiating with respect to t we find

$$\dot{U}'(C) = -[F'(K) - \delta]U'(C),$$

which is, of course, Ramsey's rule again.

This intuitive argument is reminiscent of the introduction of canonical variables mentioned before. Indeed, suppose that we were to introduce a demand price $p(t)$ for the capital good, and a rental rate $R(t)$ for its service. If we approach the saving problem using a maximum principle, we form a Hamiltonian

$$H = -[B - U(C)] + p(t)[F(K) - \delta K - C],$$

and deduce that a condition necessary for a saving policy to be optimal is that there exist a continuous price p satisfying

$$\dot{p} = -p[F'(K) - \delta]$$

where

$$\dot{K} = F(K) - \delta K - C$$

and C is selected so as to maximize H over $0 \leq C \leq F(K)$. Observing that $\partial H/\partial C = U'(C) - p(t)$, we conclude that if C can always be chosen to make $\partial H/\partial C = 0$, then $U'(C) = p(t)$ and the Euler equation

$$-\dot{U}'(C) = U'(C)[F'(K) - \delta]$$

may equivalently be written

$$\frac{\dot{p}}{p} + \frac{R}{p} = \delta \qquad \text{where} \qquad R = pF'(K) \qquad \text{as usual.}$$

(It should be re-emphasized that the identification of p with $U'(C)$ is an equilibrium condition—a characteristic of an interior solution to the static maximization problem—and not simply a definition.)

Moreover, the conditions that $U(C) \to B$ and $U'(C) \to 0$ entail $p(t) \to 0$. Thus, in this formulation the requirement that the system approach Bliss yields the additional boundary condition—a terminal valuation on the capital good.

The discussion of this section may be quickly summarized. We attempted to extend the discussion of previous sections in order to reflect the fact that economic problems have no natural stopping time and that valuations require consideration of events beyond any finite horizon. The extension to our infinite horizon problem involved some difficulties with convergence of the criterion functional; to circumvent these difficulties we introduced (following Ramsey) a different criterion based upon the existence of some "saturation" path. The new criterion dictated that attention be confined to a limited class of paths, namely those that converged ultimately to the "Bliss" or "saturation" path. This restriction provided a boundary condition that enabled us to evaluate one constant of the Euler necessary condition for an optimal path, and thus it enabled us to derive Ramsey's rule characterizing an optimal policy.

When we attempted to interpret this rule in terms of a conventional balancing of marginal costs and benefits (for durable assets), we found ourselves led back to auxiliary variables of the kind introduced before, and we were thus led to reformulate the problem in terms of these variables. Sketching the necessary conditions for a maximum, we found that the requirement of convergence to Bliss provided the additional boundary condition we had sought, a transversality condition that dictated that the asset price tend to zero in the limit.

A similar transversality condition plays a role in the discussion of the possible inefficiency of competitively determined saving plans. It is useful to keep in mind that the condition was developed here not as a necessary condition arising from variational analysis but from the definition of the criterion itself.

11–4. The One-Sector Model with Labor Force Growth

The Model

So far in this chapter we have studied the problem of optimal saving only under the assumption that the labor force and population are stationary. More generally we wish to study problems arising in an economy that shows an underlying force for growth, most particularly through continuing growth of the population and labor force. In this section we will again adopt the one-sector model familiar from Chapter 2, except that the determination of saving is left open. Instead we select a saving policy that realizes a maximum to some criterion functional purporting to represent social welfare.

There are two distinct issues raised by the fact of a growing population. One is that the labor force and productive capacity grow over time, and continual capital widening is therefore necessary to maintain factor proportions. A second separate issue is that selection of a saving policy entails an allocation of the community's consumption between people now and people later, these latter being greater in number but possibly distant in time, and not present to vote on the allocation issue.

We will concentrate on the production aspect of labor force growth first, adopting for the purpose a criterion functional that will be reconsidered later in this chapter. We assume, then, as before, the existence of an instantaneous utility function $U(c)$, but we argue now that per capita consumption c, rather than total consumption C, is the appropriate index of the community's welfare at any particular moment, perhaps because we anticipate equitable redistribution of goods, in which case $U(C/L)$ is the utility flow attained by the "representative man," or perhaps because per capita consumption simply seems an appropriate measure of the aggregate performance of the economy at any moment. We take as a welfare measure the integral of instantaneous utilities discounted by an exponential weighting factor, so that our criterion functional is

$$J = \int_0^\infty \exp(-\gamma t)U(c)\, dt, \tag{59}$$

provided that this improper integral converges.

The technology of the one-sector model yields a constraint on the optimizing problem, namely,

$$\dot{k} = f(k) - (g + \delta)k - c = sf(k) - (g + \delta)k, \qquad k(0) = k_0 > 0 \tag{60}$$

where

$$c = (1 - s)f(k) \qquad \text{and} \qquad 0 \le s \le 1 \tag{61}$$

and where the additional nonnegativity constraint on the state variable k can be ignored because of the form of the differential equation.

Defining the maximum sustainable capital/labor ratio $\bar{k}$ by the relation

$$f(\bar{k}) = (g + \delta)\bar{k},$$

we see that if $k_0 \le \bar{k}$, then $k(t) \le \bar{k}$ for all $t \ge 0$. Hence,

$$c \le f(\bar{k})$$

and

$$U(c) \le U[f(\bar{k})],$$

and thus convergence of the integral J is guaranteed for $\gamma > 0$.

As in our opening sections of this chapter, we will suppose $U(c)$ to have the following properties:

$$U'(c) > 0, \qquad 0 \le c \le f(\bar{k}),$$
$$U''(c) < 0, \qquad 0 \le c \le f(\bar{k}),$$

and

$$\lim_{c \to 0} U'(c) = \infty.$$

The last property is in no way essential, but it is convenient in excluding the boundary case in which all output is saved.

We thus seek a maximum to (59) subject to (60) and (61). That is, among all feasible accumulation paths satisfying (60) and (61), we seek that which ranks highest in the (rather special) preference ordering adopted here in equation (59).

Sufficient Conditions for an Optimal Path

The problem posed at the end of the last section is in a standard form that should seem quite familiar by now. We have to choose a saving plan $s(t)$ $(0 \leq t)$; when we have done so the differential equation (60) determines an associated path $k(t)$ of capital accumulation. Equation (61) indicates the resulting consumption stream, and the criterion (59) ranks it in the community's preferences. If we could be sure that output would never be specialized either to consumption or to investment, then we could simply apply the traditional calculus of variations and write down the Euler equation (after substituting (60) and (61) into (59)) as a necessary condition that must be satisfied if any path $k(t)$ is to be optimal. Instead we do not commit ourselves on the composition of output and, rather than characterizing the whole optimal path $k(t)$ directly by the Euler differential equation (of second order), we will use the maximum principle to characterize the saving policy at each instant. The maximum principle, it will be recalled, tells us that if a (piecewise continuous) policy $s(t)$ and the associated path $k(t)$—associated through the differential equation (60)—are to yield a maximum to (59), it is necessary that there exist also a continuous (price) function $q(t)$ having the following properties:

(i) Given the Hamiltonian function

$$H = U[(1 - s)f(k)] \exp(-\gamma t) + q[sf(k) - (g + \delta)k],$$

then

$$\dot{q} = -\partial H/\partial k$$

(evaluated at the "candidate" policies s, k under discussion).

(ii) At each time t, for the values of $q(t)$ given by the differential equation in (i), and for $k(t)$ given through (60), the value $s(t)$ yields the maximum to H over all admissible choices of s.

If these conditions are not satisfied, then the value of the criterion function J could be improved by a feasible alteration of the path, and the policy $s(t)$ could not be optimal. Hence, an optimal path must satisfy an auxiliary equation

$$\dot{q} = -U'[(1 - s)f(k)] \exp(-\gamma t)(1 - s)f'(k) - q[sf'(k) - (g + \delta)]$$

where s is chosen to maximize H—i.e., where s satisfies the standard Kuhn-Tucker [57] necessary conditions for an inequality-constrained maximum, namely,

$$\frac{\partial H}{\partial s} \leqq 0, \qquad s \frac{\partial H}{\partial s} = 0, \qquad \text{and} \qquad s \geqq 0.$$

For our purposes these conditions mean simply that there are two cases to consider:

(a) $s = 0,$ $q \leqq U'[(1 - s)f(k)] \exp(-\gamma t) = U'[f(k)] \exp(-\gamma t),$

and

(b) $1 > s > 0,$ $q = U'[(1 - s)f(k)] \exp(-\gamma t).$

To eliminate the inconvenient exponential term involved in these equations we may shift, just as we did before, to a current, undiscounted price

$$p = q \exp(\gamma t)$$

rather than the discounted price associated with the planning criterion J. Thus we find

$$\dot{p} = \dot{q} \exp(\gamma t) + \gamma q = -U'[(1 - s)f(k)](1 - s)f'(k) - psf'(k)$$
$$+ (g + \delta + \gamma)p.$$

We learn, therefore, that if a saving policy s and the associated accumulation path k are to be optimal, the following pair of differential equations must be satisfied:

$$\dot{k} = sf(k) - (g + \delta)k, \qquad k(0) = k_0 > 0$$
$$\dot{p} = -[U'\{(1 - s)f(k)\}(1 - s) + ps]f'(k) + (g + \delta + \gamma)p. \tag{62}$$

The side conditions

$$p = U'[(1 - s)f(k)] \qquad \text{and} \qquad s(p - U') = 0 \tag{63}$$

determine s.

The reader may verify, as an exercise, by analyzing the properties of the locus of points satisfying

$$\dot{k} = 0, \qquad \dot{p} = 0, \qquad \text{and} \qquad s = 0,$$

that these equations (62) and (63) yield the phase diagram illustrated in Figure 48. As a further exercise, show that the characteristic roots of the associated linear system at the equilibrium point (k^*, p^*) are real and of opposite sign, implying that the equilibrium is locally a saddlepoint.

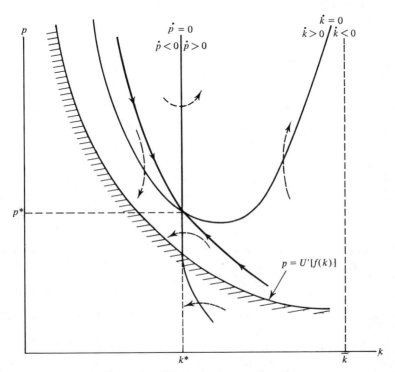

Figure 48. *The optimum growth path.*

We are not yet quite finished, however, since our objective is not to predict the behavior of a system along a specified growth path from a specified initial point, but rather to select an optimal growth path. We must not conclude prematurely that there is any significance to any intersection of two curves in our phase diagram. Even though in this case we will in fact learn that an optimal path is one that converges to the saddlepoint equilibrium, it is a conclusion that requires demonstration.

Figure 48 illustrates the trajectories of a system obeying the necessary conditions for optimality; a policy resulting in a path not lying along one of these trajectories cannot be optimal. We also have the initial capital stock k_0. What we must determine is the initial point on that vertical line through

k_0; that is, what we have yet to choose is an initial price for capital goods (or, equivalently, an initial consumption rate). How is this to be done?[21]

The answer lies in the following theorem, which is a special case of a more general sufficiency theorem proved by Mangasarian [65]. (Exercise 19 asks the reader to complete a sketch of Mangasarian's result.)

Theorem 2. *Let U and f be strictly concave; let (s^0, k^0) be a feasible policy satisfying (60)–(63) with s^0 piecewise continuous, and also satisfying the transversality condition*

$$\lim_{t \to \infty} p \exp(-\gamma t) = \lim_{t \to \infty} q(t) = 0. \tag{64}$$

Let (s, k) be any other feasible policy with s piecewise continuous. Then

$$J^0 = \int_0^\infty U[(1 - s^0)f(k^0)]\exp(-\gamma t)\, dt$$

$$\geq \int_0^\infty U[(1 - s)f(k)]\exp(-\gamma t)\, dt = J.$$

with strict inequality unless $s(t) \equiv s^0(t)$, $k(t) \equiv k^0(t)$.

Proof: By introducing a multiplier z, the side condition (63) may also be written in a standard form $-U' + f + z = 0$, $zs = 0$, $z \geq 0$, $s \geq 0$. It is also convenient for the moment to let $(\bar{s}, \bar{k})$ represent the candidate-

---

[21] If our problem were a finite time problem, necessary conditions would give a terminal condition as well as the price equations. But transversality conditions in the infinite horizon problem are open to some question. Whether we are entitled to assert, by analogy with the usual transversality condition for finite time problems, that $\lim_{t \to \infty} q(t) = 0$, or rather, under what conditions we can confidently assert this as a necessary condition, is apparently still a matter for investigation. We will see that such a condition, together with the conditions (62) and (63), is sufficient to ensure optimality in some strictly concave problems. When the optimizing curve is also unique, the conditions are then necessary. Shell [90] discusses this issue in some detail.

It is easy to see that the condition $\lim_{t \to \infty} q(t) = 0$ cannot always be necessary; indeed, the well-known extension by Koopmans [55] of the Ramsey analysis to a growing economy provides a counter example: when the discount rate γ is zero, the prices p and q coincide, and when p approaches a constant $p^* > 0$ asymptotically, so also does q. We shall verify Koopmans' result that p does approach p^* along an optimal path, and hence may conclude that on this optimal path q violates the condition $\lim_{t \to \infty} q(t) = 0$.

The discussion of terminal conditions for finite time problems as in exercises 7 or 12 suggests that one could look also at the value (per capita) of terminal capital stock, requiring $\lim_{t \to \infty} q(t)k(t) = 0$. For cases with γ positive and k is bounded away from zero and infinity, this requirement is obviously equivalent to $\lim_{t \to \infty} q(t) = 0$.

Finally, lacking definitive necessary transversality conditions, we may attempt to proceed by elimination, showing that any path which does not approach (k^*, p^*) either may be dominated by some comparison path, or ultimately violates the nonnegativity requirement on k. This approach is set out in Arrow. [2, p. 101].

optimal path, to let $\bar{f}$ denote $f(\bar{k})$, the output per capita along that candidate path, and to have $\bar{U}$ denote $U[(1 - \bar{s})f(\bar{k})]$, the utility enjoyed along the candidate path. Likewise $\bar{f}'$ and $\bar{U}'$ are to be interpreted as functions evaluated along the candidate-optimal path. Then

$$\int_0^\infty \{U[(1 - \bar{s})f(\bar{k})] - U[(1 - s)f(k)]\}\exp(-\gamma t)\, dt$$

$$\geq \int_0^\infty \{-(\bar{s} - s)\bar{U}'\bar{f} + (\bar{k} - k)\bar{U}'(1 - \bar{s})\bar{f}'\}\exp(-\gamma t)\, dt$$

$$\text{(by calculation using the concavity of } U \text{ and } f)$$

$$= \int_0^\infty \{-(\bar{s} - s)(\bar{p} + \bar{z})\, f - (\bar{k} - k)(\bar{p}[\bar{s}\bar{j} - (g + \delta + \gamma)] + \dot{\bar{p}})\}$$

$$\exp(-\gamma t)\, dt \qquad \text{(by (62) and (63))}$$

$$= \int_0^\infty \{-(\bar{s} - s)(\bar{p} + \bar{z})\, f - (\bar{k} - k)\bar{p}[\bar{s}\bar{f}' + (g + \delta)] + \bar{p}(\dot{\bar{k}} - \dot{k})\}$$

$$\exp(-\gamma t)\, dt + \bar{p}\exp(-\gamma t)(k - \dot{k})\,|_0^\infty$$

$$\text{(integrating } \int_0^\infty \dot{\bar{p}}(\bar{k} - k)\exp(-\gamma t)\, dt \text{ by parts)}$$

$$= \int_0^\infty \{\bar{p}[-(\bar{s} - s)f - (\bar{k} - k)(\bar{s}\bar{f}' - (g + \delta + \dot{k} - \dot{k}]$$

$$-(\bar{s} - s)\bar{z}f\}\exp(-\gamma t)\, dt \qquad \text{(by (64))}$$

$$\geq \int_0^\infty (s - \bar{s})\bar{z}f\exp(-\gamma t)\, dt \qquad \text{(by (62) and the concavity of } f)$$

$$\geq 0 \qquad \text{(by (63)).}$$

Thus we obtain the required terminal condition. Moreover we note that the terminal condition is satisfied by a trajectory that converges to the equilibrium point (k^*, p^*); if it is possible to select the initial value p_0 so as to ensure this convergence, then the trajectory satisfies all the other necessary conditions enunciated before. That this is the case for problems of the type we have been considering is shown by Arrow [2, pp. 102–103]. Thus there exists a feasible path satisfying all the sufficient conditions for optimality.

Our analysis leaves us, then, with the following conclusion. Given a concave utility function and a social rate of time preference strictly greater than zero there is an optimal policy for accumulation of capital in a one-sector model. This policy calls for the capital/labor ratio k to approach a constant level at a value defined by the Modified Golden Rule

$$f'(k^*) = g + \gamma + \delta.$$

Moreover the policy may be realized by permitting producers to select, at each instant, the composition of output that would be warranted if the price p were taken as the demand price for new capital goods and $U'(c)$ were treated as the opportunity cost of the consumption goods foregone to produce

capital goods. Thus, referring back to a point raised in the discussion of one-
and two-sector models, we see how a social preference ordering can replace
arbitrary saving assumptions in selecting at each moment a point on the production possibility frontier. Not by defining a utility function over output
flows of investment goods as well as consumption goods, but instead by
computing a measure of the value of a present capital good in terms of the
consumption-goods flow yields in the future, we are able to determine the
composition of output at each instant. Indeed, it is indicative of the extent to
which Pontryagin's maximum principle may be interpreted as a theorem of
economics that it gives us precisely the conditions to carry out this reduction
of the intertemporal problem to one of static optimization.

It is possible to overstate the pure competition implications of this procedure, however. In principle the price equation (62) has an obvious interpretation as a zero-profit condition, or as an arbitrage condition if we think
of a market for funds as well as capital goods, but it must be remembered
that this is an optimizing problem, a planning problem, and the initial price
$p(0)$ is not historically given but is assigned by the optimizing agent. Were
there shocks in the system it would be the duty of the planning agent instantly
to reassign corrected prices that restore the economy to the optimal path.[22]
Thus the formal instability of the equilibrium point has only analytical
significance in this optimizing problem. Indeed it has been observed that if the
equilibrium point were not formally a saddlepoint, central planners would
have very little justification for drawing a salary since the unguided system
would tend unerringly to the equilibrium point in any case, under any assignment of prices. We began with a planning problem, and it is still with us.

We have said nothing about the adjustment of actual capital-goods prices
toward the perfect shadow price, so we cannot discuss the stability or effectiveness of a competitive mechanism as a decentralized system intended to realize
the optimal policy.

All these results are obtained under the assumption that the effective rate
of time discount γ is positive. However, our welfare criterion J is based upon
a utility of per capita consumption, and it may be argued that if people are
to be treated equally between generations as well as within, then the performance of the economy at any moment should look at total utility in some
sense—that is, should weight the utility of per capita consumption at any
moment by the population enjoying that per capita consumption at that
moment. In other words, it is argued that the "representative man" measure
$U(c)$ might be appropriate with unchanging population, but it distorts the
comparison between performance at times of larger population and times of
smaller. The correct procedure according to this argument is to add up the
utilities of all people at a particular moment, i.e., to weight $U(c)$ by the

---

[22] See Samuelson [E52–383].

population $L_0 \exp(gt)$.[23] The effect of this is to introduce a negative component into the discount factor γ; hence γ may be written $\rho - g$ where ρ is intended to reflect discounting of the future, whereas g reflects the scaling for population size.

This would be simply a notational change, except for the fact that there now remains no compelling reason why the restriction $\gamma > 0$ should hold. We may note that if we consider a limiting case with $\gamma = 0$ in the foregoing analysis, the optimal trajectories remain well defined, and, indeed, in the limit the equilibrium point for the system is the familiar Golden Rule point. But for the limiting case the criterion function J does not converge; it is therefore not obvious what significance can be attached to the trajectories for this case. The next section turns to this issue and Koopman's original analysis of it.

A Bliss Point Again

We opened this chapter with a discussion of a finite horizon planning problem with a constant population. In response to difficulties created by the assumption of a fixed finite terminal date, we adopted a different model based on allocation of consumption over the whole infinite future. This change introduced the possibility that the criterion function might diverge, and indeed, in the absence of time discounting, divergence problems did arise. As a result we adopted a different criterion based on Ramsey's notion of a Bliss point. Using this modified criterion we were able to obtain a ranking of consumption paths and to select a "best" policy from among all feasible policies.

Subsequently we introduced growth in the labor force and again obtained a characterization of the accumulation policy optimal under an integral criterion reflecting per capita utility, provided that the rate of time discount was positive. But at the end of the last section we observed that in the presence of population growth there may be a strong case arguing that future per capita utility flows should not be discounted, but should perhaps even be scaled up. This argument spotlights the problem of determining the optimal policy when population grows but there is no discounting of the utility of future per capita consumption. In such a case the criterion functional used in the previous section may diverge, but we can find a modified criterion just as Ramsey did—a modified criterion that agrees with the original if the original converges, but discriminates among paths even when the original diverges.

---

[23] Note that this is not quite the same as arguing that larger population should be weighted positively in the utility function. Many people who argue that there are substantial diseconomies due to larger population (through congestion, crowds, and general contamination) might nevertheless agree that choices between generations ought to attempt to weight individuals equally once they are in fact in existence.

The Bliss point we require for the purpose is simply the familiar Golden Rule growth track. That this is the case should not be surprising: we know that Ramsey's Bliss point arose either from utility saturation or from capital saturation, and we saw before that the Golden Rule path has a simple interpretation as a point of capital saturation[24] when we choose among paths with constant capital/labor ratios. Koopmans [55], elaborating on this idea, proved that the Golden Rule path may indeed be taken as a suitable comparison path from which to measure utilities in the growing economy.

What we must do, therefore, is define the Golden Rule path by

$$f'(\hat{k}) = g + \delta, \qquad \hat{c} = f(\hat{k}) - (g + \delta)\hat{k}, \qquad \hat{U} = U(\hat{c}),$$

and then define a criterion $\hat{J} = \int_0^\infty [U(c) - \hat{U}]\, dt$ to be maximized.

Given earlier sufficiency proofs it is an easy matter, which we omit, to show that for the concave technology and concave utility function specified before the criterion $\hat{J}$ is bounded above.

Second, we observe that the criterion $\hat{J}$ attains its maximum, for given initial k_0, at the path (s, k) obtained by letting the parameter γ tend to zero in the previous analysis. Indeed, we observe that mathematically the form of the problem is unaltered from that analysis,[25] and from the original Ramsey problem; all that is required is the selection of a criterion function that is meaningful.

This analysis—the adoption of the Golden Rule track as a Bliss point—thus enables us to extend the earlier analysis, which was valid only for a positive rate of time discount, to the case of a zero rate of time discount. Unfortunately the same trick will not work for the negative rates of discount that might arise from an attempt to weight individuals equally. To handle these cases it is necessary to adopt a different type of criterion functional, upon which we will comment in Section 11-5.

The Consumption Turnpike

What conclusions can be drawn from analysis of the optimal saving policy? One characteristic feature follows from the fact of a saddlepoint equilibrium. This feature, described variously as a catenary property or a consumption turnpike, refers to the tendency of optimal trajectories to arch toward the saddlepoint equilibrium at the Modified Golden Rule value of the capital/

[24] It is a point of capital saturation in the sense that it shows the highest sustainable flow of output net of capital requirements.

[25] One part of the argument does not carry over directly. For the present problem it is necessary to demonstrate explicitly that the optimal policy does converge to a definite limit (and in particular that it does not oscillate). Koopmans [55] does this by showing that it can never be optimal to follow a path that has a "bulge" such that $k(t_1) = k(t_2) < \hat{k}$ and $k(t) < k(t_1)$ for any $t \in (t_1, t_2)$.

labor ratio, so that along an optimal path the system generally spends a substantial fraction of the total plan period in the neighborhood of the saddlepoint equilibrium.

More precisely, the property refers to the fact that for any prescribed neighborhood of the equilibrium point and any prescribed fraction θ, we may choose a plan period T sufficiently long that the fraction of time the system point is within the prescribed neighborhood exceeds the prescribed fraction θ for all problems with planning horizons exceeding T.

This property is demonstrated by Samuelson [82] who exploits the fact that the equilibrium point is a saddlepoint such that as the planning period lengthens optimal trajectories pass closer to the saddlepoint and such that the velocity of the system point is reduced as one approaches the saddlepoint. A somewhat more formal analysis of the differential equation system (62) and (63) and the corresponding phase diagram leads to the following theorem. (See Cass [16, 17].)

Theorem 3: *Given $\varepsilon > 0$, define a neighborhood $N(\varepsilon)$ of the Modified Golden Rule path (k^*, p^*) by*

$$N(\varepsilon) = \{(k, p) : |k - k^*| < \varepsilon, \quad |p - p^*| < \varepsilon\}.$$

Then for the unique path (k, p), optimal for prescribed initial and terminal capital k_0 and k_T and prescribed horizon T, there exist two finite times T_1 and T_2 such that $[k(t), p(t)] \in N(\varepsilon)$ whenever $T_1 \leqq t \leqq T - T_2$.

The proof of this theorem is based on an analysis of a phase diagram similar to the one in Figure 48. For details the reader is referred to Cass [17]. (Note that the theorem remains true for the case $\gamma = 0$, where (k^*, p^*) is the Golden Rule path.) Thus, by taking the horizon T to be sufficiently large (specifically, by taking $T > (T_1 + T_2)/(1 - \theta)$), one may ensure that the proportion θ of time spent by the system in an arbitrarily small neighborhood of (k^*, p^*) is as close to unity as desired. The parallel with the turnpike results of the previous chapter is obvious.

11–5. Extensions and Further Issues

The literature on optimal economic growth is by now far too vast to permit discussion in detail of all, or even any substantial number, of the individual original contributions. The previous sections have outlined the basic analytical structure; here we will try to sketch some main features of a number of issues that extend beyond the standard analysis.

Optimal Growth in the Two-Sector Model

The construction described in Section 11-1 suggests that there is really only one consideration leading toward interior solutions to the problem of the optimal composition of output and hence to smooth optimizing paths satisfying the classical Euler equation, namely, sufficient curvature in the transformation curve describing the choices open to the community at each moment. We saw that even in a one-sector model with a linear production possibility frontier, adoption of a strictly concave utility function implied curvature of the trade-off curve relating the utility of consumption to the value of the investment accomplished by foregoing consumption. (With sufficiently high marginal utility as consumption tends to zero, we obtained sufficient curvature to eliminate altogether the possibility that output would be specialized to investment.) On the other hand, when a linear utility function is combined with the linear transformation function, the static optimization problem (determining the composition of output) reduces to the maximization of a linear form subject to linear constraints, and boundary solutions at extreme points of the feasible set must be expected.[26]

An alternative specification leading to curvature in the static optimization problem is found in the two-sector model described in Chapter 4. In this model the transformation curve relating the outputs of the two sectors is strictly concave if the two sectors have different neoclassical production functions.[27] Therefore, even in the presence of a linear utility function the static composition of output problem may have an interior solution. On the other hand, the curvature of the production possibility frontier may be limited, causing specialization of output either to consumption or to investment.

Srinivasan [93], Uzawa [101], and Shell [89] have investigated the problem of optimal growth in the two-sector model, giving conditions for the times of switching from specialized to nonspecialized production and verifying the existence of a Modified Golden Rule equilibrium having the same characteristics as the one-sector model investigated before.

Heterogeneous Capital Goods

The introduction of additional sectors producing different consumption goods—or, for that matter, additional nonproduced, nontradable assets—does not add anything except some marginal utility or marginal productivity

---

[26] Saving policies are derived for such cases by Cass [16] and Shell [90].

[27] This assertion has to be qualified slightly by recognition that there may exist some capital/labor ratios at which both sectors select the same capital intensities, implying that the production possibility frontier is momentarily a straight line.

conditions to the necessary conditions for optimal accumulation just given. But the introduction of distinct durable and tradable capital goods does create problems not encountered in the one-sector model developed previously in this chapter. We have to decide upon the extent of saving and investment, as before, and also upon the composition of investment as between the different capital goods.

We encountered this problem before, it will be recalled, when the introduction of money into a descriptive model offered alternative ways to hold wealth and thus gave rise to portfolio composition problems. Perhaps on the basis of that discussion, and of the discussion of descriptive models with many capital goods, it will not be surprising to find that the resolution of the optimal accumulation problem takes the following simple form.

(i) Specification of an optimal accumulation problem entails an implicit social rate of time discount implied by the criterion function, and optimal decisions may be expected to make the own-rate of return on the *numeraire* good equal to this implied social rate of time discount.

(ii) Given the own-rate of return on the *numeraire* good pegged at the social rate of time preference, capital market trading realizes the dynamic efficiency conditions of Samuelson [80]—the arbitrage conditions or auxiliary equations—which force all capital-goods prices to change at a rate that makes the yield on each capital good equal to that on the *numeraire* good. This determines (through a differential equation) the prices of all capital goods, *assuming* that initial values can be specified in accord with terminal requirements.

(iii) Given the prices of all capital goods and the demand price for the consumption good (that is, the opportunity cost, indicated by the criterion function, of diverting resources from consumption), producers in each sector attempt to maximize current profit. The resulting outputs determine the extent and composition of investment.

(iv) Given the outputs of each sector, the growth of various assets is determined by the customary accumulation equations; consequently asset stocks are all determined once initial conditions are given. Hence we have prices and endowment levels determined at each instant, and the whole evolution of an optimal path is established from given initial conditions.

This sketch indicates a way in which optimal control of a system with distinct capital goods could be realized. We are arguing that the requirements for an optimal path may be summarized as follows.

(i) There must exist continuous asset prices such that the yield on all assets is equal, and their common value is the social rate of time discount implied by the criterion function.

(ii) The initial prices must be chosen to satisfy some transversality conditions.

(iii) With asset prices and the endowment levels given at each instant, the composition of output must be selected to yield a maximum value of net national product (evaluated, however, in terms of some utility measure).

A decentralized system may be expected to realize condition (iii) through the actions of suppliers and to equalize asset yields as in condition (i) through arbitrage. It remains for the planning agency to assign initial asset prices that will satisfy transversality conditions and to force the common yield on assets into equality with the social rate of time preference.

If proper representation of a saving decision and a market for funds were to bring asset yields into balance with time preference—as is the role of markets for funds—then only the assignment of initial asset prices remains.

If, finally, futures markets were able to look into the distant future and recognize the satisfaction of transversality conditions—or, more precisely, were able to recognize the eventual violation of one of the auxiliary equations as a result of a failure to satisfy transversality conditions—then the assignment of initial prices would also be realized as required for optimal growth. (This result was conjectured by Samuelson [84] and investigated by Shell and Stiglitz [91] in the context of a simple model.)

In a complete system of perfect markets, therefore, the planning agency becomes otiose; every one of the conditions for optimal growth can be realized by a decentralized system of independent decision makers. Academician Pontryagin and his colleagues have thus enunciated a newer and more powerful principle of an invisible hand; the maximum principle of Pontryagin is seen to be the culmination of a logical sequence originating in the maximum principle of Adam Smith.

Of course, it goes without saying that the principle holds only for an ideal system of perfect markets; it applies equally to a decentralized socialist economy and a free market capitalist economy. It is a theorem about allocation mechanisms and not about income distribution. But is it not fascinating that the evolution of a free enterprise system has included development of some form (often quite imperfect) of every market structure required in principle to realize the theoretically optimal decentralized control system?

In a remarkable anticipation of the maximum principle and of a literature to burgeon a decade later, Samuelson and Solow [85] suggest many of the foregoing ideas in their analysis of the Ramsey problem with heterogeneous capital goods. The dynamic efficiency conditions were also developed in a model [80] with no explicit criterion functional depending upon consumption, but instead with the weaker criterion of efficiency familiar from the literature on turnpike theorems surveyed in the previous chapter.

Radner [76] and Chakravarty [21] deal with the issue of optimal growth in multicapital models, and a great deal of further analysis is contained in the *Symposium on Optimal Infinite Programmes* [35].

Decentralized Systems

The previous paragraphs have suggested that the market mechanisms present in an idealized capitalist system may realize in a decentralized fashion the control necessary to guide the system along an optimal trajectory. The discussion there also isolated the requirement that the common own-rate established by asset trading be brought into balance with the social rate of time preference, and the requirement that initial prices be assigned in conformity with terminal conditions as the two conditions least naturally established by a descriptive model of a market system. Whether a capitalist system has, in principle, a mechanism to meet these conditions, and the consequences if it has not, have been subjects for recent discussion.

Hahn [43] showed that in one model in which no explicit intertemporal optimization is considered at all, but in which an arbitrary hypothesis determining total saving instead serves to determine the common own-rate of return at each instant, and in which transversality conditions are not considered but initial asset prices are instead taken to be historically given, then the system does not in general converge to a stable balanced growth equilibrium as the one-sector Solow model does. Rather it diverges from the balanced growth equilibrium which is a saddlepoint in the price-quantity space. Hahn concluded that the presence of many capital goods was responsible for this result, and apparently felt that the result itself cast doubt upon the desirability of a system of capitalist markets for guiding a complex economy along an accumulation path.

Samuelson [84] and Shell-Stiglitz [91] argued that the result was a consequence of incomplete specification and that a full specification of an idealized capitalist system should include possible futures markets. They argued, further, that if equilibrium in all of a complete set of futures markets over an infinite horizon were required, then only the unique initial prices leading to balanced growth would be tenable as an initial price assignment in a competitive capitalist system. In other words, any path that did not converge to the saddlepoint balanced growth equilibrium would ultimately reveal itself to be incompatible with nonnegativity constraints and market clearing conditions. However, thus far Samuelson's conjecture has been proved only for special cases such as that considered by Shell-Stiglitz.

Burmeister, Dobell, and Kuga [15] suggested that Hahn's result should be assessed in terms of its specification as to portfolio behavior, which requires asset holders to be prepared to accept the promise of infinite capital gains (confidently expected) as a perfect offset to an infinite gap between actual earning streams of two different assets. They showed that an alternative (still unrealistic) assumption concerning the determination of investment composition results in a unique balanced growth equilibrium that is globally stable. The path to balanced growth will not, in general, satisfy Samuelson's dynamic efficiency conditions, but the equilibrium track may be a Golden Rule path, and cannot in any case display Phelps-Koopmans inefficiency.

Kurz [59] adopts still another point of view, suggesting that a saving assumption must be describing the consequences of some decision process, and, in particular, the constant saving hypothesis adopted by Solow could be interpreted as the result of an analysis of optimal policy along the lines of that given before in this chapter. The optimal policy is then summarized in a saving rule from which the prices (auxiliary variables) have been "integrated out" to leave a feedback rule or synthesized policy. Kurz displays the criterion function that must have been in mind in order for the optimal policy to take the constant saving propensity form.[28] Drawing on results known in the control literature (and reminiscent of the literature on dual stability), Kurz suggested that the equilibrium solution to an optimizing problem is a saddlepoint in the price-quantity space. He concluded that the Solow model was stable (in the quantity space) because the prices do not appear explicitly when the optimal saving policy is synthesized (i.e., is solved and expressed as a function of quantities alone). Hahn's model, on the other hand, is unstable (in the price-quantity space) because prices do appear explicitly, and the control—i.e. the determination of the composition of output—is not synthesized but depends on the prices.

We do not propose to pursue this issue here, except to emphasize that we must be very clear as to (1) the space within which the characteristics of the equilibrium point are to be studied, (2) the complete specification of all market relations and side conditions within the system to be studied, and (3) the complete set of price adjustment conditions. Here, as before, lags in the adjustment of actual asset prices to the perfect asset prices generated by the auxiliary equations may lead to a more stable system. But again these considerations introduce all the problems of specifying the formation of expectations and disequilibrium behavior.

Technical Change

We have seen before that the effect of technological progress is to make the production function depend explicitly on time. In some special cases of the one-sector model technological progress can be represented as an increase in the efficiency of particular productive factors. If, for example, technical change is Harrod neutral (purely labor augmenting), then all the previous analysis remains valid if we measure labor in efficiency units.

If, however, technical change is not Harrod neutral, then the system of differential equations arising from the necessary conditions for optimality

---

[28] The calculation is an example of the so called "inverse optimal problem," a problem like that of reasoning back from demand curves to find the utility function that generated them. See Kurz [58].

will be nonautonomous, i.e., will depend explicitly on time. It is generally difficult to carry out qualitative analysis of such systems.

Shell [89] has studied one- and two-sector models with disembodied technical change of the Hicks-neutral type. In these models we may define a Golden Rule point at each instant, but the Golden Rule capital/labor ratio rises with time. This moving target may serve, just as before, as a turnpike toward which optimal paths will arch, but because the target is moving we have to be sure that the system can, in fact, grow fast enough to reach the target. Moreover, even when it can, the formal turnpike property need not hold; with a low terminal target on capital the time required for terminal decumulation from the turnpike to the terminal target may not shrink (as a proportion of the plan period), to zero, and hence the proportion of time spent in a neighborhood of the turnpike may not approach unity as the horizon becomes indefinitely long. Otherwise the qualitative results of the earlier analysis remain largely unaltered by the introduction of technical change into these simple one- and two-sector models. (Mirrlees [67] deals in detail with some further issues on this subject.)

One of the essential features of technical change is uncertainty. We anticipate that technical progress will expand the productive opportunities of future generations, but not just how or when. What should be the response of the community—should it be saving more or less as a consequence of uncertain technical change? Mirrlees [68] studied this problem under the assumption that technical progress enters in a Harrod-neutral exponential fashion, but the exponent is a random variable with normally distributed increments. The analysis is intricate, but only local conclusions emerge.

There are other considerations to be taken into account. If technical change is embodied in new equipment, then optimal rates of saving must be influenced. If learning-by-doing results in more efficient production as experience accumulates, then again the optimal policy cannot be established without taking into consideration the external benefits created by production and investment. Some results in dealing with such questions have been obtained by Sheshinski [92], Stiglitz [94], and others.

Models of induced technological progress such as that discussed in Chapter 3 may also lead to complex problems of optimal policy. Kamien and Schwartz [53] consider the problem of optimal induced technical change at the level of the firm; Drandakis and Hu, in an unpublished paper, discuss optimum growth policies in the Kennedy-type models described in Chapter 3.

Finally, the question of induced technological progress leads to a discussion of education and training. Uzawa [100] undertakes an analysis of the optimal allocation of labor between a production sector where goods are produced and an education sector where the efficiency of labor in production is determined. Related issues arise in the surplus-labor models to be discussed in the next section.

Surplus Labor

Until now the analysis has assumed that the labor force is given exo-genously and utilized fully in production. But there are a number of reasons why we might wish to consider development patterns that entail some un-employment. The first is that in many situations initial conditions force us to begin with unemployed labor, and plans ought to say something about the path by which this unemployed labor should be absorbed into production. (Stoleru [95] attempts to do exactly this.) The difficulty, analytically, is that we have assumed labor to be available as required, have assumed that utiliza-tion rates are control variables to be set at the planner's discretion, and have assumed that there are no costs to absorbing labor into production. If labor has a positive marginal product, therefore, an optimal policy could never display unemployment.

Several considerations suggest that there are social costs to absorbing labor into production. In the type of dual economy in which unemployment is a serious problem, there is an urban industrial sector and a residual rural subsistence sector. Moving a laborer from the latter to the former will generally involve some capital costs for social housekeeping expenditures, such as urban housing, and personal transfer costs. Alternatively, the fact that a capital cost is entailed in training labor to a level of skill adequate for participation in an industrial sector provides a barrier to instant elimina-tion of all unemployment in an optimizing model. Marglin [66] and Dixit [27] have studied the question in the context of the dual economy, giving con-sideration also to the fact that the rate of capital accumulation may be accelerated by presence of a larger surplus of revenues over wages in the industrial sector. Dobell and Ho [30] analyzed the question on the assumption of a capital cost of training labor for entry into production. As is to be ex-pected, the analytical structure of the two problems is almost identical, and the results can be interpreted in terms of traditional cost-benefit computations.

It should be emphasized that the unemployment portrayed in these cal-culations is not due to deficient aggregate demand, but is rather a supply side phenomenon reflecting inadequate human capital or inadequate social capital. If there is unemployment of people in these models it is because it costs too much to settle people where they can enter production or costs too much to endow them with sufficient training. The analysis separates the concept of human capital, which may be fully employed, from a straight population count, which may exhibit some unemployment. If there is such unemployment along an optimal path, it will be because it costs too much to create the training necessary for entry into production.

There is an interesting issue to be pursued here, though we cannot follow it at this time. Dobell and Ho began with the question of whether there is any logical basis for the argument that in modern society it may be optimal to leave substantial amounts of unemployment, with income redistribution undertaken to compensate those unemployed. They showed that the presence of a fixed capital cost of training could not by itself account for the presence of persistent unemployment along an optimal path, unless it happened that the capital cost was so high that a laborer's wage could not cover the competitive interest payments on the loan necessary to finance training. This extreme case being deemed implausible, the conclusion was that constant capital costs for training alone cannot justify abandoning a social commitment to full employment. Subsequently they argued [31] that if training costs rise with the employment rate—presumably because the remaining pool of untrained labor is less suited to training or production—then persistent unemployment could be optimal, but it would be for very conventional reasons, namely the wage that could be paid in a competitive system could not cover the competitive interest costs on the *marginal* capital cost of training.

This conclusion, however, depends on the idea of a single threshhold level of skill required for production. If the extent of training may be varied, along with employment rates, then the foregoing conclusion need not hold. Indeed, Dobell [29] has shown in a simple model with both training and employment decisions to be optimally determined that the Golden Rule path can never show unemployment if the training level is always optimally chosen. These results bear upon important questions dealing with the role of decentralized institutions in the provision and financing of education. The social consequences of various distortions in individual decisions on these issues (e.g., as a result of asymmetric tax policy or capital market failure) may be extremely significant.

Microeconomic Decisions in Optimizing Models

We have referred before to the fact that many of the components of simple models of economic growth are intended to be summary representations of individual optimizing decisions. We have also suggested that the more such individual optimizing takes place, the more indirect must be the instruments by which the central government influences individuals and implements its own socially optimal policies.

In principle the components for a dynamic model with individual optimizing behavior are available. For the consumer, theories of lifetime allocation are well developed (see Modigliani-Brumberg [69] and Yaari [107]). For the producer, decision rules for adjusting production and capacity utilization rates have been derived (see Holt, Modigliani, Muth, and Simon [49]). Theories of optimal capacity creation—or, more accurately, theories of a desired capital stock—have been elaborated by Eisner and Strotz [33] and Jorgenson [52], and theories of capital stock adjustment are given by Gould

[42] and Lucas [62]. Individual portfolio decisions have been studied in detail. Combining such building blocks into some comprehensive model would leave the planning agency with influence only to the extent that it could affect these individual decisions by operating on a limited range of instruments: money supply, bond issues and debt management, taxes and transfers, and other social capital expenditures.

Such a representation of the problems of optimal policy is presumably of far more relevance to the actual issues of economic policy determination than most of our foregoing analysis. It also goes some way toward bridging the gap between theories of optimal accumulation and econometric policy models being developed for evaluation of alternative uses of economic instruments. Analyses of these more limited instruments are undertaken by Arrow and Kurz [7] and Foley and Sidrauski [36]. We have touched upon the issue in Chapter 6.

The Criterion Functional

Any saving policy, whether deduced from optimality conditions or not, has significant implications for the allocation of consumption between individuals living at different times. One of the difficulties in arriving at an equitable solution to the problem of choosing a saving policy is that many of those affected are not able to vote on the decision because they belong to generations not yet in existence.

There is a rather substantial literature dealing with one aspect of the problem. Initiated by Samuelson [79], this literature attempts to establish conditions under which a market determined rate of interest may bring about an optimal distribution of consumption in a growing economy. Work of Lerner [61], Diamond [26], and Cass-Yaari [18] deals with the issue, and Samuelson [83] also has returned to the question.

Some of the debate relates to the question of whether a terminal date and terminal decumulation are permitted to enter the criterion function. This issue in turn relates to the notion of Phelps-Koopmans inefficiency discussed before. If, as Lerner argues, we weight the integrand function by population size and take the enjoyment of terminal decumulation into account, then a growing society may deepen capital to the point of actual physical capital saturation, since the decumulation of this capital stock at a time of many people always yields benefits sufficient to outweigh the sacrifices of accumulation undertaken at a time of fewer people. If, on the other hand, we consider a representative individual and take the horizon to be truly infinite (in which case no account is taken of terminal decumulation), then, as Samuelson [83] argues, we must respect the prohibitions of Phelps-Koopmans inefficiency and must not accumulate beyond the Golden Rule point. (Again, of course, independently formulated individual saving decisions need not be consistent with this social goal.)

The question of weighting the integrand by population brings us back to the question of the convergence of the criterion functional. In planning problems with an infinite horizon, we saw that (because capital/labor ratios, and hence per capita consumption, were bounded above) a positive rate of time discount would generally guarantee convergence of our standard integral criterion functional, while some trick of measuring utility from a Golden Rule or Bliss point yields a slightly different criterion function that allows the boundary case in which the effective social rate of time discount is zero. But if a positive weighting by population offsets the negative weight of time preference, the effective social rate of time discount could well be negative. In this case neither of the previous two criterion functionals defines a sensitive ordering on the class of alternative consumption paths. Rather, these functionals diverge for many paths, assigning the value plus infinity to distinct paths among which the planner or the community could express definite preference.

To meet this problem, the so-called "overtaking" or partial-sum criterion was suggested: we seek a path $c^0(t)$, $0 \leq t$, such that for any other path $c(t)$ there exists $T^0 > 0$ such that

$$J^0 = \int_0^T U(c^0, t) \, dt \geq \int_0^T U(c, t) \, dt = J$$

for all $T \geq T^0$. Von Weizsäcker [105], McFadden [63], and Gale [37] discuss this criterion and the conditions under which the rankings it assigns might agree with rankings according to the earlier criterion.

An alternative procedure—that of the so-called sliding plan in which plans are recomputed each year for a specified finite plan period—is investigated by Goldman [40].

Joint Production and Nonuniqueness

Recently it has been observed that in some models a stationary solution (K^*, p^*) to the Euler–Lagrange equations need not be unique, a circumstance which raises questions about consumption turnpike theorems asserting characteristic features of optimal paths.[29] However, these results have generally been derived with a criterion function in which not only consumption flows but also state variables such as wealth or capital stocks enter. When perfect foresight and perfect certainty are assumed, it may be argued that such models are inappropriate in that they "double count" the benefits of

---

[29] The problem was studied by Richard Sutherland in an unpublished Ph. D. dissertation "On Optimal Development Programs when Future Utility is Discounted" (Brown University, 1967) and later mentioned by Gale [38]. A continuous time-analysis is given in M. Kurz, "Optimal Economic Growth and Wealth Effects" *International Economic Review* 9, 3, (October, 1968) pp. 348–357.

additional stocks—presumably in a riskless world of perfect capital markets, increments to wealth or capital stock at a point in time increase welfare only to the extent that they contribute to future consumption or the utility of future bequests, the value of which is already measured in the criterion function J.

Rather than pursue this issue directly, we shall retain our previous criterion functional and show that in principle the same nonuniqueness property may result under slightly different technological assumptions. More precisely, equation (2) of our earlier model may be replaced by a *production possibility frontier* of the form

$$C = G(\dot{K}, K) \tag{65}$$

The function has its usual simple interpretation: at any fixed time t, K is fixed; given an admissible value of net investment $\dot{K}$, the value of G gives the maximum technologically attainable consumption flow C. Further, if we assume that G is a strictly concave function in $\dot{K}$ and K, then the existence of joint production may be proved.[30]

Now consider the Euler equation for a problem of the sort analyzed in Section 11-2. At a stationary point where $\dot{K} = \ddot{K} = 0$, we must have

$$\Phi(K) \equiv \gamma G_{\dot{K}}(0, K) + G_K(0, K) = 0. \tag{66}$$

Evidently equation (66) need not have a unique positive solution if Φ_K changes sign. But by direct calculation,

$$\Phi_K = \gamma G_{\dot{K}K} + G_{KK} \tag{67}$$

and thus if $\gamma > 0$, Φ_K may indeed change sign. (When $\gamma = 0$, of course, the restriction $G_{KK} < 0$ implies $\Phi_K < 0$ everywhere.)

It is interesting, however, that such a possibility exists only if there is joint production and G is a strictly concave function. To prove this assertion, we define the net own-rate of return on capital by $r \equiv -G_K/G_{\dot{K}}$ and note that (66) holds if and only if $r = \gamma$. But since it is known that $dK/dr|_{\dot{K}=0} < 0$ in models without joint production,[31] the proof is immediate; we conclude (66) has a unique solution K^* under these circumstances.

Where joint production does exist, however, the possibility of two (or more) roots K^* and K^{**}, both satisfying (66), is definitely present. The existence of

---

[30] In making this observation we are implicitly assuming the existence of an underlying fixed labor force which is fully employed, so that all the variables may be interpreted for our purposes as per capita quantities. We retain this assumption throughout the remainder of this section.

[31] See Corollaries 8.1 and 8.2 in Chapter 9.

multiple stationary solutions to the Euler equation suggests that the optimal policy may depend crucially on the initial condition K_0, with the optimal $K(t)$ path arching toward a lower root K^* when K_0 is sufficiently low, but arching toward some higher root K^{**} if K_0 is sufficiently high. (It should be noted that the possibility of distinct stationary solutions to the Euler equation does not conflict with assertions that satisfaction of the Euler equation is, in these examples, a sufficient condition for a unique optimum. Indeed, since $U(C) = U[G(\dot{K}, K)]$ is a strictly concave function in both $\dot{K}$ and K, the sufficiency theorem of Mangasarian [65] applies to this case. But from this the only conclusion is that a path starting from prescribed initial conditions and satisfying the Euler equation yields a maximum to the criterion functional J. The uniqueness of an optimal path with prescribed initial conditions does not rule out the possibility that optimal paths with different initial conditions may differ drastically. In particular, taking the case $T = \infty$, consider optimal paths starting from different initial capital stocks. Nothing implies that these paths must lie along a unique curve in the (K, p) space, although this outcome is characteristic of simple examples such as illustrated in Figure 48, where all the optimal infinite paths start on, and follow along, the stable arm leading to the saddlepoint.)

An example of a problem with such multiple turnpike behavior has been given by Liviatan and Samuelson.[32] In their particular example there are three distinct values of the capital stock (or capital/labor ratio) serving as stationary solutions to the Euler equation. Labelling these values K_1^*, K_2^*, K_3^* in order of increasing magnitude, they show that K_1^* and K_3^* are (locally) saddlepoints while K_2^* is (locally) an unstable node. (See Figure 49a. The similarity to results known in the analysis of non-conservative physical systems may be noted.)

Liviatan and Samuelson show that a local turnpike property holds with respect to these saddlepoints K_1^* and K_3^*; for $K_0 \in (0, K_2^*)$ the fraction of time an optimally guided system spends in the neighborhood of K_1^* may be made as close to unity as desired by selection of sufficiently large T. Likewise for $K_0 \in (K_2^*, \bar{K})$, the saddlepoint K_3^* serves as a turnpike, independently of terminal conditions.

On the other hand, inspection of Figure 49a suggests that for $K_0 \in (K_1^*, K_2^*)$ and $K_T > K_3^*$, there can still be optimal paths which arch toward K_3^* and spend a large fraction of the total plan period in the neighborhood of that value. From the resulting time path of capital accumulation one might conclude (wrongly) that K_3^* serves as a turnpike for the problem. Instead of the optimal paths approaching K_3^* more closely as the horizon T grows, however, there comes a time when the system point on an optimal path lies

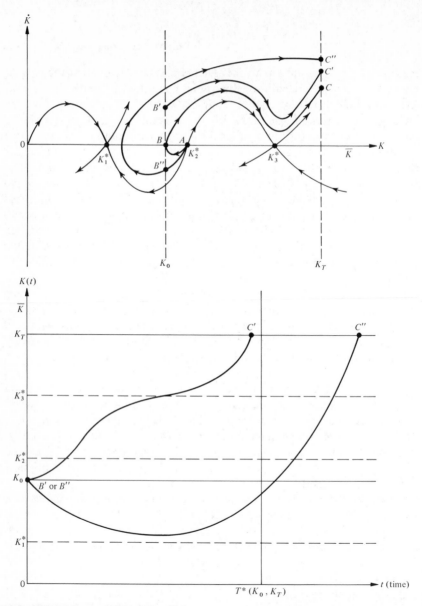

Figure 49(a)/Figure 49(b). *The Euler equation has multiple stationary solutions at* K_1^*, K_2^*, *and* K_3^*. *For the illustrated initial and terminal conditions,* K_0 *and* K_T, *respectively, the critical time* $T^*(K_0, K_T)$ *is the time it takes to move from point B to point C along the path ABC in Figure 49(a).*

Consider an optimal program for a fixed time T. If $T > T^*(K_0, K_T)$, *the solution is a path similar to* $B''C''$ *which spends a high proportion of time near the relevant turnpike* $(K_1^*, 0)$ *in* $(K, \dot{K})$ *space or* $K = K_1^*$ *in* (t, K) *space, as illustrated in Figures 49(a) and (b). However, if* $T \leqq T^*(K_0, K_T)$, *the optimal program is represented by a path such as* $B'C'$, *and this path "arches toward" the point* $(K_3^*, 0)$ *in 49(a) and the line* K_3^* *in 49(b).*

close to K_1^* for "most" of the plan period, and with further increases in the horizon T the usual turnpike properties re-emerge, with K_1^* serving as the true turnpike for paths beginning at the prescribed initial value.

By separating those paths which, starting from K_0, do not move toward the value K_1^* from those paths which do begin to move toward K_1^*, we obtain some idea of how significant this spurious turnpike-like "short horizon" behavior might be. The following theorem shows that for some initial conditions one might have to take very long horizons indeed before the value K_3^* could be revealed as only a pretender to the turnpike role.

Theorem[33]: *Assume* $0 < K_1^* < K_0 < K_2^* < K_3^* < K_T < \overline{K}$. *There exists a finite time* $T^*(K_0, K_T)$ *such that the optimal finite time program will have the following behavior*: *If* $T \le T^*$ *the optimal path will be such that* $\dot{K}(0) \ge 0$ *and will arch towards the turnpike* K_3^*; *and if* $T > T^*$ *the optimal path will be such that* $\dot{K}(0) < 0$ *and will arch towards the turnpike* K_1^*.

Proof: Consider the path ABC in Figure 49a, starting at the unstable node A, tangential to K_0 at B and reaching K_T at C. Let $T^*(K_0, K_T)$ denote the time to travel from B to C on this path. Clearly T^* is the *maximum* time to get from K_0 to K_T over all paths with $\dot{K}(0) \ge 0$. This T^* defines the critical time in the statement of the theorem.

Consider now any other path $B'C'$ with $\dot{K}(0) > 0$. Since

$$\dot{K}(t)|_{B'C'} > \dot{K}(t)|_{BC},$$

the time to go from K_0 to K_T along this path is less than T^*.

Suppose now there exists a path taking time $T < T^*$, starting from K_0 with $\dot{K}(0) < 0$, such that it arches toward K_1^* and meets the terminal condition $K(T) = K_T$. By continuity there must exist some other path like $B'C'$ with $\dot{K}(0) > 0$ which arches toward K_3^* and takes the *same time* T. However, since the integrand function is concave, we know the optimal path is unique and hence we have a contradiction. Thus for $T \le T^*$, the optimal path must have the property $\dot{K}(0) \ge 0$ and approach the turnpike K_3^*.

Finally, for $T > T^*$, since T^* has the stated maximum properties with respect to K_0 and K_T, it is clear that the only feasible path from K_0 to K_T (taking time $T > T^*$) must start with $\dot{K}(0) < 0$ and arch toward K_1^*.

QED

(Of course we may expect that a symmetric result obtains in a case with $K_0 \in (K_2^*, K_3^*)$ and $K_T < K_1^*$.)

---

[33] This result was obtained in collaboration with Stephen J. Turnovsky.

Such results teach us that we must forego some of the simplicity of earlier characterizations of optimal paths. The original turnpike literature asserted that optimal plans developed with respect to sufficiently long horizons would follow close to a unique turnpike path, independently of either initial or terminal conditions. In the face of multiple stationary paths, the global turnpike results clearly have to fall, but there remain local turnpike properties independent of terminal conditions. That is, the optimal long-horizon programs will not longer be independent of initial conditions, but remain independent of terminal conditions.

For sufficiently long plans, of course, independence of terminal conditions is hardly surprising; terminal conditions at infinity impose no restrictions on the optimal path at any finite time, and the optimizing system can act as if they were irrelevant. The optimizing system can, in effect, substitute its preferred transversality conditions for imposed terminal targets.

What our theorem suggests is that, depending on initial conditions, the horizon may have to be very long indeed before the true turnpike is revealed. In the meantime, as Figure 49b illustrates, optimal paths may not "arch toward" the turnpike appropriate to the prescribed initial conditions, but may indeed "arch toward" quite distinct values.

If a nation developing from an initial position K_0 (satisfying $K_1^* < K_0 < K_2^*$) to the target $K_T > K_3^*$ has a plan period, of, say, 10 years, the optimal plan may call for it to begin accumulating at once toward its target, taking advantage of (arching towards) the turnpike K_3^* along the way. As the horizon is lengthened, however, so that the nation can afford to decumulate (ignore the terminal target) initially, then it will be led toward the turnpike K_1^* appropriate to the given initial condition. As the horizon lengthens and the target recedes in the distance, ultimately all motions approach the true turnpike K_1^*.

The presence of time preference is crucial to any intuitive explanation of these results. Thus we finish up not with a technology-oriented turnpike theorem, but with a utility-oriented country-lane result: not "Accumulate! Accumulate! Accumulate!" along a path of maximal growth, but "To travel hopefully (with high consumption) is better than to arrive." We lose the simplicity of earlier turnpike results, but perhaps we gain in recognizing the influence of nontechnological considerations.

Robust Controls

Finally, we will close this section with the observation that the search for optimal policies becomes more difficult as more complex portfolio decisions, investment decisions, or saving decisions are introduced, and still more so as we attempt to take account of uncertainty. Eventually our search must turn from a concern with exact optimality to a concern with the identification of policies that lead to satisfactory values of the criterion function and that are robust against shocks or possible misspecification.[34] This search can be expected to bring economists closer to the work of control engineers seeking policies which, although not precisely optimal, may have the property of inexorably reducing some convenient measure of distance from a target. In addition, work of numerical analysts is relevant: the search for "methods" that yield "good" results for a whole class of problems (though not necessarily optimal results for any one problem in that class), and work on the concept of fuzzy sets and fuzzy algorithms (which may permit approximate solution of imperfectly specified problems), suggest possibilities.

Thus it can truly be argued that although the analysis of optimal economic growth has developed a rather stereotyped appearance at this stage, the really imaginative work is still to come.

Exercises

1. Show that the usual Kuhn-Tucker conditions applied to the problem

$$\text{Max } U(C) + pI$$

subject to

$$C + I = F(K)$$

$$C \geqq 0, I \geqq 0,$$

yield the conditions given in (5) provided that U satisfies the hypotheses described in Section 11-1. Interpret these as a tangency condition such as that given in Figure 43.
2. Give an economic justification for equation (7) when the solution to the problem of Exercise 1 yields positive consumption. Explain why equation (7) may fail if output is specialized to investment.
3. Carry out the differentiation indicated in equation (8).
4. Verify equation (19).
5. Determine the condition under which equation (25) may be solved to yield $\dot{K}$ as a function of K, t, and q.

[34] We know, for example, that in the model discussed by Burmeister, Dobell, and Kuga [15], the selection of sectoral saving rates $s_i = 1$ (entailing the reinvestment of all capital good rentals in further capital goods of the same type) ensures the stable convergence of the system to the same Golden Rule equilibrium balanced growth path as an optimal accumulation policy. The rule is also robust against shocks. If the utility loss in comparison to the optimal policy is not too great, we might elect to sacrifice some utility in order to gain some assurance of stability in an uncertain world.

6. Verify (27)–(29).
7. Prove that the conditions of the Theorem on page 373 are necessary for a candidate path to be optimal.
8. Prove that the conditions of the Theorem on page 373 are sufficient for a candidate path to be optimal.
9. Derive equation (43).
10. Verify equations (45) and (46).
11. Verify that the function given by equation (44) does yield a unique solution to the problem formulated on page 374.
12. Derive the natural boundary condition (49) as a necessary condition for optimality with free right-hand end point.
13. Verify the result asserted on page 378.
14. Show that in the special case that time does not appear explicitly in the integrand function, the Euler equation always has a first integral.
15. Analyze the system (62) and (63) in a phase diagram.
16. Verify that the equilibrium point with positive, finite k and p is locally a saddlepoint.
17. Consider the problem of finding a maximum to $\hat{J}$ as defined on page 400.
    (a) Show that $\hat{J}$ is bounded above.
    (b) Determine the saving policy that yields a maximum to $\hat{J}$ subject to the stated technology.
18. Investigate the optimal policy in case the utility function $U(c)$ is linear, so that $U(c) \equiv c$, but otherwise the planning problem is as posed on page 392.
19. Consider the problem of finding the maximum to

$$J = \int_0^\infty L(x, u, t)\, dt$$

subject to

$$\dot{x} = g(x, u, t) \tag{E2}$$

$$h(x, u, t) \geq 0 \tag{E3}$$

$$x(0) = x_0. \tag{E4}$$

Theorem:

Let L, g, and h be differentiable and concave in x and u. If there exist $\bar{u}$, $\bar{x}$, $\bar{v}$, and $\bar{w}$ satisfying (E2)–(E4) with $\bar{x}$, $\bar{v}$ continuous, $\bar{w}$ integrable, and such that

$$-\nabla_x[\bar{L} + \bar{v}\bar{g} + \bar{w}\bar{h}] = \dot{\bar{v}}, \qquad \nabla_u[\bar{L} + \bar{v}\bar{g} + \bar{w}\bar{h}] = 0$$

$$\lim_{t \to \infty} \bar{v}(t)\bar{x}(t) = 0$$

$$\bar{w} \geq 0, \qquad \bar{w}\bar{h} = 0, \qquad \bar{v} \geq 0,$$

then $\bar{u}$, $\bar{x}$ will yield a maximum to J subject to (E2)–(E4).

Proof: Consider

$$J[\bar{u}, \bar{x}] - J[u, x] = \int_0^\infty (\bar{L} - L)\, dt$$

$$\geq \int_0^\infty [(\bar{x} - x)\nabla_x \bar{L} + (\bar{u} - u)\nabla_u \bar{L}]\, dt$$

$$= \int_0^\infty [-(\bar{x} - x)(\nabla_x \bar{v}\bar{g} + \nabla_x \bar{w}\bar{h} + \dot{\bar{v}})$$

$$- (\bar{u} - u)(\nabla_u \bar{v}\bar{g} + \nabla_u \bar{w}\bar{h})]\, dt$$

$$= \int_0^\infty [-(\bar{x} - x)(\nabla_x \bar{v}\bar{g} + \nabla_x \bar{w}\bar{h}) + (\bar{g} - g)\bar{v}$$

$$- (\bar{u} - u)(\nabla_u \bar{v}\bar{g} + \nabla_u \bar{w}\bar{h})]\, dt - (\bar{x} - x)\bar{v}\Big|_0^\infty$$

$$\geq \int_0^\infty [\bar{v}(g - \bar{g}) + \bar{w}(h - \bar{h}) - (g - \bar{g})\bar{v}]\, dt - (\bar{x} - x)\bar{v}\Big|_0^\infty$$

$$= \int_0^\infty \bar{w}(h - \bar{h})\, dt - (\bar{x} - x)\bar{v}\Big|_0^\infty$$

$$= \int_0^\infty (\bar{w}h)\, dt - (\bar{x} - x)\bar{v}\Big|_0^\infty$$

$$\geq \bar{v}(\infty)x(\infty) - \bar{v}(\infty)\bar{x}(\infty)$$

$$\geq 0.$$

Exercise: Justify all the steps of this proof.

20. Consider $J = \int_{t_0}^{t_1} U[F(K) - \dot{K}]\exp(-\gamma t)\, dt$

$$\equiv \int_{t_0}^{t_1} L(K, \dot{K}, t)\, dt.$$

Show that the Hessian $M \equiv \begin{bmatrix} L_{KK} & L_{K\dot{K}} \\ L_{\dot{K}K} & L_{\dot{K}\dot{K}} \end{bmatrix}$ is negative definite if U and F are both concave functions. Hence, conclude that the necessary conditions cited in Exercise 7 are in fact sufficient if the Hessian M is everywhere negative definite.

21. Consider the stable Burmeister-Dobell-Kuga model [15] with the savings-investment equations $p_i y_i = s_i w_i k_i$, $0 < s_i \leq 1$, $i = 1, \ldots, n$. Prove that the Samuelson dynamic efficiency conditions are satisfied asymptotically if and only if $s_i = (g + \delta_i)/(\gamma + g + \delta_i)$ for all $i = 1, \ldots, n$. Verify, therefore, that the unique equilibrium is at the Modified Golden Rule point where $r_0 = g + \gamma$.

Answers and Hints

PROBLEM 2. Consider the marginal product of the (services of) the capital good. Observe that the value of that marginal product depends upon the composition of output.

PROBLEM 4. To derive equation (19), we should first establish the Euler equation itself. This derivation can be completed in a general form, and the special case then follows directly by substitution. For development of the Euler equation as a necessary solution, see Gelfand and Fomin [39, pp. 14–15].

PROBLEM 5. Apply the simplest implicit function theorem.

PROBLEM 7. Consider the problem of selecting a function $s(t)$ so as to maximize

$$J = \int_0^T L[K(t), s(t), t] \, dt$$

subject to the constraint that

$$\dot{K} = sF(K) - \delta K.$$

Following a procedure reminiscent of Lagrange multiplier rules in ordinary calculus (and in the classical calculus of variations), one may adjoin the constraint to the integrand function and write

$$J = \int_0^T \{L(K, s, t) + q(t)[sF(K) - \delta K - \dot{K}]\} \, dt.$$

Letting $H = L(K, s, t) + q(t)[sF(K) - \delta K]$ and integrating the last term of the integral by parts yields

$$J = \int_0^T \{H + \dot{q}K\} \, dt - q(t)K(t)|_0^T.$$

(Note that the last expression is simply the value of inheritances less the value of bequests; this reformulation of the criterion functional therefore lends itself to very direct economic interpretation.) The variation dJ due to a change ds in the policy functions may be estimated as

$$dJ = \int_0^T \left\{ \left(\frac{\partial H}{\partial K} + \dot{q}\right) dK + \frac{\partial H}{\partial s} \, ds \right\} dt - q(T) \, dK(T) + q(0) \, dK(0).$$

By analogy with the conventional static Lagrange multiplier procedure, we may choose the multiplier function to ensure the vanishing of terms involving dK. Thus choosing q so that

$$\dot{q} = \frac{\delta H}{\delta K}, \quad q(0)\, dK(0) = q(T)\, dK(T) = 0,$$

we find

$$dJ = \int_0^T \left\{ \frac{\partial H}{\partial s}\, ds \right\} dt.$$

(Note that the end conditions are satisfied automatically without restriction on q if the boundary values of K are prescribed.)

In order that the original candidate policy be optimal, it is necessary that the variation dJ be zero for all admissible changes in policy. Hence we find the necessary condition (the maximum principle)

$$\frac{\partial H}{\partial s} = 0.$$

By suitably adjoining the control constraint $0 \leq s \leq 1$ to the Hamiltonian H, we may extend the above argument to accommodate this additional restriction. (For details of this argument see Bryson and Ho [14, pp. 47–49, and following sections]. A more complete proof of necessity for this finite time problem can be found in Pontryagin et al [75, Th 3*, p. 63].)

PROBLEM 8. Let max $[U'(C), p]$ be denoted α, and observe that for any policy s, with an associated trajectory $K(t)$, $C(t)$, one may write (by virtue of the constraints imposed on admissible paths)

$$J^* - J = \int_0^T U(C^*)e^{-\gamma t}dt - \int_0^T U(C)e^{-\gamma t}\, dt$$

$$= \int_0^T \{ [U(C^*) - U(C)] + \alpha[(1 - s^*)F(K^*) - C^* - (1 - s)F(K) + C]$$

$$+ p[s^*F(K^*) - \delta K^* - \dot{K}^* - sF(K) + \delta K + \dot{K}] \} e^{-\gamma t}\, dt.$$

Employing first the concavity of the function U, then the definition of α and the nonnegativity of C and s, then the concavity of F, one concludes

$$J^* - J \geq \int_0^T \{ [\alpha F'(K^*) - p\delta](K^* - K) + p(\dot{K} - \dot{K}^*) \} e^{-\gamma t}\, dt.$$

Integrating the last term by parts, and employing the auxiliary equation satisfied by p, and noting the boundary conditions on K, one finds

$$J^* - J \geq 0.$$

Hence the conditions given in the theorem are sufficient to ensure that no other feasible path may yield a greater value to the criterion functional J. (Proofs along these lines may be found in Cass [16] or Shell [90, p. 252].)

(Note that the strict concavity of U ensures that any feasible policy different from s^* on any interval yields a strictly lower value to J. Hence the trajectory satisfying the cited sufficient conditions must be unique. Since we find (by reference to the phase diagram) one such path for the problem under discussion, we may thus arrive at a rather indirect proof of the necessity of the conditions derived in Exercise 7.)

PROBLEM 11. Apply the sufficiency conditions cited in Theorem 1.

PROBLEM 12. Consider any admissible variation with unspecified righthand value, perform the integration by parts, and observe that the condition cited is necessary if the variation is not to lead to an increase in the criterion functional. See Gelfand and Fomin [39, pp. 25–26].

PROBLEM 13. Observe that for any feasible path, $K(T) = S(T) + \bar{K} \geq S(0) + \bar{K} = K_0$ we may confine attention to cases with $K_0 > 0$. Then, save for the form of the terminal condition, this exercise is the same as Exercises 7 and 8. Employing the condition $q(T) = 0$ in place of $K(T) = K_T$, after integrating by parts, one may follow the same argument as used in Exercises 7 and 8.

PROBLEM 15. See Figure 48.

PROBLEM 16. Consider the associated linear system obtained by expanding the functions describing $\dot{k}$ and $\dot{p}$ around the equilibrium point, and examine the characteristic roots of the matrix of coefficients in the associated linear system.

PROBLEM 18. Separate the boundary cases $s = 0$, $s = 1$, and the interior case $0 < s < 1$. Observe that there can be equilibrium only in the interior case.

PROBLEM 19. Observe that the result asserted is nothing more than a full statement of the conditions in the maximum principle. (The notation $\nabla_x[L]$ denotes the vector of partial derivatives of the function L with respect to the components of the vector x.) See also the hints to Exercise 8.

References

[1] AKHIEZER, N. I., *Calculus of Variations*. New York: Blaisdell, 1962.

[2] ARROW, K. J., "Applications of Control Theory to Economic Growth," *Lectures in Applied Mathematics*, **12** (Mathematics of the Decision Sciences— Part 2), 1968, pp. 85–119.

[3] — "Optimal Capital Policy, the Cost of Capital and Myopic Decision Rules," *Annals of the Institute of Statistical Mathematics*, **16** (1964), pp. 21–30.

[4] — "Optimal Capital Policy with Irreversible Investment," in *Value, Capital, and Growth* (J. N. Wolfe, Ed.). Chicago: Aldine, 1968, pp. 1–19.

[5] — *Social Choice and Individual Values*, 2nd ed. New York; Wiley, 1963.

[6] — and A. ENTHOVEN, "Quasi-Concave Programming," *Econometrica*, **XXIX**, 4 (October, 1961) pp. 779–800.

[7] — and M. KURZ, *Public Investment, the Rate of Return, and Fiscal Policy*, Resources for the Future, forthcoming.

[8] ATHANS, M., and P. FALB, *Optimal Control*. New York: McGraw-Hill, 1966.

[9] BARDHAN, P. K., "Optimum Accumulation and International Trade," *Review of Economic Studies*, **XXXII**, *91* (July, 1965), pp. 241–244.

[10] BHARADWAJ, R., and T. MANOHARAN, "On the Theory of Optimal Savings with Finite Planning Horizon," *Southern Economic Journal*, **XXXIII**, *2* (October, 1966), pp. 264–267.

[11] BLACK, J., "Optimal Savings Reconsidered, Or Ramsey without Tears," *Economic Journal*, **LXXII**, *286* (June, 1962), pp. 360–366.

[12] BLISS, G. A., *Lectures on the Calculus of Variations*. Chicago: University of Chicago Press, 1959.

[13] BOSE, S., "Optimal Growth and Investment Allocation," *Review of Economic Studies*, **XXXV**, 104 (October, 1968), pp. 465–480.

[14] BRYSON, A. E., and Y. C. HO, *Applied Optimal Control*. Waltham, Mass.: Blaisdell, 1969.

[15] BURMEISTER, E., R. DOBELL, and K. KUGA, "A Note on the Global Stability of a Simple Growth Model with Many Capital Goods," *Quarterly Journal of Economics*, **LXXXII**, *4* (November, 1968), pp. 657–665.

[16] CASS, D., "Optimum Growth in an Aggregative Model of Capital Accumulation,"*Review of Economic Studies*, **XXXII**, *91* (July, 1965), pp. 233–240.

[17] — "Optimum Growth in an Aggregative Model of Capital Accumulation: A Turnpike Theorem," *Econometrica*, **34**, *4* (October, 1966), pp. 833–850.

[18] — and M. YAARI, "Individual Saving, Aggregate Capital Accumulation, and Efficient Growth," in *Essays on the Theory of Optimal Economic Growth* (K. Shell, Ed.). Cambridge: MIT Press, 1967, pp. 233–268.

[19] CHAKRAVARTY, S., "The Existence of an Optimum Savings Program," *Econometrica*, **30**, *1* (January, 1962), pp. 178–187.

[20] — "Optimal Savings with Finite Planning Horizon," *International Economic Review*, **3**, *3* (September, 1962), pp. 338–355.

[21] — "Optimal Programme of Capital Accumulation in a Multi-Sector Economy," *Econometrica*, **33**, *3* (July, 1965), pp. 557–570.

[22] —, "Optimal Investment and Technical Progress," *Review of Economic Studies*, **XXXI**, *87* (June, 1964), pp. 203–206.

[23] CHARNES, A., R. W. CLOWER, and K. O. KORTANEK, "Effective Control Through Coherent Decentralization with Preemptive Goals," *Econometrica*, **35**, *2* (April, 1967), pp. 294–330.

[24] —, J. DREZE, and M. MILLER, "Decision and Horizon Rules for Stochastic Planning Problems: A Linear Example," *Econometrica*, **34**, *2* (April, 1966), pp. 307–330.

[25] DIAMOND, P. A., "Optimal Paths of Capital Accumulation under the Minimum Time Objective—A Comment," *Econometrica*, **34**, *4* (October, 1966), 886–887.

[26] —, "National Debt in a Neoclassical Growth Model," *American Economic Review*, **LV**, *5* (December, 1965), pp. 1126–1150.

[27] DIXIT, A. K., "Optimal Development in the Labour-Surplus Economy," *The Review of Economic Studies*, **XXXV**, *101* (January, 1968), pp. 23–34.

[28] DOBELL, A. R., "Optimization in Models of Economic Growth," invited address given at the Society for Industrial and Applied Mathematics, Toronto, June, 1968.

[29] —"An Optimal Unemployment Rate (Reply)," *Quarterly Journal of Economics* **LXXXIII**, *3* (August, 1969), pp. 521–524.

[30] — and Y. C. HO, "Optimal Investment Policy: An Example of a Control Problem in Economic Theory," IEEE *Transactions on Automatic Control*, **AC-12**, *1* (February, 1967), pp. 4–14.

[31] — "An Optimal Unemployment Rate," *Quarterly Journal of Economics*, **LXXXI**, *4* (November, 1967), pp. 675–683.

[32] DREYFUS, S., *Dynamic Programming and the Calculus of Variations*. New York: Academic Press, 1965.

[33] EISNER, R., and R. STROTZ, "Determinants of Business Investment," pp. 160–337, in *Impacts of Monetary Policy*, Commission on Money and Credit. Englewood Cliffs, N.J.: Prentice-Hall, 1963.

[34] FINDLAY, R., "Optimal Investment Allocation Between Consumer Goods and Capital Goods," *Economic Journal*, **LXXVI**, *301* (March, 1966), pp. 70–83.

[35] FARRELL, M., and F. HAHN, (Eds.), *Infinite Programmes in Economics*. Edinburgh: Oliver and Boyd, 1967.

[36] FOLEY, D., and M. SIDRAUSKI, *Monetary and Fiscal Policy in a Growing Economy*, to be published by Macmillan.

[37] GALE, D., "On Optimal Development in a Multi-Sector Economy," *Review of Economic Studies*, **XXXIV**, *97* (January, 1967), pp. 1–18.

[38] — "A Mathematical Theory of Optimal Economic Development," *Bulletin of the American Mathematical Society*, **74**, 2, (March, 1968) pp. 207–233.

[39] GELFAND, I. M., and S. V. FOMIN, *Calculus of Variations* (R. A. Silverman, Trans.). Englewood Cliffs: Prentice-Hall, 1963.

[40] GOLDMAN, S., "Optimal Growth and Continual Planning Revision," *Review of Economic Studies*, **XXXV**, *102* (April, 1968), pp. 145–154.

[41] GOODWIN, R. M., "Optimal Growth Path for an Underdeveloped Economy," *Economic Journal*, **LXXI**, *284* (December, 1961), pp. 756–774.

[42] GOULD, J. P., "Adjustment Costs in the Theory of Investment of the Firm," *Review of Economic Studies*, **XXXV**, *101* (January, 1968), pp. 47–55.

[43] HAHN, F. H., "Equilibrium Dynamics with Heterogeneous Capital Goods," *Quarterly Journal of Economics*, **LXXX**, *4* (November, 1966), pp. 633–646.

[44] — "The Stability of Growth Equilibrium," *Quarterly Journal of Economics*, **LXXIV**, *2* (May, 1960), pp. 206–226.

[45] HALL, R. E., "Technical Change and Capital from the Point of View of the Dual," *Review of Economic Studies*, **XXXV**, *101* (January, 1968), pp. 35–46.

[46] HAQUE, W., "A Pseudo-Classical Dynamic Programming Model of Capital Accumulation," *International Economic Review*, **6**, *1* (January, 1965), pp. 32–46.

[47] — "Dynamic Programming in a Multi-Product Model of Economic Development," *International Economic Review*, **7**, *1* (January, 1966), pp. 93–108.

[48] — "Intertemporal Optimality and von Neumann Equilibrium in Non-Linear Activity Analysis: Corrections," *Metro-Economica*, **XVII**, *1–2* (July-August, 1965), pp. 45–46.

[49] HOLT, C., F. MODIGLIANI, R. MUTH, and H. SIMON, *Planning Production, Inventories, and Work Force*. Englewood Cliffs, N.J.: Prentice-Hall, 1960.

[50] HOTELLING, H., "A General Mathematical Theory of Depreciation," *Journal of the American Statistical Association*, **XX**, *150* New Series (September, 1925), pp. 340–353.

[51] JORGENSON, D., "A Dual Stability Theorem," *Econometrica*, **28**, *4* (October, 1960), pp. 892–899.

[52] — "Capital Theory and Investment Behavior," *American Economic Review*, **LIII**, *2* (May, 1963), pp. 247–259.

[53] KAMIEN, M., and N. SCHWARTZ, "Optimal 'Induced' Technical Change," *Econometrica*, **36**, *1* (January, 1968), pp. 1–17.

[54] KENDRICK, D., and L. TAYLOR, "Numerical Methods and Nonlinear Optimi-

zing Models for Economic Planning," Discussion Paper No. 48, Harvard Institute for Economic Research (January, 1968).

[55] KOOPMANS, T. C., "On the Concept of Optimal Growth," pp. 225–300, in *The Econometric Approach to Development Planning*. Chicago: Rand McNally, 1965.

[56] — "Objectives, Constraints and Outcomes in Optimal Growth Models," *Econometrica*, **35**, *1* (January, 1967), pp. 1–15.

[57] KUHN, H. W., and TUCKER, A. W., "Nonlinear Programming," pp. 481–492, in *Proceedings of the Second Berkeley Symposium on Mathematical Statistics and Probability*. Berkeley: University of California Press, 1950.

[58] KURZ, M., "On the Inverse Optimal Problem" in *Mathematical Systems Theory and Economics*, **I** (H. Kuhn and G. Szegö, Eds). New York: Springer-Verlag, 1969, pp. 189–201.

[59] — "The General Instability of a Class of Competitive Growth Processes," *Review of Economic Studies*, **XXXV**, *102* (April, 1968), pp. 155–174.

[60] LEE, E. B., and L. MARKUS, *Foundations of Optimal Control Theory*. New York: Wiley, 1967.

[61] LERNER, A. P., "Consumption-Loan Interest and Money (Reply)," *Journal of Political Economy*, **LXVII**, *5* (October, 1959), pp. 523–525.

[62] LUCAS, R. E., "Tests of a Capital-Theoretic Model of Technological Change," *Review of Economic Studies*, **XXXIV**, *98* (April, 1967), pp. 175–189.

[63] McFADDEN, D., "The Evaluation of Development Programmes," *Review of Economic Studies*, **XXXIV**, *97* (January, 1967), pp. 25–50.

[64] MALINVAUD, E., "Croissances Optimales dans un Modele Macroeconomique," pp. 301–384, in *The Econometric Approach to Development Planning*. Chicago: Rand McNally, 1965.

[65] MANGASARIAN, O. L., "Sufficient Conditions for the Optimal Control of Nonlinear Systems," *Journal of the Society for Industrial and Applied Mathematics (Control)*, **4**, *1* (1966), pp. 139–152.

[66] MARGLIN, S., "The Rate of Interest and the Value of Capital with Unlimited Supplies of Labor," pp. 141–163, in *Essays on the Theory of Optimal Economic Growth* (K. Shell, Ed.). Cambridge: MIT Press, 1967.

[67] MIRRLEES, J., "Optimal Growth When Technology is Changing," *Review of Economic Studies*, **XXXIV**, *97* (January, 1967), pp. 95–124.

[68] — "Optimum Accumulation under Uncertainty," *Econometrica*, forthcoming.

[69] MODIGLIANI, F., and R. BRUMBERG, "Utility Analysis and the Consumption Function: An Interpretation of Cross-Section Data," pp. 388–436, in *Post Keynesian Economics* (K. K. Kurihara, Ed.). London: Allen & Unwin, 1955.

[70] PEARCE, I. F., "The End of the Golden Age in Solovia," *American Economic Review*, Vol. LII, *5* (December, 1962), pp. 1088–1097. See also Phelps, E. S., "Comment," same issue, pp. 1097–1099.

[71] PHELPS, E. S., "The Golden Rule of Accumulation: A Fable for Growthmen," *American Economic Review*, **LI**, *4* (September, 1961), pp. 638–643.

[72] — *Golden Rules of Economic Growth*. New York: W. W. Norton, 1966.

[73] — "Second Essay on the Golden Rule of Accumulation," *American Economic Review*, **LV**, *4* (September, 1965), pp. 793–814.

[74] — "The Ramsey Problem and the Golden Rule of Accumulation," Cowles Foundation Discussion Paper No. 194. New Haven, Conn.: Yale University (1967).

[75] PONTRYAGIN, L. S., *et al.*, *Mathematical Theory of Optimal Processes* (K. N. Trirogoff, Trans.). New York: Interscience, 1962.

[76] RADNER, R., "Optimal Growth in a Linear-Logarithmic Economy," *International Economic Review*, **7**, *1* (January, 1966), pp. 1–33.

[77] — "Efficiency Prices for Infinite-Horizon Production Programmes," *Review of Economic Studies*, **XXXIV**, *97* (January, 1967), pp. 51–66.

[78] RAMSEY, F. P., "A Mathematical Theory of Savings," *Economic Journal*, **XXXVIII**, *152* (December, 1928), pp. 543–559.

[79] SAMUELSON, P. A., "An Exact Consumption-Loan Model of Interest With or Without the Social Contrivance of Money," *Journal of Political Economy*, **LXVI**, *6* (December, 1958), pp. 467–482.

[80] — "Efficient Paths of Capital Accumulation in Terms of the Calculus of Variations," in *Mathematical Methods in The Social Sciences* (K. Arrow, S. Karlin, and P. Suppes, Eds.). Stanford: Stanford University Press, 1960, pp. 77–88.

[81] — "The Two-Part Golden Rule Deduced as the Asymptotic Turnpike of Catenary Motions," *Western Economic Journal*, **VI**, *2* (March, 1968), pp. 85–89.

[82] — "A Catenary Turnpike Theorem Involving Consumption and the Golden Rule," *American Economic Review*, **LV**, *3* (June, 1965), pp. 486–496.

[83] — "Turnpike Refutation of the Golden Rule in a Welfare-Maximizing Many Year Plan," in *Essays on the Theory of Optimal Economic Growth* (K. Shell Ed.), Cambridge, pp. 269–280.

[84] — "Indeterminacy of Development in a Heterogeneous-Capital Model with Constant Saving Propensity," pp. 219–231, in *Essays on the Theory of Optimal Economic Growth* (K. Shell, Ed.). Cambridge, Mass.: MIT Press, 1967.

[85] — and R. SOLOW, "A Complete Capital Model Involving Heterogeneous Capital Goods," *Quarterly Journal of Economics*, **LXX**, *4* (November, 1956), pp. 537–562.

[86] SENGUPTA, J. K., "Truncated Decision Rules and Optimal Economic Growth with a Fixed Horizon," *International Economic Review*, **7**, *1* (January, 1966), pp. 42–64.

[87] — "On the Relative Stability and Optimality of Consumption in Aggregative Growth Models," *Economica*, *124* (February, 1964), pp. 33–50.

[88] SHELL, K. (Ed.), *Essays on the Theory of Optimal Economic Growth*. Cambridge, Mass.: MIT Press, 1967.

[89] — "Optimal Programs of Capital Accumulation for an Economy in which there is Exogenous Technical Change," pp. 1–30, in *Essays on the Theory of Optimal Economic Growth* (K. Shell, Ed.). Cambridge, Mass.: MIT Press, 1967.

[90] — "Applications of Pontryagin's Maximum Principle to Economics," in *Mathematical Systems Theory and Economics*, **I** (H. Kuhn and G. Szegö, Eds.). New York: Verlag-Springer, 1969, pp. 241–292.

[91] — and J. E. STIGLITZ, "The Allocation of Investment in a Dynamic Economy," *Quarterly Journal of Economics*, **LXXXI**, *4* (November, 1967), pp. 592–609.

[92] SHESHINSKI, E., "Optimal Accumulation with Learning by Doing," in *Essays on the Theory of Optimal Economic Growth* (K. Shell, Ed.). Cambridge, Mass.: MIT Press, 1967, pp. 31–52.

[93] SRINIVASAN, T. N., "Optimum Savings in a Two-Sector Model of Economic Growth," *Econometrica*, **32**, *3* (July, 1964), pp. 358–373.

[94] STIGLITZ, J. E., "A Note on Technical Choice under Full Employment in a Socialist Economy," *Economic Journal*, **LXXVIII**, *311* (September, 1968), pp. 603–609. (See also "Further Notes on the Choice of Technique," unpublished.)

[95] STOLERU, L. G., "An Optimal Policy for Economic Growth," *Econometrica*, **33**, *2* (April, 1965), pp. 321–348.

[96] TINBERGEN, J., "The Optimal Rate of Savings," *Economic Journal*, **LXVI**, *264* (December, 1956), pp. 603–609.

[97] — "Optimum Savings and Utility Maximization," *Econometrica*, **XXVIII**, *2* (April, 1960), pp. 481–490.

[98] TOBIN, J., "Life-Cycle Saving and Balanced Growth," in *Ten Economic Studies in the Tradition of Irving Fisher* (W. Fellner *et al.*, Eds.). New York: Wiley, 1967, pp. 231–256.

[99] TSUKUI, J., "The Consumption and the Output Turnpike Theorems in a von Neumann Type of Model: A Finite Term Problem," *Review of Economic Studies*, **XXXIV**, 97 (January, 1967), pp. 85–93.

[100] UZAWA, H., "Optimum Technical Change in an Aggregative Model of Economic Growth," *International Economic Review*, **6**, *1* (January, 1965), pp. 18–31.

[101] — "Optimal Growth in a Two-Sector Model of Capital Accumulation," *Review of Economic Studies*, **XXXI**, *85* (January, 1964), pp. 1–24.

[102] VIND, K., "Control Systems with Jumps in the State Variables," *Econometrica*, **35**, *2* (April, 1967), pp. 273–277.

[103] WAN, H. Y., "Intertemporal Optimization with Systematically Shifting Cost and Revenue Functions," *International Economic Review*, **7**, *2* (May, 1966), pp. 204–225.

[104] VON WEIZSÄCKER, C. C., "Lemmas for a Theory of Approximate Optimal Growth," *Review of Economic Studies*, **XXXIV**, *97* (January, 1967), pp. 143–151.

[105] — "Existence of Optimal Programs of Accumulation for an Infinite Time Horizon," *Review of Economic Studies*, **XXXII**, *90* (April, 1965), pp. 85–104.

[106] WINTER, S. G., Jr., "The Norm of a Closed Technology and the Straight-Down-the-Turnpike Theorem," *Review of Economic Studies*, **XXXIV**, *97* (January, 1967), pp. 67–84.

[107] YAARI, M., "On the Consumer's Lifetime Allocation Process," *International Economic Review*, **5**, *3* (September, 1964), pp. 304–317.

Chapter 12 Summary

We have come to the end of our book. It is now time to draw together the main strands in this long discussion and to highlight the essential themes.

Our goal has been to isolate the central economic issues arising in the study of an evolving economy. Our results have generally been in the established classical tradition: the principles of analysis developed to describe the static economy have extended to our more elaborate dynamic framework.

Chapter 1 simply states that conventional microeconomics forms, in principle, the foundation for all the subsequent analysis. Growth models are a natural vehicle for macroeconomic reasoning, and macroeconomics is itself only an approach to summarizing and condensing the features of a Walrasian general equilibrium system so as to focus on relations between a few crucial markets. Thus the functions introduced into a macroeconomic model or, more particularly, a growth model, may be considered derived, explicitly or implicitly, from some underlying microeconomic specification. Indeed, the trend of development in the growth literature is clearly toward even fuller treatment of individual household decisions, individual decisions of firms and other institutions, and adjustment processes in the various markets that bring together and reconcile these individual decisions. We began, however, by neglecting most of the underlying general equilibrium structure. Instead we assumed full utilization of all factor stocks, including labor, and guaranteed automatic clearing of the goods market by taking aggregate demand always equal to potential supply (determined by the full utilization assumption). The behavior of the aggregate model was then easy to trace.

Chapter 2 set out the logic of the one-sector supply-oriented model. The key observation was that when we focus on potential output, it is necessary to know only the growth path of factor (capital and labor) stocks and the capacity output that these stocks can sustain at any moment. A labor growth equation, a saving (capital growth) equation, and a production function yield all the information necessary to determine the evolution of the system from any specified initial point. (Since saving will generally depend upon output or income distribution, and this in turn depends upon the path of capital accumulation, the system develops a simultaneous structure, but analysis is not difficult.) The first step in our study of dynamic models was to determine the characteristic features of such a growth process.

The dominant feature we isolated was the fundamental stability of the process. This stability stems from the requirement that all saving volunteered must be absorbed, and in this model saving can be absorbed only by the widening or deepening of capital. If capital widening fails to absorb all resources offered for accumulation, then capital deepening must occur. Since capital deepening itself automatically increases the size of the resource flow necessary to sustain a constant capital/labor ratio, the inherent stability of this supply-determined growth process is obvious. Moreover, since equilibrium is always realized where the capital/labor ratio is constant and capital is expanding at the same rate as the exogenously growing primary factor labor, it is possible to assert that saving policy or habits of thrift exert absolutely no influence on the long-run growth rate of the system.

We saw that these conclusions regarding the inherent stability of the system and the irrelevance of fiscal policy designed to affect saving rates require several qualifications.

(i) If the specification of production conditions in the basic model is altered, then the dynamic system may have a stable equilibrium other than at balanced growth. In particular, if substitution is either too easy or too difficult, the capital/labor ratio may diverge to infinity or decay to zero rather than approach a constant equilibrium value. We saw that these cases may be associated with situations in which the imputed share of capital in national income approaches unity, and we may therefore be inclined to discount their empirical relevance.

(ii) If population growth is influenced by the development of the economic system, then there need no longer be a unique stable equilibrium for the growth process. Instead low-level stable equilibrium "traps" and high-level unstable equilibria may appear. On the other hand, the possibility that labor supply may be responsive to wage rates is unlikely to change the equilibrium characteristics of the system.

(iii) If, in fact, the automatic absorption of saving by passive investors cannot be assumed, then we may have to face reservations, such as those voiced by Harrod, to the effect that the process of capital deepening may be limited by the willingness of owners of capital to continue to accumulate at the reduced rental rates brought about by the capital deepening itself. If this is the case, then again the existence of stable equilibria away from balanced growth is possible. This reservation is one aspect of the general criticism that the one-sector model we study lacks an explicit demand side and explicit representation of investors' decisions. We have not dealt at all with the class of multiplier-accelerator models based on a condition of equilibrium between independently determined aggregate demand and potential supply functions.

The basic growth model thus rests on the specification of three economic components, and our specification of each of these is subject to qualification. Acceptance of any of these qualifications leads to the logical possibility that the smooth convergence to balanced growth asserted in the basic model may not occur.

A qualification of a somewhat different order was mentioned and is worth emphasizing. It suggests that even if all our basic specification is correct, conclusions drawn from phase diagrams and qualitative analysis of dynamic systems may have little relevance to real issues of economic policy. Such conclusions, since they are inherently qualitative rather than quantitative, yield no explicit information on time or duration. Asymptotic conclusions may focus attention on results whose importance is negligible in comparison to transitory paths whose influence, though ultimately small, may persist and dominate for a very long time.

All the foregoing is descriptive economics. We took one step toward development of criteria for economic policy by enunciating the Golden Rule of accumulation. We observed that it provides a criterion for eliminating a class of policies that are demonstrably inefficient because they lead to growth paths which can be dominated by other attainable paths. With this criterion we were able to show, following Diamond's analysis, that a growth model in which aggregate saving is constructed from maximizing decisions of mortal individuals could lead to a path that is dynamically inefficient in the Phelps-Koopmans sense. The question whether, or under what conditions, a competitive economy with rational savers and investors planning over a long horizon will be led to reject such inefficient growth paths was not resolved by our discussion.

In Chapter 3 we checked some properties of our one-sector growth model against a few features supposedly characteristic of recent economic history, and we found the model lacking. One reason is obviously the failure to recognize improving technology. We found that some classes of technological change could be represented in a convenient factor-augmenting form. Specifically we learned that only the particular labor-augmenting representation of technical progress is consistent with a balanced growth equilibrium and our list of stylized facts. We also observed that early concern with the effect of technological change upon the welfare of labor resulted in a natural classification of "neutral" and "biased" forms of such technological progress.

The economic content of such classification schemes is not great, however. We would prefer to know whether there is any reason why technological progress might tend to be Harrod neutral. Indeed, the representation of technological change as just "happening" is thoroughly unsatisfactory; it is obviously necessary to account for decisions on research and development and investment generally in some explicit way, thereby bringing these decisions within the framework of the model.

A first step in this direction involves the assumption of an "invention possibility frontier" from which individual enterprises may select the pattern of technological change that appears to maximize the present rate of cost decrease. This approach is only a first step, however; the decision rule is short-sighted, and the invention possibility frontier is itself not explained within the model. Nevertheless, it is interesting that this analysis of induced technological change does lead ultimately to observed Harrod neutrality, as required if the growth model is to sustain an economically meaningful balanced growth equilibrium.

A different modification of the analysis relates the productivity of capital equipment to its date of manufacture, and it brings the age distribution of the capital stock explicitly into the discussion. Investment policy which has the effect of reducing the average age of capital may then have a stronger effect than otherwise would be estimated. On the other hand, such effects appear to be transitory; the age distribution of capital stock approaches an asymptotic distribution which is not affected by the fact that technological change may be embodied rather than disembodied. Since such long-run considerations may be irrelevant to any analysis of actual social policy over a decade or two, we must go beyond such limited conclusions, however, and attempt to deal with shorter run effects of saving policy when technological change is embodied.

The introduction of embodied technological change also enables us to investigate factors determining the economic life of machines and the effects of economic obsolescence, as well as the allocation of labor over machines of different vintages. The presence of optimizing decisions governing this allocation makes it possible under some circumstances to construct measures of aggregate capital from which aggregate output may be estimated using an apparently conventional aggregate production function. Because these circumstances are very special, the significance of this result should not be overestimated.

Finally, we observed that growth models with embodied technological change should include some mechanism to explain the rate and direction of technical progress, just as in earlier models with disembodied change. One approach to such a model is based on the idea of "learning by doing": productivity rises as the scale of the economy and the experience of labor in production increases. Again it is possible to answer questions as to the existence and stability of possible balanced growth equilibrium paths. Perhaps the more interesting issue in these models, however, is the presence of increasing returns to saving and an excess of the social rate of return to saving over the private. All these issues were raised in our discussion, but we omitted details and referred instead to extensive literature on the topic.

Chapters 4 and 5 deal with the two-sector model of economic growth. Analytically the important feature of this discussion is the more elaborate (static) general equilibrium structure it entails. The allocation of factors between sectors must be determined explicitly, whereas demand for the output of each sector may depend upon the relative price of the two output goods or upon income distribution (through differing marginal propensities to save). As a result, determination of the static equilibrium becomes more complex, and the causality of the system is called into question. But if the system remains causal, analysis of the dynamic behavior of the system is largely unaltered from the earlier one-sector model.

Chapter 6 raised a new issue, that of the determination of portfolio composition. By introducing a second durable asset, but one which is not produced within the system, we studied the effects of an alternative store of value. Not surprisingly we found that to the extent that wealth-holders are prepared to accept paper assets as an alternative to real assets, the system may approach an equilibrium with a reduced level of real assets per capita and a reduced consumption per capita. However, our analysis suggests that this equilibrium is unstable, and that for all initial price levels exceeding a prescribed minimum, (and starting from given initial stocks of nominal money and physical capital), the system asymptotically approaches an equilibrium with zero real balances per capita and the same equilibrium capital/labor ratio as in the original one-sector model. The primary analytical point in Chapter 6 was the role of price changes as a mechanism to persuade portfolio managers to hold the existing supplies of both assets. From this mechanism and the fact that all nominal balances are treated as outside money whose real value is counted as part of real wealth by portfolio managers and savers, there follows intuitive justification for all the results in Chapter 6.

In Chapters 7, 8, and 9 we studied models with several produced assets. The variety of results developed is too great to permit summary, but the procedure in each case was to develop conditions assuring the existence of a meaningful static equilibrium in which prices and outputs are nonnegative. From such calculations we were able to establish conditions under which, for given factor endowments, specification of a common own-rate of return to assets suffices to determine the complete static equilibrium. In this way factor-price frontiers and nonsubstitution theorems are established.

Dynamic models attempt to express the evolution of prices and quantities by employing the static equilibrium so determined in accumulation equations and capital market equilibrium equations. A fundamental dual stability feature usually emerged when the resulting price and quantity systems were analyzed as part of a single system subject to specified initial conditions.

After a discussion of planning models in Chapter 11, we were able to suggest that the differences between planning models and descriptive models of the type discussed in Chapters 7–9 are: (1) the substitution of a social rate of time preference for a saving hypothesis that determines the yield on assets, and (2) the substitution of transversality conditions for the initial conditions on prices. As a result of the latter change, values in the planning model flow backward from prescribed terminal conditions rather than forward from initial values. Indeed, we might then view the planning problem as having a quantity system flowing forward in a stable fashion from prescribed initial conditions, and a price system flowing backward in a stable fashion from prescribed terminal conditions. The asserted instability of the descriptive model thus stems from its inability to alter initial prices to conform to prescribed transversality conditions.

Chapter 10 broke from the pattern of descriptive economics that included specification of market conditions and behavioral relations. Instead we took only the technological constraints upon production possibilities as given, and we imposed an efficiency criterion in various forms. That is, we imposed the requirement that the economy not follow any path on which the output of some desirable good could be increased without sacrificing any other desirable output, and we asked what are the characteristics of paths satisfying this efficiency requirement. One conclusion was that conditions equivalent to the requirement of equilibrium in factor markets and in capital markets as outlined earlier in the descriptive models are necessary conditions for efficient growth. A second conclusion was that these conditions lead to a characteristic relative stability property (for infinite horizon problems) or a characteristic turnpike property (for finite horizon problems). Thus the single requirement of dynamic efficiency is seen to be sufficient to eliminate from consideration all those technologically feasible paths that do not possess this unique turnpike feature.

Finally, Chapter 11 discussed the selection of particular efficient growth paths by appeal to a social welfare function. With this strong criterion imposed, all freedom remaining in the models of Chapter 9 (which already embody the dynamic efficiency conditions of Chapter 10 through their capital market conditions and the static efficiency conditions through their factor market conditions) is eliminated and the model has a determinate future without recourse to arbitrary saving hypotheses. That is, the maximization of the social welfare function determines the appropriate allocation between consumption and investment, and hence this approach eliminates any need for saving hypotheses. The resulting paths again reveal the characteristic catenary properties arising in the turnpike results, and earlier, from the dual stability features of the price-quantity systems.

These models we study omit a number of important considerations. There is little discussion of government decisions and government policies, although these are present in the background from the beginning. They contain no representation of corporation financing decisions or dividend policy, and in fact no consideration of the private paper assets (debt and equity) which separate the firm from the household. The analysis contains discussion of capital market trading, but no mention of complications introduced by transactions costs, imperfect foresight, and uncertainty. Recent work is directed toward introducing some of these considerations; now that much of the basic structure has been elaborated and clarified, we can expect rapid extension of the model to include other institutions and other decisions. The goal of a full model described in stochastic terms undoubtedly remains distant. In addition, a completely rigorous disequilibrium model (in which, for example, training costs, imperfect information, etc., create unemployment) must be constructed from the individual microeconomic level, and much basic research is required before such considerations can be incorporated into elaborate growth models. However, we recognize that all the foregoing problems are of practical importance, and certainly they will be incorporated in future work as economic theory progresses.

Throughout this book the focus has been on analysis of idealized systems. We have not thought that we were describing accurately any real economy, nor that we were defending any particular social or economic organization. We have simply traced carefully the implications of a limited set of assumptions about idealized economic relations. We have dealt primarily with the consequences of saving rules when wealth consists of only a single ubiquitous capital good, a portfolio containing a capital good and a paper asset, or a portfolio containing several produced capital goods. In this sense the first nine chapters (with the exception of a brief discussion of Harrod's famous model and of the dynamic input-output system) are really multigood extensions of Solow's seminal 1956 contribution to the theory of economic growth: they examine the evolution of an economy in which there is full utilization of resources and saving desires are realized.

We repeat that one major consideration is omitted from this discussion, and that is the role of the firm or corporation as an independent entity, particularly as purchaser and operator of capital goods. Independent investment functions do not appear in our analysis, which is only to say that we have not dealt with demand-oriented models of economic growth. If we were to attempt to justify this omission further, it would be on the grounds that an approximate treatment of long-run trends in an economy committed to full employment may legitimately omit some considerations that might be crucial in a study of cyclical problems. With a strong commitment to full employment, economic policy will be designed to ensure that the labor market and the goods market clear by bringing saving and investment desires into balance. Believing that the policies adopted are likely to influence investment desires rather than saving plans, we find it of interest to follow the course of full employment models in which saving plans are realized and no investment equation appears. This idea was stated and qualified in Chapter 1.

Of course, we do not justify this procedure as the last word, but rather as the first step toward a full treatment of disequilibrium growth models in which the adjustment of demand toward potential supply is explicitly considered. But an understanding of the basic relationships we have studied is clearly prerequisite to that extended work.

Second, our analysis of Chapters 10 and 11 tells us that any program of economic growth, whether guided through socialist planning or capitalist markets, must satisfy all the relations we have postulated in descriptive models (up to the determination of aggregate saving or the yield on assets) if it is not to waste scarce resources. Necessary conditions for growth which is efficient (in the sense that it does not waste resources that could go toward satisfying the desires of the people) demand that the path of growth closely resemble those we have studied, except that descriptive models do not include the social decision as to the division of output each period between consumption and accumulation.

Thus our analysis here, though it defends no particular social organization, does leave us, as members of particular societies, with an important lesson. We have seen that the effectiveness of a market mechanism in solving complex economic problems is not confined to static resource allocation alone, but applies also to dynamic problems of growth and accumulation. Had we no markets at all, we—as social planners—would have had to invent them, at least for computational purposes. The most striking lesson of modern control theory applied to large systems may be the observation that optimal control can be (perhaps must be) implemented through a decentralized scheme modeled on a price system. Apolitical numerical analysts devise algorithms based on a pricing mechanism to solve maximization problems. Socialist planners reintroduce prices to rationalize allocation decisions.

The moral is that where it may be possible to devise a workable price system to effect social decisions, this procedure may be the most successful. A perfect price system entails no coercive power, yet realizes (at least within the scope of the models we have considered) effective use of available resources. The conclusion is the more remarkable because the evolution of social institutions has generated in a natural way a market system which, rudimentary and imperfect as it is, mirrors in some ways the mathematical ideal.

In this book we have opened the door on a number of hard questions. How much should a nation save? How can the interests of future generations be adequately represented in present economic planning? Can the rate or direction of economic growth be influenced by social policy in a community dedicated to individual choice and free markets? We do not claim to have answered any of these questions, but we hope our exposition will have suggested some principles to guide the reader in his own assessments. At least the complexity of these problems, even in the highly simplified cases we study, should demonstrate that no solution to these hard choices will be found in facile dicta urging that we need only "expand the public sector" (or "eliminate it"), "extend GM" (or "break it up"), or "all remain under thirty years of age."

The problems are hard, but they are also exciting and worth our careful attention. Artificial as our analysis may seem, decisions taken every day on such issues affect the welfare of many individuals, both living and not yet born. Study of mathematical theories of economic growth is intended to clarify some of the theoretical implications of such decisions. To the extent that it does, we all benefit.

Appendix

Mathematical Properties of Nonnegative Square Matrices

Certain properties of nonnegative square matrices are used extensively in the text and, indeed, throughout the economic literature. This appendix sets out a few of the major results and suggests references for further reading.

Consider two vectors $x = (x_1, x_2, \ldots, x_n)$ and $y = (y_1, y_2, \ldots, y_n)$ representing points in Euclidean n-space. Following the usual notation, we write

(i) $x > y$ if $x_i > y_i$ for all $i = 1, \ldots, n$;

(ii) $x \geq y$ if $x_i \geq y_i$ for all $i = 1, \ldots, n$ and $x_i > y_i$ for

at least one i (in this case we say x dominates y);

(iii) $x \geqq y$ if $x_i \geqq y_i$ for all $i = 1, \ldots, n$.

If the vector x satisfies (i), (ii), or (iii) for $y = 0$, we say that x is *positive*, *semipositive*, or *nonnegative*, respectively; and if $-x$ satisfies (i), (ii), or (iii) for $y = 0$, x is *negative, seminegative*, or *nonpositive*, respectively.

Similarly, a matrix $b = [b_{ij}]$ is *positive* if $b_{ij} > 0$ for all i and j or *nonnegative* if $b_{ij} \geqq 0$ for all i and j. Likewise, a matrix b is *semipositive* if it is nonnegative and in addition $b_{ij} > 0$ for at least one pair (i, j).[1] A negative, seminegative, and nonpositive matrix are defined analogously.

Many well-known results on properties of semipositive matrices may be summarized in the following Lemmas.[2]

Let $b = [b_{ij}]$ be a semipositive $n \times n$ matrix; then:

Lemma 1: *The matrix b has a dominant characteristic root λ^* which is real and nonnegative.*

---

[1] Although the stated definition of a semipositive vector is widely used, some authors may use a different definition for a *semipositive matrix*.

[2] Many of these results may be found in Gantmacher [6], Vol. II, Chapter 13; Morishima [9], p. 195; or Solow [10]. In the preceding text we have referred to these results as L.1, L.2, and so on.

Lemma 2: *Associated with λ^* there is a semipositive eigenvector $x^* \geq 0$.*

Lemma 3: $\partial \lambda^* / \partial b_{ij} \geqq 0$.

Lemma 4: *λ^* is not less in modulus than any other characteristic root of b.*

Lemma 5: $[\lambda I - b]^{-1} \geq 0$ *if and only if* $\lambda > \lambda^*$.

Lemma 6: *A scalar λ satisfies $\lambda > \lambda^*$ if and only if*

$$\lambda - b_{11} > 0, \quad \det \begin{bmatrix} \lambda - b_{11} & -b_{12} \\ -b_{21} & \lambda - b_{22} \end{bmatrix} > 0, \quad \ldots, \quad \det[\lambda I - b] > 0.^3$$

Lemma 7:
$$[\lambda I - b]^{-1} = \frac{1}{\lambda} \left[I - \frac{b}{\lambda} \right]^{-1}$$
$$= \frac{1}{\lambda} \left[\sum_{i=0}^{\infty} \left(\frac{b}{\lambda} \right)^i \right] \qquad \textit{if and only if} \qquad \lambda > \lambda^*.$$

Definition: A semipositive matrix b is called *indecomposable*[4] if there exists no permutation of like rows and columns for which b may be written in the form

$$\begin{bmatrix} b_I & b_{II} \\ 0 & b_{III} \end{bmatrix}$$

with square submatrices b_I and b_{III} on the diagonal; if such a permutation does exist, the matrix b is *decomposable*.[5]

Lemmas 1–5 apply to a decomposable matrix b; if b is indecomposable, the results may be strengthened as follows.

Let $b = [b_{ij}]$ be an indecomposable semipositive matrix; then:

Lemma 1′: *The matrix b has a dominant characteristic root λ^* that is simple, real, and positive.*

Lemma 2′: *The eigenvector x^* associated with λ^* is positive, and no other characteristic root has an associated nonnegative eigenvector.*

---

[3] See Gantmacher [6], Vol. II, p. 74. These conditions are a generalization to $\lambda \neq 1$ of the Hawkins-Simon conditions [7].

[4] See Dorfman, Samuelson, and Solow [3] pp. 254 ff. for an economic interpretation of indecomposability.

[5] If, in addition, b_{II} is a null matrix, b is called *completely decomposable*; see, e.g., Ando, Fisher, and Simon [1], p. 67. Some authors use the terms *irreducible*, *reducible*, and *completely reducible* in place of *indecomposable*, *decomposable*, and *completely decomposable*, respectively.

Lemma 3′: $\partial\lambda^*/\partial b_{ij} > 0$.

Lemma 4′: *If b is primitive, then λ^* is larger in modulus than any other characteristic root of b.*[6]

Lemma 5′: $[\lambda I - b]^{-1} > 0$ *if and only if* $\lambda > \lambda^*$.

Many results in the literature on economic growth, particularly stability properties, depend upon inclusion theorems for characteristic roots. A survey of such theorems may be found in Varga [11]. Further results of particular interest to economists have also been proved by McKenzie [8] and Fisher [4, 5], and the following results extend those above concerning any non-negative $n \times n$ matrix $b = [b_{ij}]$.

Lemma 8:[7] *The characteristic roots of b are less than one in modulus if and only if the matrix $[I - b]$ has a positive dominant diagonal, i.e., there must exist positive numbers $d_1, \ldots, d_n$ such that*

$$d_i(1 - b_{ii}) > \sum_{j \neq i} d_j b_{ij}, \qquad (i = 1, \ldots, n).$$

Lemma 9:[8] *The matrix b may always be written in the canonical form*

$$b = \begin{bmatrix} B_1 & & & \\ & B_2 & & \\ & & \ddots & \\ 0 & & & B_k \end{bmatrix}$$

where the submatrices B_i are all square and indecomposable. (If b is itself indecomposable, then $b \equiv B_1$.) The characteristic roots of b are all less than one in modulus if (1) all the column (row) sums of b are at most unity, and (2) among the set of columns (rows) which form each submatrix B_i at least one column (row) sum of b is strictly less than unity $(i = 1, \ldots, k)$.

---

[6] A matrix b is *primitive* if there exists no permutation of like rows and columns for which b may be written in the form

$$\begin{bmatrix} 0 & B_1 & 0 & \ldots & 0 \\ 0 & 0 & B_2 & \ldots & 0 \\ \vdots & \vdots & \vdots & & \vdots \\ 0 & 0 & 0 & \ldots & B_{n-1} \\ B_n & 0 & 0 & \ldots & 0 \end{bmatrix}$$

where B_i are square submatrices. Obviously a matrix with $b_{ii} > 0$ for at least one i is primitive. The concept of a primitive matrix is important in Chapter 10.

[7] See McKenzie [8], p. 58.

[8] This sufficiency result is proved by Solow [10] and Fisher [4].

Lemma 10:[9] *Let d be an n × n diagonal matrix with positive diagonal elements $d_1, \ldots, d_n$. Define $b^* \equiv dbd^{-1}$. The characteristic roots of b are all less than one in modulus if and only if there exists a matrix d such that b^* satisfies the sufficiency conditions stated in* Lemma 9.

Note that b^* defines new units of measurement; e.g., if b is a matrix of Leontief input coefficients and the jth good is measured in new units twice as large, then the jth row and column of b must be divided and multiplied by two, respectively. Hence, in new units $b^* = dbd^{-1}$ where $d_j = 1/2$ and $d_i = 1, i \neq j$.

References

[1] ANDO, A., F. M. FISHER, and H. A. SIMON, *Essays on the Structure of Social Science Models*. Cambridge, Mass.: MIT Press, 1963.

[2] DEBREU, G., and I. N. HERSTEIN, "Nonnegative Square Matrices," *Econometrica*, **21**, 4 (October, 1953), pp. 597–607.

[3] DORFMAN, R., P. A. SAMUELSON, and R. M. SOLOW, *Linear Programming and Economic Analysis*. New York: McGraw Hill, 1958.

[4] FISHER, F. M., "Choice of Units, Column Sums, and Stability in Linear Dynamic Systems with Nonnegative Square Matrices," *Econometrica*, **33**, 2 (April, 1965), pp. 445–450.

[5] —, "An Alternative Proof and Extension of Solow's Theorem on Nonnegative Square Matrices," *Econometrica*, **30**, 2 (April, 1962), pp. 349–350.

[6] GANTMACHER, F. R., *The Theory of Matrices* (K. A. Hirsch, Trans.). New York: Chelsea Publishing Co., 1964.

[7] HAWKINS, D., and H. A. Simon, "Note: Some Conditions of Macroeconomic Stability," *Econometrica*, **17**, 3–4 (July-October, 1949), pp. 245–248.

[8] MCKENZIE, L., "Matrices with Dominant Diagonals and Economic Theory," in *Mathematical Methods in the Social Sciences, 1959* (K. Arrow, S. Karlin and P. Suppes, Eds.). Stanford: Stanford University Press, 1960, pp. 47–62.

[9] MORISHIMA, M., *Equilibrium, Stability, and Growth*. Oxford: Clarendon Press, 1964.

[10] SOLOW, R. M., "On the Structure of Linear Models," *Econometrica*, **20**, 1 (January, 1952), pp. 29–46.

[11] VARGA, R., *Matrix Iterative Analysis*. Englewood Cliffs, New Jersey: Prentice-Hall, 1962.

---

[9] The necessity condition is stated without proof in Dorfman, Samuelson, and Solow [3], p. 256. Fisher [4] provides a proof.

Index

441